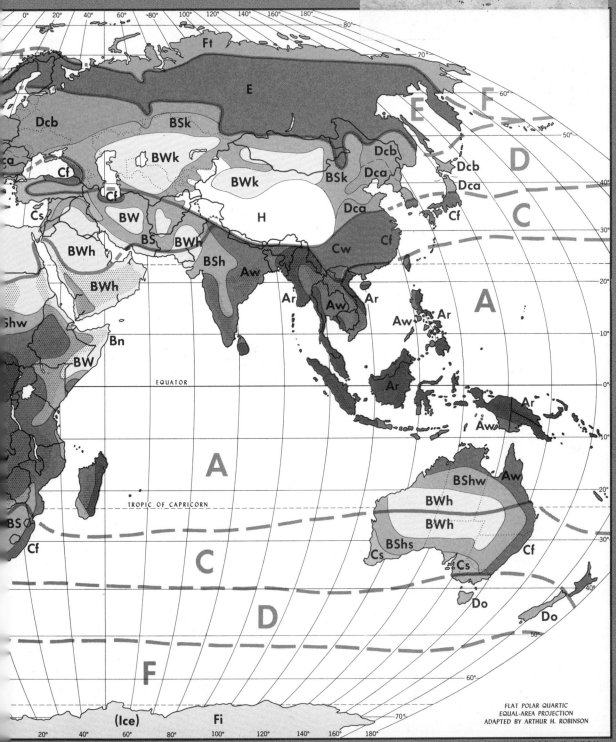

FLAT POLAR QUARTIC
EQUAL-AREA PROJECTION
ADAPTED BY ARTHUR H. ROBINSON

ELEMENTS OF GEOGRAPHY by G. T. Trewartha, A. H. Robinson,
and E. H. Hammond. © McGraw-Hill Book Co., N.Y., 1967.

AN INTRODUCTION TO CLIMATE

McGRAW-HILL SERIES IN GEOGRAPHY

John C. Weaver, *Consulting Editor*

Vernor C. Finch was Consulting Editor of this series from its inception in 1934 to 1951.

FOURTH EDITION

AN INTRODUCTION TO CLIMATE

GLENN T. TREWARTHA
Emeritus Professor of Geography
University of Wisconsin

Cartography by Randall D. Sale

McGRAW-HILL BOOK COMPANY
New York   St. Louis   San Francisco   Toronto   London   Sydney

PREFACE

The present book has three forebears. It probably should have more, since fourteen years have elapsed since the last edition appeared. In that time the added years of experience in teaching the geography of climate to college students and a greatly expanded body of materials in atmospheric science have provided the author with new ideas relative to the selection and organization of the materials to be incorporated in this fourth edition. It is no wonder that the book has had to be largely rewritten. Significant modifications of earlier editions include the following:

1. Much greater emphasis has been placed upon dynamic processes as genetic factors in climatic origins. Consequently Part One on the elements and controls of climate has been generally expanded, with particular attention to the materials on solar radiation and the earth's energy budget.

2. As indicated by the map inside the front cover, the classification of climates is new in many important respects, although it still has some resemblance to the modified Köppen scheme of the third edition. Teachers who still wish to use Köppen's classification will find it illustrated on the map following page 393 and described in the Appendix.

3. In Part Two on the world pattern of climates, synoptic weather types have been given more emphasis as ingredients of climatic description and interpretation. Climate is inseparably linked to the dynamic element of weather.

4. The appendix providing supplementary data for selected stations has been eliminated, and additional station data have been put into the body of the text. The sections in Part Two dealing with resource potentials of individual climatic realms have also been eliminated as belonging more properly to other courses.

5. Part Two's descriptions of each climatic type have been rounded out with brief analyses of certain individual climatic regions within the type on the various continents. The concept of "problem," or anomalous, climates is introduced in connection with regions which show significant departures from their general type.

6. Just as the text has been revised and modernized, so most of the old illustrations have been modified or redrawn, and scores of new ones have been added.

However, the overall two-part organization of *Introduction to Climate* remains the same as in previous editions. Part One, which deals with the individual elements and controls of climate, focuses on distribution and interrelation, both spatial and temporal. It describes world distribution patterns of the main climatic elements—solar energy, temperature, precipitation, and atmospheric circulations—and shows how their arrangements are conditioned by the climatic controls.

This emphasis on distribution reflects the book's design for what is mainly a geographic audience. The author regards descriptive analysis alone as inadequate, so that enough background on atmospheric processes has been provided to make the distribution patterns intelligible. For example, material on jet streams, mid-troposphere long waves, and general circulation is introduced mainly because these topics contribute to an understanding of atmospheric disturbances and fronts, and hence of temperature and precipitation distribution patterns. It is the author's conviction that a climatology which omits or seriously slights genesis and explanation is not only dull but also inadequate for the needs of geographers.

Part Two opens with a brief analysis of climatic classification and of the classificatory scheme used in this book. After introducing the concept of climatic regions, types, and groups deriving from a synthesis of the climatic elements, it describes the world pattern of climates based on these groups and types. Climatic genesis is emphasized by focusing on the characteristic locations of types and groups of climate with respect to latitude, wind and pressure systems, and air masses. On the other hand, precise definitions and the exact locations of climatic boundaries between types are deemphasized. As the text points out, these should be thought of an approximations at best. Description, distribution, and explanation of core climates form the basic approach.

Sections devoted to applied climatology, or the influence of climate on life forms, including humans, do not appear in the book because the author believes that the place for them is elsewhere. Also omitted are such topics as ancient climates and microclimates (those on the smallest scales). It is the purpose here to concentrate on climates having large dimensions—usually those on a world or regional scale.

Since the text has been kept relatively short so that it will provide a concise introduction to the geography of climate, some instructors and students will want more material on various topics than is given. For their convenience, supplementary readings and references have been listed for each of the two parts and for each chapter. With this framework a more comprehensive or a more advanced treatment of selected topics can be provided.

There is no long list of acknowledgments here, because the author is indebted to so many people that an inclusive list would be tedious to the point of defeating the purpose of gratitude. Prominent in any list of benefactors would certainly be my numerous students, who have also been my teachers. Special recognition should also be given to Professors Lyle H. Horn (meteorology) and Michael E. Sabbagh (geography) at the University of Wisconsin, and to Professor Wesley Calef (geography) at the University of Chicago, who have read parts or all of the manuscript and made invaluable improvements in it.

GLENN T. TREWARTHA

CONTENTS

THE EARTH'S OCEAN OF AIR

The planet earth is composed of a solid-liquid inner sphere whose radius is about 4,000 miles. This core is surrounded by an air ocean which, at its extreme limits, is several times as deep. Since the atmosphere is just as much a part of the planet as the solid-liquid core, the actual surface of the earth is the outer limit of the atmosphere. So life—including human life—dwells deep within the planet earth, not on its surface. It is only because air is so transparent, and so nearly weightless when compared with land or water, that the land-water surface is ordinarily referred to as the earth's surface. As a bottom-crawling organism in the densest part of the air ocean, man is of course greatly influenced by his atmospheric environment.

It is the air ocean that maintains the planet's habitable range of temperature and moisture. Without its fluid energy-distribution properties, the high latitudes would be lifeless because of unbearable cold, the tropics because of inconceivable heat. Through certain of its chemical and physical properties, the air also regulates the amount and kinds of energy that reach the land-water surface. Ozone in the high atmosphere shields terrestrial life from the sun's lethal ultraviolet radiation. The whole atmosphere above about 7 miles protects the surface from bombardment by highly charged particle radiation from the sun. Water vapor and carbon dioxide, which occur mainly in the lower atmosphere, act to retard the escape of the converted solar energy and thereby ensure adequate warmth at the surface.

The science of climate.   To laymen and specialists alike, climate relates to the air ocean and in this respect is one branch of atmospheric science. But climate is also a part of physical geography, which studies the physical earth as the home of man.

Climate is a layman's as well as a scientist's term, although scientists have given it various shades of meaning and have subdivided it into a number of specialized fields, such as dynamic climatology, synoptic climatology, and regional climatology. These need not be defined here; nor will even a comprehensive definition of climate itself be given in this introductory book. Instead, the following paragraphs will simply present some of the attributes of climate.

Climate and weather have much in common, yet they are not identical. The weather of any place is the sum total of the atmospheric variables for a brief period of time. Thus we speak of today's weather, or of last week's. Climate, on the other hand, refers to a more enduring regime of the atmosphere. It represents a composite of the day-to-day weather conditions, and of the atmospheric elements, for a long period of time. It is more than "average weather," for no adequate concept of climate is possible without an appreciation of seasonal and diurnal change and of the constant weather variations which occur. While the emphasis in a study of climate may be given to the norm, departures, variations, and extremes are also important.

Climate always applies to atmospheric conditions for a given period of time—a month, season, year. But not for one January, or one summer, or a single year. A sufficient number of these calendar units must be involved to provide a true composite.

Furthermore, climate is not an abstraction; it applies to places and regions. We speak of the climate of Chicago, the climates of Japan and of the American Great Plains. This place attribute of climate makes it highly geographic. And since much

geography has an anthropocentric quality, a geography of climate tends to emphasize those features and elements which have resource potential for man. Moreover, just as the science of geography in general emphasizes distribution, arrangement, and pattern, so also does the science of climatology.

Unfortunately, or so this writer believes, too much climatology has been largely descriptive, with little attempt to explain the phenomena described. But like any other science, climatology is potentially both descriptive and explanatory, the only limitations being the writer's competence and the adequacy of the data.

For its basic information, climatology depends mainly upon hourly and daily observations made at official weather stations, which form a network varying in density over the earth. The weather records of these stations are organized by calendar units—days, months, seasons, and years—based upon periodic sun control. Consequently it is only natural that climatic description has also been organized around these calendar units, which are based on the sun's control of the weather and hence are periodic (cyclical) in character.

Nevertheless, there is another important weather unit in addition to the periodic one reflecting sun control. This is the nonperiodic weather episode which is associated with a particular temporary weather disturbance or atmospheric circulation pattern. Such episodes are of various scales of size and duration, but they all have the attribute that they do not fit the solar-controlled calendar units. They may cover part of a day, several days, or even several weeks, but their beginnings and endings have little or nothing to do with day or night, noon or midnight. Hence the observations and records at official weather stations provide no summaries of data in terms of these nonperiodic units, or weather types. In the statistics, their effects are blurred by daily, weekly, and monthly summaries that cut across the periods in which individual episodes were in control of the weather.

Yet the nonperiodic weather element cannot be neglected in climatic analysis. It operates over the whole earth in varying degrees of intensity; in some regions and in some seasons it is more dominant than sun control. Unfortunately science cannot at present provide a comprehensive quantitative climatology of weather types. Much remains to be discovered about the kinds and distribution of the atmospheric disturbances which affect weather in different parts of the world, and likewise about the quantitative distribution of the weather elements (temperature, rainfall, etc.) associated with these disturbances. Moreover, every classification of weather types is open to question, since there is no single parameter which delineates the totality of weather conditions within a disturbance. As a consequence, statistical averages of the individual climatic elements are still used in this book as an important method of climatic description. On the other hand, they are supplemented wherever possible by information about the various kinds of disturbance types or weather situations, the composites of which comprise a climate. *For climate cannot be divorced from the dynamics of weather.*

Elements of weather and climate.   As noted earlier, weather and climate are not identical. Yet the nature of both is expressed by the same elements in combination. Primarily these elements are solar energy, temperature, humidity-precipitation, and to a lesser degree, winds. These are called the *elements* of weather and climate; they are the variables out of which the many weather and climatic types are compounded.

Controls of weather and climate.   Weather varies from day to day, and climate differs from region to region, because of variations in the amount, intensity, and distribution over the earth of the weather and climatic elements—particularly solar energy, temperature, and precipitation. What causes these climatic elements to vary temporally and regionally, so that some places and some seasons are hot and others are cold, some are wet and others dry? The answer is found in the operation of the climatic *controls*. Each of the climatic elements named in the previous section—solar energy, temperature, precipitation-humidity, and winds—also functions as

a climatic control and influences each of the other elements. Other important climatic controls are altitude, the distribution of land and water, mountain barriers, the great semipermanent high- and low-pressure cells, air masses, atmospheric disturbances of various kinds, and ocean currents. It is the controls, acting in different combinations and with different intensities, that produce the variations in temperature and precipitation which in turn give rise to the changing patterns of weather and climate.

Although it is climates and their world distribution that are of chief interest to geographers, some knowledge of the individual climatic elements and controls is essential to an understanding of world climates. In this book Part One, dealing with solar energy, temperature, winds and pressure, moisture and precipitation, air masses, and atmospheric disturbances, provides essential background for Part Two's discussion of the origin of the various types of climate and their patterned arrangement on the earth.

The nature of the atmosphere.   Although the earth's atmosphere is a mixture of a number of gases, nitrogen (78 percent) and oxygen (21 percent) make up 99 percent of the total volume of dry air. What little remains is composed of argon, carbon dioxide, neon, krypton, ozone, and a number of other gases. The relative percentages of these permanent gases remain almost constant horizontally over the earth and also at different altitudes. But ordinary surface air differs somewhat from this description, for in addition to the permanent gases, it contains variable amounts of water vapor and many organic and inorganic impurities, including dust, and condensed water and ice particles. Although the amount of water vapor in the air varies greatly from time to time and place to place, it rarely exceeds 3 percent by volume, even in the humid tropics. Yet as far as climate is concerned, it is the paramount ingredient of the lower atmosphere, as will be explained later.

The nongaseous substances, collectively known as dust, held in suspension chiefly in the lower atmosphere, are essentially pollutants. Some have hygroscopic properties and so provide the nuclei around which atmospheric condensation takes place. In many localities, particularly in the vicinity of large cities and industrial districts, air pollution has become a grave and rapidly worsening problem. Its recent increase is the result of man's burgeoning consumption of the fossil fuels—coal, petroleum, and gas. A major source of these atmospheric impurities is factory smokestacks. The chief offender, however, is the exhaust fumes from the swelling tide of motor vehicles. Every day in the United States, 350,000 tons of pollutants are exhausted into the atmosphere by 90 million cars—probably more than that released by all other pollutant sources combined. Poisoning of the air over cities has become a serious menace to the health and comfort of urban populations.

The main characteristics of any gas, including the atmosphere, are its extreme mobility and its unusual capacity for expansion and compression. Gas has far greater fluidity and mobility than water. Air may appear weightless and insubstantial, but everyone knows how much force is exerted by a strong wind, and how much resistance is offered even by quiet air to an object moving rapidly through it.

Within the *troposphere*, which is approximately the lowest 6 to 10 miles of the air ocean, both air temperature and air density decline with altitude. The density decrease continues indefinitely, but the decrease in temperature does not. Since the main heat source for the lower atmosphere is the sun-heated land-water surface, it is understandable why normally the air is colder with increasing distance from that surface. But this decline stops at about 30,000 to 50,000 ft, at what is called the *tropopause*. The tropopause represents a boundary separating the troposphere, or mixing layer, below, where vertical air movement is widespread, from the *stratosphere*, or stratified layer, above, where rapid up and down movement is largely absent. In the stratosphere at a height between about 15 miles (24 km) and 31 miles (50 km), where the atmosphere's small amount of ozone is concentrated, temperature rises with altitude. This is because a

small fraction of the incoming solar radiation is almost completely absorbed at the top of the ozone layer. Thus at an altitude of about 31 miles, air temperature reaches a second maximum—one which is nearly as high as that at the surface. Above this high-level maximum, the temperature declines up to about 50 to 55 miles, then rises rapidly again.

It is the lower 6 to 10 miles of atmosphere, the troposphere, which is the turbulent, convective layer. In it are concentrated a very large percentage of the atmosphere's dust, water vapor, and cloud, as well as most of the weather phenomena. The troposphere has several subdivisions. There is the extremely shallow laminar boundary layer which is in immediate contact with the earth's land-sea surface. Since it is so shallow that it lies below the level of weather-station instruments, information concerning this layer must be obtained largely from non-official sources. Only in the lowest surface layer is conduction, or molecular activity, an important factor in the vertical energy transfer between the land-sea surface and the air. In the laminar surface layer, vertical changes in temperature and moisture are exceedingly rapid. Above it is the so-called friction layer, which is about 1,000 meters (3,000 ft) deep. Here the vertical heat transfer is chiefly accomplished by turbulence or eddy motion. Here also, changes in temperature within the daily period are large. Above the friction layer is the free atmosphere, where winds are stronger and vertical energy transfer is carried out mainly through the formation of clouds.

GENERAL REFERENCES FOR PART ONE

Alissow, B. P., O. A. Drosdow and E. S. Rubinstein, *Lehrbuch der Klimatologie,* VEB Deutscher Verlag der Wissenschaften, Berlin, 1956.

Aviation Weather, U.S. Federal Aviation Agency and U.S. Weather Bureau, Washington, D.C., 1965.

Blair, Thomas A., and Robert C. Fite, *Weather Elements,* 5th ed., Prentice-Hall, Inc., Englewood Cliffs, N.J., 1965.

Blumenstock, David I., *The Ocean of Air,* Rutgers University Press, New Brunswick, N.J., 1959.

Blüthgen, Joachim, *Allgemeine Klimageographie,* Walter de Gruyter and Co., Berlin, 1964; 2d ed., 1966.

Brooks, C. E. P., *Climate through the Ages,* revised ed., McGraw-Hill Book Company, New York, 1949.

Brooks, Charles Franklin, *Why the Weather?* Harcourt, Brace & World, Inc., New York, 1935.

Byers, Horace Robert, *General Meteorology,* 3d ed., McGraw-Hill Book Company, New York, 1959.

Climate and Man, Yearbook of Agriculture, 1941, U.S. Department of Agriculture, Washington, D.C. See particularly Parts 1 and 4.

Compendium of Meteorology, Thomas F. Malone (ed.), American Meteorological Society, 1951.

Conrad, V., *Fundamentals of Physical Climatology,* Harvard University, Blue Hill Meteorological Observatory, Milton, Mass., 1942.

————, and L. W. Pollak, *Methods in Climatology,* 2d ed., Harvard University Press, Cambridge, Mass., 1950.

Court, Arnold, "Climatology: Complex, Dynamic and Synoptic," *Ann. Assoc. Amer. Geographers,* Vol. 47, no. 2, pp. 125–136, 1957.

Critchfield, Howard J., *General Climatology,* 2d ed., Prentice-Hall, Inc., Englewood Cliffs, N.J., 1966.

Garbell, Maurice A., *Tropical and Equatorial Meteorology,* Pitman Publishing Corporation, New York, 1947.

Geiger, Rudolph, *The Climate near the Ground,* Harvard University Press, Cambridge, Mass., 1965.

Gentilli, J., *A Geography of Climate,* The University of Western Australia Press, Perth, 1958.

Griffiths, John F., *Applied Climatology: An Introduction,* Oxford University Press, Fair Lawn, N.J., 1966.

Hare, F. K., *The Restless Atmosphere,* Harper & Row, Publishers, Incorporated, New York, 1963.

Haurwitz, Bernard, and James M. Austin, *Climatology,* McGraw-Hill Book Company, New York, 1944.

Heyer, Ernst, *Witterung und Klima,* B. G. Teubner Verlagsgesellschaft, Leipzig, 1963.

Kendrew, W. G., *Climatology,* 2d ed., Oxford University Press, Fair Lawn, N.J., 1957.

Koeppe, Clarence E., and George C. De Long, *Weather and Climate,* McGraw-Hill Book Company, New York, 1958.

Landsberg, Helmut, *Physical Climatology,* 2d ed., Gray Printing Company, Inc., Du Bois, Pa., 1958.

Leighly, John, "Climatology since the Year 1800," *Trans. Amer. Geophys. Union,* Vol. 30, no. 5, pp. 658–672, 1949.

Miller, A. Austin, *Climatology,* 3d ed., E. P. Dutton & Co., Inc., New York, 1953.

Pédelaborde, Pierre, *The Monsoon* (translated by M. J. Clegg), Methuen & Co., Ltd., London, 1963.

Péguy, Charles P., *Précis de climatologie,* Masson et Cie, Paris, 1961.

Petterssen, Sverre, *Introduction to Meteorology,* 2d ed., McGraw-Hill Book Company, New York, 1958.

Reiter, Elmar R., *Jet-stream Meteorology,* The University of Chicago Press, Chicago, 1963.

Reiter, Elmar R., *Jet Streams,* Doubleday and Company, Inc., Garden City, New York, 1967.

Riehl, Herbert, *Introduction to the Atmosphere,* McGraw-Hill Book Company, New York, 1965.

————, *Tropical Meteorology,* McGraw-Hill Book Company, New York, 1954.

Schwarzbach, Martin, *Climates of the Past: An Introduction to Paleoclimatology,* D. Van Nostrand Company, Ltd., London, 1963.

Sellers, William D., *Physical Climatology,* The University of Chicago Press, Chicago, 1965.

Symposium on Tropical Meteorology, Rotorua, New Zealand, 1963, J. W. Hutchings (ed.), New Zealand Meteorological Service, Wellington, 1964.

Watts, I. E. M., *Equatorial Weather,* University of London Press, Ltd., London, 1955.

Willett, Hurd C., and Frederick Sanders, *Descriptive Meteorology,* 2d ed., Academic Press Inc., New York, 1959.

PART ONE

THE ELEMENTS AND CONTROLS OF CLIMATE

CHAPTER ONE

SOLAR RADIATION

Energy of the atmosphere. Radiant energy from the sun provides 99.97 percent of the total energy of the atmosphere. It is also the prime source of energy for terrestrial life, as well as for the natural processes which go on in the oceans and in the upper layers of the solid earth. Temporal and regional differences in solar radiation give rise to weather and climate. Solar radiation which is absorbed by the atmosphere takes the form of either thermal energy (heat) or kinetic energy denoted by air in motion (wind). These two forms of atmospheric energy are readily converted from one to the other.

A huge and continuous flow of radiant energy streams out into interplanetary space in all directions from the sun, whose surface has an estimated temperature of about 12,000°F (6000°C). The planet earth, about 93 million miles distant, intercepts less than one five-billionth of the sun's total energy output. Nevertheless, solar radiation energy is the great engine which drives the earth's atmospheric and oceanic circulations, generates the weather, and makes the planet a livable place for plants and animals, including humans. The coal, gas, electricity, and petroleum that heat our homes and power our engines are only transformed solar energy.

Nature of radiation.   All bodies or objects, irrespective of their temperatures, give off radiant energy in the form of electromagnetic waves. These waves, traveling at a speed of about 186,000 miles a second, transport energy just as waves on the sea do. Electromagnetic radiation exists in a variety of conditions—solar energy, heat from a stove, radio and television transmission, warmth from the earth, x-rays. These differ from each other mainly in their wavelengths, or the linear distance between wave crests. Wavelengths of radiant energy range from the exceedingly short waves of cosmic rays and x-rays (10^{-8} to 10^{-5} microns[1]) to the long radio waves of several hundred meters (10^8 microns). In the whole range of known radiation wavelengths, those given off by the sun and earth are intermediate in their dimensions (between 10^{-3} and 10^2 microns).

Wavelength depends on the temperature of the radiating body: it increases as the temperature of the body decreases. Thus high-temperature solar radiation is in the form of shorter waves than those given off by the much cooler earth. Earth radiation waves are roughly 20 times longer than those of solar radiation. Only about one-fifth of the range of the solar spectrum can be perceived as light; there are other wavelengths, some shorter (ultraviolet), and others longer (infrared), which cannot be seen. Still, in terms of energy output, the visible part of the solar spectrum comprises a great share of the total solar radiation output.

Radiation is energy in transit. When it meets an object or substance it may be *transmitted, reflected,* or *absorbed,* in proportions which depend on the nature of the medium and the wavelength of the radiation. Only that part of the radiation which is absorbed by a medium is effective in heating it. Clear air or glass transmits most of the sunlight falling upon it and so retains very little heat. Fresh snow reflects most of the sunlight, so that it too is not much heated. But a dark soil absorbs a great part of the incident sunlight, and as a consequence its temperature is markedly increased.

A *blackbody* is a hypothetical object which by

[1] A micron equals one-millionth (10^{-6}) of a meter.

definition is the most efficient possible absorber and emitter of radiation. Theoretically it absorbs all the radiation incident upon it, reflecting and transmitting none. At the same time, it also emits the highest possible radiation for a given temperature. A true blackbody does not exist in nature, but radiation from the sun and from the earth's land-sea surface approximates that of a blackbody. By contrast, the atmosphere does not perform like a blackbody, for it absorbs and emits radiation only selectively; that is, in certain wavelengths but not in others.

Solar energy as a climatic element.   Since solar radiation is the single important source of atmospheric energy, its distribution over the earth is a major determinant of weather and climatic phenomena. Solar energy is the ultimate cause of all changes and motions of the atmosphere, and the single most important control of climate. But solar energy is not just a *control* of climate; it is also a climatic *element* of the highest importance. Quite apart from its influence on air temperature, solar radiant energy directly affects the growth and character of plants and animals, including humans. It does this both through illumination, as controlled by the visible part of the solar spectrum which is perceived as light, and through the nonvisible radiation.

The natural illumination regime, or the varying lengths of day and night, determines the period of photosynthesis, which for some plants is a critical factor. Solar radiation falling upon plants has three immediate and direct effects: At certain critical periods in their growth, it may produce burning; in green plants it largely determines the vegetative rates of growth; and it directly influences the rate of transpiration, or water loss, and consequently the water requirements of plants.

Human health and comfort, and the nature and distribution of human diseases, are likewise greatly affected by the duration and intensity of sunlight. For most outdoor workers, such as farmers, sunlight is an important part of the work environment. For people in general it is a feature of the natural environment which importantly affects outdoor recreation and enjoyment. At least for the cooler parts of the earth outside the tropics, sunshine is a relished feature of weather and climate. Its psychological effect is to add zest to living, buoy up the spirits, and dispel gloom, so much so that a cheerful, genial person is said to have a sunny disposition.

PRIMARY FACTORS DETERMINING DISTRIBUTION

Obviously the climate near ground level, where life forms are concentrated, is geographically of the greatest importance. But it is simpler at first to consider the distribution of solar radiation as it exists at the top of the earth's atmosphere, or as it would exist near ground level if there were no atmosphere.

Because of the spherical shape of the earth, half its surface is always in darkness, and even much of the lighted half receives solar beams at a fairly oblique angle. Consequently a unit of the surface at the outer boundary of the atmosphere receives on the average only one-fourth of the total solar radiation flux that would be intercepted by a similar plane surface at the same distance from the sun and perpendicular to the solar beam. This one-fourth of the solar radiation flux received by the earth is distributed very unevenly over its outermost atmospheric surface. The amount received in any latitude at any time of year depends primarily upon two factors: (1) the intensity of solar radiation, which is chiefly a function of the angle at which the beam of sunlight reaches that portion of the curved earth, and (2) the duration of solar radiation, or length of day compared with night.

When the noon sun is directly overhead in a particular area, and the beam of solar energy is therefore vertical at the surface, that area is receiving a maximum intensity of solar energy. When the noon sun is farther away from the zenith, so that its beam is more oblique, the area will intercept less energy. At the latitude of New York City, where in winter the altitude of the noon sun is about 64° away from the vertical, a unit surface intercepts only 44 percent of the solar energy which would be delivered by a perpendicular ray. In summer, when the noon sun at New York is only about 17° away from the zenith, the comparable figure is 95 percent. Of course, the sun's rays themselves don't actually change in intensity. Moreover, they are always parallel. Their varying angles, and therefore varying intensities, are only the result of the curvature of the earth's surface. Because an oblique solar ray is spread out over a larger segment of the earth's curved surface than a vertical one, it delivers less energy per unit area (Fig. 1.1). Moreover, although for the moment the effects of an atmosphere are being omitted, it should be added that an oblique ray also passes through a thicker layer of scattering, absorbing, and reflecting air which likewise greatly reduces its intensity (see table, page 13, top). For these two reasons, therefore, winter sunlight is much weaker than that of summer. Also, early morning and late afternoon sunlight is much weaker than that of midday.

As regards the second factor, duration of solar radiation, obviously the longer the period of daylight and the shorter the night, the greater the amount of solar energy received, all other conditions being equal (see table, page 13, bottom). In the latitude of southern Wisconsin, say, the longest summer days (15+ hr) have 6+ hr more of daylight than the shortest winter days (9− hr) do (Figs. 1.2, 1.3, 1.4). It is quite understandable, then, why in the middle latitudes summer temperatures are so much higher than winter temperatures: in summer (a) the sun's rays are less oblique and (b) the days are much longer.

Because length of day and angle of the sun's rays are equal on all parts of the same parallel, it follows that all places on a parallel receive the same amount of solar energy (except for differences in cloudiness and in transparency of the atmosphere). By the same reasoning, different parallels or latitudes receive varying amounts of solar energy which de-

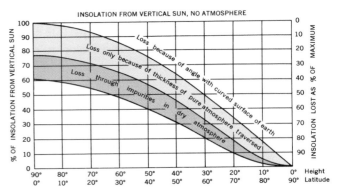

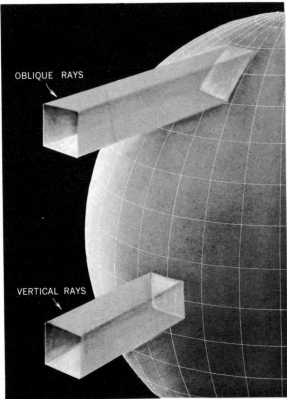

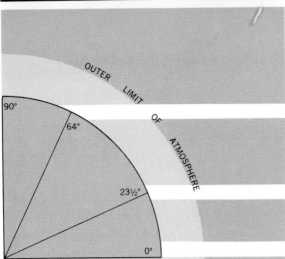

Figure 1.1 Oblique solar rays deliver less energy at the earth's surface than vertical rays, both because their energy is spread over a larger surface (*top*), and because they pass through a thicker layer of reflecting and absorbing atmosphere (*bottom*).

Figure 1.2 The effects of the angle of the incident ray on the intensity of solar radiation. Maximum solar radiation (100 percent on graph) is received from a vertical ray on a horizontal surface without an atmosphere. The top curve shows the intensity of the radiation received at varying angles from 90° to 0° (scale marked "height" of sun), disregarding the effects of an atmosphere. At 30° the intensity is half that at 90°. The middle curve on the graph shows the additional depleting effects of a pure, dry, cloudless atmosphere with a transparency of 78 percent. The third curve shows the further reduction resulting from impurities in the atmosphere. (*From S. Gentilli, A Geography of Climate.*)

crease from equator to poles for the year as a whole.

If solar radiation were the only control of atmospheric phenomena, all places in the same latitude would have identical climates. And while they are certainly not identical, the strong climatic resemblances within latitude belts testify to the dominant, although not exclusive, rank of sun control.

A plane surface perpendicular to the solar beam intercepts the largest possible amount of radiation. At the outer limits of the atmosphere, such a surface receives solar energy amounting to 2 cal (calories) per sq cm per min. This is called the solar constant. Since the spherical earth's surface intercepts only one-fourth as much solar radiation as a perpendicular plane surface would, the solar constant for the earth is only 0.5 cal per sq cm of the earth's surface per min, averaged over the whole globe. There is an insignificant variation in the solar constant due to slight changes in the distance of the earth from the sun at different positions in the earth's orbit. The fact that the Northern Hemisphere is in the middle of its winter season at the time when the

Intensity of solar radiation (Transmission coefficient 78 percent)

Sun's altitude	Distances rays must travel through atmosphere*	Radiation intensity on a surface perpendicular to rays	Radiation intensity on a horizontal surface
90°	1.00	78	78
80°	1.02	77	76
70°	1.06	76	72
60°	1.15	75	65
50°	1.31	72	55
40°	1.56	68	44
30°	2.00	62	31
20°	2.92	51	17
10°	5.70	31	5
5°	10.80	15	1
0°	45.00	0	0

* Expressed in atmospheres.

earth is about 3 million miles closer to the sun only serves to emphasize that this item of distance is minor compared with the varying length of daylight and the angle of the sun's rays reaching the earth.

Earth and sun relations

The earth is held in space by the combined gravitational attraction of other heavenly bodies and has motions that are controlled by them. The two principal earth motions are rotation and revolution.

Rotation The earth rotates upon an imaginary axis, the ends of which are the North and South Poles. Owing to the earth's slight bulging at the equator and slight flattening at the poles, this axis is its shortest diameter. The time required for the earth to rotate once upon its axis determines the length of a day. During that time (approximately 24 hr), places on the sphere are turned alternately toward and away from the sun. They go through a period of light and a period of darkness, and they are swept over twice by the circle of illumination (i.e., boundary between light and dark): at dawn and again at twilight. The direction of earth rotation is toward the east. This not only determines the direction in which the sun, moon, and stars appear to rise and set, but is related to other earth phenomena of far-reaching consequence, such as the prevailing directions of winds and ocean currents.

Length of day in various northern latitudes (In hours and minutes on the 15th of each month)

Month	0°	10°	20°	30°	40°	50°	60°	70°	80°	90°
Jan.	12:07	11:35	11:02	10:24	9:37	8:30	6:38	0:00	0:00	0:00
Feb.	12:07	11:49	11:21	11:10	10:42	10:07	9:11	7:20	0:00	0:00
Mar.	12:07	12:04	12:00	11:57	11:53	11:48	11:41	11:28	10:52	0:00
Apr.	12:07	12:21	12:36	12:53	13:14	13:44	14:31	16:06	24:00	24:00
May	12:07	12:34	13:04	13:38	14:22	15:22	17:04	22:13	24:00	24:00
June	12:07	12:42	13:20	14:04	15:00	16:21	18:49	24:00	24:00	24:00
July	12:07	12:40	13:16	13:56	14:49	15:38	17:31	24:00	24:00	24:00
Aug.	12:07	12:28	12:50	13:16	13:48	14:33	15:46	18:26	24:00	24:00
Sept.	12:07	12:12	12:17	12:23	12:31	12:42	13:00	13:34	15:16	24:00
Oct.	12:07	11:55	11:42	11:28	11:10	10:47	10:11	9:03	5:10	0:00
Nov.	12:07	11:40	11:12	10:40	10:01	9:06	7:37	3:06	0:00	0:00
Dec.	12:07	11:32	10:56	10:14	9:20	8:05	5:54	0:00	0:00	0:00

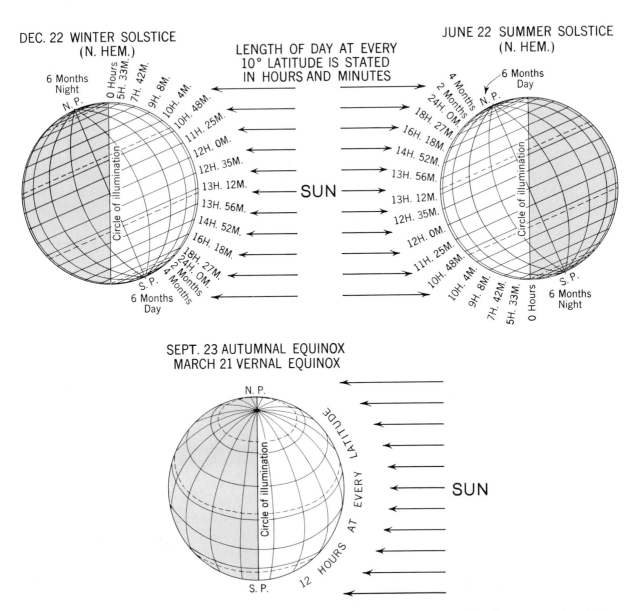

Figure 1.3 At the times of the two equinoxes, when the sun's noon rays are vertical at the equator, the circle of illumination cuts all parallels in half, so that days and nights are equal (12 hr) over the whole earth. At the times of the solstices, the sun's vertical noon rays have reached their greatest poleward displacement, 23½° north or south. The circle of illumination then cuts all parallels except the equator unequally, so that days and nights are unequal in length except at latitude 0°.

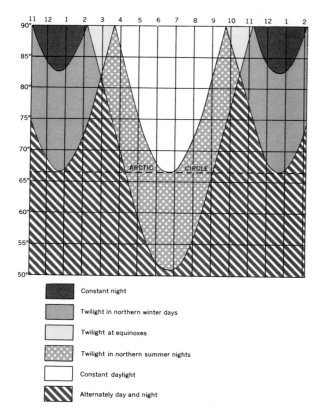

Figure 1.4 The annual march of light conditions poleward from 50°N. (*After W. Meinardus.*)

Legend:
- Constant night
- Twilight in northern winter days
- Twilight at equinoxes
- Twilight in northern summer nights
- Constant daylight
- Alternately day and night

Revolution. The rotating earth revolves in a slightly elliptical orbit about the sun, keeping an average distance of about 93 million miles from it. The time required for the earth to pass once completely around its orbit fixes the length of the year. During the time of one revolution, the turning earth rotates on its axis approximately $365\frac{1}{4}$ times, thus determining the number of days in the year.

An imaginary plane passed through the sun and extended outward through all points in the earth's orbit is called the plane of the ecliptic. The axis of the earth's rotation has a position that is neither parallel with nor vertical to that plane. Instead, it is inclined about $66\frac{1}{2}°$ from the plane of the ecliptic (or $23\frac{1}{2}°$ from an imaginary line vertical to it). This position is constant, and therefore the axis at any time during the yearly revolution is parallel to the position that it occupies at any other time (Fig. 1.3). This is called the *parallelism* of the axis.

The degree of inclination of the earth's axis and the parallelism of that axis, together with the earth's shape, its rotation on its axis, and its revolution about the sun, produce a number of features in the earth's environment that are very important to man. One of the most fundamental is the changing distribution of solar energy over the earth and the accompanying changes of seasons.

The march of the seasons

Equinoxes: spring and fall. Twice during the yearly period of revolution, on about March 21 and September 23, the sun's noon rays are directly overhead, or vertical, at the equator (Fig. 1.3). At these times, therefore, the circle of illumination, marking the position of the tangent rays, passes through both poles and so cuts all the earth's parallels exactly in half. One-half of each parallel (180°) consequently is in light, and the other half is in darkness, so that days and nights are equal (12 hr each) over the entire earth. From this fact the two dates March 21 (spring equinox) and September 23 (autumn equinox) get their names, for *equinox* is derived from Latin words meaning equal night. At these seasons the maximum solar energy is received at the equator, from which it diminishes regularly toward either pole, where it becomes zero.

Solstices: summer and winter. On about June 22 the earth is midway in its orbit between the equinoctial positions, and the North Pole is inclined $23\frac{1}{2}°$ *toward* the sun (Fig. 1.3). As a result of the axial inclination, the sun's rays are shifted northward by that same amount ($23\frac{1}{2}°$), so that the noon rays are vertical at the Tropic of Cancer ($23\frac{1}{2}°$N), and the tangent rays in the Northern Hemisphere pass over the pole and reach the Arctic Circle ($66\frac{1}{2}°$N), $23\frac{1}{2}°$ on the opposite side of it. In the Southern Hemisphere the tangent rays do not reach the pole but terminate at the Antarctic Circle, $23\frac{1}{2}°$ short of it. Thus while all parts of the earth north of the Arctic Circle are in constant daylight, similar latitudes in the Southern Hemisphere (poleward from the Antarctic Circle) are entirely without sunlight. All parallels, except the equator, are cut unequally by the circle of illumination. Those in the Northern Hemisphere have the larger parts of their circumferences toward the sun, so that days are longer than nights. Longer days, plus more nearly vertical rays of the sun, result in a maximum receipt of solar energy in the Northern Hemisphere at this time. Summer, with its associated high temperatures, is the result, and north of the equator June 22 is known as the *summer solstice*. In the Southern Hemisphere, all these conditions are reversed: nights are longer than days, the sun's rays are relatively oblique, solar radiation is at a minimum, and winter conditions prevail (Fig. 1.4). The sun seems to stand briefly still for about 5 days at the time of the summer solstice before reluctantly starting southward, during which time there is almost no change in the time of sunrise or sunset. It appears almost as if the momentum gained during 6 months of northward travel must be first overcome before it can shift into reverse. The same happens at the winter solstice.

On about Dec. 22, when the earth is in the opposite position in its orbit, it is the South Pole that is inclined $23\frac{1}{2}°$ toward the sun (Fig. 1.3). The noon rays are then vertical over the Tropic of Capricorn ($23\frac{1}{2}°$S), and the tangent rays pass $23\frac{1}{2}°$ over the South Pole to the other side of the Antarctic Circle ($66\frac{1}{2}°$S). Consequently south of $66\frac{1}{2}°$S there is constant light, while north of $66\frac{1}{2}°$N there is none. All parallels of the earth, except the equator, are cut unequally by the circle of illumination, with days longer and the sun's rays more nearly vertical in the Southern Hemisphere. This, therefore, is summer south of the equator but winter in the Northern Hemisphere (*winter solstice*), where opposite conditions prevail.

EFFECTS OF AN ATMOSPHERE

In passing through the air ocean, the solar beam is depleted by an amount varying with latitude and with the season, and with local conditions. This weakening occurs because the sun's rays are scattered, reflected, and absorbed in varying degrees by the atmosphere's gases and by tiny particles suspended in the air (Fig. 1.5, left side).

Figure 1.5 To illustrate terrestrial heat balance. Note that the number of energy units absorbed by the earth's atmosphere and land-water surface just equals the units of energy radiated by the earth to space. Only about two-thirds of the total incoming solar radiation is utilized in heating the earth, one-third being reflected and scattered back to space. (*Adapted from Houghton.*)

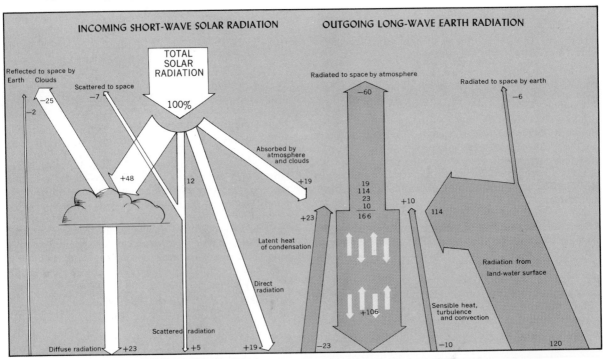

Scattering, reflection, and absorption. When a beam of solar energy passes through a relatively transparent medium such as air, some of the wavelengths are deflected from the direct beam by air molecules and very fine dust, including smoke haze, and sent in all directions. This phenomenon is known as *scattering.* True scattering occurs only when the diameters of the obscuring particles are smaller than the wavelengths of the radiation. Since the process is selective, with the shorter waves being affected most, various sky colors may result. A blue sky, for example, is the consequence of a more complete scattering by air molecules of the shorter wavelengths in the solar radiation beam. On the other hand, the sun appears red when seen through a smoke haze, because the blue light has been subtracted. Similarly, the ruddy cloud colors of sunset and sunrise result from cloud illumination by beams of light from which the blue portion of the spectrum has been removed by scattering. Because of scattering, there is a smaller amount of ultraviolet light in cities, where smoke is prevalent, than in the open country.

When the diameters of the obscuring particles are larger than the wavelengths of light, the result is *diffuse reflection,* which is caused by cloud droplets and larger dust and salt particles in the air. Being nonselective and therefore equally effective for all wavelengths, diffuse reflection does not affect sky color but rather light intensity. Thus the light reflected from a cloud when the sun is back of the observer is pure white. Also, the sun appears white when seen through a fog of water droplets.

The lengths of the solar waves do not change during the process of scattering and reflection, however; they are still fairly short waves and consequently the atmosphere does not absorb them readily.

The atmospheric gases are transparent to most of the wavelengths in the solar beam, and the air ocean transmits or reflects most sunlight. Those gases that do *absorb* are selective in their action, absorbing more of some wavelengths than of others. Water vapor is the controlling agent in atmospheric absorption; it absorbs six times as much solar radiation as all the other gases combined. Thus most absorption occurs in the lower atmosphere, where water vapor is found in greatest abundance.

The earth's albedo. A part of the solar energy which is scattered and reflected by clouds, the atmosphere, and the earth's land-sea surface is sent back to space and is therefore lost to the earth. This reflection from the earth (its *albedo*) causes the planet to shine brilliantly. It is earthshine that faintly illuminates the dark portion of the new moon, so that one sees the earth-lit part as "the old moon in the new moon's arms." The average earth albedo is estimated to be about 34 percent of the total solar radiation intercepted. The albedo varies with latitude, however. In the tropics and subtropics, probably about 30 percent of the solar radiation is reflected back to space. But in polar latitudes, the albedo increases to over 50 percent owing to the heavy cloud deck in high latitudes in summer, the long trajectory of oblique solar rays through the atmosphere, and the lasting winter snow cover which, like clouds, is an efficient reflecter. The albedo of different earth surfaces varies greatly, as these averages show:

Fresh snow	75–90 percent	Forests	3–10 percent
Old snow	50–70 percent	Grass	15–30 percent
Sand	15–25 percent	Bare	
		ground	7–20 percent

Diffuse daylight. Some of the solar energy scattered and reflected in the atmosphere, however, is not lost to space but reaches the earth's land-sea surface in the form of diffuse blue light from the sky, called diffuse daylight. At the surface it is transformed into heat and other forms of energy. It is diffuse daylight which prevents absolute darkness on cloudy days, indoors, or in the shade, where direct sunlight is absent. The energy transmitted to the earth in this form may constitute 25 to 30 percent of the total incoming solar energy. The more oblique the ray of sunlight, the thicker the layer of reflecting and scattering atmosphere through which it must pass. When the sun is only 4° above the horizon, the solar rays have to penetrate an atmosphere more than twelve times thicker than those coming from the sun at altitude 90°. This explains why one can look at the sun at sunrise and sunset without being blinded. In the higher latitudes, where the sun is never very far above the horizon and direct sunlight is consequently weak, diffuse daylight is the source of a large part of the solar energy received at the earth's surface. At Stockholm, Sweden (59°23′N), for example, 25 percent of the total solar energy in May, and 80 to 90 percent in winter, is in the form of diffuse daylight. At the poles, probably not more than 18 percent of the total solar radiation reaches ground level.

Amount of depletion.   The amount of depletion of solar radiation by scattering, reflection, and absorption depends upon two factors: the length of the passage through the atmosphere (in other words, the angle of the sun's rays), and the transparency of the atmosphere (Fig. 1.2). The length of the passage can be computed mathematically, but the transparency varies according to time and place, for it is affected by the amount of cloudiness and the turbidity of the atmosphere, as Fig. 1.2 shows. Quantitative estimates of the depletions of solar radiation passing through the atmosphere are difficult to arrive at, vary considerably between authorities, and must be considered as only approximate. One such approximation (after Houghton and others), made in terms of 100 units (or 100 percent) of solar radiation is as follows:

Reflected to space		
By clouds	25	
By the earth's land-sea surface	2	
Scattered by molecules of air and fine dust	7	34 units
Absorbed in the atmosphere		
By the atmosphere	17	
By clouds	2	19 units
Transmitted through the atmosphere and absorbed at the land-sea surface		
As direct sunlight	19	
As diffused radiation through clouds	23	
As scattered radiation	5	47 units
		100 units

According to this estimate 34 percent of the total solar radiation arriving at the outer limits of the atmosphere is returned to space in its original short-wave form (Fig. 1.5, left part). It plays no part in heating either the land-sea surface or the atmosphere. Only 19 percent of solar radiation is absorbed in the atmosphere and thereby heats it directly. The remaining 47 percent reaches the land-water surface, is absorbed by it, and heats it.

Thus only about two-thirds of the total incoming solar radiation (19 percent absorbed by the atmosphere and its clouds directly, and 47 percent absorbed by the earth's land-sea surface) becomes effective for heating the atmosphere. Also, a much larger percentage (47 percent) is absorbed by the earth's surface than by the atmosphere directly (19 percent). The solar energy absorbed by the earth's land-sea surface, therefore, represents by far the largest part of the total solar energy absorbed by the whole earth environment—surface and atmosphere. Consequently the atmosphere gains most of its heat indirectly, i.e., by transfer from the earth's land-sea surface. For a shallow ground layer of air, this is almost entirely true. *It is of the utmost climatic significance that the atmosphere is fueled mainly from below.*

The amount of solar radiation absorbed at the earth's surface, varies greatly over short periods of time and from one region to another. This is mainly because of variations in the amount of cloudiness and contrasts in the albedos of different land surfaces, for to a large extent these factors determine the amount of solar energy reflected to space. Such temporal and regional variations naturally have marked climatic effects. For example, since the average surface-air temperature lags behind the maximum solar radiation by about 4 to 8 weeks, it is obvious that a region's excess or deficiency of solar radiation at the earth's surface will have much to do with determining the future air temperature over a period of time such as a week or a month. The land-water surface acts as a great heat reservoir. It is able to absorb vast amounts of solar radiation, and it is warmed to considerable depths by this energy. Subsequently the stored energy is given up gradually to the atmosphere.

DISTRIBUTION OF SOLAR RADIATION

As discussed earlier, the belt of maximum solar radiation swings back and forth across the equator during the course of a year, following the shifting rays of the sun. Two variables, the angle of the sun's rays and the length of day, largely determine the amount of solar energy received at any time or place (effects of the atmosphere omitted).

Variations from pole to pole. *For the year as a whole,* solar radiation reaches a maximum at the equator and diminishes gradually and regularly toward minima at either pole (see the table below and Fig. 1.6a). At the poles the total amount of solar radiation received for the entire year is about 40 percent of that received at the equator.

Total annual solar radiation for various latitudes (Effects of an atmosphere omitted)

Latitude	Thermal days*	Latitude	Thermal days*
0°	365.2	50°	249.7
10°	360.2	60°	207.8
20°	345.2	70°	173.0
30°	321.0	80°	156.6
40°	288.5	90°	151.6

* The thermal day is the average total daily solar energy at the equator.

At the time of the equinoxes (about March 21 and September 23), when the sun's noon rays are vertical at the equator and the tangent rays reach the poles, latitudinal distribution of solar radiation resembles that for the year as a whole, since the maximum is at the equator with minima at the poles (Fig. 1.6b). Although the symmetrical curves representing annual and equinoctial latitudinal distributions of solar radiation are relatively similar in form, they differ in that solar radiation declines to zero at the poles at the time of the equinoxes, while this is not the case with annual distribution.

Not only does the latitudinal distribution of solar energy in spring and fall resemble that for the year as a whole, but patterns of temperature, pressure, winds, and precipitation over the earth in these transition seasons most closely approximate yearly averages. This is because it is in spring and fall that the Northern and Southern Hemispheres are receiving approximately equal amounts of solar radiation. The result is that temperature conditions in the two hemispheres are most nearly similar then, and pressure, wind, and precipitation conditions are likewise more in balance to the north and south of the equator.

At the time of the two solstices (about June 22 and December 22), when the noon rays of the sun are vertical on the $23\frac{1}{2}°$ parallels north or south, and the length of day increases from $66\frac{1}{2}°$ in the winter hemisphere to the pole in the summer hemisphere,[2] solar radiation is very unequally distributed in the two hemispheres. The summer hemisphere actually receives two to three times the amount of solar radiation received by the winter hemisphere. Neglecting for the moment the effects of the atmosphere, on about June 22 the zonal solar energy curve, beginning at zero at the Antarctic Circle, continues to rise steadily up to about latitude 44°N, in spite of the fact that the sun's rays are increasingly more oblique north of $23\frac{1}{2}°$N (Fig. 1.6c). North of this latitude, however, there is a slight decline in solar radiation, which continues to about latitude 62°N, because the more oblique rays of the sun offset the increased length of day. But the solar energy curve again rises north of 62°N and reaches an absolute maximum at the North Pole. The counterpart of this solar radiation curve, simply reversed as to hemisphere, occurs at the time of the winter solstice (Fig. 1.6d). The curve of solar energy distribution from pole to pole at the time of the solstices is complicated because it is a compromise between the effects of two important controls of solar radiation—angle of the sun's rays and length of day—which do not coincide in their latitudes of maximum effect. Thus on June 22, although

[2] By "summer" hemisphere is meant the hemisphere that has summer. Thus in July the Northern Hemisphere is the summer hemisphere and the Southern Hemisphere is the winter hemisphere. In January this situation is just reversed.

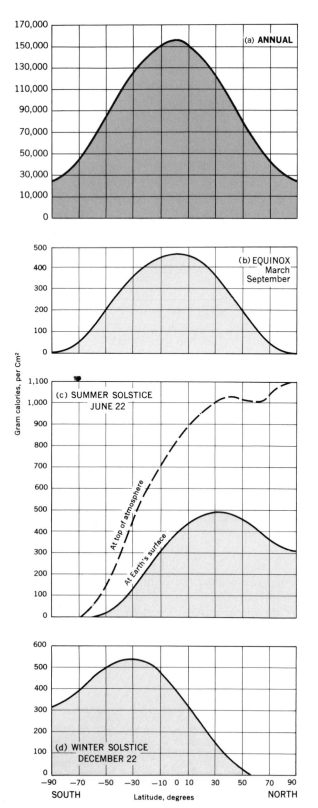

Gram calories, per Cm²

the sun's noon rays are vertical at parallel $23\frac{1}{2}°$N, days are longest beyond the Arctic Circle.

It can be seen from Fig. 1.6c that at the time of a solstice the latitudinal profiles of solar radiation are significantly different at the top of the atmosphere and at the earth's land-sea surface. Not only is there a general depletion of solar energy as a consequence of its passage through the atmosphere, but also there are some differences in the latitudinal locations of the peaks and hollows in the two profiles. For example, at the land-sea surface the peak of solar radiation does not occur at a pole; instead there is a broad maximum zone in the vicinity of latitude 40°, while the pole receives less radiation than the equator. In the summer hemisphere, solar energy is distributed fairly uniformly with latitude, so that there is no sharp maximum in any particular latitude, and the parallels in middle latitudes receive more than the equator does. Therefore the maximum surface-air temperatures in summer usually occur over land masses in the lower middle latitudes rather than at the equator. In the winter hemisphere, the latitudinal rate of change (gradient) in solar energy is greater.

These characteristics of solar radiation distribution at the seasonal extremes of summer and winter furnish the basic explanations for many features of global weather and climate. Some of these are (1) the striking latitudinal shifts of temperature, pressure, wind, and precipitation belts from summer to winter following a similar migration of solar radiation; (2) the high summer temperatures of the lower middle-latitude continents, where solar energy receipts are at a maximum; (3) the much greater latitudinal rate of change in temperatures in the winter hemisphere compared with the summer

Figure 1.6 Latitudinal distribution of solar energy at the earth's surface. For the year as a whole and at the two equinoxes, solar energy is symmetrically distributed between the Northern and Southern Hemispheres. There is a maximum in equatorial latitudes and minima at the North and South Poles. At the solstices, solar energy is very unequally distributed, with the summer hemisphere receiving two to three times the amount that the winter hemisphere does.

hemisphere—a situation which approximates the distribution of solar radiation; and (4) the greater storminess and variability of weather in the winter hemisphere compared with the summer hemisphere —a feature which is related to the steeper rate of temperature change (gradient) in the former.

Annual march by latitudes.   Annual solar radiation curves fall naturally into three groups: low-, middle-, and high-latitude curves (Fig. 1.7).

1. The low-latitude, or tropical, curve, which is characteristic of the belt lying between the Tropic of Cancer and the Tropic of Capricorn, remains constantly high, with little seasonal variation. This accounts for the continuously high year-round temperatures of the tropics. During the course of a year, all places situated between the two tropics are passed over twice by the vertical rays of the sun, so that the solar radiation curve for the low latitudes shows two weak maxima and two weak minima.

2. The middle-latitude curve for the belts lying between $23\frac{1}{2}°$ and $66\frac{1}{2}°$ in each hemisphere shows a single strong maximum and a single minimum, both of which coincide with the solstices. Like the tropics, the middle latitudes have no period

when solar radiation is absent, so that the curve does not reach zero at any time. Nevertheless, it shows far greater seasonal extremes, which are reflected in greater seasonal extremes of temperature.

3. The polar solar radiation curve for latitudes poleward of the Arctic and Antarctic Circles resembles that of the middle latitudes in that it has one maximum and one minimum, coinciding with the summer and winter solstices. It differs from both the other curves in that it does reach zero; during a portion of the year, the high latitudes have no direct sunlight (Fig. 1.4).

Annual march at top and bottom of atmosphere.   At stations in high latitudes, there is a close correspondence between the annual march of solar radiation upon a horizontal surface at ground level and that at the top of the atmosphere. In other words, for both levels the maximum and minimum occur close to the solstice dates.

In middle latitudes, while the correspondence between the march of solar radiation at the top and bottom of the atmosphere is not as close as in high latitudes, the two curves still show peaks and depths occurring at the same general times. The maximum ground-level radiation is most commonly received during May to July in the Northern Hemisphere, the minimum during November to January—periods which include the solstices.

But in the wet tropics of equatorial latitudes, there is little correspondence between the annual march of solar radiation at the top of the atmosphere and that at ground level. Indeed, they are characteristically out of phase, in part because of the small annual range of solar radiation in low latitudes, but mostly because the belts of cloud (and rainfall) commonly follow the sun in low latitudes, so that cloudiness is at a maximum during the period of high sun. This is less true outside the tropics. Consequently the equatorial latitudes have a wider diversity of low-level solar radiation regimes than the middle and high latitudes do.

At the equator, for example, the annual variation in the daily value of solar radiation at the top of the atmosphere is only 13 percent, and at latitude

Figure 1.7 Annual march of solar radiation received at the outer limits of the earth's atmosphere at different latitudes. In the very low latitudes close to the equator, the amount of solar energy received at the top of the atmosphere is large, and varies little throughout the year. In the middle and higher latitudes, there are large seasonal differences in the receipts of solar energy.

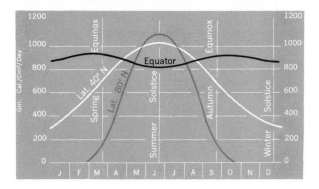

10° N and S, it is only 22 percent. But because of variations in cloudiness, atmospheric turbidity, and diffuse reflection in the atmosphere, radiation received at the ground in the tropics ranges anywhere from about 20 to 80 percent of that received at the outer atmosphere. With the solar radiation regime at the top of the atmosphere so nearly uniform within the broad belt of the wet tropics, radiation at ground level becomes chiefly a function of cloudiness. For instance, Rangoon, Burma, at about 17°N, receives nearly 75 percent more ground-level radiation in low-sun February than in high-sun July, even though in July the outer-atmosphere radiation is 20 percent greater. Greater cloudiness in July offsets the effects of higher sun. Thus in equatorial latitudes there is a close inverse relationship between cloudiness and ground-level solar radiation.

Distribution of observed solar energy. The distribution of observed annual solar radiation by latitude belts at the earth's land-sea surface is shown in Fig. 1.8. Note the slight decline in radiation in the cloudy equatorial latitudes. (Compare Figs. 1.8 and 1.6a.) On the map (Fig. 1.9) showing average *annual* distribution of solar radiation at ground level, the following facts can be observed:

1. The values range from a low of under 70 kilogram calories per square centimeter, found only in the high latitudes, to a high of over 220 in the eastern Sahara of North Africa. The highest value is thus more than three times the smallest.

Figure 1.8 Total annual solar radiation, direct and diffuse, received at the earth's land-sea surface by latitude belts (in kg cal per cm² per year). (*Data from Budyko.*)

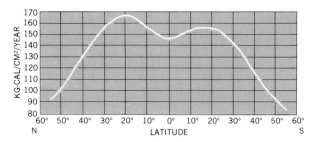

2. A general zonal pattern of distribution is conspicuous in the middle and higher latitudes, with the values declining poleward. Solar radiation in higher latitudes is primarily a seasonal phenomenon: little radiation is received in winter, and a very large part of the year's total is concentrated between the spring and autumn equinoxes.

3. In the high latitudes, the lowest annual radiation values are over oceans. In general these areas of least radiation coincide with the abundant cloud associated with the great semipermanent, oceanic, low-pressure cells, which will be described in Chapter 3.

4. A zonal pattern of distribution is not conspicuous in the tropics, where the amount of cloud is highly variable from region to region.

5. Even though equatorial latitudes have the greatest receipts of solar radiation at the outer limits of the atmosphere, they show a weak secondary minimum at the land-water surface (Figs. 1.8, 1.6a). This reflects the cloudiness of the inner tropics. Within the equatorial belt, centers of least solar radiation tend to coincide with the warm continents, where convection is strong and cumulus cloud abundant. Thus cloudy inner Amazonia in South America receives less than 120 kg cal per cm²—about on a par with central and southern Japan, the Great Lakes region of North America, and southern France and northern Italy. Equatorial West Africa also shows relatively low radiation values.

6. The zonal maxima of solar radiation are in the subtropics, where high-pressure cells, many large deserts, and relatively little cloud, especially over the land, are the rule. The largest continuous area of high solar radiation values generally coincides with the extensive dry lands of northern Africa and southwestern Asia. Other important centers of high radiation values, all of which are dry regions with little cloud, are located in the southwestern United States and northern Mexico, northern Chile and northwestern Argentina, southern (and especially southwestern) Africa, and Australia.

Seasonal maps. At the time of the solstices in June and December, when the sun's vertical rays

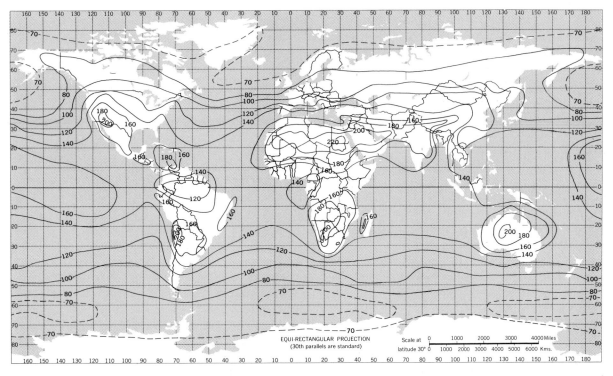

Figure 1.9 Total solar radiation received at the earth's land-sea surface during the entire *year* in kg cal per cm² per year. (*After Landsberg.*)

have shifted to their extreme northern and southern limits, naturally the distribution of solar radiation at the earth's land-sea surface is markedly different from the annual averages.

In *June,* as during the whole year, the zonal pattern of distribution still continues to be much more conspicuous in the high latitudes than in the low latitudes (Fig. 1.10). The highest values, of course, are in the Northern Hemisphere, although their centers (usually located between about latitudes 20 and 40°N over the land) are not very far north of the centers of highest value on the annual map. The most striking changes are those in radiation values for the high latitudes of the Northern Hemisphere and the middle latitudes of the Southern Hemisphere. For example, in June the latitudinal rate of change (gradient) in radiation over the Northern Hemisphere is weak, so that Arctic North America

receives almost as much radiation as the region of maximum values in the subtropics, and more than most equatorial regions. In the winter hemisphere south of the equator, radiation values are relatively low, as would be expected. Actually, northernmost North America receives up to thirteen times as much radiation as the cloudy southernmost extremity of South America.

In *December* there is a large-scale reversal of the June distribution, although a zonal pattern still prevails in the higher latitudes of both hemispheres (Fig. 1.11). In the Northern Hemisphere high latitudes, where days are short and the sun's rays oblique, daily mean values of radiation drop below 50 gm cal. The highest values are in the relatively cloudless continental deserts of the Southern Hemisphere, which receive much more radiation than the cloudier equatorial latitudes.

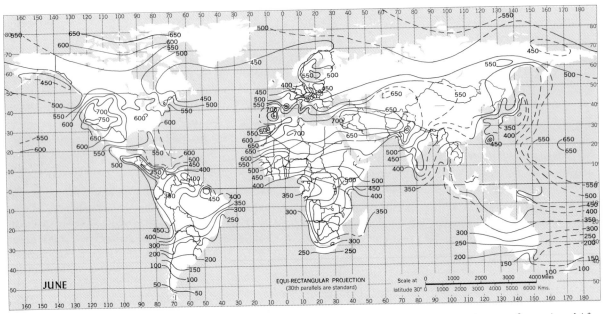

Figure 1.10   Total solar radiation received at the earth's land-sea surface in *June*, in gm cal per cm² per day. (*After Löf, Duffie, and Smith.*)

Figure 1.11   Total solar radiation received at the earth's land-sea surface in *December*, in gm cal per cm² per day. (*After Löf, Duffie and Smith.*)

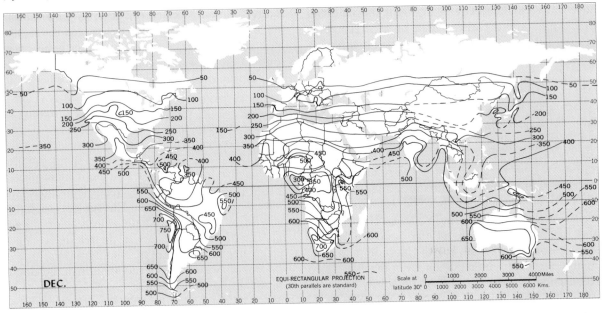

SELECTED REFERENCES FOR FURTHER STUDY OF TOPICS IN CHAPTER ONE

Note: References are inclusive. In order to avoid repeating long titles, reference many times is made to a particular book through the author's last name only. For the complete title of any book, its publisher, and date of publication, see the list of general references on pp. 4–5.

1. **Solar energy: its nature, transmission, and distribution.**   Blair and Fite, pp. 61–78; Blüthgen, pp. 44–61; Byers, pp. 1–44; *Compendium of Meteorology*, pp. 13–33, pp. 379–389; Critchfield, pp. 14–22; Conrad, pp. 1–15; Haurwitz and Austin, pp. 1–21; Kendrew, pp. 1–13; Landsberg, pp. 120–134; Alissow, Drosdow, and Rubinstein, pp. 23–61; Petterssen, pp. 87–99; Riehl, *Introduction to the Atmosphere*, pp. 31–47.

2. **General references on solar radiation.** M. I. Budyko, *The Heat Balance of the Earth's Surface* (translation), U.S. Weather Bureau, Washington, D.C., 1958; M. I. Budyko et al., "The Heat Balance of the Surface of the Earth," *Soviet Geog.: Rev. Transl.* Vol. 3, pp. 3–16, May, 1962; Farrington Daniels, *Direct Use of the Sun's Energy*, Yale University Press, New Haven, Conn., 1964; H. E. Landsberg, "Solar Radiation at the Earth's Surface," *Solar Energy*, Vol. 5, no. 3, pp. 95–98, 1961; H. E. Landsberg, H. Lippmann, K. H. Paffen, and C. Troll, *World Maps of Climatology*, 2d ed., E. Rodenwaldt and H. J. Jusatz (eds.), Springer-Verlag OHG, Berlin, 1965: Map 1, Mean January Sunshine (hours), by Lippmann; Map 2, Mean July Sunshine (hours), by Lippmann; Map 3, Total Hours of Sunshine (annual), by Landsberg; Map 4, Generalized Isolines of Global Radiation (Kcal/cm^2/yr), by Landsberg; Map 5, Seasonal Climates of the Earth, by Troll and Paffen (each map 1 : 45,000,000); G. O. G. Löf, J. A. Duffie, and C. O. Smith, *World Distribution of Solar Radiation*, Engineering Exp. Sta. Rep. 21, The University of Wisconsin, Madison, 1966.

CHAPTER TWO

TEMPERATURE OF THE ATMOSPHERE

As discussed in Chapter 1, the ultimate source of the atmosphere's energy, thermal and otherwise, is solar energy. But because high-temperature solar energy is in the form of such short wavelengths, probably less than 20 percent of the solar rays entering the earth's atmosphere are absorbed directly by it. In order to be readily absorbed by the air, short-wave solar energy first must be converted into low-temperature, long-wave terrestrial energy.

This conversion takes place mainly at the earth's land-sea surface, which is able to absorb much more of the incident solar energy than the relatively transparent atmosphere can. Solar energy absorbed at the earth's land-sea surface is converted into heat and other forms of energy. The earth itself then becomes a radiating body, but at a much lower temperature (averaging about 60°F or 15°C)[1] than the sun, so that the wavelengths of radiation are far longer. Thus the atmosphere receives

---

[1]Unless stated otherwise, temperatures are given in °F. Conversion from °F to °C, and vice versa, can be made by means of the following formulas (see also Fig. 2.1):

$$°C = \tfrac{5}{9} \, (°F + 40) - 40 \text{ or } °C = \tfrac{5}{9} \, (°F - 32)$$
$$°F = \tfrac{9}{5} \, (°C + 40) - 40 \text{ or } °F = \tfrac{9}{5} \, °C + 32$$

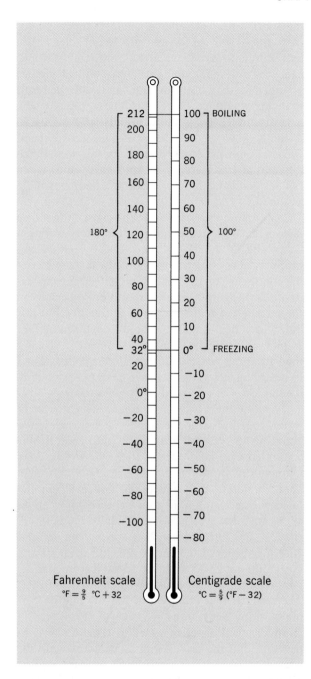

Figure 2.1   Temperatures can be converted from °F to °C, and vice versa, by a direct comparison of the two scales, or by using a conversion formula.

most of its heat indirectly from the sun and directly from the earth's surface, which in turn had previously absorbed, and itself been warmed by, solar energy. It has been estimated that the atmosphere absorbs nearly seven times more energy from the earth's land-sea surface than from solar radiation directly. On a sunny day, the striking decrease in temperature from the solar-heated hot sand or soil to the air above at a height of a few feet demonstrates that the main heat source for the lowest atmosphere is the ground. Thus a sandy beach may reach a midday temperature of 140°; in the air a quarter inch above the sand, the temperature can still be 135°; but at 3 ft, it may be down to 105°; and at the height of man, or about 6 ft, it may be only 98°—a difference of 42° within a 6-ft layer.

Differential heating of land and water surfaces. Various kinds of land and water surfaces react differently to incident solar energy in terms of reflection, absorption, and transmission, so that their potential for heating the atmosphere varies. Naturally, the surfaces which absorb relatively larger proportions of solar energy and retain it in a relatively thin surface layer are the ones which will themselves heat (and cool) most quickly, and so will have the promptest effect on the air above.

Considering land areas alone, there are marked differences in the heating characteristics of various types of solid surface. Dissimilar reflecting properties account for some of the differences, since solar energy does not heat a surface that reflects it. Snow, which reflects 70 to 90 percent of the solar radiation that falls on it, heats very slowly indeed. On the other hand, dry black soil reflects only 8 to 14 percent of the sun's rays, grass 14 to 37 percent, and coniferous forest less than 10 percent. Solar energy retained by the ground is disposed of mainly in three ways: by heat flux downward into the soil, heat flux upward to the air, and evapotranspiration (evaporation + transpiration) from moist surfaces, including vegetation. Surfaces from which evaporation is great heat more slowly. The same is true of those with high soil conductivity, which transmit a larger proportion of the heat they receive downward to lower layers.

Although the heating properties of the many kinds of land surfaces vary considerably, the greatest contrasts are those between land and water surfaces, which react so differently to solar radiation that they produce two unlike climates: oceanic and continental. The surfaces of relatively deep bodies of water heat and cool slowly compared with land surfaces. By far the most important reason for this slowness of temperature change is that in highly mobile matter such as water (and also air), redistribution of heat occurs mainly through turbulence. Heat in the solid earth is redistributed by molecular heat conduction, and so proceeds by moving from particle to particle; but ocean waves, drifts, currents, tides, and convectional overturning systems all act to disperse the absorbed solar energy throughout a large mass. Obviously no such mixing can occur on land. Therefore when land and water surfaces have identical amounts of solar energy falling on them, the land surface heats more rapidly and reaches a higher temperature.

Moreover, when a water surface begins to cool, vertical convectional movements are set up, and the cooler, heavier surface layers sink to be replaced by warmer water from underneath, Consequently the whole mass of water must be cooled before the surface layers can be brought to a low temperature. Thus a larger mass of water than land can impart its heat to the surrounding air, and for a longer period of time. As a consequence the water surface cools more slowly.

There are other contrasts between the properties of land and water which contribute to their differential heating and cooling, but these are much less important compared with mixing due to turbulence and convectional overturning. The effects on surface temperatures of land-water differences in reflection, specific heat, transmission of solar radiation, and evaporation all appear to be minor. For example, the average reflection (albedo) from the great variety of the earth's land surfaces is not very much different from that of the oceans. And volume for volume,

the specific heat of water is only 2.5 times greater than that of soil. As for transmission of solar radiation, it might seem that water's transparency would cause the rays of the sun to penetrate a much greater volume of it than of the opaque land, with the result that this would be one of the major reasons why a land surface heats more rapidly and intensely. Actually, however, the longer of the solar spectrum waves do not penetrate water very far, so that the differential transparency of land and water, while not insignificant, is less important than might be assumed.

Differential evaporation is also one of the minor factors creating temperature differences between water and land surfaces, since over water, evaporation is always at a maximum. In large areas of the continents, on the other hand, effective evaporation is less than potential evaporation, especially in the interiors of middle-latitude continents. But this differential does not always hold true, for in the wet tropics, evaporation from the continents is greater than from the oceans. Large-scale evaporation and its retarding effects on excessive heating and cooling is therefore not restricted to ocean surfaces.

Thus the turbulence and mixing which occur in water, together with the minor factors mentioned above, cause water to heat and cool to great depths compared with land. Observations show that daily temperature variations do not penetrate more than about 3 ft into the solid earth, and even annual temperature changes go to a depth of only about 47 ft. In quiet water, however, daily temperature changes are felt at least 20 ft below the surface. And it is believed that in oceans and deep lakes a layer 600 to 2,000 ft thick is subject to annual temperature variations, owing chiefly to turbulence. The result is that radiation in the summer or during a sunny day in any season will slowly heat a relatively thick layer of water to a moderate temperature, but on land a thin layer will usually be heated to a high temperature. In winter and at night, water draws upon heat reserves accumulated within a large volume and so cools slowly, but a land surface, being shallowly heated, loses heat rapidly.

Continental and oceanic climates. With the same amount of incident solar energy, a land surface reaches a higher temperature, and reaches it more quickly, than a water surface. Conversely, a land surface cools more rapidly and cools to a lower temperature than a water surface. Land-controlled, or continental, climates are therefore characterized by large daily and seasonal extremes of temperature, with the maximum and minimum air temperatures closely following the times of maximum and minimum solar radiation. By contrast, ocean-controlled, or marine, climates have moderate air temperatures, smaller daily and seasonal ranges of temperature, and a greater time lag of the maximum and minimum seasonal temperatures after the maximum and minimum of solar radiation. In the middle and higher latitudes there are striking differences between the temperatures of marine and continental climates, principally because the solid earth does not store up so large an amount of heat. The ocean, on the other hand, has a vast potential for heat storage, mostly because it distributes energy absorbed at the surface throughout a great volume. At the ocean surface, temperatures probably do not change more than 1° between day and night, and seasonal changes also are very small.

HEATING AND COOLING THE ATMOSPHERE

The atmosphere is heated by solar energy, directly through absorption, and indirectly through processes involving conduction, radiation, and condensation. The heat acquired by these processes is then transferred from one part of the atmosphere to another by vertical and horizontal currents.

Atmospheric absorption of solar radiation

As Chapter 1 discussed, only some 19 percent of the incoming solar radiation is absorbed by the gases of the atmosphere, mostly by water vapor. About one-half of this absorption takes place in the lower 2 km of air, where water vapor is concentrated. But since a layer of air 2 km thick is a large mass through which to spread 9 to 10 percent of the original solar beam, the process of absorption is not a large factor in producing the normal daytime rise in surface-air temperature. For example, on a clear, cold winter day, when the land surface is blanketed by a reflecting snow cover, surface air temperatures may remain extremely low in spite of a bright sun. At the same time, the air close to the south side of an absorbing brick wall or building, where short-wave sun energy is being converted into long-wave terrestrial energy, may be comfortably warm.

Conduction

When two bodies of unequal temperature are in contact with one another, energy in the form of heat passes from the warmer to the colder until they both attain the same temperature. In the absence of a snow cover, the solid earth during daylight hours reaches a higher temperature than the air above. This is because land is a more efficient absorber of solar energy than air. Then, by conduction, a thin layer of air resting immediately upon the warmer earth becomes heated. But air is a poor conductor, so that heat from the warmed lower layer of air is transferred only very slowly to the layers above. Heating the atmosphere by molecular conduction, which is primarily a daytime and a summer phenomenon, is negligible in importance, except where turbulence constantly replaces the heated lowest surface layer of air. Even so, however, conduction is not a major process of atmospheric heating and heat transfer.

Just as a warm land surface on a summer day heats the air layer next to it by conduction, so a cold surface, chilled by terrestrial radiation on a winter night, cools the adjacent air. As a result of radiation, and to a lesser degree conduction, the lowest layer of air on clear, calm winter nights frequently becomes colder than the layers some hundreds of feet higher. This effect, called a temperature inversion, will be discussed later in the chapter.

Earth radiation

As described earlier, the 47 percent of the short-wave solar energy which is absorbed at the earth's land-sea surface is transformed into heat or consumed in evapotranspiration. Through this absorption and conversion of solar energy, the heated land-water surface becomes a radiating body whose average temperature is about 60°. As already discussed, the spectrum of earth radiation is composed of long-wave energy, so that unlike solar radiation, it is not visible to the human eye. Although the atmosphere is relatively transparent to short-wave solar energy, it is able to absorb and retain perhaps as much as 80 to 90 percent of the outgoing long-wave earth radiation (see Fig. 1.5).

Among the atmosphere's gases, the chief absorber and emitter of earth radiation is water vapor, and to a lesser degree, carbon dioxide. Water vapor absorbs selectively in the terrestrial radiation spectrum, being much more transparent to certain wavelengths than to others. The larger the amount of water vapor in the air, the greater the amount of absorption. In deserts, for example, where dry air and clear skies permit a swift escape of earth energy to space, rapid night cooling is the rule.

It can be seen that the effect of the atmosphere is that of a heat trap, which permits 70 to 75 percent (47 units) of the effective solar energy (66 units) to reach the ground before it is absorbed, but allows only some 5 percent (6 units) of the upward moving long-wave radiation from the ground (120 units) to escape directly to space (Fig. 1.5). It is because the atmosphere is able to absorb so much of the earth radiation, and to retard its eventual escape to space through a repeated and complex radiation exchange between ground and atmosphere, that night cooling is slowed. This process is sometimes called the *greenhouse effect* of the atmosphere, for the glass roof and sides of a greenhouse permit easy entrance of short-wave solar energy but largely absorb the

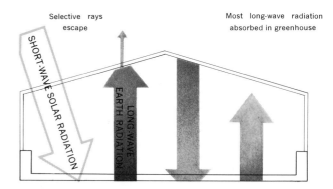

Figure 2.2 Illustrating the "greenhouse effect" of the earth's atmosphere. The glass in the roof and sides of the greenhouse, like the atmosphere, is relatively transparent to short-wave solar energy, but relatively opaque to long-wave earth radiation.

long-wave heat energy and so greatly delay its escape (Fig. 2.2, right side). A more universal illustration of the greenhouse effect is the superheating of the inside of an automobile that occurs on a sunny day when the car is parked with its windows closed.

If there were no atmosphere, probably about 80 units of the total solar radiation would be absorbed by the ground, and the average loss to space (albedo) would approximate 20 percent. This would produce a mean earth temperature of about 15° instead of the present 60°. Thus the greenhouse effect creates an average earth temperature which is markedly higher than it would be otherwise. A further consequence of the greenhouse effect is that it greatly retards night cooling and thereby moderates the diurnal range of surface temperature.

Radiation under clear skies.   Although, as the previous section said, an average of 6 units of the total earth radiation (5 percent) escapes directly to space, the rate of loss by regions varies greatly with differing atmospheric conditions. The maximum loss occurs under cloudless skies. But even the rate of loss with clear skies is variable, since the water vapor in the air is by far the most effective absorber of earth radiation among the atmosphere's gases, and the amount of water vapor is extremely variable both with regions and with time. Heat loss is least when the air's moisture content not only is high, but also is concentrated in the lower few thousand feet of air, where temperatures are highest.

Most of the long-wave earth radiation is absorbed by the water vapor, which in turn sends out long-wave radiation to the layers of atmosphere both above and below it, and also back down to the ground surface. Each successive absorbing layer of water vapor goes through the same process of absorption and radiation. The total result of this complex pattern of upward and downward streams of radiation is the greenhouse effect: retardation of the loss of heat from the earth to space. An atmosphere with high moisture content in its lower layers absorbs and reradiates downward more earth radiation than a dry atmosphere. This is a main reason why the daily range of temperature is greater in dry than in humid air. Since water vapor, the chief absorber of both solar and terrestrial radiation, diminishes rapidly with altitude (half of all the atmosphere's water vapor lies below 6,600 ft), both the incoming and the outgoing radiation increase with altitude. Thus high mountains may be called the "radiation windows" of the earth.

Radiation of terrestrial energy from the earth's surface upward toward space is a continuous process. During the daylight hours up to about midafternoon, however, more energy is received from the sun than is radiated from the earth, so that surface-air temperatures usually continue to rise until two to four o'clock in the afternoon. During the night, when receipts of solar energy cease, a continued loss of energy through earth radiation results in a cooling of the land surface and a drop in air temperature. Being a more efficient radiator than air, the ground during the night usually becomes cooler than the air above it. When this happens, the lower layers of atmosphere lose heat by radiation to the colder ground as well as upward toward space. During long winter nights when skies are clear and the air is dry and relatively calm, excessively rapid and long-continued out-radiation takes place.

Effects of a cloud cover. Radiation conditions under a cloud cover are very different from those under a clear sky, even when the air is equally humid in both cases. Water vapor, a gas, is selective in its absorption of earth radiation, letting some wavelengths escape and absorbing others. But a cloud sheet, composed of water droplets or ice particles, absorbs and radiates in all wavelengths, like a blackbody (the hypothetical object described in Chapter 1). That is, at the base of a cloud all upward-moving radiation in all wavelengths is completely absorbed. The returning stream of radiation from cloud to earth consequently includes all the wavelengths the cloud received, whereas water vapor, since it allows some wavelengths to escape through the atmosphere to space, sends less total radiation back to earth.

Because of the total absorption by clouds, the effect of a cloud cover is to considerably retard night cooling of the solid earth and the lower atmosphere. (In addition, the cloud deck may actually be warmer than the land surface, either because the clouds have moved in from warmer latitudes, or because of the extra heat which condensation releases into the air.) Under a night sky covered with low cloud, the net loss of heat from the ground is only about one-seventh the loss with clear skies. The higher the cloud cover, the less effective it is in retarding the heat loss from the ground. Thus the net loss under cirrostratus clouds located at a height of about 4 miles is nearly 80 percent of that for clear skies, while the loss is only 14 percent under nimbus and stratus clouds somewhat less than 1 mile high. In contrast to the effects of clouds at night, a daytime cloud cover reflects much of the incoming solar radiation and sends it back to space, in this way retarding surface heating and reducing the stored-up energy in the earth.

Since a cloud deck makes for warmer nights and cooler days, its net effect on *average* temperature for the 24 hours may be small. So while clear skies promote high daytime and low nighttime temperatures, and therefore large diurnal ranges, clouds result in a greater uniformity of temperature and small diurnal ranges. In the Sahara's cloudless skies and dry air, there are cases of daytime temperatures of 90° or above being followed by night temperatures slightly below freezing.

Effects of a snow surface.   A snow cover favors low temperatures. Daytime heating during short winter days is slight, for most of the solar radiation is reflected by the snow and thus does not heat the ground under it. At night the snow, which is an efficient radiator but a very poor conductor of heat, allows little heat to come up from the soil below to replenish that lost by radiation from the top of the snow surface. As a result the snow surface becomes excessively cold, and then so does the air layer resting upon it.

Effects of a water surface.   Water, like land, is a good radiator, but the cooled surface waters keep constantly sinking and are replaced by warmer water from below. Extremely low temperatures over water bodies are therefore impossible until they are frozen over, after which they act like a snow-covered land surface.

Latent heat of condensation

A large proportion of the solar energy which reaches the earth's surface is used in evaporating moisture from the land-water surface and from vegetation. The process of evaporation changes the moisture into water vapor, one of the atmosphere's gases. This transformed solar energy is thus contained in the air in latent or potential form. When condensation takes place, the latent energy is again released into the atmosphere and heats it. The air retains this heat when the condensed water falls to the ground as precipitation. (See Fig. 1.5.)

It appears that the single most important heat transfer process at the earth-atmosphere interface is evaporation, which provides about half the atmosphere's fuel, in the form of water vapor.[2] More than

[2] Michael Garstang. "Sensible and Latent Heat Exchange in Low Latitude Synoptic Scale Systems." *Proc. Sea-Air Interaction Conference.* Tallahassee, Fla., Feb. 23–25, 1965. U.S. Weather Bureau, Washington, D.C., Aug. 20, 1965.

half this fuel is supplied to the lower atmosphere by tropical oceans between 30°N and 30°S. So latent energy represented by water vapor derived from evaporation constitutes the most important single component of the atmosphere's heat budget. Above a shallow surface layer a few thousand feet thick (in which turbulence is the major factor), the latent heat contained in clouds is responsible for most of the upward heat transfer throughout the troposphere.

Transfer of heat by air currents

The energy acquired by the atmosphere through conduction, radiation, and condensation, as well as through direct absorption of solar energy, can be transferred from one part of the atmosphere to another by vertical and horizontal currents. Such a transfer, and the accompanying mixing processes, leads to changes in air temperature.

Vertical mixing by turbulence.   While for the atmosphere as a whole, the air remains suspended without rising or falling (see Chap. 3), individual masses of air do move upward and downward, and by such a process transfer heat. This is called turbulence. (See Fig. 1.5.)

Some turbulence is thermally induced. On a clear summer morning the ground heats up from solar radiation and, by conduction and radiation processes, in turn heats a shallow layer of air adjacent to it. The expanded warm air is buoyant, like a cork held under water, and tends to rise. The original small updrafts often combine into columns of rising air called *thermals*. The rising warm air mixes with that which it displaces, and the warm air particles give up some of their heat to the cooler air above. In the spaces between the thermals or rising air columns, there is a compensating downward motion. Such a vertical exchange, or convection system, creates a mixed layer which gradually becomes thicker as the day advances, shrinks as evening approaches, and disappears during the night as the ground air becomes chilled and convection halts. Over oceans, where daily variations in temperature are almost absent, vertical mixing by thermal turbulence continues both night and day as long as sea-surface temperature exceeds air temperature.

Another form of up-and-down motion is created by a process called mechanical turbulence. Internal eddying produces some mechanical turbulence, but most of it is the result of friction in fast-moving air as it passes over a rough land surface. The main roughnesses are associated with terrain features, such as mountains; but trees and buildings can also cause mechanical turbulence. Its effect on vertical temperature distribution is the same as that of thermal convection: heat carried upward from the land-sea surface creates a mixed lower layer of atmosphere, varying from a few hundred to several thousand feet in thickness. This is called the friction layer. As a method of heat transfer, turbulence of whatever kind is most important in that part of the atmosphere below the height of the cloud-base level.

Horizontal mixing by advection.   Advection refers to the transportation of any atmospheric property, such as temperature or humidity, by the horizontal movement of air (that is, by wind). In the Northern Hemisphere's middle latitudes, for example, a south wind is usually associated with unseasonably high temperatures. As an air mass of tropical origin advances northward over the central and eastern United States, it carries with it the heat and temperatures acquired in its source region, where high temperatures are normal.

Such an importation of southerly warmth in winter results in mild weather, with melting snow and sloppy streets. In summer, several days of south wind may produce a heat wave, with maximum temperatures higher than 90°. In the same way, advection of air from polar latitudes, or from the cold interior of a winter continent, causes a drop in temperature. Air from over an ocean brings a continent not only moderating temperatures, but also vast amounts of water vapor, creating an environment favorable to cloud and precipitation. An invasion of dry desert air, on the other hand, sharply diminishes the atmosphere's moisture content.

HEAT BALANCE OF THE EARTH

Referring again to the left-hand portion of Fig. 1.5, which shows the effects of the atmosphere upon incoming solar radiation, note that in all, some 66 percent of the solar radiation received at the outer limits of the earth's atmosphere is absorbed either by the atmosphere (19 percent) or by the earth's land-sea surface (47 percent). This 66 percent is called the *effective solar radiation,* for it is the portion which is available for heating the atmosphere. The remaining 34 percent is simply returned to space in the form of short-wave solar radiation. Since the yearly mean temperature of the earth as a whole is neither increasing nor decreasing, it follows that the 66 percent of solar radiation gained is balanced by an equal amount of energy radiated back to space in the form of long-wave earth radiation. This is spoken of as the *terrestrial heat balance.*

The right-hand side of Fig. 1.5 illustrates one estimate of the operation of the terrestrial heat balance. Of the 120 units of energy radiated upward from the ground, 6 units pass directly through the atmosphere to space, and consequently play no part in heating the air. The remaining 114 units are absorbed by the atmosphere. But 106 of these are reradiated back to the ground surface, resulting in a net gain of 8 units by the atmosphere. The atmosphere also gains 10 units by heat transport from the earth's surface through turbulence and convection currents. Another 23 units are transferred as evaporated moisture from the ground to the atmosphere, where subsequently they will be released as latent heat of condensation.

So far, we have 19 (solar energy units absorbed directly by the atmosphere) + 114 + 10 + 23 = 166 units, or the total earth radiation absorbed by the atmosphere. Of this, 106 units are reradiated

Incoming solar radiation and outgoing earth radiation (Northern Hemisphere)*

Latitude	0°	10°	20°	30°	40°	50°	60°	70°	80°	90°
Incoming radiation absorbed	0.339	0.334	0.320	0.297	0.267	0.232	0.193	0.160	0.144	0.140
Outgoing radiation lost	0.271	0.282	0.284	0.284	0.282	0.277	0.272	0.260	0.252	0.252
Difference	+0.068	+0.052	+0.036	+0.013	−0.015	−0.045	−0.079	−0.100	−0.108	−0.112

* Annual means are given for each latitude in gm cal per cm² per min.

Source: After Simpson.

back to the ground, while 60 are radiated by the atmosphere to space. These 60, plus the 6 which were radiated directly to space by the ground, total 66 earth radiation units—just equal to the 66 units of solar radiation absorbed by the ground and the atmosphere.

On first thought, it may seem odd that the earth's land-sea surface radiates more than it receives from the sun, but actually this is logical in view of the complex streams of up-and-down radiation involved in the atmosphere's greenhouse effect. Keep in mind, however, that the figures given above are largely intelligent estimates subject to revision as more accurate measurements or computations are made.

Latitudinal heat balance

While for the earth as a whole, gains in solar energy equal losses to space of earth energy, this is not the case for most latitudes (see Fig. 2.3 and the table above). In the low latitudes equatorward from about 35–40°, the earth and atmosphere together gain more heat from solar radiation than they lose to space by earth radiation; in the middle and high latitudes poleward from 40°, the opposite is true. Thus there is a continuing net gain of energy in low latitudes and a net loss in middle and higher latitudes. The tropics are not becoming progressively warmer and the polar regions colder, however;

Figure 2.3 In the lower latitudes equatorward of about 37°, the annual amount of incoming solar radiation exceeds the losses from outgoing earth radiation. The reverse is true for the middle and higher latitudes, where losses from outgoing earth radiation exceed the gains from incoming solar radiation.

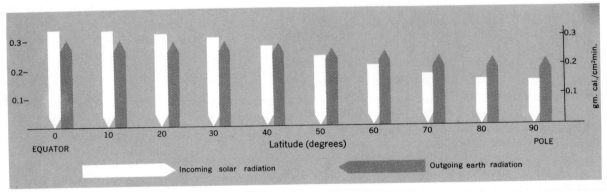

instead, a continuous large-scale transfer of heat from low to high latitudes is carried out by atmospheric and oceanic circulations.

In order to preserve the heat balance in the various latitudes of the earth, the following average quantities of heat must be carried poleward:

Lat, North	10^{19} cal per day
0°	0
10°	4.05
20°	7.68
30°	10.46
40°	11.12
50°	9.61
60°	6.68
70°	3.41
80°	0.94
90°	0.00

Heat transfer from the tropics poleward takes place throughout the year, but at a much slower rate in summer than in winter. The reason is that the temperature difference between low and high latitudes is considerably smaller in summer than in winter—only about half as large in the Northern Hemisphere. As would be expected, the winter hemisphere has a net energy loss and the summer hemisphere a net gain. Most of the summertime gain is stored in the surface layers of land and ocean, mainly in the ocean.

The unequal latitudinal distribution of solar and terrestrial radiation is the ultimate cause of the earth's atmospheric and oceanic circulations. Only through the transfer of heat by winds and ocean waters can latitudinal energy imbalances be equalized. Of the total heat transport in subtropical and middle latitudes, about 75 percent is carried out by atmospheric circulation and 25 percent by ocean water movements. Not only is the great system of planetary winds involved, but also most other phenomena of weather and climate, including atmospheric disturbances (storms). As the table above shows, the greatest transfer of heat is required in the middle latitudes. Naturally the greatest turbulence and storminess is found in regions where there is a maximum of advection and air-mass movement.

Components of the heat budget

As described above, the polar and middle latitudes consistently show a negative heat balance and the tropics a positive one. But both in the troposphere and at the land-sea surface, these net balances have different components of heat gain and loss in various latitudes.

Heat budget components in the troposphere. In the tropical belt, 0–15°, there are three components of heat gain (solar radiation, 60 units; heat of condensation, 150; vertical transfer of sensible heat by

Figure 2.4 Heat budget constituents of the atmosphere's main layer of weather activity by 15° belts, in millicalories per cm² per min. The algebraic sum of the four gains or losses is shown as the centrally located numeral in each 15° belt. Note that the two belts 0°–15° and 15°–30° show an excess of energy; all the others a deficiency. (*After Heinz H. Lettau.*)

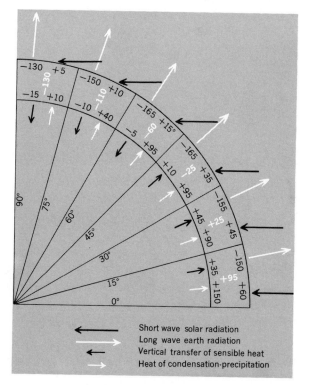

Short wave solar radiation
Long wave earth radiation
Vertical transfer of sensible heat
Heat of condensation-precipitation

Components of the heat balance at the earth's surface (Mean values in kcal per cm² per year)

Latitude	Oceans				Land			Earth			
	R	E	T	C	R	E	T	R	E	T	C
70–60°N	23	33	16	+26	20	14	6	21	20	9	+ 8
60–50°	29	39	16	+26	30	19	11	30	28	13	+11
50–40°	51	53	14	+16	45	24	21	73	59	23	+ 7
40–30°	83	86	13	+16	60	23	37	96	73	24	+ 9
30–20°	113	105	9	+ 1	69	20	49	106	81	15	+ 1
20–10°	119	99	6	− 14	71	29	42	105	72	9	−10
10–0°	115	80	4	−31	72	48	24	105	76	8	−24
0–10°S	115	84	4	−27	72	50	22	104	90	11	−21
10–20°	113	104	5	− 4	73	41	32	94	83	15	− 3
20–30°	101	100	7	+ 6	70	28	42	80	74	11	+ 4
30–40°	82	80	8	+ 6	62	28	34	56	53	9	+ 5
40–50°	57	55	9	+ 7	41	21	20	28	31	10	+ 6
50–60°	28	31	10	+13	31	20	11				+13
Earth as a whole	82	74	8	0	49	25	24	72	59	13	0

R = Net radiation balance
E = Loss of heat by evaporation
T = Turbulent heat transfer

C = Redistribution of heat by ocean currents

Source: After Budyko et al.

turbulence, 35; total, 245 units) and one of heat loss (150 units lost through earth radiation)—resulting in a net troposphere gain of +95 units (Fig. 2.4). This is by far the largest net gain for any of the six 15° latitude belts. With increasing distance from the equator, the four components of heat exchange vary in different degrees. Obviously solar radiation will steadily decline poleward, but the other components are not so consistent (see Fig. 2.4). For example, in latitude belt 45–60° there are only two positive components: +15 units of solar radiation and +95 units of heat of condensation, or a total of +110 units. Negative components are a loss of −5 units by vertical transfer of sensible heat from the atmosphere to the ground, and −165 units lost by earth radiation—a total of −170. The result is a net loss of −60 units.

Heat balance of the earth's land-sea surface.[3] Distribution of the components of the surface heat bal-

[3] M. I. Budyko et al. "The Heat Balance of the Surface of the Earth." *Soviet Geog.: Rev. and Translation.* Vol. 3, pp. 3–16, May, 1962.

ance by latitude belts is shown in the above table. Only one component, the radiation balance (R), has a similar distribution on land and sea. Over both continents and oceans, the maximum net heat gain from radiation is in the tropics and the minimum values are in higher latitudes. In both cases too, the balance of radiation remains almost constant within the tropics. The greatest land-water contrasts in amounts of net gain from radiation are also in the tropics, where the values for land are only about two-thirds those for oceans. With increasing latitude, land and water balances become more alike (Fig. 2.5).

As the table shows, the values for heat loss by evaporation (E) over land and oceans change with latitude in different ways. On land there is a strong maximum in equatorial latitudes, where heavy rainfall and lush vegetation provide abundant evaporable moisture, and a rapid decline in subtropical latitudes, where settling air in anticyclones creates dry climates (Fig. 2.6). But over oceans the loss of heat by evaporation is at a maximum in the subtropics, where solar radiation is greater because

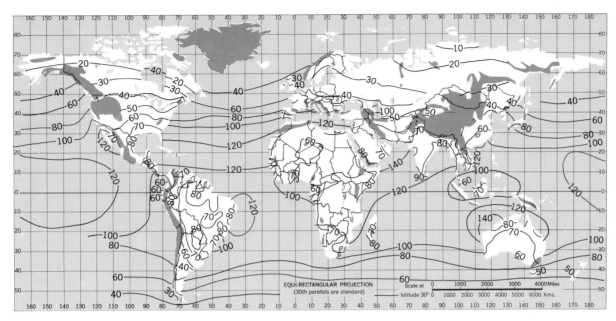

Figure 2.5 Radiation balance; annual values in kg cal per cm² per year. (*After Budyko et al.*)

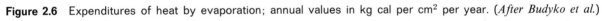

Figure 2.6 Expenditures of heat by evaporation; annual values in kg cal per cm² per year. (*After Budyko et al.*)

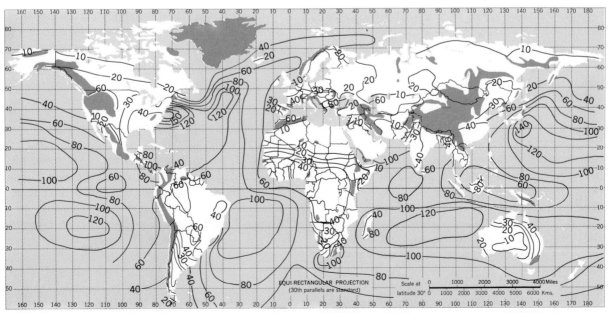

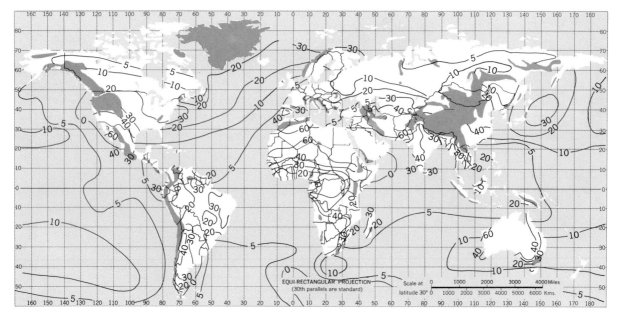

Figure 2.7   Turbulent heat exchange; annual values in kg cal per cm² per year. (*After Budyko et al.*)

there is less cloudiness. Closer to the equator, greater cloudiness reduces the solar energy received, and evaporation over oceans declines.

From the columns headed T in the table, it can be seen that the values of turbulent heat transfer from the ocean surface to the atmosphere are relatively small in all latitudes (Fig. 2.7). One reason, a point which was discussed earlier, is that sunlight does not heat a water surface intensely, as it does a land surface. On land the surface layer can become so hot that it causes strong convectional overturning in the air above it. Turbulent heat values over oceans increase with higher latitude, where warm currents warm the air in the cold season. On land, not only is turbulent heat transfer greater than it is over water, but the latitudinal distribution is also different. The highest values are in the subtropical latitudes where, because of the average minimal cloudiness and dry air, solar surface heating and convection are strong, while the expenditure of heat for evaporation is low.

As for the redistribution of heat by ocean currents (C), the table shows that heat is transported out of

a zone situated between 20°N and 20°S. The currents carry it poleward and release most of it to the atmosphere in latitudes 50° to 70° (see Fig. 3.42).

Many other facts about the earth's heat balance can be learned from this table of latitudinal heat balance components. The student of climate should also become familiar with world maps of radiation balance, heat loss by evaporation, and turbulent heat exchange (Figs. 2.5, 2.6, and 2.7).

Heat balance of individual continents.   As shown in the table on page 39, average heat balances vary widely among continents. Greatest net radiation gains (R) are in South America, Australia, and Africa, all of which lie in tropical-subtropical latitudes. The radiation balance is lowest in Europe, whose average latitude is relatively high. South America loses by far the most heat from evaporation (E), since it is located largely in the humid tropics. Africa, which is bisected by the equator, ranks next, but well below South America because of its extensive regions with dry climates. Drought is also the cause of Australia's low evaporation,

Heat balance of individual continents (In kcal per cm² per year)

	R	E	T
Europe	39	24	15
Asia	47	22	25
Africa	68	26	42
North America	40	23	17
South America	70	45	25
Australia	70	22	48

R = Net radiation balance
E = Loss of heat by evaporation
T = Turbulent heat transfer

Source: After Budyko et al.

while similarly low values in Asia and North America result both from their extensive regions with dry climates and from their high-latitude location. In Europe, on the other hand, the chief cause of low evaporation is high latitude alone. Turbulent heat transfer (T) is greatest in Australia and Africa, where hot deserts and steppes cover vast areas.

TEMPORAL DISTRIBUTION OF TEMPERATURE

All average temperatures for a month, a season, a year, or even a long period of years are built upon the *mean daily temperature* as the basic unit. The daily mean is thus the individual brick out of which the general temperature structure is formed. It is usually computed by the formula

$$\frac{\text{maximum temperature} + \text{minimum temperature}}{2}$$

or in other words, by taking an average of the highest and the lowest temperatures recorded during the 24-hr period.

Daily march, or cycle. The mean daily "march" of air temperature, or rhythm between night and day, closely follows the temperature of the land surface—which in turn reflects the balance between incoming solar radiation and outgoing earth radiation (Fig. 2.8). From about sunrise until 2 to 4 P.M., when energy is being supplied by incoming solar radiation faster than it is being lost by earth radiation, the air-temperature curve usually rises (Figs. 2.8, 2.9). From about 2 to 4 P.M. to sunrise, when loss by terrestrial radiation exceeds receipts of solar energy, the curve usually falls. It is noticeable, however, that the time of highest temperatures (2 to 4 P.M.) does not exactly coincide with that of maximum solar radiation (12 noon, sun time). This lag occurs because temperature continues to rise as long as the amount of incoming solar radiation exceeds the outgoing earth radiation. Thus although energy receipts begin to decline after noon, they continue to exceed the energy losses until ±3 P.M. Moreover, it requires some time for heat to pass up from the ground to the height where thermometers are usually located.

While daily air-temperature variations closely follow those of the land surface, the range is greatest

Figure 2.8 The march of incoming solar radiation and of outgoing earth radiation for the daily 24-hr period at about the time of an equinox, and their combined effects upon the times of daily maximum and minimum temperatures.

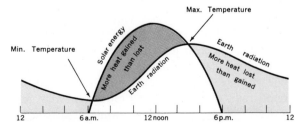

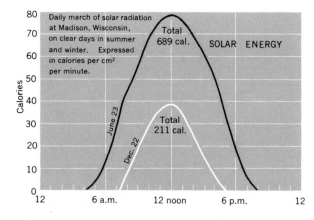

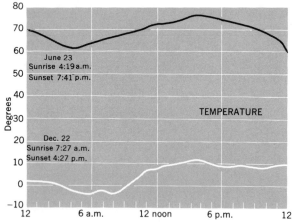

Figure 2.9 Daily march of solar radiation and temperature on clear days at the times of the summer and winter solstices at Madison, Wisconsin. The total solar energy recorded was 3.27 times as great on June 23 as on December 22. Note that temperature lags somewhat behind solar radiation. Advection by southerly winds prevented normal night cooling on Dec. 22.

next to the ground and decreases upward. The daily range is also much larger on clear days than on cloudy ones. On a clear day solar radiation quickly warms the solid earth, and it in turn heats the air above it. On a clear night rapid out-radiation from the earth similarly results in quick cooling. But as an earlier section has described, an overcast sky greatly reduces incoming solar radiation by day and so decreases daytime heating, while night cooling

Mean daily temperature range at different heights on the Eiffel Tower, Paris

Height, ft	Range, °F
6.6	13.7
403.0	9.5
646.0	8.5
991.0	7.0

is similarly retarded. The result is a flattened daily temperature curve (Fig. 2.10). Small diurnal ranges are also characteristic of oceans and their windward coasts, for since a water surface shows little temperature change during the 24-hr period, neither does the air above it (Fig. 2.11). Continental stations have larger diurnal ranges (Figs. 2.11, 2.12).

Often the daily air temperature curve does not have a periodic rise and fall corresponding to the rise and fall of solar radiation. Along coasts, land and sea breezes may modify this diurnal rhythm. And atmospheric disturbances—both because of their variable cloudiness which affects both incoming and outgoing radiation and because of their

Figure 2.10 Daily march of air temperature at Washington, D.C., on clear and cloudy days. The data represent deviations from the 24-hr mean. Each curve is the mean of 10 days at about the time of the autumn equinox, when days and nights are nearly equal. Days were selected when there was a minimum of advection. (*After Helmut Landsberg, Physical Climatology.*)

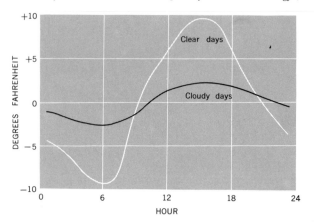

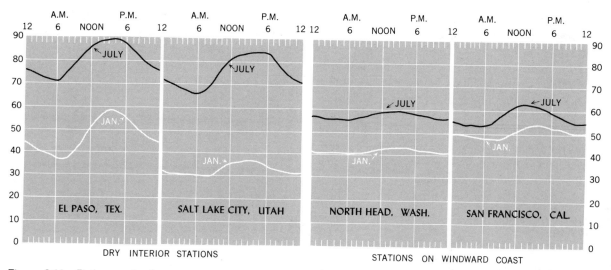

Figure 2.11 Daily march of temperature at marine and continental stations, calculated using average hourly temperatures. This is not the same as the daily range, which is based on the daily extremes regardless of hours of occurrence. Small daily variations of temperature are characteristic of marine climates (North Head and San Francisco), and large ones of the interior stations. (*After Kincer, in Atlas of American Agriculture, U.S. Department of Agriculture.*)

wind systems which advect air of contrasting temperatures from higher and lower latitudes—greatly alter the sun-imposed rhythm of night and day temperatures. In Fig. 2.9, for example, south winds and a cloud cover prevented a normal decline of temperature on the afternoon and night of December 22. In the stormy middle latitudes it is even possible for midnight to be warmer than noon.

Figure 2.12 Change in the amplitude of daily temperature (°C) variation with distance from the ocean. Latitude about 40°; elevations not over 500 meters (1650 ft). Numerals indicate locations of stations. Station 1 is an island. Station 2 is at the coast. (*After H. Landsberg, Physical Climatology.*)

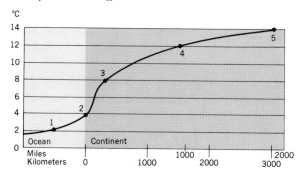

If a station's daily maximum and minimum temperatures are plotted for a period of several weeks, two controls usually stand out. First of all, the periodic or diurnal control determined by the sun induces a regular rise of temperature by day and a fall at night. But superimposed upon this sun-controlled pattern is a second one, nonperiodic in character, that is controlled largely by the passage of atmospheric disturbances and their associated air masses. Such disturbances, which occur at irregular periods, drastically modify temperatures through their associated cloud decks and their wind systems. Periodic and nonperiodic controls of temperature are illustrated again and again in Part Two of this book, in the graphs showing maximum and minimum daily temperatures for warm and cold months at selected stations. For example, see Figs. 8.7, 8.19, 9.19, 10.17. In general these graphs demonstrate that while diurnal, or sun, control of temperature is dominant in the tropics and often in middle-latitude summers, nonperiodic control associated with atmospheric disturbances and their air masses is very important in the middle and high latitudes, especially in winter.

In the middle latitudes particularly, the temperature differences between successive days, or inter-diurnal temperature changes, are greater in winter than in summer. This reflects the steeper temperature gradients and stronger air-mass control usually found in winter. As the table below shows, inter-diurnal temperature changes are also larger in continental than in marine locations.

Temperature differences between successive days in middle latitudes

	Winter	Summer	Year
Central North America and central Asia	8.5°	4.1°	6.3°
West coast of North America	3.6°	1.8°	2.7°

Annual march.   The annual march or cycle of temperature reflects the daily increase in solar energy (and therefore in heat accumulated in the air and ground) from midwinter to midsummer, and the decrease from midsummer to midwinter (Fig. 2.13). This is the rhythm of the changing seasons. Usually air temperature lags 30 to 40 days behind the periods of maximum or minimum solar radiation, a delay which reflects the balance between incoming solar and outgoing terrestrial energy. The lag is even greater over the oceans in middle latitudes, where in the Northern Hemisphere, August is often the warmest month and February the coldest. Strongly ocean-dominated land climates—for instance, west coasts in middle latitudes—also may show this typical oceanic lag (Fig. 2.14). In the interior parts of middle-latitude continents, however, July in the Northern Hemisphere is almost universally the warmest month, and January the coldest. Amplitude or range is modest in marine climates and larger in the continental interiors (Fig. 2.14).

Annual temperature is the average of the 12 monthly means, and each of these means in turn

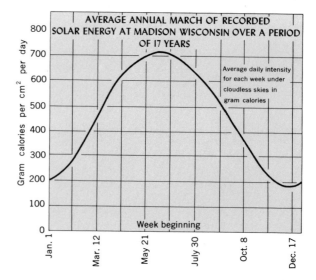

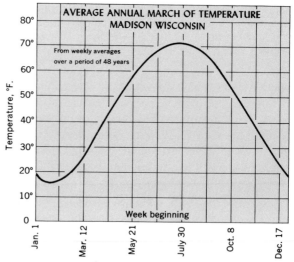

Figure 2.13   Note that the temperature maximum and minimum lag a month or so behind maximum and minimum solar radiation. The solar radiation curve has been smoothed slightly.

is the average of the 28 to 31 daily means. Both the average daily and annual marches, or variations, of temperature for any station can be represented by means of thermoisopleths on a single diagram. These show lines of equal temperature, both for hours of the day and for months of the year, and

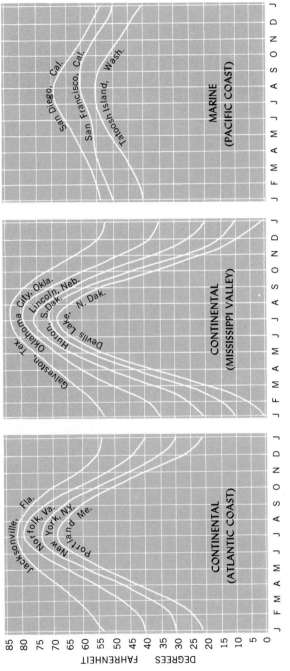

Figure 2.14 Annual march of temperature at marine and continental stations in the United States. Temperature range is large in the interior and along the leeward Atlantic coast, although continentality is somewhat modified in the latter location. Range is small along the windward Pacific coast. At the continental stations, temperature change from north to south is much greater in winter than in summer. (*After Kincer.*)

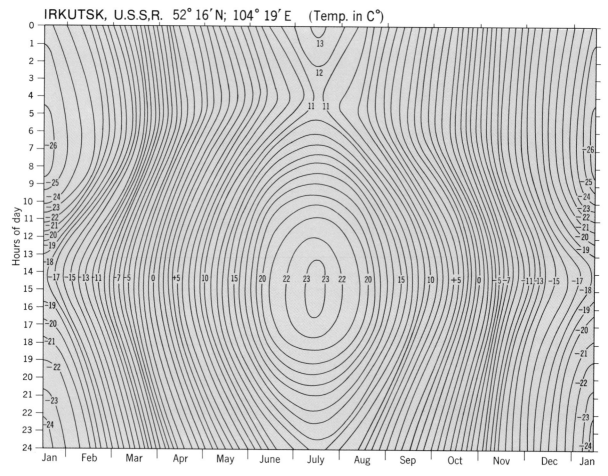

Figure 2.15 Thermoisopleth graphs for two contrasting stations. Irkutsk, U.S.S.R., represents a severe continental climate with large annual and daily variations in temperature. Macquarie Island typifies a strongly marine climate in

thereby make it easy to compare the annual and diurnal temperature regimes. Examples of thermo-istopleth diagrams, which appear throughout Part Two of this book, are given here in Fig. 2.15. One is a severe-climate continental station in the middle latitudes (Irkutsk, U.S.S.R.); the other represents a cool oceanic climate (Macquarie Island).

Temperature singularities. When plotted from monthly means, a station's annual variation of temperature is a fairly smooth curve. But if the annual variation is plotted from daily means obtained over a long period of observation, or even from 5-day means, the result is a somewhat zigzag line whose general form follows the curve plotted from monthly means. In the annual profile obtained from daily means there appear to be sudden jumps and drops in temperature, signifying warm spells and cold spells which occur in many years at about the same calendar date.

These spells of weather, called *singularities*, do not match in all parts of the world; they are regional rather than universal. Among the better-known singularities are the following: (1) "January thaw"

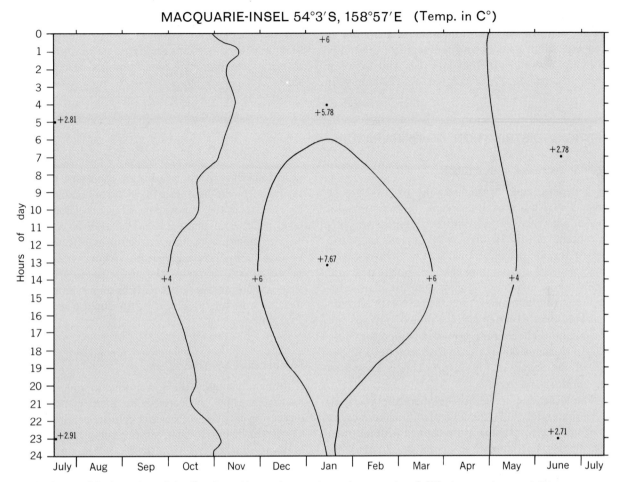

MACQUARIE-INSEL 54°3′S, 158°57′E   (Temp. in C°)

the higher middle latitudes of the Southern Hemisphere, where the annual and daily temperature variations are very small. (*After Troll.*)

of the northeastern coastal United States, a warm period centered around January 20 to 23; (2) "Ice Saints" of western and central Europe, a cold spell bringing frost in May; (3) "Indian Summer," a spell of sunny, warm autumn weather in late October and November in much of the central and eastern United States; (4) a cold spell around mid-October in the central United States, which is often the first genuine outbreak of cold polar air ushering in the winter season.

The reality of climatic singularities is still a controversial topic. Even the most pronounced singular-

ities occur in only 50 to 60 percent of the years on record, and in any particular year a singularity may be absent or untimely. They are not a very useful tool in long-range weather forecasting.

The causes of singularities, while not wholly understood, may be of the following nature. The principal control of the annual course of weather is the march of solar radiation. This in turn generates the atmospheric circulation and its seasonal changes. Such fixed terrestrial controls as the distribution and arrangement of land and sea, and the position of great mountain ranges, also play a part in the sequence of weather. In the annual march of weather events, contrasts in such atmospheric elements as pressure, wind systems, and temperature gradually build up between different latitudes and between land-surface features in much the same fashion year after year. When these contrasts reach certain threshold values, sudden shifts in large-scale pressure and circulation patterns appear to occur and in turn to initiate temperature and humidity-precipitation shifts.

VERTICAL DISTRIBUTION OF TEMPERATURE

Normal decrease with altitude

As a general rule, throughout the troposphere or lower 5 to 7 miles of atmosphere, temperature decreases with increasing elevation. Exceptions to this rule occur mostly in the lowest several thousand feet of the air ocean, known as the friction layer, where diurnal temperature changes are greatest and nighttime inversions of temperature are characteristic. The rate of temperature decrease with altitude is not uniform; it varies with the time of day, season, and location. The average, however, is approximately 3.5°F for each 1,000-ft rise in elevation (0.65°C per 100 m), as shown in Fig. 2.16B. This is known as the *normal lapse rate.*

The lapse rate, or vertical temperature gradient, is approximately 1,000 times greater than the average horizontal rate of temperature change with latitude. The steeper the lapse rate, or the more rapid the vertical temperature decrease, the closer to a horizontal position is the temperature-altitude line on a graph chart. A vertical temperature-altitude line indicates an isothermal condition in which there is no change in temperature with altitude.

The fact that air temperature is normally highest at low elevations next to the earth clearly indicates that most of the atmosphere's energy is received directly from the earth's surface and only indirectly from the sun. But the lower air is warmer not only because it is closest to the direct source of heat, but also because it is denser and contains more water vapor, water particles, and dust. These make it a more efficient absorber of terrestrial radiation than the thinner, drier, clearer air aloft. Also remember that vertical temperature distribution throughout the lowest few thousand feet of atmosphere is maintained not only through radiation processes, but also through upward heat transfer by turbulent overturning. Higher in the troposphere, above the cloud-base level, release of heat of condensation in clouds is an additional important mechanism affecting the vertical temperature structure. Above the tropopause, which separates the troposphere from the stratosphere, temperature distribution is more complex, as was described in the introductory section to Part One.

Temperature inversions

Although normally the lower several miles of atmosphere show a decrease in temperature with increasing altitude, often this condition is reversed at certain levels, so that temperatures temporarily or locally increase with altitude. When the colder air lies underneath the warmer air, and closer to the earth's surface, the normal temperature lapse rate is reversed, a phenomenon which is appropriately named a *temperature inversion.*

Surface inversions. One of the commonest forms of temperature inversion occurs at low levels close to the land surface. Over land areas in middle and high latitudes, surface inversions probably develop on a majority of nights. Usually they are the result of radiation cooling of the lower air by the underlying cold land surface. Since a land surface is a more effective radiator than the atmosphere, nighttime cooling is more rapid at the ground than higher in the air, and consequently the coldest air may be found next to the land surface (Figs. 2.16A, 2.20).

Ideal conditions for surface inversions are (1)

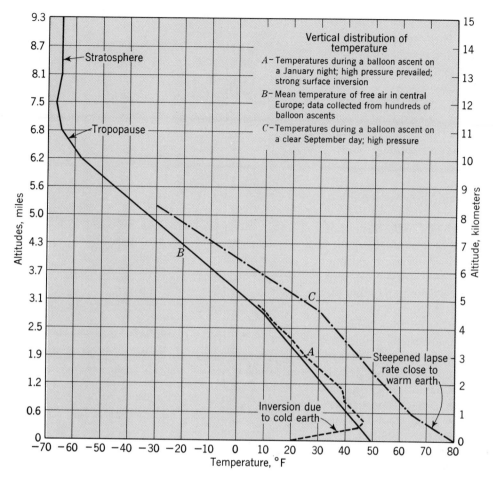

Figure 2.16 Contrasts in the vertical temperature distribution (lapse rates) *A*, on a winter night; *C*, on a summer day; and *B*, under average conditions. On the *B* lapse rate, plotting of temperature is continued up to 15 km (9+ miles) so that the tropopause and the stratosphere are represented.

long nights, as in winter, in which there is a relatively long period when outgoing earth radiation exceeds incoming solar radiation; (2) clear skies, or skies with only high cloud, so that loss of heat by terrestrial radiation is rapid and unretarded; (3) relatively dry air that absorbs little earth radiation; (4) calm air, so that little vertical mixing occurs and the surface stratum can rapidly acquire the temperature of the underlying ground surface; and (5) a snow-covered surface which, owing to reflection of solar energy, heats little by day, and being a poor conductor, re-

tards the upward flow of heat from the ground below.[4] A porous sandy soil with low heat conductivity further lowers the temperature of air next to the ground.

While night and winter provide the best conditions for them, surface inversions are common even in summer, although then they usually disappear

[4] At Milton, Massachusetts, on February 9, 1934, C. F. Brooks recorded a temperature of −27° on the surface of the snow and +24° 7 in. below the surface—a difference of 51°.

by day because of surface heating. Throughout the year at the Eiffel Tower in Paris, temperature increases upward from base to top between midnight and 4 A.M. Over polar areas, temperature inversions are the normal condition, in summer as well as winter. They are also normal for the night hours of the colder months over the snow-covered land masses of the higher middle latitudes (Fig. 2.16). The mean depth of the polar inversion layer is about 0.6 miles, while in the middle latitudes it is usually only a few hundred feet.

When cooler, denser air underlies warmer air, as it does in an inversion, the circumstances are opposed to all upward movement and hence to the formation of rain-bearing clouds. The air is strongly stable; convective overturning is stifled. When nighttime surface inversions form over cities, dust, smoke from chimneys, automobile exhaust fumes, and other atmospheric impurities collect underneath the inversion lid to form dense smoke fogs, or smog. Whether in city or country, surface inversions favor the development of lowland fog, since temperatures are relatively low and relative humidity is usually high within the stable layer (see Chap. 4). A close relationship also exists between surface temperature inversions and frost, for the same conditions are conducive to both (see page 64). While surface inversions are common on flattish land surfaces, they occur far more often in topographic depressions.

Besides being produced by radiation cooling, low-level temperature inversions may be caused by the advection of cold air at the surface, or of warmer air aloft. Such an advection inversion ordinarily covers a more extensive area than inversions of radiation origin. The widespread and intense surface inversions over the great lowland areas of northern Eurasia and North America in the colder months are at least partly caused by advected air masses.

Contrasts between continents and oceans. Since a land surface ordinarily has a wide range of temperatures between day and night, the layers of air next to the land also show large diurnal variations in vertical structure. During the day the surface air has a steep lapse rate, with the warmest air closest

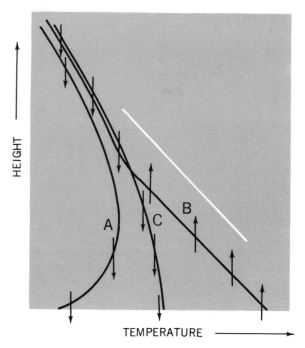

Figure 2.17   Diurnal variations in vertical distribution of temperature, and of stability conditions, over a land surface. *A*, night and early morning; *B*, midday; *C*, evening. White line is the dry adiabat. Arrows indicate direction of eddy transfer of heat. (*From Petterssen.*)

to the ground. At night there is usually a surface inversion (Fig. 2.17).

But over seas, where the daily water-temperature change is slight, the changes in surface air temperature are also slight. In fact, somewhat higher up, where temperature changes are controlled largely by radiation, diurnal variations are greater than they are close to the ocean surface. This results in a slightly steeper lapse rate by night than by day —just the reverse of the situation over land (Fig. 2.18).

Surface inversions and air drainage. In regions where the land surface is uneven, the density of the cold inversion stratum of air causes it to drain gradually off the uplands and slopes into the surrounding lowlands (Figs. 2.19, 2.33). The collecting of cold, dense surface air in valleys and lowlands, where as a result the inversion becomes deeper and more

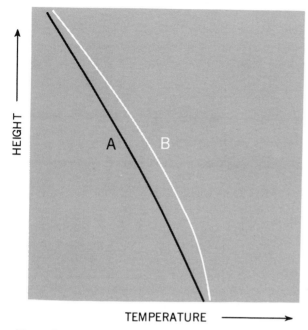

Figure 2.18 Diurnal variations in vertical distribution of temperature over oceans. *A*, night; *B*, midday. Note that the lapse rate in the lower layers is steeper at night than at midday—the reverse of conditions over land. (*After Petterssen.*)

intense, is a phenomenon referred to as *air drainage*. It is because of air drainage that the first freeze in autumn and the last in spring occur in bottomlands, and that the lowest minima on calm, clear winter nights are found in low spots. On one occasion during a winter cold spell, a minimum night temperature of −8.9° was recorded on top of Mount Washington, New Hampshire, while the surrounding valleys registered temperatures as low as −23° and −31°.

In California, citrus orchards, which cannot tolerate frost, are planted on slopes rather than in the chillier valleys. Coffee plantations in Brazil are situated on the rolling uplands, not in the valleys. Many resort hotels in the Swiss Alps are built on the sunnier, milder slopes above the cold, foggy valleys. Some high hill lands and mountains in middle latitudes have a "thermal belt"—an intermediate zone along the slope. Here nighttime freezing temperatures are less likely to occur than at lower levels (where air drainage creates a greater frost hazard) or at higher levels (where low temperatures are related to the normal lapse rate).[5] (See Fig. 2.19.)

Above-surface inversions. Inversions may also develop at various atmospheric levels well above the earth's surface. A few of these are due to radiation at high levels, but this is a relatively unimportant cause. Others are frontal in origin—that is, they are associated with the convergence of air masses which have contrasting temperatures and densities. Still others are caused by mechanical processes such as subsidence and turbulence. Because of their wide-

[5] Gary S. Dunbar. "Thermal Belts in North Carolina." *Geog. Rev.,* Vol. 56, pp. 516–526, 1966.

Figure 2.19   Air drainage and thermal belts on the slopes of some middle-latitude valleys.

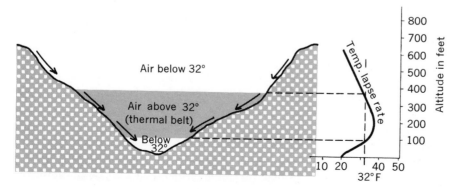

spread distribution and their inhibition of rainmaking processes, the inversions caused by subsidence are climatically the most significant.

Subsidence, or slow sinking of the air, has two major effects. First, the subsiding air is heated by compression, which reduces its relative humidity and hence increases its aridity. Second, it is made more stable (see Chap. 4), or nonbuoyant, so that it opposes upward movement, which is essential for cloudy condensation and precipitation.

Above-surface inversions associated with subsidence are produced in the following way. Turbulence, involving upward and downward movements of air currents, is almost always present near the ground, because of friction created by land-surface features. Since this prevents the lower air layers from participating in the general subsidence, they do not share in the general rise of temperature, and the inversion ordinarily does not reach down to ground level. Consequently a temperature inversion develops between the lower turbulent layer and the subsiding warmed layers aloft (Fig. 2.20). Within the lower turbulent air the lapse rate is normal, so that temperature decreases with altitude. But at the top of the turbulence layer, there is a sharp increase in temperature and a marked decrease in relative humidity. Throughout the inversion layer, which may reach a thickness of 5,000 to 10,000 ft, temperature continues to *increase* with elevation. Further aloft above the subsidence, however, the normal lapse rate is resumed. The inversion layer may extend down to within 1,500 ft of ground level, or even lower. The lower the inversion layer, the thicker it is, and the lower the humidity within it, the less favorable the conditions are for rainmaking processes. The higher the base of the inversion and the greater the turbulence and convection in the lower layers of surface air, the greater the opportunity for rainfall. The inversion layer acts as a lid or ceiling which limits the height of ascending air currents and thus stifles the precipitation mechanism. It is not uncommon, however, for a layer of stratus cloud to develop at the base of the inversion layer.

Subsidence is characteristic of high-pressure systems or anticyclones, especially those which are stationary or slow-moving. Hence the most exten-

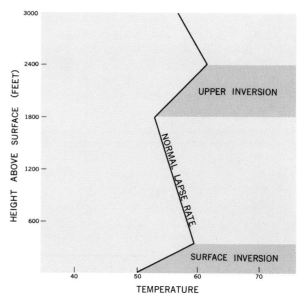

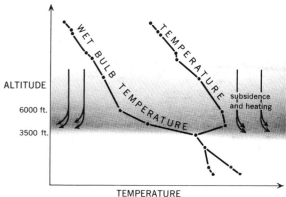

Figure 2.20 *Top:* A vertical temperature distribution showing a radiation surface inversion, and a subsidence inversion aloft.
Bottom: Vertical temperature observations taken in the heart of the maritime trade winds in the eastern South Atlantic Ocean, showing a well-developed subsidence inversion. Above the base of the inversion layer, temperature rises sharply, while the wet-bulb temperature, reflecting a corresponding fall in relative humidity, declines. (*After Kuhlbrodt and Reger.*)

sive and perfectly developed above-surface inversions are found in the warm anticyclones typical of subtropical latitudes and the cold anticyclones which are common in winter over large continents in the middle and high latitudes. Largely because of these inversions, annual rainfall is modest in the subtropical latitudes and winter precipitation is light over the interiors of cold continents. The earth's largest deserts are associated with the subtropical anticyclones and their trade winds. It is especially the poleward parts of the trade winds along the equatorial flanks of the high-pressure cells which are characterized by strong inversions, but these become weaker and are located at increasingly higher levels as the winds approach the equatorial, convergence zone (see Figs. 2.21 and 3.35). This helps to explain why the trade winds, or "trades," are dry near their source region in the subtropical highs, and increasingly showery as they approach the equatorial convergence. Within the subtropical anticyclonic cells over the oceans, the inversion is ordinarily much stronger and lower in the eastern portion of each of the cells than along its western margin. Greater stability and intensified drought therefore characterize the eastern parts of the oceanic subtropical highs and their trade winds.

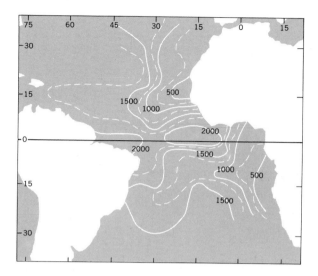

Figure 2.21   Height in meters of the base of the trade-wind inversion over the tropical Atlantic Ocean. Note that the inversion is lowest in altitude toward the eastern side of the oceanic trades. (*After H. Riehl, in Tropical Meteorology.*)

HORIZONTAL DISTRIBUTION OF TEMPERATURE

Isothermal maps.   Temperature distribution over the earth is shown in Figs. 2.22 and 2.23 by means of isotherms—lines connecting places which have the same air temperature. Thus all points on these maps through which any one isotherm passes have identical average temperatures for the period indicated. A world map covered with numerals representing the temperatures of hundreds of stations would be very cumbersome to use. But on a map which shows isotherms, many of the significant facts of thermal distribution can be seen at a glance.

In Figs. 2.22 and 2.23 all temperatures have been reduced to sea level to eliminate the effects of altitude. If this were not done, the complications caused by mountains and other relief forms would obscure the general worldwide isothermal patterns resulting from latitude and land-water distribution. For farmers, engineers, and others who need to put their data to practical use, these maps of sea-level isotherms are not so useful as maps showing actual surface temperatures.

As Figs. 2.22 and 2.23 show, isotherms in general trend east-west, roughly following the parallels. This is logical, since all places along the same parallel receive identical amounts of solar energy, except for differences in the atmosphere's transparency associated chiefly with cloudiness. The east-west trend of isotherms is additional evidence that solar radiation, which is a function of latitude, is the single greatest cause of temperature contrasts. On no parallel of latitude at any season are temperature differences so great as those between poles and equator.

In some parts of the earth the isotherms are closely spaced, indicating that air temperature changes rapidly in a horizontal direction. In other parts they are widely spaced, showing that horizontal temperature differences are slight. The rate of

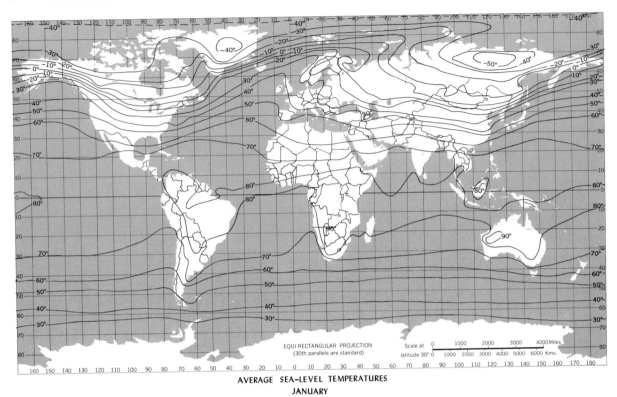

AVERAGE SEA-LEVEL TEMPERATURES
JANUARY

Figure 2.22

change of temperature is called the *temperature gradient*. Closely spaced isotherms signify a steep horizontal temperature gradient, widely spaced ones a weak temperature gradient.

Average annual temperature distribution. In general the average annual temperature of a place is not a very significant figure, since for much of the earth it is the mean of large seasonal extremes. Only in equatorial latitudes is the air temperature difference between the extreme months small enough so that the average annual temperature becomes meaningful.

The highest average annual temperatures are in the tropics and subtropics, where the largest amounts of solar energy are received in the course of a year. Lowest average temperatures are found in the vicinity of the poles, the regions of least annual

solar energy (Fig. 1.8). In most parts of a low-latitude zone about 45 to 50° wide, there are only very slight temperature differences in a meridional direction. This near-absence of north-south temperature gradients within much of the tropics is partly a result of more cloud near the equator. In these rainier parts of the inner tropics, less solar energy is received at ground level than in the clearer subtropical areas farther from the equator.

The table on page 53 shows that mean annual temperatures for comparable latitudes are usually somewhat higher in the Northern Hemisphere than in the Southern. In part this reflects the gigantic cold source of Antarctica; for tropical and subtropical latitudes it is also evidence of the larger land masses north of the equator. The table also shows that the belt of highest mean annual temperature is not located at the equator but at about 10°N.

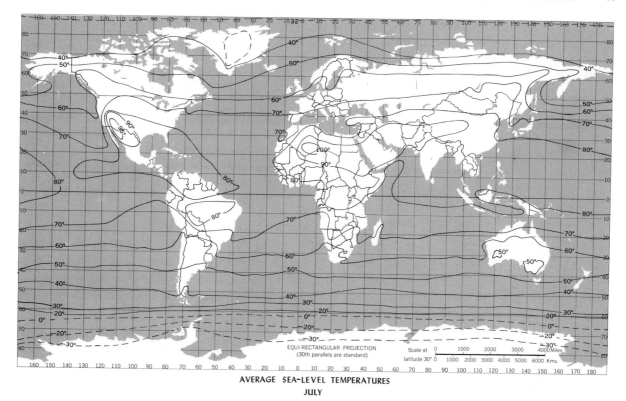

Figure 2.23

This belt, from which temperatures decrease toward either pole, is called the thermal equator. For the year as a whole the main cold pole of the earth is the Antarctic icecap, while the ice plateau of Greenland forms a secondary cold center.

January and July temperatures. For the earth in general, January and July temperatures ordinarily represent the seasonal extremes. As can be seen in Figs. 2.22 and 2.23, isotherms tend to be straighter,

have fewer "kinks," and are also more widely spaced in the Southern Hemisphere, whose surface is more homogeneous, being largely water. The isotherms deviate most from an east-west course where they seem to buckle as they pass from continents to oceans, or vice versa. These kinks are caused by the thermal effects of ocean currents and by the unlike heating and cooling properties of land and water surfaces. Next to latitude or sun control, land and water contrasts are the second greatest control of temperature

Mean annual temperature for different latitudes (°F)

	0°	10°	20°	30°	40°	50°	60°	70°	80°
Northern Hemisphere	79.2	80.1	77.5	68.5	57.2	42.3	30.2	14.0	1.9
Southern Hemisphere	79.2	77.5	73.4	65.1	53.6	42.1	31.6	11.3	−3.6

Source: From Landsberg.

distribution. Cool ocean currents off the coasts of Peru and northern Chile, southern California, and southwestern Africa result in a strong equatorward bending of the isotherms. Similarly, warm currents in higher latitudes cause isotherms to bend poleward, as they do off the coast of northwestern Europe.

Following are some of the more significant features of temperature distribution as shown on the seasonal maps in Figs. 2.22 and 2.23:

1. Comparison of the two maps reveals a marked latitudinal shifting of the isotherms between July and January, following the latitudinal migration of solar radiation belts.

2. The migrations of isotherms are much greater over continents than over oceans, because land has greater seasonal extremes of temperature than water (Fig. 2.24).

3. The highest temperatures are found in the tropical-subtropical land areas of the summer hemisphere.

Figure 2.24 Comparative amplitude of isotherm seasonal migration over land and over water in middle latitudes. The difference results from the contrasting heating and cooling properties of land and water surfaces.

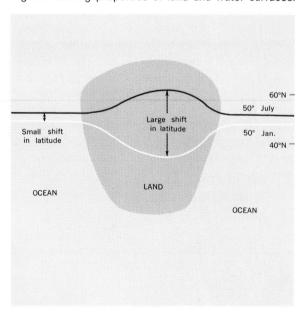

4. The lowest temperatures occur over land in the winter hemisphere. In January, the cold poles are northeastern Asia, northwestern Canada, and Greenland in the Northern Hemisphere, and ice-covered Antarctica in the Southern Hemisphere, even though it is summer there. In July, the earth's cold pole is Antarctica.

5. In the Northern Hemisphere the January isotherms bend abruptly equatorward over the colder continents and poleward over the warmer oceans. In July exactly the opposite happens.

6. No such seasonal contrasts between land and water are to be found in the Southern Hemisphere, for it has no large land masses in the higher middle latitudes.

7. On the January map the lowest temperature is over northeastern Asia—the leeward side of the largest land mass in higher middle latitudes. The next-lowest temperatures are over Greenland and North America.

8. Temperature gradients, like solar energy gradients, are steeper in winter than in summer, especially in the Northern Hemisphere with its large continents. Close spacing of isotherms is particularly conspicuous over the continents of the Northern Hemisphere in January. Gradients are less steep in the Southern Hemisphere, although between about 42 and 50°S over the open ocean, where frigid, heavy water from Antarctica sinks below the warmer surface water of the westerly wind belt, the rate of latitudinal temperature change is rapid.[6]

9. Great seasonal reversals of temperature are not characteristic of the Southern Hemisphere, again because its land area is negligible in the higher middle latitudes.

Annual range of temperature. The difference between the average temperatures of the warmest and coldest months, usually January and July, is the annual range of temperature for a given location. The largest annual ranges occur over the Northern Hemisphere continents, which become alternately hot in summer and cold in winter (Fig. 2.25). Ranges

[6]Harry van Loon. "On the Annual Temperature Range over the Southern Oceans." *Geog. Rev.,* Vol. 56, pp. 499–503, 1966.

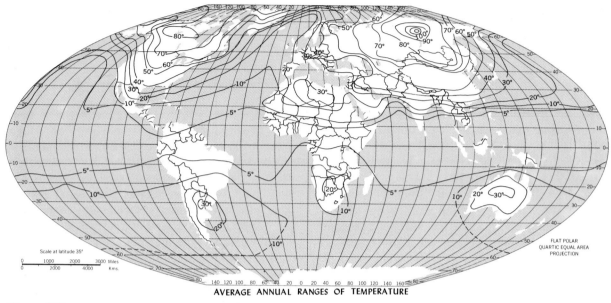

AVERAGE ANNUAL RANGES OF TEMPERATURE

Figure 2.25

are never large near the equator, where solar radiation is fairly constant throughout the year. Nor are there great variations over large water bodies—which accounts for the small ranges found everywhere in the middle latitudes of the Southern Hemisphere. In general, annual ranges increase toward the higher latitudes, but much more markedly over the continents than over the oceans (Fig. 2.26).

Extreme temperatures.   The extremes of heat and cold on the earth, as measured 5 ft above the land-water surface, cover an unbelievably large range of 261°F (146°C)—from 136° above zero in Libya in northern Africa to 125° below zero in east-central Antarctica. At elevations closer to the ground than 5 ft, extremes of heat and cold are considerably larger.

Most of the world's highest temperatures have been recorded in and close to the Sahara in North Africa. For extremes of winter cold, next to Antarctica comes northeastern Siberia, where one station has recorded a minimum of about 110° below zero and another −92°. It is fortunate that over most of the earth the seasonal extremes do not ap-

proach these figures. About one-sixth of the earth's land area has temperatures which do not rise above 100° or fall below zero.

Figure 2.26   Mean surface-air temperature for January and July, and seasonal temperature range, around the earth at 50°N. Note the abrupt change at the North American west coast compared with the gradual change across Europe. (*After H. Riehl, Introduction to the Atmosphere.*)

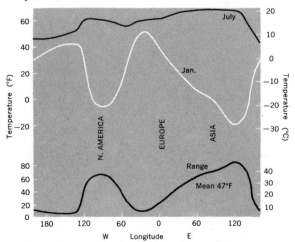

Mean annual range of temperature for different latitudes (°F)

	0°	10°	20°	30°	40°	50°	60°	70°	80°
Northern Hemisphere	1.4	2.0	11.5	22.9	34.4	45.2	53.6	59.4	63.5
Southern Hemisphere	1.4	4.3	9.7	13.0	11.9	9.7	19.4	38.5	45.0

Source: From Landsberg.

Isanomalous temperatures. The temperature distribution shown on an isothermal map of the world is caused by (1) the balance between incoming solar radiation and outgoing earth radiation on a homogeneous surface, upon which is superimposed (2) a field of disturbances produced by such terrestrial phenomena as unequal heating and cooling of land and water surfaces, ocean currents, prevailing streams of airflow, etc. The effects of (1) and (2) can be separated by computing the mean temperatures of the parallels as they would be if temperature were controlled only by radiation on a homogeneous earth, and subsequently determining the difference between the observed mean temperatures of places and the mean temperatures of their parallels. This difference, called a thermal anomaly, represents the amount of deviation from the latitude normal. Lines called *isanomals* can be drawn on a world map to join places which have equal thermal anomalies, producing an isanomalous map (Figs. 2.27, 2.28).

The greatest thermal anomalies are in the Northern Hemisphere, where not only oceans but also extensive land masses occupy middle-latitude locations. In the relatively homogeneous Southern Hemisphere, temperature deviations from the latitude normal are much smaller.

On the *January* map in the Northern Hemisphere,

Figure 2.27 Isanomalies of temperature, January. Temperatures in °C; °F equivalents in parentheses. (*After Hann-Süring.*)

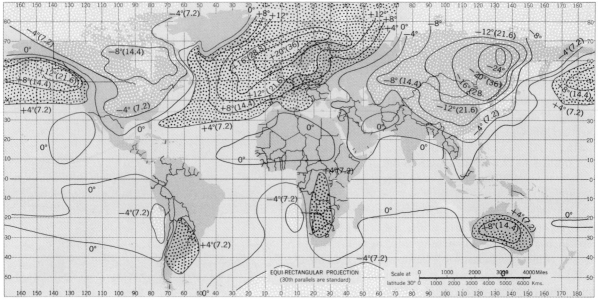

JANUARY

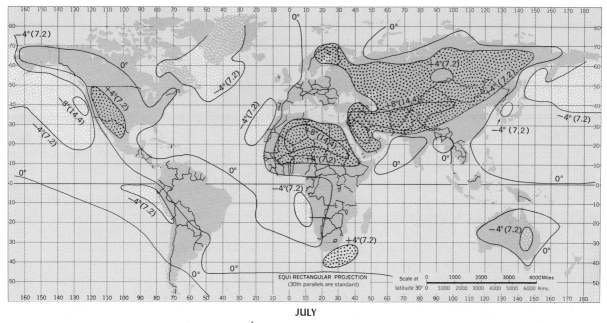

Figure 2.28 Isanomalies of temperature, July. (*After Hann-Süring.*)

positive anomalies are found over the oceans and negative ones over the continents. The greatest positive anomalies are along the eastern sides of middle-latitude oceans and the adjacent western margins of the continents—locations where warm ocean waters prevail. Nothwestern Europe has the extreme positive anomaly on the earth: a small town on the Norwegian coast at 63°N is 46° too warm for its latitude in January. The extreme negative anomaly is in northeastern Siberia, which is 46° colder than the average for its parallel. In the middle latitudes, where westerly winds prevail, both the positive anomalies over the oceans and the negative anomalies over the continents are shifted away from the centers of the land or water areas toward the eastern or leeward sides. In *July* the situation is reversed, and the Northern Hemisphere continents have positive anomalies while the oceans have negative ones. For the year as a whole, the continents show negative anomalies poleward from about latitude 40° and positive anomalies farther equatorward.

Air temperature and sensible temperature

Correct air temperature can be obtained only from an accurate thermometer properly exposed. One of the main principles of correct exposure is that the thermometer must not be in the sun; otherwise it receives energy not only from the surrounding air but from the absorption of solar radiation as well. It should also be protected from direct radiation from the ground and adjacent buildings and from the open sky.

Sensible temperature refers to the sensation of temperature that the human body feels, as distinguished from the actual air temperature recorded by a properly exposed thermometer. Unlike a thermometer, which has no temperature of its own, the human body, as well as that of every warm-blooded animal, is a heat engine, generating energy at a relatively fixed rate when at rest. Consequently anything that affects the rate of loss of heat from the body affects physical comfort.

A certain amount of heat produced by the body

must be got rid of in order to maintain the proper heat balance. If the climate is so hot that it prevents sufficient heat loss, the person feels uncomfortable, and may even have a heat stroke if the condition continues. On the other hand, if the weather is so cold and windy that heat losses from the body cannot be compensated for by internal heat generation, then chilling, and eventual death, may result.

The factors controlling the thermal comfort of the human body are numerous.[7] Air temperature is the major influence, but wind, relative humidity, and radiation also have important effects. Thus a humid hot day is more uncomfortable than a dry hot one, since loss of heat by evaporation is retarded when the air is humid. A windy cold day feels uncomfortable because the body is losing heat too rapidly; not only does the wind speed up evaporation, but it conducts heat more rapidly away from the body by continually replacing the warm air surrounding it with cold air. A sunny day in winter feels less cold than its air temperature may indicate, owing to the body's absorption of direct solar radiation. Cold air containing liquid moisture particles is especially penetrating, since the skin becomes moist and evaporation results, while further loss of heat follows from contact with the cold water. Because of its sensitiveness to these factors, the human body is not a very accurate instrument for measuring air temperature.

Although no instrument can accurately measure the human body's feeling with respect to a temperature condition, a wet-bulb thermometer probably comes closest to it. This is just an ordinary thermometer whose bulb is covered with saturated gauze or some other freely evaporating surface. Evaporation from the saturated gauze reduces the temperature of the wet-bulb thermometer below that of the dry bulb by an amount varying inversely with the relative humidity of the atmosphere. For example, in southwestern Arizona the average depression of the wet-bulb thermometer in July during the hottest part of the day is over 30°. Such a depression indicates a very dry atmosphere with a high potential evaporation. Because of this distinctly lower sensible temperature, the extremely high daytime temperatures of that region are not so unbearable as they might appear.

OTHER TEMPERATURE DATA AND THEIR USES[8]

Means, frequencies, and deviations.   The arithmetic mean, which is the sum of all observations divided by the number of observations, is the factor most often used to represent climatic conditions. Mean annual temperature, mean monthly temperature of January, July, or some other month, mean of the daily maximum and minimum temperatures for July or January—such commonly used means have been referred to again and again in this chapter. Their computation is simple. For example, the mean January temperature for a station is found by adding the average January temperatures for each of the years in which observations exist, and dividing this sum by the number of years represented.

Means alone, however, give an imcomplete picture of actual climatic conditions. For example, the mean annual temperatures of Boston and Oxford (England) are both approximately 49°F.; yet the monthly means from which the annual means were computed are very different. At Oxford, the monthly means are grouped more closely about the annual mean, the coldest month being only 11° below and the warmest month 13° above the mean. At Boston, the warm month is 22° warmer than the yearly

[7] See Werner H. Terjung. "Physiologic Climates of Conterminous United States; A Bioclimatic Classification Based on Man." *Ann. Assoc. Amer. Geographers,* Vol. 56, pp. 141–179, 1966.

[8] For a brief treatment of the use of climatological data, see Helmut Landsberg, *Physical Climatology,* 2d ed., Gray Printing Co., Du Bois, Penn., pp. 66–106. For a more detailed treatment, see V. Conrad and L. W. Pollok, *Methods in Climatology,* 2d ed., Harvard University Press, Cambridge, Mass., 1950.

Mean monthly and annual temperatures (°F)

	J	F	M	A	M	J	J	A	S	O	N	D	Yr
Boston	27	28	35	45	57	66	71	69	63	52	41	32	49
Oxford	38	40	42	47	53	59	62	61	57	49	44	40	49

average, and the cold month 22° colder. It is obvious that there are striking temperature differences between Boston and Oxford even though they have similar mean annual temperatures. The same criticism applies to other temperature means, and to means of rainfall, winds, and the rest of the climatic elements.

A more comprehensive picture of climate is obtained by combining arithmetic means with data on the frequency of occurrence of certain climatic values. Frequency is defined as the number of times a value occurs within a specified interval; for example, the frequency of hours during which the temperature at a station was within a certain limit. A very important type of frequency is the number of occurrences of a specific deviation or departure from the mean. For example, the average temperature at Philadelphia for a period of 60 years was 54.4°. The departures of the individual yearly averages from 54.4° were computed and their mean determined, with the results shown in the following table. When the

Frequencies of annual temperature deviation from 60-yr mean at Philadelphia (°F)

Temperature deviation	−3	−2	−1	0	+1	+2	+3
Number of cases	4	5	10	17	18	4	2

Source: From Landsberg.

Mean departures of monthly means (°C)

	Winter	Summer	Mean
Interior of North America	2.54	1.20	1.95
Northern Russia	3.43	1.61	2.33
Northern Germany	2.02	0.93	1.28
Northern slope of Alps	2.28	1.06	1.56
England	1.41	0.95	1.24

Source: From Hann.

same technique is applied to monthly means, the deviations are ordinarily more striking. For example, the mean departure of the monthly mean temperature for winter months in northern European Russia is as much as 3.43°C, and in interior North America it is 2.54°C.

Annual temperature curve (march of temperature). The annual course or march of temperature, as represented by a line joining the 12 monthly means, provides information on a number of temperature characteristics. One is the *range of variation,* i.e., the difference between the temperature of the warmest and coldest month, or *annual range.*

A second characteristic is the *phase,* which refers to the month with the highest and the month with the lowest temperature. At most land stations in the middle latitudes, July is the warmest month and January the coldest, so that the lag of temperature behind solar radiation is about a month or a little less. But over the oceans and at various marine stations located on islands or on windward coasts, August and February may be the months of maximum and minimum (Fig. 2.14). Although January is the coldest month at San Francisco, for example, September is the warmest. In regions of strong monsoons, such as India, the highest temperature is frequently in May, before the summer solstice. This is because the monsoon, which is the time of maximum cloudiness and rainfall, comes in June, July, and August, and greatly diminishes the amount of solar radiation received at the surface during those months (Fig. 8.17).

A third characteristic of the annual temperature curve is *symmetry* or *asymmetry.* There are two axes of symmetry, and therefore symmetry can be analyzed in two directions. As shown in Fig. 2.29, one axis of symmetry is the straight line B-7, which is

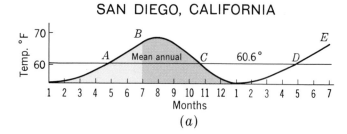

Figure 2.29 Contrasting symmetry of the annual temperature curves for a marine and a continental weather station.

the ordinate of the month of July. In a symmetrical curve the area 1-A-B-7 should equal the area 7-B-C-1. In the annual curve for Barnaul, a typical continental station, this is approximately true, but it is not the case in the San Diego curve. At San Diego the latter half of the year is considerably warmer than the first half; that is, fall is warmer than spring. The importance of this fact for all forms of life is obvious.

The second axis of symmetry (Fig. 2.29) is the straight line ACD, which is the mean of the monthly mean temperatures. Symmetry with respect to this axis is determined by comparing the length of the upper part of the curve with that of the lower part. In the Barnaul curve, AC is somewhat longer than CD, while in the San Diego curve, CD is longer than AC. On the whole, curves that are above the mean a longer time than they are below indicate a longer period of vegetation growth.

Mean duration of certain temperatures.   There are certain temperatures which are recognized as critical: for example, 32°, the freezing point of water; 40 or 42°, the approximate temperature at which seeds germinate and plants begin to grow; and perhaps 50°, often given as the lower limit of human comfort. The dates on which an annual temperature curve rises above such important thresholds and sinks below them, and the length of time between these dates, are of great significance climatically.

Although most plants are not killed by cool temperatures above 32°, many species do not start growing until the daily temperature rises to 40° or a little more. The effectiveness of temperature in promoting plant growth, or the *temperature efficiency,* may therefore be measured by the number of days with a temperature above 40°, and the amount of temperature rise above that point (Fig. 2.30). A high temperature efficiency is obviously an advantage, for more different kinds of crops can be grown. Each crop has its own basic temperature at which growth begins, and each crop also requires a certain number of heat units to bring it to maturity. Thus peas germinate at a temperature of 40°F, but sweet corn requires 50°F. As a rule the rate of maturing is approximately doubled for each 10°C, or 18°F, increase in temperature. For peas, each Fahrenheit degree above a mean daily temperature of 40° is a *growing degree-day,* or heat unit. For sweet corn, each unit above the mean daily temperature of 50° is a heat unit. In the case of corn, a series of 3 days whose mean temperatures are 55, 60, and 65° would be counted as 5, 10, and 15 degree-days, or a total of 30 in all. Data on growing degree-days serve as a guide in crop planting and in forecasting dates of crop maturity. If 1,500 heat units are required

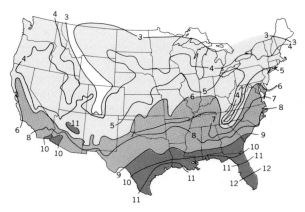

Figure 2.30 Temperature efficiency during the average frost-free season. In most plants active growth in spring does not begin until the mean daily temperature rises to, or somewhat exceeds, 40°F. The temperature efficiency of an area is the effectiveness of temperature in promoting plant growth. It varies with the number of days that have mean temperatures above 40°F, and with the amount of rise above this point. Numbers on the map represent efficiency units in hundreds.

for maturity, corn will theoretically be harvested when this number has actually accumulated. However, the tendency in agriculture at present is toward a use of more complex indices for plant growth than the concept of degree-days provides (Fig. 2.31).

Another type of degree-day is used by heating engineers, who have discovered that the difference between 65°F and the mean outside temperature for a day, a week, or any other period, is an accurate index of the fuel required for heating a building. Thus the heating fuel consumed in a month which has an average daily mean temperature of 15°F, as compared with a month whose average daily mean is 40°F, would be (65 − 15)/(65 − 40) = 50/25, or twice as great. The unit used is the *heating degree-day,* which is defined as a departure of 1° per day from 65°. If the mean outside temperature for a day is 25°, the number of degree-days for that 24-hr period would be 65 − 25, or 40. The degree-days for any longer period are computed by determining the number of degrees by which the mean temperature for each individual day falls below 65° and totaling them for the period. Degree-day

records compiled over a period of many years are used by the Weather Bureau in establishing monthly averages of degree-days for the entire country. These form the basis for estimating the fuel requirements. Shortly after the close of each month, the Weather Bureau computes daily degree-day totals for more than 300 locations and publishes them.

Period without freeze. One of the most important limiting values in temperature is the freezing point of water—32°F or 0°C. The period between the last day in spring which has a minimum temperature below 32° and the first day in fall with the same minimum is often called the "frost-free season" or "growing season." In reality, however, there is no simple relationship between plant growth and

Figure 2.31 Growing degrees increase rapidly in late spring and summer. (*U.S. Weather Bureau.*)

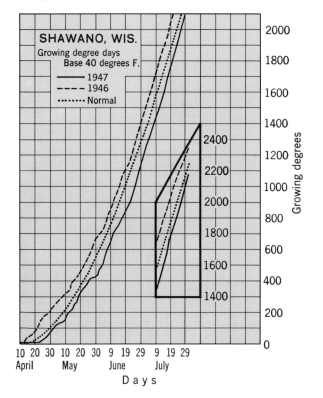

SHAWANO, WIS.
Growing degree days
Base 40 degrees F.
——— 1947
- - - - 1946
········· Normal

a freezing temperature. Some hardy plants can withstand severe freezes, while other sensitive ones are injured by low temperatures well above freezing. The term frost is also rather ambiguous. "Killing frost" is too vague to be very helpful. In addition, the occurrence of frost is extremely localized, its distribution depending largely on the irregularities of the land surface. Thus the soundest concept to use is the 32° point marking the limit of freezing temperatures, and it is in relationship to this point that the terms frost and growing season are used here.

A short freeze-free period greatly limits the number and kind of crops that can be grown in a region. Where the freeze-free period is less than 90 days, the opportunities for agricultural development are extremely meager. The greater diversity of crops which is possible with a long freeze-free season increases the stability of agriculture and tends to make it more profitable. Figure 2.32 shows in a very generalized way the duration of the freeze-free period for the land areas of the earth. As a rule, the extensive areas in the tropics where a freezing temperature has never occurred are not the regions of largest present-day agricultural development. These regions do have great potentialities, however.

Protection from freeze

Throughout almost all the middle latitudes, freezing temperatures are most serious as a menace to crops in autumn and spring. In subtropical latitudes such as California and Florida, however, midwinter freezes are the critical ones, because sensitive crops are grown during that season. In the southern parts of boreal or subarctic Canada and the U.S.S.R., summer freezes sometimes do serious damage to cereal crops. In tropical lowlands, freezing temperatures usually do not occur.

Figure 2.32   Average length of the frost-free period, or growing season, in days. (*From The Great Soviet World Atlas, Vol. 1.*)

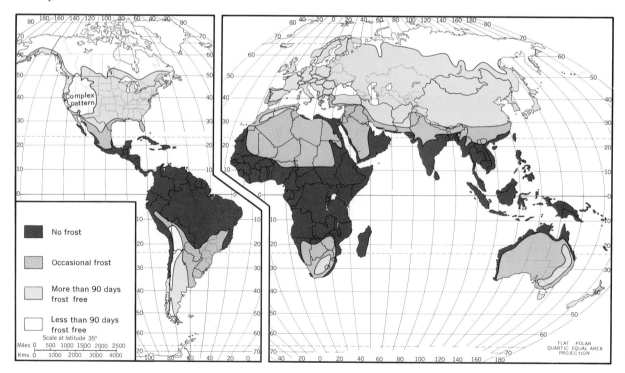

Conditions favorable to frost. Ideal conditions for a freeze are those which favor rapid and prolonged surface cooling: importation of a mass of chilly polar air, followed by a clear, dry, calm night during which the surface air, by radiation and conduction, is reduced below freezing. The original importation provides the necessary mass of air which is already cool, although still somewhat above freezing. Further rapid loss of heat by earth radiation during the following clear night is all that is necessary to reduce the temperature of the surface air below freezing. But even though these conditions may prevail over extensive areas, the destructive effects of the frost ordinarily are local and patchy, depending chiefly on surface configuration, air drainage, and soil conductivity.

Artificial protection. The problem of artificial protection from freeze is important only in regions of highly sensitive and valuable crops which occupy restricted areas. It is obviously impossible to protect such extensively grown field crops as corn or small grains, even when Weather Bureau warnings are issued 12 to 24 hr in advance. Most field crops in the middle latitudes are annuals planted late enough in spring to avoid frost. If fall-sown, they do not reach a stage in which they can be injured by frost until the danger from a spring freeze is past. Ordinarily these crops of annuals are harvested in summer or early fall before frosts are likely to occur, although in the latitude of southern Wisconsin, corn is sometimes damaged by early fall frosts.

Orchards such as the valuable citrus groves of California and Florida, and important truck and market gardens occupying small areas, are the crops which require special precautions to minimize the danger of frost. This may be done either by planting them on a site where there is least danger of a freeze, or by adopting special measures for preventing frost occurrence. Two types of sites which are freer from frost than the surrounding countryside are the lower slopes of highlands and coasts situated on the windward side of fairly large bodies of water (Fig. 2.33). Slopes are warmer than valleys owing to air drainage, which was discussed in an

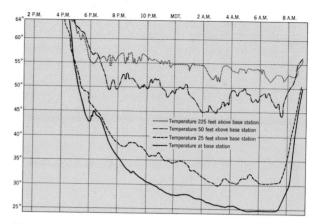

Figure 2.33 Actual temperature recordings from 4 P.M. to 9 A.M. at the base, and at different heights above the base, along a steep slope on a clear, still night in spring. In this instance, air drainage resulted in a minimum temperature of 25°F at the foot of hill, causing freeze damage to fruit. This was 26°F lower than the temperature 225 ft up the slope. (*U.S. Weather Bureau.*)

earlier section. Coasts are protected because an adjacent body of water has regulatory effect upon the temperatures of land, a feature which is conspicuous only along its windward side. The major fruit belts along the southeastern shore of Lake Michigan, and the south shores of Lakes Erie and Ontario, illustrate the protective influence of water bodies.

But dangerous freezes are occasionally inevitable even on the most favorable sites. Damage to sensitive crops which occupy restricted areas may be prevented or lessened in two ways: either the loss of heat from the earth can be retarded, or a temperature above freezing can be maintained immediately around the threatened crop by artificial heating. Heat loss from the land may be checked by spreading over the crop some nonmetallic covering such as paper, straw, or cloth, thereby intercepting the heat being radiated from the ground and plants. The purpose of the cover, quite obviously, is not to keep the cold out but to keep the heat in. This inexpensive type of frost protection is the one used by the housewife to save her garden plants from freezing. It is not so well suited to the protection of extensive orchard areas, however.

In California and Florida, the huge losses in the citrus areas resulting from an occasional freeze have inspired the most careful and sustained experimentation in frost-fighting methods. A single freeze in California can cause citrus losses amounting to tens of millions of dollars. Many protective devices, some of them of little or no practical value, have been constructed and tried out in the citrus groves. The two most effective and practical ones appear to be orchard heaters, consisting of sheet metal cylinders in which diesel fuel is burned, and huge fans, which agitate the lower few meters of air so that the surface inversion is dissipated. In the cranberry areas of Wisconsin and New England, the bogs are usually flooded if killing frost seems probable. The water surface created by flooding cools more slowly than a land surface and thereby lessens the freeze hazard. Moreover, a protective cover of light fog is likely to develop over the flooded fields.

SELECTED REFERENCES FOR FURTHER STUDY OF TOPICS IN CHAPTER TWO

1. **Heating and cooling the atmosphere.** Byers, pp. 11–44; Haurwitz and Austin, pp. 14–22; Landsberg, pp. 118–126, 141–146; Petterssen, pp. 77–99; Hare, pp. 9–16; Kendrew, *Climatology,* pp. 13–22; Miller and Parry, pp. 38–57.

2. **Distribution of temperature over the earth.** Blüthgen, pp. 66–97; Byers, pp. 45–60; Critchfield, pp. 28–36; Conrad, pp. 16–38; Haurwitz and Austin, pp. 23–43; Kendrew, *Climatology,* pp. 23–30; Koeppe and De Long, pp. 42–47; Landsberg, pp. 146–165; Miller and Parry, pp. 48–54; Willett and Saunders, pp. 38–81.

3. **General references on temperature.** M. I. Budyko, *The Heat Balance of the Earth's Surface* (translation), U.S. Weather Bureau, Washington, D.C., 1958; Arnold Court, "Duration of Very Hot Temperatures," *Bull. Amer. Meteorol. Soc.,* Vol. 33, no. 4, pp. 140–149, 1952; D. M. Houghton, "Heat Sources and Sinks at the Earth's Surface," *Meteorol. Magazine,* Vol. 87, pp. 132–142, 1958; Henry G. Houghton, "On the Annual Heat Balances of the Northern Hemisphere," *J. Meteorology,* Vol. 11, pp. 1–9, 1954; W. H. Ransom, "Solar Radiation and Temperature," *Weather,* Vol. 8, pp. 18–23, 1963; K. A. Salishchev, "The Cold Pole of the Earth," *Geor. Rev.,* pp. 684–685, 1935; R. Stone, "Solar Heating of Land and Sea," *Geography,* Vol. 40, p. 288, 1955; Carl Troll, "Thermische Klimatypen der Erde," *Petermanns Geograph. Mitt.,* Vol. 89, pp. 81–89, 1943.

CHAPTER THREE

WIND AND PRESSURE SYSTEMS

It is chiefly as *controls* of temperature and precipitation, rather than as *elements* of climate, that atmospheric pressure and winds are crucial to life on earth. Pressure as a climatic element does not seem to make a great difference to life forms with its slight variations and changes that occur at the earth's surface. Winds are more important than pressure as an element, for wind speed does have an effect on plant life, and also on man's comfort and safety. Moreover, wind influences the rate of evaporation and therefore affects sensible temperatures. But on the whole, the winds of a place do not contribute as much to its climatic environment as solar energy, temperature, and precipitation do.

As climatic controls, however, pressure and winds rank among the highest. Although very small pressure changes are imperceptible to human beings, they may induce remarkable variations in general weather conditions. Also, they are usually the cause of wind, and wind is a powerful determinant of the air temperature and moisture conditions of a place. In fact, it can be said that pressure and winds operate as climatic controls mainly through their effects upon temperature and precipitation—two climatic elements of critical importance as far as living things are concerned.

Winds serve two basic climatic functions.

1. By transporting heat, in either sensible or latent form, from the lower to the higher latitudes, winds are the principal agent in maintaining the latitudinal heat balance of the earth. They operate to correct the unbalanced receipt of solar radiation between low and high latitudes.

2. Winds also provide the land masses with much of the moisture necessary for precipitation, since they transport the water vapor which is evaporated over the oceans to the lands, where subsequently a large part is condensed and falls as rain. Because rainfall distribution over the earth is much affected by the atmospheric circulation, this chapter on pressure and winds precedes Chapter 4's discussion of moisture and precipitation.

Measurement of atmospheric pressure. Atmospheric pressure is a measure of the weight of the atmosphere above the height of observation. The total weight of the air ocean is over 5,600 trillion tons. If this weight of air were to be replaced by the same weight of water, the water would form a layer about 34 ft (10+ meters) deep over the whole earth. In spite of its great total weight, the atmosphere as a whole does not fall toward the solid-liquid earth. Rather, it remains suspended, neither rising nor sinking, except for individual air masses. This is because the downward pull of gravity on the air ocean is just balanced by another force urging it upward, a force created by the decrease in atmospheric pressure with height. Such equilibrium is called *hydrostatic balance*.

A column of air 1 sq in. in cross-sectional area extending from sea level to the top of the atmosphere weighs nearly 15 lb. This weight is balanced by a column of mercury 29.92 in., or 760 mm, tall having the same cross-sectional area. The value 29.92 in., or 760 mm, is accepted as the normal value of atmospheric pressure at sea level at latitude 45°. Thus it is customary to measure air pressure in terms of its equivalent weight expressed in inches or millimeters of a column of mercury—in other words, to measure it by a mercurial barometer.

Another measurement unit of atmospheric pressure, called a millibar, has been widely adopted by the national weather services of the world. The millibar is a force equal to 1,000 dynes per cm² and a dyne is a unit of force approximately equal to the weight of a milligram. Sea-level pressure (29.92 in. or 760 mm) under this system of measurement is 1,013.2 millibars (mb). One-tenth of an inch of mercury is approximately equal to 3.4 mb. On all United States weather maps published since January, 1940, pressure readings have been in millibars instead of inches. These maps have *isobars* (lines of equal surface pressure) drawn for every 4 mb of pressure, an arrangement that closely corresponds to the interval of $\frac{1}{10}$ in. previously used.

Barometric pressure equivalents

Millibars	Inches of mercury	Millimeters of mercury
940	27.76	705.1
950	28.05	712.5
960	28.35	720.1
970	28.65	727.7
980	28.94	735.1
990	29.24	742.7
1,000	29.53	750.1
1,010	29.83	757.7
1,013.2*	29.92*	760.0*
1,020	30.12	765.0
1,030	30.42	772.7
1,040	30.71	780.0
1,050	31.01	787.7

* Pressure at sea level at latitude 45°.

Types of pressure systems and their origins. Pressure systems vary greatly in both size and duration. At one extreme are the immense semipermanent cells of high and low pressure which can be seen on average monthly, seasonal, and annual pressure charts of the earth. But in addition there are many smaller, short-lived moving pressure systems which show up chiefly on the daily weather map. These are closely identified with daily weather changes.

The two main types of pressure are high-pressure systems and low-pressure systems. Centers of relatively low pressure are designated as *depressions*,

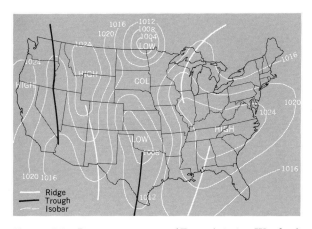

Figure 3.1 Pressure systems. (*From Aviation Weather.*)

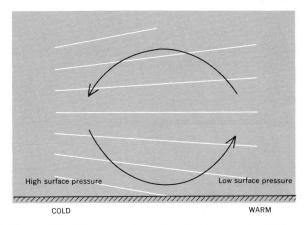

Figure 3.2 What may be called the expected relationship between air temperature on the one hand and surface pressure and atmospheric circulation on the other. Sloping white lines indicate surfaces of equal pressure.

cyclones, or *lows.* Elongated lows are called *troughs.* Centers of high pressure are called *anticyclones* or *highs.* An elongated high is a *ridge* (Fig. 3.1).

At present several features of average pressure distribution over the earth, and many of the pressure changes which occur from day to day, cannot be satisfactorily explained. Since a column of hot air is less dense and weighs less than a column of cold, heavy air of the same length at the same height, it seems likely that some surface lows are at least partly caused by high surface temperature, and some highs by low surface temperature (Fig. 3.2). Most pressure systems, however, appear to be related to nonthermal, or mechanical, factors affecting air in motion, such as frictional effects, centrifugal force, and the blocking effects of highlands. These mechanical forces operate in various ways to either remove or pile up air, thereby producing low- and high-pressure systems. Thus while pressure differences can induce air movement, the circulation of the air in turn may act to generate new pressure differences. So it is not always easy to say which comes first and is the primary cause.

DISTRIBUTION OF ATMOSPHERIC PRESSURE

Vertical distribution

Since air is very compressible, air weight, or pressure, decreases rapidly with height. The lower layers of the atmosphere are the densest, because the weight of all the layers above rests upon them. The change in pressure with height is proportional to density, so that it is possible to determine approximate elevation by the pressure of the atmosphere at that level.[1] For the first few thousand feet above

[1]Accurate determination would require an adjustment for temperature.

sea level, the rate of pressure decrease is about 1 in., or 34 mb, of pressure for each 900 to 1,000 ft of elevation. At higher altitudes the air rapidly becomes much thinner and lighter. Although the air ocean extends upward for thousands of miles, at an elevation of about 18,000 ft one-half the atmosphere by weight is below the observer, and at 36,000 ft three-quarters lies below. Since the human body is not physiologically adjusted to the low pressures and low oxygen content of the air at high altitudes, nausea, faintness, and nosebleed often result from a too rapid ascent. Oxygen tanks are a part of the normal equipment of aircraft operating at high altitudes.

Atmospheric environment

Altitude (ft)	Pressure		Temperature (°C)
	Inches of mercury	Millibars	
70,000	1.3	44.0	−55.2
50,000	3.4	115.1	−56.5
35,000	7.0	237.0	−54.0
18,000	14.9	506.0	−20.6
10,000	20.6	697.5	−4.8
5,000	24.9	843.1	5.1
Mean sea level	29.92	1013.2	15.0 (59.0° F)

Horizontal distribution at sea level

As the accompanying table shows, pressure declines rapidly with increasing altitude. Consequently it is necessary to adopt a standard height of observation when comparing pressure readings for stations at different elevations. This standard is the sea-level surface.

Average annual conditions. Just as temperature distribution is represented on maps by isotherms, so atmospheric pressure distribution is shown by isobars. These are lines connecting places having the same atmospheric pressure at a given elevation. Pressure distribution charts are constructed for sea level and also for a number of different constant-pressure surfaces in the free atmosphere—commonly the 700-mb surface at about 10,000 ft and the 500-mb surface at about 18,000 ft. On the sea-level pressure charts (see Figs. 3.6 and 3.7) the effects of different elevations on the continents have been eliminated by reducing all pressure readings to sea level.

Where isobars are closely spaced, there is a rapid change of pressure in a direction at right angles to the isobars. The rate and direction of pressure change is called the *pressure gradient*. The gradient

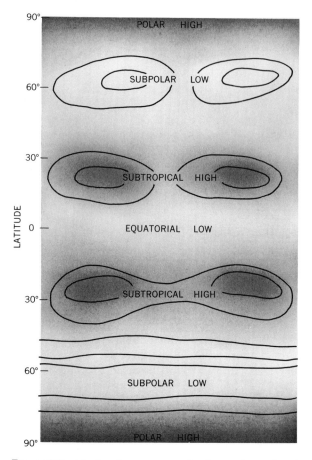

Figure 3.3 Idealized arrangement of zonal sea-level pressure. Except in the higher latitudes of the Southern Hemisphere, the zonal pressure "belts" are cells of low or high pressure arranged in belts which are concentrated in particular latitudes.

is weak where isobars are widely spaced and steep where they are closely spaced. The horizontal pressure gradient may therefore be defined as the decrease in pressure per unit distance in the direction in which the pressure decreases most rapidly (see Figs. 3.6, 3.7, and 3.9).

The earth's average sea-level pressure shows something of a zonal arrangement in latitudinal belts (Fig. 3.3). But while a belted pattern is fairly conspicuous, especially when pressure is averaged for all longitudes, some of the so-called belts are more accurately described as centers, or cells, of pressure whose long axes are aligned roughly east-west. The belted arrangement is much more conspicuous in the relatively homogeneous Southern Hemisphere—a fact which suggests that the great continents, with their seasonal temperature contrasts, their frictional effects on winds, and their highland barriers that obstruct the free flow of air currents, have much to do with the cellular pattern visible on the seasonal pressure maps.

Generalized sea-level pressure patterns as represented in Figs. 3.3 and 3.8 show these outstanding features:

1. The dominant element is the series of high-pressure centers or cells which form discontinuous belts of high pressure, one in either hemisphere, located at about 25–35° N and S. These are the subtropical highs. Although they represent what is probably the key factor in the earth's surface pressure, their origin is not fully understood—except that it is definitely mechanical or dynamic and not directly thermal.

2. Surface pressure declines equatorward from the two subtropical high-pressure belts. Thus there is a general trough of low pressure between them in the vicinity of the geographic equator.

3. Pressure likewise decreases poleward from the subtropical highs toward cells of low pressure located at about the latitudes of the Arctic and Antarctic circles. These are the subpolar cells or troughs of low pressure. They form individual oceanic cells of low pressure in the Northern Hemisphere, but in the Southern Hemisphere they consist of a deep and continuous circumpolar trough of low pressure. The causes of the subpolar lows are also not clear, but these pressure systems can scarcely be of direct thermal origin.

4. Poleward from about latitude 65°, aerological data are so scarce that the pressure distribution pattern cannot be described with certainty. It is generally assumed that anticyclones, partly of thermal origin, occupy the inner polar areas.

On a weather map of the world for any particular day and time, the arrangement of average zonal surface pressure shown in Figs. 3.3 and 3.8 is not so evident. This fact suggests that the generalized

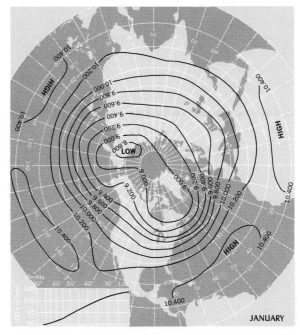

Figure 3.4 January: 700-mb pressure surface in the Northern Hemisphere. (*After Namias and Clapp.*)

Figure 3.5 July: 700-mb pressure surface in the Northern Hemisphere. (*After Namias and Clapp.*)

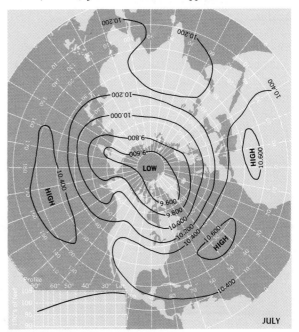

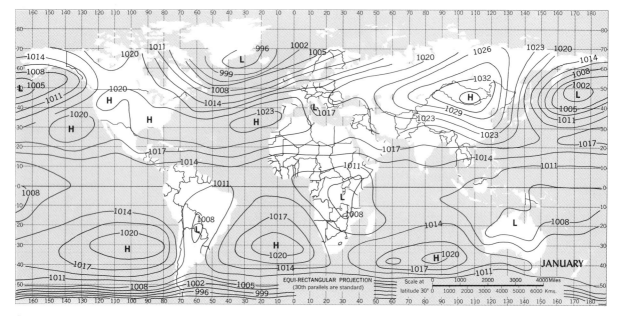

Figure 3.6   January sea-level pressure, in millibars (mb). (*After Mintz and Dean.*)

Figure 3.7   July sea-level pressure, mb. (*After Mintz and Dean.*)

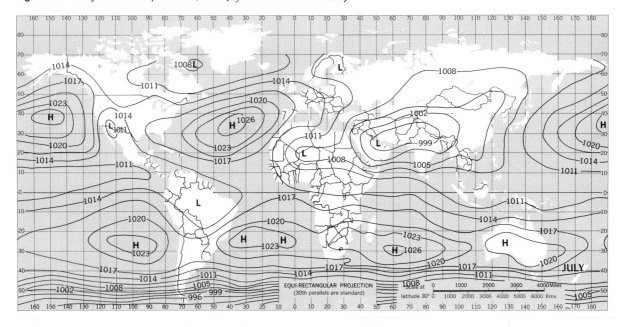

cells and belts of surface pressure are partly, at least, statistical averages of complicated day-to-day systems of smaller traveling highs and lows.

With increasing elevation above the earth's surface, the cellular pattern of pressure distribution so conspicuous at sea level gradually becomes less clear. It is only faintly discernible in the mid-troposphere at about 10,000 ft, or the 700-mb level. At this elevation there is a broad plateau of high pressure in tropical latitudes, from which pressure decreases to minima in the polar regions (Figs. 3.4 and 3.5).

Distribution in January and July.

Average sea-level pressures for the seasonal extremes, January and July, are shown in Figs. 3.6, 3.7, and 3.8. Although pressure distribution at these times retains many of the features of average annual conditions, there are some noteworthy departures:

1. Pressure belts and cells, like belts of solar energy and temperature, shift northward in July and southward in January—a fact of crucial importance to climate. This latitudinal migration is most readily observed in Fig. 3.8 showing the seasonal profiles of pressure.

2. In general, pressure is higher and pressure gradients are steeper in the winter hemisphere. Thus between summer and winter there is an enormous mass transfer of atmosphere from the warmer summer hemisphere to the colder winter hemisphere. It has been calculated that the July-to-January net flow of air across the equator amounts to about two trillion tons, or 1/2,500 of the total mass of the atmosphere.

3. The subtropical belts of high pressure are more continuous in the winter hemisphere; in the summer hemisphere, they are weakened by the heated continents. As a rule these subtropical cells are best developed over the eastern sides of the oceans and tend to be weaker toward the western sides. In the Northern Hemisphere in July, the subtropical highs along the eastern sides of the oceans extend well poleward and into the middle latitudes, strongly affecting the climate of the western sides of the continents.

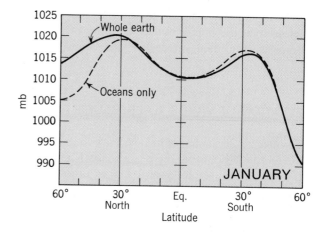

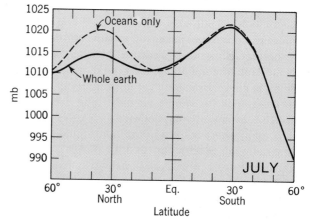

Figure 3.8 Profiles of sea-level pressure from 60°N to 60°S, averaged for all longitudes, at the time of the extreme seasons. Equatorial low, subtropical highs, and subpolar lows are conspicuous features of both profiles. Note the seasonal north-south displacements of the pressure belts following the sun.

4. In the Southern Hemisphere, the subpolar low is very deep and forms a continuous circumpolar trough in both winter and summer. But because of the great continents in the Northern Hemisphere, the subpolar low there is represented by individual oceanic cells which are strongly seasonal in character. In January a deep cell of low pressure occupies both the North Pacific (Aleutian Low) and the North Atlantic (Iceland Low), but in July these oceanic lows are only faintly discernible.

5. In January a strong cell of high pressure develops over the higher middle latitudes of the cold Eurasian continent; a weaker one appears over smaller North America. In July these same continents, now warm, develop weaker thermal lows in somewhat lower latitudes.

RELATION OF WINDS TO PRESSURE

Chapter 2's discussion of heat balance in the atmosphere pointed out that there is a general convective transport of heat from lower to higher altitudes, and an advective or horizontal transport of heat from lower to higher latitudes, in order to correct the earth's radiational imbalance. It is for this reason that the atmosphere is a restless medium in which circulations of all sizes are normal. While vertical motions (properly spoken of as currents) are very important climatically because they help produce cloud and precipitation, their total magnitude is small in comparison with the horizontal movements of wind. Wind is simply air moving in a direction which is essentially parallel with the earth's surface. The atmosphere is fixed to the solid-liquid earth in gravitational equilibrium and so moves with the earth in its west-to-east rotational movement. Wind, therefore, is air movement *in addition to* that associated with rotation.

In large-scale circulations covering several thousand miles, horizontal motion or wind greatly exceeds vertical motion. Thus, a wind which takes several days or even a week or more to cross an ocean may move up or down only a few miles. The vertical component of movement is much greater in small-scale circulations such as thunderstorms and tornadoes. In a thunderstorm, air may ascend to the top of the troposphere (± 6 miles) in a half hour to an hour.

Wind is complex in origin. Usually its direct cause lies in differences between atmospheric densities resulting in horizontal differences in air pressure. That is, it represents nature's attempt to correct pressure inequalities. When these horizontal pressure differences develop, so that there is a high in one location and a low in another, a slope or gradient of pressure exists between them, analogous to the slope or gradient of level which separates a hill from an adjacent valley. But in spite of the direct part played by pressure differences, the ultimate source of energy for generating and maintaining winds against the drag of friction is derived mainly from the differences in heating and cooling between high and low latitudes.

Forces governing winds

Four forces operate to determine the speed and direction of winds: (1) pressure gradient force, (2) the deflecting force of the earth's rotation (Coriolis force), (3) friction, and (4) centrifugal force.

Pressure gradient force. This force sets the air in motion and causes it to move with increasing speed along the gradient. If a mass of air is subjected to higher pressure on one side than on the other, there is a net pressure force moving it from the higher toward the lower pressure.

Pressure gradient force has both magnitude and direction. The *magnitude* is inversely proportional to the isobar spacing: the closer the spacing, and hence the steeper the gradient, the stronger the accelerating force and the greater the wind speed. Weak winds are associated with widely spaced isobars; calms with a near-absence of isobars (Figs. 3.9 and 3.10). The *direction* of the pressure gradient force is represented by a line drawn at right angles to the isobars. Since the gradient slopes downward, from high to low pressure, direction of airflow is from high to low pressure, or along the pressure gradient. But because of the operation of another force, that of earth rotation, the trajectory of an air particle moving from high to low pressure is very indirect, except close to the equator.

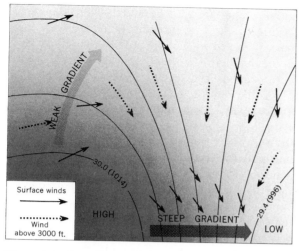

Figure 3.9 Pressure gradient is the rate and direction of pressure change. It is represented by a line drawn at right angles to the isobars. Gradients are steep where isobars are closely spaced and weak where they are far apart. Winds move from high to low pressure, but because of earth rotation they do so indirectly. At the surface, friction causes them to cross the isobars at an angle of 10 to 30°, but aloft they nearly parallel the isobars.

Figure 3.10 Relation of isobaric surfaces in the atmosphere to isobaric lines at the earth's sea-level surface (*xy*).

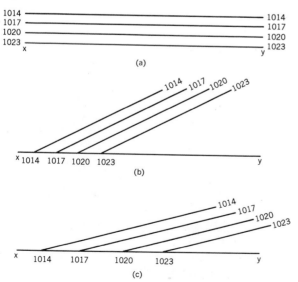

Coriolis force. The second force, which affects only the direction of winds, is *the deflecting force of the earth's rotation,* known as the *Coriolis force.* Except at the equator, winds and all other moving objects, no matter what their direction, are deflected to the right of the gradient in the Northern Hemisphere and to the left in the Southern Hemisphere (Fig 3.11). The force always acts at right angles to the direction of motion.

In reality, Coriolis force is not a real force but only an apparent one. It arises because a moving

Figure 3.11 The apparent deflection of the planetary winds on a rotating earth. White arrows indicate wind direction as it would develop from pressure gradient force alone. Black arrows indicate the direction of deflected winds resulting from earth rotation.

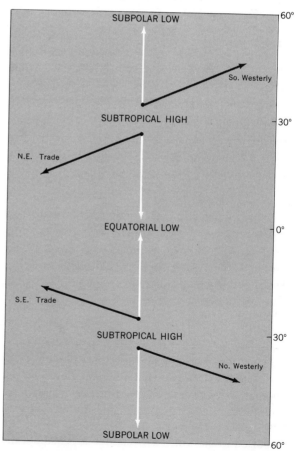

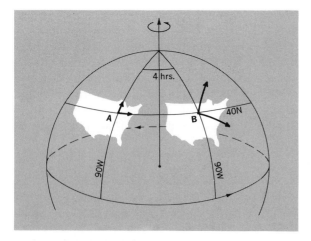

Figure 3.12 Showing the rotation of the United States (in white) around the earth's axis as the earth turns during about 4 hr, or one-sixth of a complete rotation. In its initial position *A*, one wind is shown blowing from the south and another from the west at 40°N and 90°W. But 4 hr later these winds are from the southwest and the northwest, as indicated in the second position *B*. They have undergone an apparent deflection to the right. (*After H. Riehl in Introduction to the Atmosphere.*)

object like the wind tends to keep its original direction fixed with respect to a point in space. By contrast, directions on the earth's surface are related to a coordinate system of meridians and parallels which themselves rotate and change absolute direction as the earth turns on its axis.

This is illustrated in Fig. 3.12, where the United States is shown as moving from west to east as the earth turns on its axis. Assume for the moment that there is no friction and no horizontal pressure force. The wind will therefore maintain its original absolute direction with respect to a point in space, while the earth underneath turns. In position *A* a wind from the south is shown along the 100°W meridian and a wind from the west along the 40°N parallel. Four hours later, the earth has turned 60° on its axis. Meridians and parallels have rotated counterclockwise and changed absolute directions, and the United States area has similarly rotated with respect to the axis. But these rotations are not imparted to the winds above. So to a person on the

ground, unaware that he and his directions have been turning, it will appear that the winds have been deflected to the right (or to the left, if he is in the Southern Hemisphere) of their original starting direction. And so they have, from his point of observation on the rotating earth where directions are changing. Thus four hours later, the original south wind appears to be from the southwest, and the west wind from the northwest. To an observer on the earth, it appears that the winds have been deflected to the right by some force exerted to the right of the wind. (The right-hand deflection of winds in the Northern Hemisphere and their left-hand deflection in the Southern Hemisphere will not be apparent, however, unless the observer's back is toward the wind so that he faces the direction in which the wind is blowing.)

This deflective force of earth rotation can be illustrated by an analogy. Figure 3.13 shows a circular disk rotating counterclockwise, as indicated by the arrows. If an object at point *C* is moved toward point *P* beyond the rotating disk, an outside observer would see the object move from *C* to *P* along the straight dashed line. An observer *T* riding *on* the disk, however, would be at point *T* when the object started from *C*, but because of rotation of the disk, would find himself at *T'* when the object arrived

Figure 3.13 The deflecting force of earth rotation.

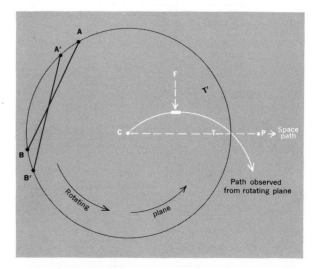

at *P*. It would appear to this observer on the disk that a force *F* had caused the moving object to be pushed to the right of its original path. This apparent force is the Coriolis force. Both observers would be right in their observations, for the one in space observed the object's absolute motion, while the one on the rotating disk observed its relative motion (see also Fig. 3.14).

Thus on a nonrotating earth, air set in motion by pressure gradient force will move in a straight line from high to low pressure. On a rotating earth, air starts toward the low pressure, but to an observer on the earth it is

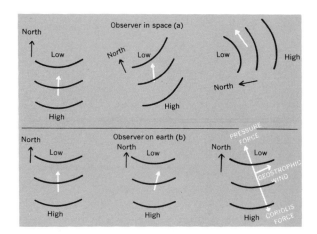

Figure 3.15 The solid black lines are isobars, drawn parallel with the latitude circles. The white arrows indicate the position of the air particle and its direction of motion as seen *a* by an observer in outer space, and *b* by an observer in a fixed position on the earth. N = local north. (*After H. Riehl in Introduction to the Atmosphere.*)

deflected more and more to the right of its initial path until, in the absence of friction, it moves parallel with the isobars (Fig. 3.15). To an observer in space the situation looks different. He sees the air start out toward the low pressure along a straight line in space. But it cannot get to the low directly, because the pressure system rotates as the earth turns on its axis. The air is obliged to continuously turn in response to the changing positions of low and high pressure. Eventually it moves parallel with the isobars and at right angles to the gradient.

The magnitude of the Coriolis force is proportional to (1) the speed of the wind, and (2) the degree of inclination of the earth's spherical surface with respect to the earth's axis (i.e., the latitude). The effect of the changing inclination of the earth's surface is illustrated in Fig. 3.16, which makes it necessary to distinguish clearly between two different rotations. There is, first, the turning of the entire earth on its axis once in 24 hr. But second, there is a rotation of meridians and parallels, and so of surface areas on the earth with respect to the axis. At the pole, where the earth's surface is inclined 90° to the axis, an area will rotate in a plane perpendicular to the axis and make a complete

Figure 3.14 Deflective effect of earth rotation at the North Pole. Illustrated is a flat disk tangent at the North Pole. The arrows paralleling the circumference indicate the west-to-east rotation of the earth. Any body that is set in motion in a given direction tends to keep that direction unless acted upon by some external force. Based upon the preceding principle, a south wind, illustrated by arrow 1*A*, continues to keep its direction constant as the earth rotates. When the earth has turned through 45°, the original south wind is still moving in the same direction with respect to space, for arrow 2*A* is parallel with 1*A*. But in terms of directions on the rotating earth, whose meridians and parallels are constantly changing positions, the 2*A* is from the southwest. Similarly, the west wind 1*B* becomes northwest wind 2*B*; north wind 1*C* becomes northeast wind 2*C*; and east wind 1*D* becomes southeast wind 2*D*. (*After Koeppe.*)

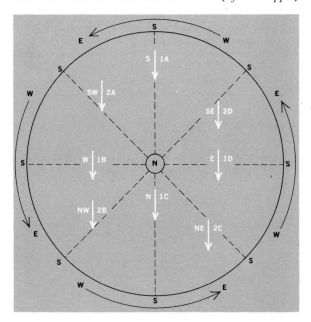

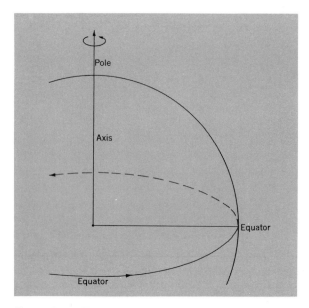

Figure 3.16 The surface of the earth is perpendicular to the axis at the pole and parallel to it at the equator. So during a complete earth rotation a person near the pole would turn through 360° and consequently experience a complete change in directions. But a person at the equator would experience no change in direction. (*After H. Riehl in Introduction to the Atmosphere.*)

360° rotation once in 24 hr. For this reason Coriolis force is strongest in high latitudes. With increasing distance from the pole, the earth's spherical surface is more and more turned away from the axis, so that the component of area rotation acting parallel to the earth's surface decreases. At latitude 30°, this component is only half what it is at the pole. At the equator, where the earth's surface is parallel with the axis, the whole rotation of surface areas takes place in a plane perpendicular to the earth's surface. Hence Coriolis force disappears there.

When a wind (in this case called a *geostrophic wind*) blows parallel with the isobars, the Coriolis force is just balanced by the pressure gradient force (Fig. 3.17). Outside the atmosphere's friction layer, which extends 1,500 to 3,000 ft above the earth's surface, winds actually do blow in a direction almost parallel with the isobars, with low pressure on the left and high pressure on the right (in the

Northern Hemisphere). The air may then be thought of as flowing between the isobars, in the same way that a river flows between its banks. Where the channel is narrow, the flow is faster; where it is wider, the flow is slower, If the spaces between the isobars are thought of as tubes of constant transport, the speed of the air above the friction layer is nearly inversely proportional to the width of the channel, or the space between the isobars (Fig. 3.18).

Friction. Both wind speed and wind direction are affected by friction, the third of the forces governing winds. Friction between the moving air and the earth's land-sea surface tends to slow the air's movement—a factor which is important mainly in the lower few thousand feet of the air ocean. It likewise produces turbulence, or vertical motion. An air mass itself in which the wind changes with height also has a slight amount of internal friction.

Because of the frictional effects of the land-sea

Figure 3.17 A geostrophic wind results when pressure gradient force is balanced by the deflecting force. Straight (or nearly straight) isobars and a similar airflow are assumed. The geostrophic wind blows parallel with the isobars, with high pressure to the right (Northern Hemisphere). Winds are essentially geostrophic in character above about 1,000 m. (When isobars are strongly curved, and the path of a moving parcel of air is as well, the effects of a third force, centrifugal force, should be included. Then the flow of air which is necessary to balance pressure gradient, deflection, and centrifugal forces is called a *gradient wind*.)

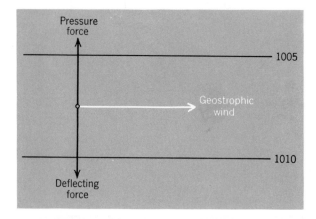

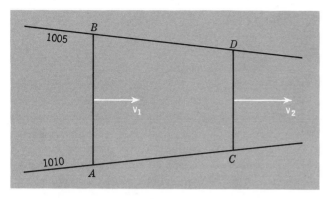

Figure 3.18 The spaces between the isobars may be thought of as channels of constant transport, so the speed of the air is inversely proportional to the width of the channel. Consequently the amount of air that flows through section CD equals that flowing through section AB where the channel diameter is greater. It follows that the air must have a higher velocity (V_2) at CD than at AB (V_1).

surface upon air flowing over it, surface air does not flow essentially parallel with the isobars as it does aloft, but instead crosses them at an oblique angle (Fig 3.19). The greater the friction, the wider

Figure 3.19 The effects of friction on the direction of surface winds. Over the sea surface, where friction is slight, winds cross the isobars at a small angle. The angle is much greater over a rough land surface.

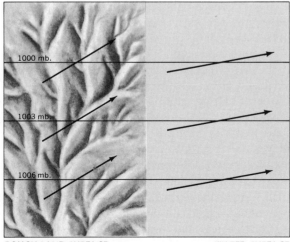

ROUGH LAND SURFACE   WATER SURFACE

is the angle the wind direction makes with the isobars; i.e., the closer the wind direction is to the direction of the pressure gradient. Winds over irregular land surfaces usually form angles varying from 20 to 45° with the isobars. But over oceans, where the frictional drag is less, the angle may be as little as 10°.

Centrifugal force. Fourth of the great influences on winds is centrifugal force,[2] which operates only when air moves in a curved path. It acts in a direction radially outward from the center of curvature of the air's path, and increases both with wind speed and with the shortening of the radius of curvature. Centrifugal force is a major factor only when the wind is strong and the radius of curvature small—as they are in tropical hurricanes, tornadoes, and the centers of a few unusually well-developed cyclonic storms.

Wind direction and speed

Winds are always named by the direction they come from. Thus a wind from the south, blowing toward the north, is called a south wind. The wind vane points into the wind. *Windward* refers to the direction a wind comes from, *leeward* to the direction it blows toward. Thus a windward coast is one along which the air is moving onshore; on a leeward coast, winds blow offshore. When a wind blows more frequently from one direction than from any other it is called a *prevailing* wind. Wind direction is expressed in terms of directions on a 32-point compass and is referred to by the compass point, by letter abbreviations of the directions, or by the number of degrees east of north.

Wind speed increases rapidly with height above the ground level, as frictional drag declines. Wind is commonly not a steady current but is made up of a succession of gusts, slightly variable in direction, separated by lulls. Close to the earth the gustiness is caused by irregularities of the surface, which

[2]This is scarcely a real force; it is rather a consequence of the unbalancing of the other forces when isobars are curved and wind flow is too.

create eddies. Larger irregularities in the wind are caused by convectional currents. All forms of turbulence play a part in the process of transporting heat, moisture, and dust into the air aloft.

Cyclonic and anticyclonic circulations

As discussed earlier in the chapter, sea-level pressure patterns are commonly cellular in form. On an isobaric chart they are represented as systems with closed isobars. When such a system has the lowest pressure at the center, it together with its circulation is designated as a cyclone. When a system of closed isobars has the highest pressure at the center, it together with its circulation is called an anticyclone (Fig. 3.20). The combined effects of pressure gradient force, Coriolis force, and friction cause airflow in a cyclone to be *convergent,* with surface winds flowing obliquely across the isobars toward the center. In an anticyclone the circulation is *divergent,* with surface winds moving obliquely across the isobars outward from the center.

Figure 3.20 A cyclonic circulation is a converging system of airflow around a low-pressure center, counterclockwise in the Northern Hemisphere and clockwise south of the equator. An anticyclonic circulation is a diverging system of airflow around a high-pressure center, clockwise in the Northern Hemisphere and counterclockwise in the Southern.

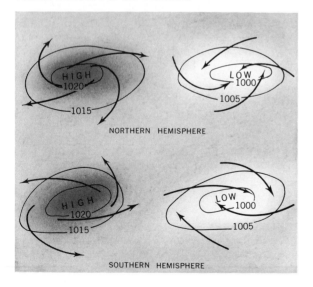

NORTHERN HEMISPHERE

SOUTHERN HEMISPHERE

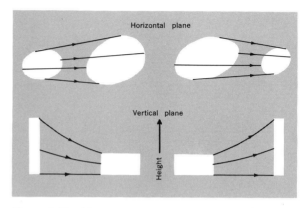

Horizontal plane

Vertical plane

Height

Figure 3.21 Mass convergence and divergence of the atmosphere, shown in horizontal and vertical planes. In the lower diagram the lowest streamlines of airflow are shown horizontal because the base of the air columns is the ground. (*After H. Riehl in Introduction to the Atmosphere.*)

Convergence and divergence

Although vertical air movement occurs on a much smaller scale than horizontal transfer, it is very important in the formation of cloud and precipitation. Vertical movement has various causes. It can be produced by thermal convection due to heating of air near the ground, or by mechanical turbulence caused by terrain irregularities. A major cause of vertical movement is lifting and subsidence associated with convergence and divergence in horizontal airstreams. Convergence occurs when the horizontal area occupied by a given mass of air decreases; divergence occurs when the area increases (Fig. 3.21). Air which converges laterally must spread vertically or stretch. In an airstream bounded by the earth's surface, this results in upward movement. Divergence and horizontal spreading in surface flow result in vertical shrinking and downward movement, or subsidence. In large-scale circulations, convergence or divergence may take place over areas covering 50,000 to 500,000 square miles. In such systems the vertical movement has a speed of only about a half mile a day.

Convergence and lifting in an airstream also occur when its speed decreases downstream. This results in a piling up of air to the rear and consequently in upward movement there. Conversely, when speed increases downstream, the air diverges and settles. In a curved airstream, convergence occurs when the air curves counterclockwise (forming a cyclonic circulation) in the Northern Hemi-sphere. When the curvature is clockwise (anticyclonic), divergence prevails. Air moving equatorward into latitudes of decreasing Coriolis force tends to diverge and subside; moving poleward, it slowly converges and lifts.

GENERAL CIRCULATION OF THE EARTH'S ATMOSPHERE

The force required to drive the gigantic circulation of the earth's atmosphere is provided by the energy contrasts between the warm energy source in tropical latitudes and the cold sources in polar latitudes. Obviously these latitudinal temperature contrasts originate because the low latitudes receive much more solar energy than the high latitudes. The atmospheric circulation (and the oceanic circulation as well) transports heat from a zone of excess energy in the tropics to a region of deficiency close to either pole. In other words, it acts like a heat engine. The poleward heat transport is mainly in the form of sensible heat (heat that is felt), and to a lesser degree in the form of latent heat traveling as water vapor acquired by evaporation. Although ultimately there must be an exchange of energy in a north-south direction (that is, there must be a meridional circulation of the atmosphere), the average circulation actually is overwhelmingly zonal, or west-east —a feature due to earth rotation and its resulting Coriolis force.

On a nonrotating earth, warm in the low latitudes and cold at the poles, the atmosphere would circulate in the form of two gigantic convectional systems, one in each hemisphere. The warm air would rise in the low latitudes and flow poleward at higher levels, where it would slowly subside to ground level and give up its heat. The cold polar air would flow equatorward as a surface current. Under these circumstances, surface pressure would be high in the polar areas and low in equatorial latitudes.

But on a rotating earth, both low-level currents moving equatorward and high-level ones moving poleward are acted upon by earth rotation. The result is that the earth's atmospheric pressure ar-rangement, as well as its atmospheric circulation, becomes unusually complicated. In fact, it is so complex that some elements of the circulation still remain uncertain, and there are no widely accepted explanations for some features that are known. For example, just how the required meridional heat exchange is accomplished in a circulation which is essentially zonal has always been something of a puzzle.

In the low latitudes between about 0 and 30°, where Coriolis force and the rotation component of meridians and parallels about the earth's axis are weak (dropping to zero at the equator), the atmospheric circulation resembles that which one would expect in a simple convectional system (Fig. 3.22). The air flows obliquely equatorward at the surface and poleward aloft, and though the high-tropospheric flow is variable, the net transfer is poleward.

This direct thermal type of circulation prevails within the tropics in spite of the fact that significant north-south contrasts in sensible temperature are lacking. The equatorial heat source is maintained chiefly by heat of condensation released in cumulus clouds in the relatively narrow belt of heavy equatorial rainfall. Significantly, the belt between 25°N and 25°S furnishes 60 percent of the earth's evaporated moisture. Tropical cumuli have effects far beyond the local region in which they originate. Indeed, they play a vital role in the fire-box and fuel-pump functions of the atmosphere's heat engine, which maintains the tropical circulation. The *mean* tropical atmosphere does not generate large-diameter cumulus towers. The trade-wind cumuli do act, however, to raise and weaken the trade inversion along the air trajectory and thereby create the pressure head which maintains the steady

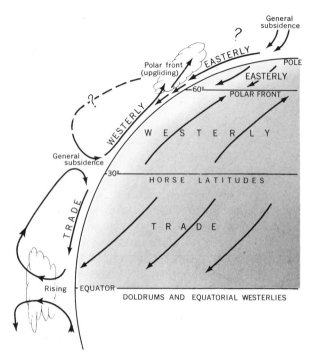

Figure 3.22 Important elements of the general circulation of the atmosphere. Some features of the upper circulation are not at present sufficiently well understood, or are too complicated, to be represented in a simple diagram.

easterly flow. But a few thousand simultaneously active giant cumulonimbus "hot towers" in the equatorial-trough zone, as well as occasional hurricanes, condense two-thirds of all the water evaporated into the atmosphere and transport aloft several hundred times as much energy as is consumed in all the global wind systems combined.[3] It is these giant hot towers, mainly equatorial, that perform the fire-box function in the tropical atmosphere's heat engine. They condense the water vapor carried equatorward by the trades, thereby releasing prodigious amounts of heat of condensation.

The tropical "cold source" is broader in latitudi-

[3] Joanne S. Malkus. "Tropical Convection: Progress and Outlook." In J. W. Hutchings (ed.). *Proc., Symposium on Tropical Meteorology, Rotorua, New Zealand, 1963.* New Zealand Meteorological Service, Wellington, 1964. Pp. 247–277.

nal spread, covering much of the whole volume of the atmosphere between about latitudes 5 or 10° and 30°. It is a consequence of radiational cooling at various levels and is accompanied by a broad area of slow settling and drying of the air in the subtropics.

In the middle latitudes, the circulation does not resemble that of a large convectional system, for in the westerly wind belts of these latitudes the surface flow is from a warm source toward a cold one. Since Coriolis force is strong, the rotation component of meridians and parallels about the earth's axis is large. Consequently the north-south heat transfer in the middle latitudes is accomplished less by steady flow than by strong, sporadic air-mass exchanges across the latitude belts. These take the form of intermittent thrusts of cold surface polar air equatorward, and of tropical air moving poleward. Outside the tropics, airflow is variable at all heights. Such individual air-mass exchanges accompany the succession of cyclones and anticyclones which move from west to east in the middle latitudes. They are also linked with the upper-tropospheric long waves (discussed in the next section), which occur in the same latitudes. It appears, therefore, that the contrasting types of general circulation inside and outside the tropics are strongly affected by variations in Coriolis force with latitude, in the same way as is the component of rotation of meridians and parallels about the earth's axis.

It is not so difficult to produce a vertical profile model of the atmospheric circulation in the low latitudes, where the airflow is reasonably steady. But constructing any such model of the mean circulation outside the tropics presents almost insuperable difficulties because of the sporadic air-mass exchange.

Least is known about the polar circulation. Although it is sporadic in nature, its overall direction of flow most likely resembles that of the tropics more than that of the middle latitudes. In other words, probably the surface-air movement is largely from higher to lower latitudes, or from a colder to a warmer source. Consequently the low-troposphere flow in middle latitudes must move in a direction

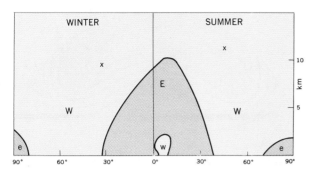

Figure 3.23 A pole-to-pole cross section of the planetary winds up to about 8 or 9 miles above the earth's surface. E = tropical easterlies or trades; W = westerlies; x = average location of the jet stream; w = the somewhat less certain belt of equatorial westerlies; e = polar easterlies. (*After Flohn.*)

opposite to those on both its high- and low-latitude margins. This cannot help but result in a clash of polar and tropical air masses within the middle-latitude westerlies. Such a clash necessarily has major effects on temperature, precipitation, and storminess. Another fact of great importance, particularly in relation to cloud and precipitation, is that the mechanism of the general circulation results in ascent of air both in equatorial and in middle latitudes, but in settling or subsidence in the subtropics and probably in the polar regions.

Figure 3.23 shows a generalized meridional cross section of the normal state of the circulation. Much the greatest volume of the atmosphere has a westerly flow. In middle latitudes these vast and deep circumpolar westerly circulations reach down to the earth's surface. The westerly direction is less obvious in the surface flow, however, because of turbulence and numerous disrupting atmospheric disturbances. Both steadiness of direction and speed of flow increase aloft in the westerlies. A sharp maximum in speed is reached in the vicinity of the jet stream (which is described in the following sections), at an altitude of about 10 or 12 km. The existence of the smaller isolated area of westerly flow in the vicinity of the equator has not been completely confirmed.

As seen in Fig. 3.23, there are two main systems of easterly circulation. First of these is the broad and deep belt of tropical easterlies, or trade winds, which extend out 30° and more on either side of the equator. The second, located in the high latitudes of each hemisphere, is the much shallower and more fickle polar easterlies, whose existence has not yet been decisively verified.

General circulation features of the upper troposphere

Airflow is predominantly in the form of wave motion. Within the troposphere there are air waves of all sizes and at all altitudes. It is the atmosphere's wave patterns, and their associated convergence and divergence, which largely govern weather occurrences on time scales ranging from periods as short as a day to those as long as a month or even more.

Upper-air long waves. The middle- and upper-troposphere westerlies contain two features—the long waves and the jet streams—which themselves are closely linked, and which are both intimately related to surface weather. Superimposed upon the circumpolar vortex of westerly winds is a system of huge, slow-moving long waves, several thousand miles in length, which radiate out from the polar cyclonic vortex (Fig. 3.24). These long waves in the upper westerlies form troughs and ridges in the constant pressure surfaces. Although they vary from three to six in number, the atmosphere appears to have a strong inclination to return to a system of four principal waves. The long waves either are stationary or move very slowly. Moreover, because the earth's surface is not uniform, the atmosphere's troughs and ridges seem to have certain preferred positions. (Fig. 3.25). Major troughs commonly are positioned as follows: (1) extending from Labrador toward Florida in eastern North America or the adjacent Atlantic, (2) extending from northern Scandinavia toward the Mediterranean, (3) extending from Alaska toward the central Pacific, and (4) possibly another from central Siberia toward Burma. However, the long waves and their troughs and

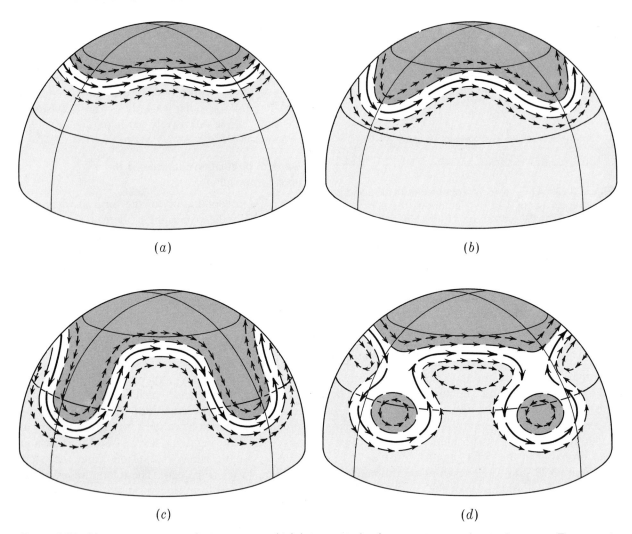

(a)

(b)

(c)

(d)

Figure 3.24 Upper-air waves on the jet stream, which bring periods of contrasting weather in their train. The typical sequence, called an index cycle, is shown in the four diagrams. The undulating jet goes into increasingly large oscillations. North of the jet lies cold polar air, and south of it warm tropical air. The great oscillations carry polar air into the middle and low latitudes and tropical air into the middle and high latitudes. Finally, the extended waves are cut off, leaving cells of cold air in the south and cells of warm air in the north. (*After Namias.*)

ridges often depart from their normal positions for variable periods. Such shifts in location cause the weather patterns of a hemisphere to shift also.

Large-scale wave motion is characteristic of the atmosphere in the middle and high latitudes, but is found much less often in the tropics. This fact is related in a cause-and-effect sense to two others of more than ordinary importance: (1) Coriolis force increases with latitude, and (2) heat transport in the tropics is achieved by a fairly steady flow resembling a convectional system, but in the westerlies of the middle latitudes, where the long waves prevail, heat exchange takes place by sporadic thrusts of cold air equatorward and warm air poleward.

In experiments with water-filled rotating basins, it was discovered that slow rotation gave rise to a steady flow, with the highest speeds near the inner cold core. At faster rotations a sinuous wave pattern developed which resembled that of the westerlies, with high speeds concentrated in a narrow band similar to the jet-stream type of current described in the next section. The basin experiments suggest that it is the more rapid rotation of earth surfaces with respect to the axis (stronger Coriolis force) in middle and high latitudes that is responsible for the long waves there, and for the associated sporadic method of heat transport. Slower rotation and weaker Coriolis force fit the tropical situation, with its near-absence of wave motion and its steady process of heat transport.

Unquestionably, the strength, frequency, and positioning of the long-wave pressure troughs and ridges have much to do with the broad-scale regional patterns of surface weather. Thus there is a close genetic connection between the upper waves and the cyclones and anticyclones at the surface. Since the air on the front of a meridionally oriented ridge or rear of a trough is from higher latitudes, polar outbreaks of deep layers of cold air often accompany the passage of a trough. The equatorial margins of these polar thrusts become the hemisphere's polar front. Subsidence below a high-level ridge is conducive to dry weather at the surface. By contrast, a trough preceded by a poleward flow of tropical air favors high humidity and rain.

Over the United States, the average midwinter

Figure 3.25 Upper-air troughs are closely associated with the location of major frontal zones, which in turn are concentrated regions of cyclogenesis. Eastern North America–western Atlantic, and eastern Asia–western Pacific are two Northern Hemisphere regions with a noteworthy concentration of upper troughs, frontal zones, and cyclone development. (*After Flohn.*)

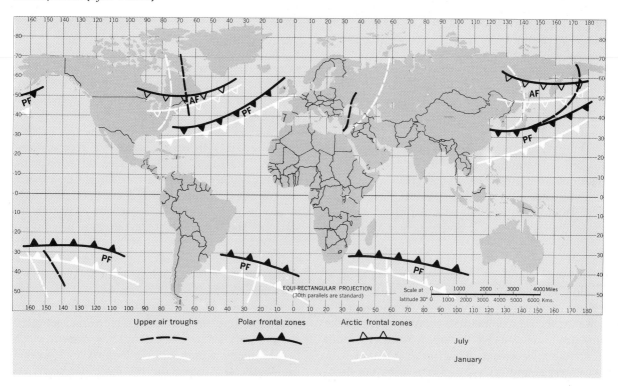

flow at 500 mb shows a meridional pressure ridge over the western half of the United States and a trough over the eastern half. In an instance cited by Riehl, the average flow in January, 1958, resembled the normal pattern except that the troughs and ridges were unusually strong. This arrangement drew warm air into the western states, while a cold northerly flow dominated the East. As a consequence the West was warm and the East abnormally cold. Precipitation was above normal along much of the Pacific Coast and also the Atlantic and Gulf Coasts. It was below normal over the interior. In January, 1949, the positioning of troughs and ridges was reversed. An upper trough with cold air dominated the West and a ridge with warm air the East. The result was cold surface temperatures in the West and warmth in the East—exactly opposite to the situation in January, 1958. Rainfall was below normal along the Pacific Coast and well above normal in the southern interior.

Troughs and ridges in the upper westerlies are definitely linked with frontal waves and cyclones and anticyclones at the earth's surface. A cold trough in the upper atmosphere usually prevails to the rear of a cyclone family at the surface, and an upper-atmosphere warm ridge of high pressure is usually positioned over, or to the east, of it. Thus the cyclone family chiefly exists in the warmer air, but it is commonly followed by a deep polar outbreak of cold air.

There is reason to believe that these dynamically induced long waves in the upper westerlies have a great deal to do with the cellular structure of pressure and atmospheric circulation at the earth's surface. The troughs and ridges in the high westerlies create convergences and divergences which probably lead to the development of the great semipermanent centers of high and low pressure at low levels. No doubt this dynamic arrangement is modified by the seasonal contrasts in surface heating over continents and oceans. Fundamentally, however, the subtropical high-pressure cells and the subpolar low-pressure cells appear to be the result of nonthermal controls which are associated with convergences and divergences caused by the high-altitude troughs and ridges. The shallow surface highs of the polar regions, on the other hand, are probably the result of radiational surface cooling. This idea of a relationship between upper-air waves and surface pressure cells is supported by the fact that the waves in the circumpolar vortex are much less pronounced (have a smaller amplitude) in the Southern Hemisphere than in the Northern Hemisphere, and the cellular structure of sea-level pressure is correspondingly less strongly marked in the Southern Hemisphere.

Jet streams. This second feature of the upper westerlies, which is intimately related both to upper long waves and to the surface weather, resembles a system of meandering torrential streams. Jet streams are relatively narrow bands of strong winds bounded by slower-moving air (Fig. 3.26). Their wind speeds vary considerably in different longitudes of their circumpolar course, but become faster in winter than summer. In winter jets, rates of 100 to 150 miles per hour are common, and instances of 300 miles per hour are known. The highest speeds occur at altitudes of about 30,000 to 40,000 ft.

On the average, the jet is positioned over the subtropical anticyclones at the surface (30 to 35°N), where horizontal temperature contrasts are great. Across the jet (or jets) horizontally, temperature changes rapidly, with cold air on its poleward side and warmer, often tropical, air on its equatorward side (Fig. 3.24). In reality, while it is true that the average "statistical jet" lies above the subtropics, there are usually several jets, with the more northerly one (or ones) showing higher speeds and also more inconstancy in position. It is because of this inconstancy of the northerly streams that the *mean* position falls in the subtropics, where the jet is fairly stationary in location. As might be expected, the jet or jets shift their average latitudinal positions with the seasons.

While the average direction of air movement in the jets is from west to east, an individual jet often shows a very sinuous or meandering pattern which is in harmony with that of the long waves described previously. It is especially the more northerly jets

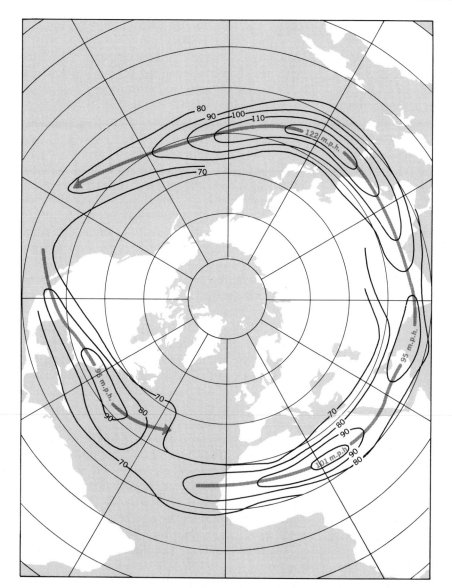

Figure 3.26 Jet-stream map for the Northern Hemisphere in January, showing average positions and speeds at elevations of 35,000 to 40,000 ft. (*After Namias.*)

which vary considerably in position and sinuosity, and it is these which are closely associated with middle-latitude weather disturbances. The meanders of the northerly jet aloft can be identified with the position of the surface polar front, where the strongest north-south temperature gradients prevail.

It is along this front that large numbers of cyclonic storms develop. It may be too much to say that the jet creates the cyclones, but doubtless it has much to do with the courses they follow over the earth's surface. By thus steering the cyclones, jets greatly influence the distribution of surface precipitation as well as temperature. This is because cyclones not only are important generators of precipitation, but also act to steepen surface temperature gradients. Rainfall appears to be concentrated in areas lying underneath the jet, where the effects of a traveling cyclone may be focused. When a jet is relatively stable in position, there may be a detectable zone of seasonal precipitation concentration underneath it, as there is in subtropical China in winter. Such a concentration is not obvious, however, when a jet and its related cyclonic storms frequently shift positions, as is the case in the central and eastern United States.

Jets also probably set in motion those deep and extensive air masses whose movements over the earth's surface bring sustained periods of remarkable heat and cold, drought and flood. The ultimate cause of the varying patterns of the jet, with their important repercussions upon world weather, is a question not completely answered.

Nonperiodic variations in the upper-air circulation. The normal state of the general circulation as represented on hemisphere or world maps is one which is never repeated in that precise form on any daily weather map, or on maps showing the mean for any week or month. For the "normal" condition is only a statistical average of the varying circulations which prevail from week to week or for other shorter or longer periods of time. The most striking of the variations are those in the circumpolar vortex west-wind circulation, which involve the interrelated phenomena of long waves, jet streams, polar fronts, and large-scale weather situations. Although they are nonperiodic, these variations are not purely random, for there is an observable sequence of episodes. The variations may be looked upon as contractions and expansions of the circumpolar westerly wind vortex toward and away from the pole. During these contractions and expansions the long waves change in length, the jet streams shift positions and alter velocity, and the planetary polar front and its associated storm tracks undergo wide oscillations. Such a period of change is called an

index cycle and usually takes from 4 to 6 weeks to complete (Fig. 3.24).

In stage 1, the jet stream is positioned well to the north. The cold polar air masses are confined to the higher latitudes, and most regions in the middle latitudes are covered by mild air. The high westerlies are strongly zonal in character, so that long waves and jet streams are weakly developed. Surface westerlies also are strongly zonal, and they lie poleward of their normal position. Pressure systems are oriented east-west, cyclonic activity is confined to the higher latitudes, and there is little latitudinal air-mass exchange between high and low latitudes. This stage is spoken of as representing a high zonal index, for the rate of change in pressure along a meridian is great.

In stage 2, the jet stream moves farther equatorward, and its waves increase in amplitude. This results in thrusts of polar air equatorward and of tropical air poleward. Stage 3 consists of a further increase in the amplitude of the jet waves. Associated with the increase are strong north-south movements of tropical and polar air masses, causing great east-west contrasts in temperature. At this stage the mean position of the jet stream is much closer to the equator.

In stage 4 of the index cycle, the waves in the jet have increased so greatly in amplitude that immense pools of tropical air are cut off and isolated in higher latitudes, while similar large masses of polar air are left stranded in lower latitudes. This condition is described as one of low zonal index, since the north-south contrasts in pressure are small. There has been a complete fragmentation of the zonal westerlies into closed cellular centers; air-mass and temperature contrasts are at a maximum in an east-west direction, and there is a north-south orientation of pressure centers and frontal systems. Such a period of strongly agitated circulation is the occasion of topsy-turvy surface weather, when Alaska may be warmer than Florida. Subsequently the circulation returns to the zonal pattern characteristic of stage 1.

As mentioned earlier, the great convolutions in

the circumpolar vortex and the jet stream are a part of the overall mechanism of latitudinal heat balance on the earth. Their mass exchanges of air between high and low latitudes represent nature's chief method of equalizing the radiation imbalance between polar and equatorial regions.

THE EARTH'S SURFACE-WIND SYSTEMS

A diagram of surface winds

It is possible to superimpose on the generalized sketch of sea-level pressure (Fig. 3.3) a very simple system of zonal surface winds (Fig. 3.27). These, of course, reflect the four forces previously described which determine the direction and speed of winds—especially pressure gradient force, Coriolis force, and friction.

Two main systems of surface winds are recognized in each hemisphere. From the subtropical highs, whose crests are located at about 25° to 35° N and S, surface winds flow along the pressure gradient toward the low-pressure trough near the equator. Coriolis force turns these into easterly winds, so that they are known as tropical easterlies or trade winds: northeast trades north of the equator and southeast trades to the south (Fig. 3.27). Poleward from the subtropical high-pressure ridges in each hemisphere, winds flow toward the subpolar troughs of low pressure. These winds are turned by Coriolis force so that their general direction of flow is from west to east. They are the middle-latitude westerlies: southwesterly in the Northern Hemisphere and northwesterly in the Southern Hemisphere. Above the shallow friction layer at the surface, both trades and westerlies are strongly zonal, flowing nearly parallel with the isobars.

Poleward from the westerlies, weather observations are scarce and the prevailing direction of surface winds is not known with any certainty. If it may be assumed that on the average there are shallow highs of thermal origin in the general vicinity of the poles, then outflowing surface easterly winds should characterize the very high latitudes.

Figure 3.27 A much idealized representation of the earth's surface winds. Average airflow is predominantly from an easterly direction in most of the low latitudes, and from a westerly direction in the middle latitudes.

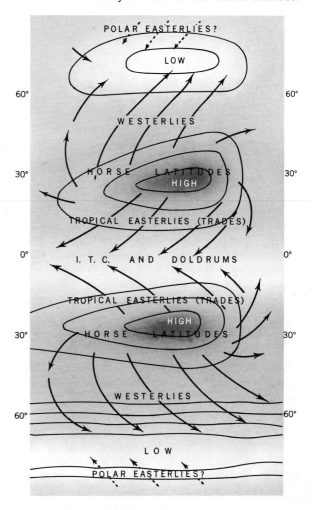

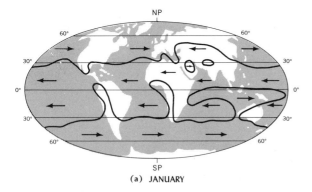

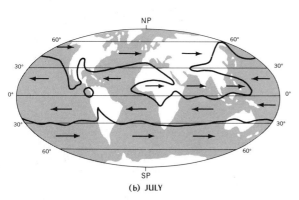

Figure 3.28 Geographical distribution of the west-east component of the mean surface wind. The heavy lines separate tropical easterlies from westerlies, both in equatorial and in middle latitudes. (*After Mintz and Dean.*)

And in fact there is considerable evidence to support this concept of polar easterlies.

To summarize surface winds, easterly winds predominate in the tropics, or low latitudes, and westerly winds prevail in the middle latitudes. Less information exists concerning average wind direction in polar latitudes (Figs. 3.28 and 3.29).

Data on average wind directions near the equator are also inadequate. It is known, however, that winds are usually variable and weak here between the converging trades in the vicinity of the equatorial pressure trough. This transition zone has been given various names—among them intertropical

convergence zone (ITC), doldrums, and equatorial belt of variable winds and calms. Along the axis of the equatorial trough there is a large-scale ascent of warm, moist air.

Figure 3.29 Zonal component (direction and speed) of the mean surface wind, averaged for all longitudes, over the oceans in meters per second. Negative speed represents easterly winds; positive speed, westerly. The zonal component drops to zero in equatorial latitudes in July. Note the latitudinal shifting of winds from January to July. (*After Mintz and Dean.*)

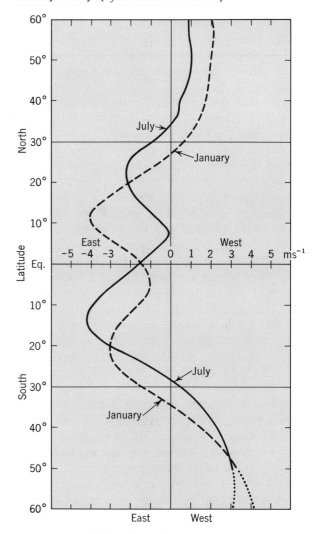

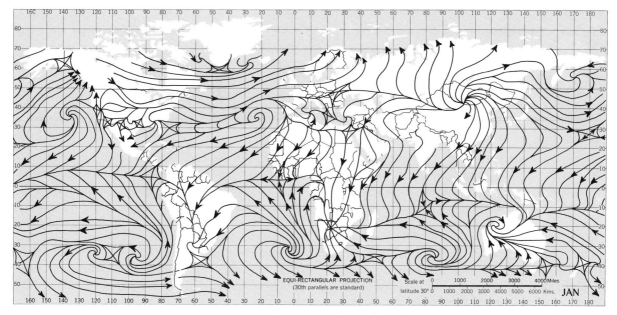

Figure 3.30   January: Direction of mean surface resultant wind. (*After Mintz and Dean.*)

Another belt of weak and variable winds occupies the intermediate area between trades and westerlies—a zone which coincides with the crests of subtropical highs. These are the *horse latitudes*, lo-

Figure 3.31   July: Direction of mean surface resultant wind. (*After Mintz and Dean.*)

cated at about 30° in either hemisphere. In the horse latitudes there is a slow but widespread settling or subsidence of air, which is fed into this area aloft from both polar and tropical sources. Along the western flanks of the individual subtropical cells, genuinely tropical air invades the realm of the middle-latitude westerlies (see Fig. 3.27); along the eastern flanks of the cells, cool polar air intrudes into the tropics.

A third transition zone occurs where polar easterlies clash with the westerlies, which have been supplied with air from the subtropics and tropics. This zone lies in the subpolar trough along a line of discontinuity known as the *polar front* (Fig. 3.22). The fluctuating and wavy polar front is the breeding ground for many of the cyclonic disturbances which infest the westerlies. In fact, probably the subpolar trough of pressure is simply the statistical average of the annual or seasonal procession of cyclonic disturbances.

Surface winds in January and July

In Figs. 3.30 and 3.31 the direction of the mean resultant surface winds in January and July, the two extreme seasons, is shown by means of atmospheric streamlines.[4] These charts portray a much more complicated pattern of surface winds than those in

[4]Resultant winds are obtained by adding separately the north and south and the east and west components of the observed winds, averaging them, and then applying these average components to obtain a resultant. This procedure is illustrated in Fig. 3.32. Here the vector pointing east (E) represents the average of the east and west components. The vector pointing south (S) represents the average of the north and south components. *R* is the resultant of these two vectors.

Figure 3.32 Procedure for obtaining resultant surface winds.

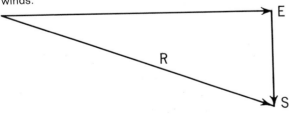

the previous section, which emphasized a simple zonal system of tropical easterlies and middle-latitude westerlies (Fig. 3.27). On the streamline maps there is, to be sure, ample evidence of the dominance of easterly winds in the low latitudes and westerlies in the middle latitudes. But at the same time these maps show modifications of, and departures from, the very elementary pattern outlined before.

Yet even the January and July streamline maps are only means of the highly variable and complicated short-time airflow patterns given on the daily weather map. Still, these mean seasonal maps are a very useful climatic tool, capable of explaining important climatic features.

Because of the meager data, no attempt is made in Figs. 3.30 and 3.31 to show wind directions poleward of latitude 65° N and S. In the other latitude belts, mean surface resultant winds exhibit cellular as well as zonal arrangements. Main circulations occur in the form of anticyclonic and cyclonic circulations around high-pressure and low-pressure centers, or cells. Some of these cellular circulations appear to persist throughout the year, for they can be seen on both the January and July charts. Others are definitely seasonal in character. As a general rule the cellular pattern of pressure and winds, and the seasonal changes in position and size of the centers of cyclonic and anticyclonic winds, are not nearly so pronounced in the more homogeneous Southern Hemisphere as they are in the Northern Hemisphere. North of the equator, the earth's wind-flow patterns are modified by thermal contrasts between large continents and oceans in winter and summer, as well as by the frictional effects of the continents and the blocking action of their high cordilleran systems. These modifications lead to cellular (as contrasted with zonal) circulations in the Northern Hemisphere.

The most prominent features of the mean surface-wind flow are the large systems of divergent anticyclonic circulation concentrated in subtropical latitudes. The equatorward flow of air from these anticyclonic circulations consists of the well-known tropical easterlies or trades, while the poleward flow is the middle-latitude westerlies. Thus the subtropical anticyclones are pivotal to both trades and westerlies, a fact which has earned them the designation "centers of action." Yet they are really centers of inaction as far as bad weather and storms are concerned, for such disturbances are steered away from their cores to circulate around their margins.

On both January and July maps the subtropical anticyclonic systems are dominant; there are no equally persistent systems of convergent cyclonic flow. The nearest approach is found in the smaller and weaker centers of converging cyclonic circulation over the oceans in the higher latitudes of the Northern Hemisphere, especially in winter. Their weakness may seem strange in view of the well-developed low-pressure centers which occupy the same areas, as shown on Fig. 3.6. In reality, however, the winter lows over the North Atlantic and North Pacific largely represent statistical averages of the numerous moving low-pressure centers whose paths concentrate on these areas. They are not durable features of the daily weather map.

January circulation.   On the January map of surface winds (Fig. 3.30), divergent anticyclonic systems are relatively weak over the Northern Hemisphere subtropical oceans, and they are largely confined to the eastern parts of the North Atlantic and North Pacific. In the Southern Hemisphere, by contrast, the subtropical anticyclonic circulations over the oceans are well developed and relatively continuous in an east-west direction. In addition to the anticyclonic wind systems over the subtropical oceans in both hemispheres, there is also one over middle-latitude eastern Asia. This diverging circulation, the Asiatic winter monsoon, is associated with an average winter high-pressure cell whose origin is related to moving cold anticyclones and to the accumulation of frigid surface air over the cold continent.

In January not only are the subtropical anticyclonic systems over the Northern Hemisphere oceans weakened, but also there is a spreading and deepening of the oceanic low-pressure centers and associated cyclonic circulations in somewhat higher latitudes. Convergent cyclonic circulations around the Aleutian Low over the North Pacific and the Iceland Low over the North Atlantic are best developed at this season. In the Southern Hemisphere, where it is summer, a relatively strong low-pressure cell and associated cyclonic wind system develop over heated Australia, and somewhat weaker ones appear over South America and southern Africa.

July circulation.   In July (Fig. 3.31), well-developed highs and strong anticyclonic circulations cover much of the North Atlantic and North Pacific Oceans with their centers at about 35° and 40°N. The pattern of the subtropical anticyclonic circulations in the Southern Hemisphere has not greatly changed from what it was in January, except that the cells are more continuous in an east-west direction as a result of the cooler continents.

In the Northern Hemisphere, the subpolar oceanic lows and their associated cyclonic circulations are weaker than in January. On the other hand, thermally induced lows with cyclonic circulations occur over the heated land areas of northwestern India, eastern Asia, and western interior North America. In India this is the well-known summer monsoon.

Lines of horizontal divergence and convergence. Prominent features of the pattern of surface-wind flow shown in Figs. 3.30 and 3.31 are the extended lines of divergence and convergence of wind direction. The most conspicuous of the great lines of divergence are those which pass through the centers of the anticyclonic systems and extend poleward and eastward, and equatorward and westward, from these centers. Along such lines of divergence in surface-wind flow there must be a compensating feeding in of dry air from aloft, with accompanying slow but extensive subsidence.

Somewhat less well developed are the extended lines of convergence of wind direction associated with the centers of the smaller, weaker cyclonic circulations. Such convergence zones are areas in which the atmosphere is undergoing slow lifting. The most prominent of all the lines of convergence ·lies between the two trades, and therefore in the vicinity of the equatorial low-pressure trough (also see Figs. 3.36 and 3.37).

SURFACE-WIND SYSTEMS AND THEIR WEATHER

Winds of the tropics

Scientific understanding of the atmospheric circulation within the tropics is still fragmentary. Even today the network of weather observatories is widely spaced in most tropical regions, their instrumental equipment is rudimentary, and competent observers are scarce. During the Second World War, the stepped-up tempo of military aviation greatly increased the number of observations both of surface and of upper winds in the low latitudes. One consequence was that many long-held concepts concerning tropical winds and weather were shattered. But the newly added observations are not always sufficiently numerous, well distributed, and long continued to permit the formulation of satisfactory substitute hypotheses and models. Thus at present our knowledge of the tropical circulation and associated weather patterns remains basically negative. Meanwhile the professional literature is full of hasty generalizations based on inadequate local observations, which in turn lead to a mass of contradictory explanations and resulting confusion.

Many of the features of weather, and the tools of weather analysis, which are accepted as standard in the middle latitudes must be discarded in the tropics. For instance, Coriolis force is weak (and absent at the equator), and the usual relation of pressure gradient to wind does not hold. Isobaric patterns are poorly defined, and recognizable pressure and wind systems seldom exist. Pressure gradients are so weak that many times they are obscured by instrumental errors. The scale of the synoptic patterns is unknown, and the same is largely true of synoptic models. Moreover, tropical disturbances often are phenomena of the middle and upper troposphere and may not appear on surface charts,

so that they are more difficult to detect and observe. Fronts have little importance in the tropics.

Because of the data collected during and since World War II, the previously held concept of zonal uniformity in winds and weather in low latitudes has had to be modified. It is now known that the tropics are affected by more atmospheric disturbances and by different kinds of them than was previously believed. Accordingly, students of the atmosphere are increasingly aware that tropical weather is not as exclusively sun-controlled and periodic as they used to think. They have also discovered that the really steady trades occupy only a fraction of the total oceanic area within the tropics, while the antitrades[5] aloft are not present everywhere.

Winds of the equatorial convergence zone. In the trough of low pressure situated between the converging trades from opposite hemispheres, wind conditions are complex and not well understood. In this zone of intertropical convergence or ITC, some longitudes have a prevalence of calms and light variable winds, a condition known as *doldrums*. In certain regions and seasons, light easterly winds are common; in others westerly winds predominate. The equatorial trough with its light and variable winds is not always continuous around the earth. In some places and on some occasions it may be greatly constricted or even wiped out by encroaching trades or monsoons; then again it may expand to twice its normal width.

It is the meridional component of the trade winds which results in their convergence in equa-

---

[5] High-altitude winds above the surface trades, flowing in a direction opposite to them.

torial latitudes. Also, it is the convergence of the trades, even more than thermal convection, which creates the widespread ascent of air in equatorial areas. Thus the intertropical convergence zone (ITC) is predominantly a region of rising air, and this in turn causes a lowering of pressure and an abundance of cumulus clouds and heavy showery precipitation. Vast amounts of latent heat of condensation are released into the air, adding to its instability. It is mainly this equatorial heat source that drives the tropical circulation. Pressure gradients are weak. The unstable and stagnant air masses are very sensitive to local variations in relief, vegetation cover, land and sea breezes, and mountain and valley breezes, so that weather is extremely localized. At four weather stations on Singapore, an island whose dimensions are only 24 by 13 miles, the same weather phenomena are rarely observed at the same time.

The concepts of air masses and density fronts,[6] which are crucial in middle-latitude weather analysis, are of negligible importance in tropical regions. Temperatures are so nearly uniform in the tropics that convergence of airstreams, including convergence of the two trade winds, rarely results in density fronts; or if it does, they appear in much weakened form.

But while genuine density fronts are rare in the tropics, horizontal convergences lacking in frontal structure are common. It is within such convergence zones that an important part of tropical weather develops. When homogeneous air masses converge and density contrasts are absent, there is no tendency for one air mass to be shoved obliquely upward above the other, separated by a sloping surface of discontinuity or front. (This is the pattern of middle-latitude weather disturbances, as will be described in Chapter 5.) Rather, the air along the axis of a pronounced field of convergence is forced vertically upward simply because of the squeeze to which it is subjected by the oppositely advancing air masses. Condensation occurs in these rising air currents

along a convergence zone, creating tall, multilayer cumulonimbus clouds, with associated convective showers and thunderstorms.

The most extended of the convergence lines or zones within the tropics is the intertropical convergence (ITC), situated between the trades arriving from the opposite hemispheres (Fig. 3.33). Some

Figure 3.33 Pressure and circulation patterns *a* when the ITC is located near the equator, and *b* when the ITC is displaced some distance north-south of the equator. (*After Sawyer.*)

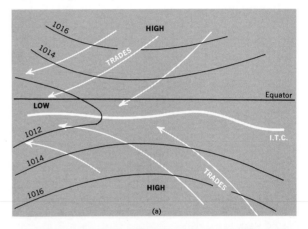

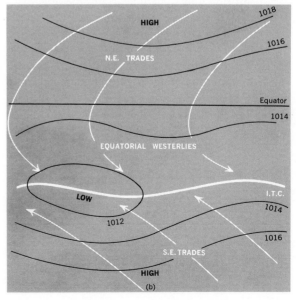

[6] Boundary surfaces separating air masses of contrasting temperatures and hence densities.

authorities consider the ITC a single zone which, on the average, is continuous around the earth, is shifted north and south with the march of the seasons, and is governed chiefly by the outward thrusting of air from the winter hemisphere. Others describe the ITC more realistically as discontinuous, for ordinarily it cannot be traced around the earth on the daily weather map. Still others describe the ITC as double in character, involving a northern intertropical convergence (NITC) and a southern one (SITC), with true equatorial air masses in the form of weak westerlies between the two (Fig. 3.34).

It has also been suggested that the NITC and SITC are not single lines of convergence but multiple ones. In this view, evaporation of the rain falling from the clouds which are developed at the convergence, and additional cooling of the air within the ITC by radiation from the cloud tops, may cause the ITC to become a local cool source with descending air. The result is the formation of new ITCs on either side of the original one. The total effect is the development of multiple ITCs and the local northward and southward displacements of the zone of convergence. From this brief description it can be seen that the literature on the intertropical convergence and its possible multiple convergences is very confusing and sometimes contradictory.

Equatorial westerlies.   A somewhat controversial element of the tropical circulation concerns the existence of an equatorial west-wind zone in the intertropical convergence area between the broader belts of easterlies (Figs. 3.23 and 3.33*a*). Some weather specialists view equatorial westerlies as re-curved trades which have crossed the equator into the summer hemisphere (Fig. 3.33*b*). Others believe that they represent the normal situation over extensive longitudes within the inner tropics. The latter group thinks of the equatorial westerlies as being located between a northern intertropical convergence, or NITC, and a southern intertropical convergence, or SITC (Fig. 3.34). With the data now available it does not seem possible to determine whether the zonal wind, averaged for all longitudes over land as well as water, would show a mean westerly current near the equator at any sea-

son. Some assert that such an equatorial west-wind zone is reasonably well established from present observations for nearly 200° of longitude, extending from western and central Africa across the Indian Ocean and including the equatorial western Pacific, and probably also the eastern equatorial Pacific and parts of northern South America. They consider the southwest monsoons of southern Asia to be only one element of the equatorial westerlies. Other students of the atmosphere are less certain that the equatorial westerlies constitute a basic element of the planet's general circulation.

The explanations offered for the equatorial westerlies, if they actually do exist as a basic current, are too diverse to warrant their presentation here. But the significant features of these winds are worth summarizing: (1) They are most extensive in the summer hemisphere. (2) They are less well developed in the transition seasons. (3) They have a directional component toward the thermal low-pressure centers located over the lands. Hence they blow toward the poles, so that they are southwest in the northern summer and northwest in the southern summer. (4) They appear to be best developed over continental regions and adjacent oceanic areas which are more or less under continental control. (5) They are more variable in time and space than the trades. And because they are directionally less constant than trades, rainfall contrasts along their windward and leeward coasts are less marked.

The relationship between direction of winds in equatorial latitudes and the frequency and amount of precipitation has unusual climatic importance. Studies by H. Flohn show that winds with either westerly or poleward components (i.e., equatorial westerlies and tropical monsoons) are more unstable and have a greater abundance of rain than tropical easterlies (trades), which normally have an equatorward component. For a rectangular area in the equatorial Atlantic bounded by the parallels 10°N and 10°S, Flohn found that westerly winds are accompanied by rain in 25.1 percent of all cases, whereas with easterly winds the rain frequency is only 8.1 percent. Winds blowing toward the equator are accompanied by rainfall in 8.1 percent of the cases,

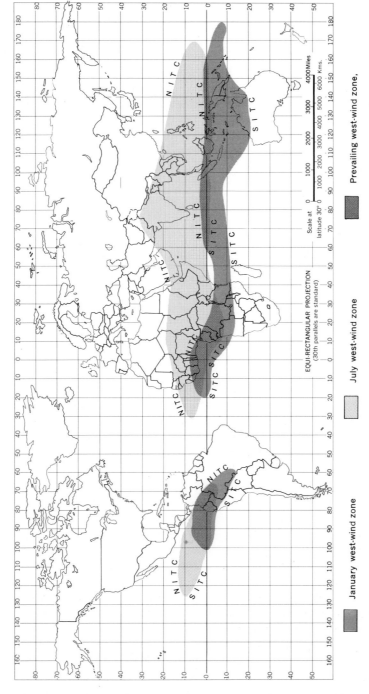

Figure 3.34 Displacement of the equatorial west-wind zone, situated between a northern and a southern ITC, in the extreme seasons. Greatest poleward displacement is over southern Asia in July. Displacement is also large over northern Africa in July and over Australia in January.

January west-wind zone

July west-wind zone

Prevailing west-wind zone,

compared with 12 percent for winds blowing away from the equator. In part, the greater rainfall of equatorial westerlies and tropical monsoons possessing a poleward component could be a matter of air-mass character. Probably the decisive factor is the greater instability of such circulations, with their increased convergence and greater vertical movement. These in turn are related to latitudinal change in Coriolis force. In short, this suggests that winds with

$$\frac{\text{westerly}}{\text{easterly}} \quad \text{and/or} \quad \frac{\text{poleward}}{\text{equatorward}} \quad \text{components}$$

have a statistical tendency toward

$$\frac{\text{upward}}{\text{downward}} \text{ movement}$$

and thus to $\dfrac{\text{instability}}{\text{stability}}$ and $\dfrac{\text{raininess}}{\text{dryness}}$

as produced by Coriolis force on the rotating earth (Flohn).

Tropical easterlies or trade winds.

Without doubt the trades are more uniform in direction and speed, and are characterized by fewer atmospheric disturbances and spells of bad weather, than either the equatorial or middle-latitude westerlies. But as mentioned earlier, the classical picture of trade-wind uniformity in direction, speed, and weather is a fiction. Steady fair-weather trades with moderate-to-fresh breezes averaging 10 to 15 miles an hour are mainly characteristic of their central latitudes and their eastern oceanic sectors. Constancy declines toward their poleward and equatorward margins. Their western oceanic parts are also more variable because of frequent interruptions there by atmospheric disturbances. In the west also, the trades have a smaller north-south directional component, and in some places they may blow parallel with the equator, or even away from it.

Weather and climate also vary in different areas of the trades. Their poleward parts are closest to the centers of the subtropical anticyclones, where subsidence and horizontal divergence are strong, and the inversion is low. Consequently these loca-

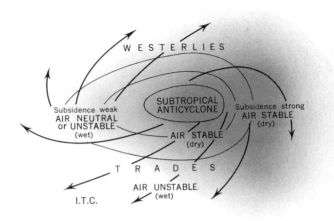

Figure 3.35 The circulation pattern around a subtropical anticyclone, with general areas of stability and instability shown. The eastern end of the oceanic cell and its trade winds are much more stable than the western end. The poleward parts of the trades are more stable than the equatorward parts. Degree of stability is suggested by the intensity of shading.

tions have few atmospheric disturbances and much dry weather and sunshine (Fig. 3.35). Here the air is stable and nonbuoyant, opposed to deep convectional overturning. As the trades move equatorward, two types of modifications gradually occur. First, as a result of traveling over great expanses of tropical ocean, they acquire large additions of moisture (hence latent energy) through evaporation. Second, the trade-wind air gradually leaves an area of strong subsidence in the subtropical anticyclones, where the temperature inversion is low, and approaches the equatorial trough of low pressure, where horizontal convergence and lifting are characteristic. Both modifications—the addition of moisture at the base, and the increasing convergence and lifting—make the trades more unstable, buoyant, and deeply humidified in their equatorward parts. In such an environment, atmospheric disturbances develop more readily, deep convectional overturning is facilitated by the absence of an inversion, and clouds and precipitation are more common. The trades evaporate great quantities of water and transport the water vapor, representing potential energy, toward the equatorial pressure trough. There it is released and returned to the land-sea surface in the form of heavy rain showers falling from towering cumulonimbus clouds, which are concentrated in synoptic disturbances.

Not only do the trades change character in a north-south direction; they also differ in their eastern and western oceanic parts and the adjacent margins of the continents. Normally the subtropical cells, on whose equatorward slopes the trades originate, are best developed toward the eastern sides of oceans. It is in these same eastern parts, where subsidence is pronounced and the inversion is strong and reaches down to low levels, that the trades are most stable and nonbuoyant, so that rain-producing disturbances are fewest (Fig. 3.35). Farther west, the anticyclone is weaker, subsidence is less, the inversion level is higher, and the air is more buoyant and inclined to rise. The result is that weather disturbances are more numerous and better developed, and clouds and precipitation are more frequent. Thus the trades are likely to be dry, fair-weather winds in their poleward and eastern oceanic parts, while their equatorward and western oceanic sectors have more weather disturbances and greater amounts of cloud and precipitation. (See Fig. 2.21.)

Winds of the subtropics

Latitudes from about 25° to 35° N and S are the centers of great anticyclonic circulations around a series of oceanic high-pressure cells elongated in an east-west direction. In these warm anticyclones there is deep and extensive subsidence of air. Their centers are associated with extended lines of mean surface-wind divergence, from which trades flow equatorward and westerlies poleward. As a consequence of subsidence and divergence the air is stable and nonbuoyant, so that these anticyclonic systems produce drought and fair weather. Pressure gradients are weak, average wind speeds are slow, constancy of wind direction is low, and resultant wind velocities are small. Thus the subtropical highs resemble the equatorial trough of low pres-

sure in many features of their surface winds. However, the two regions are greatly unlike in general weather, because one is a region of convergence and ascent, while air subsides and diverges in the other.

Although in general, constancy of wind direction is likely to be low in the subtropics, or horse latitudes, it does vary considerably from one subtropical anticyclone to another. When a particular anticyclone has a quasi-stationary character, so that its size and shape remain much the same from one daily weather map to another, the constancy of wind direction may be relatively high. But where the subtropical cell is really a mean of a large number of anticyclones migrating across the area, the constancy of direction is much lower.

Actually, the zones of the subtropical anticyclones are not longitudinally as similar throughout in winds and weather as the above description might indicate. On the margins of the anticyclonic cells, wind velocity and constancy of direction are both higher than at the centers. And what is more important, the eastern flanks of each cell show stronger subsidence, lower inversion, and fewer atmospheric disturbances than the western margins (Fig. 3.35). This pattern is like that of the trades described in the previous section.

The strong subsidence in the eastern parts of an anticyclonic cell produces a marked inversion whose base reaches down to about 500 to 1,500 meters above sea level. The air above the inversion is dry, and that together with the temperature inversion is responsible for the meager rainfall. Some of the driest regions of the earth are located along the east sides of oceans and the adjacent west coastal margins of continents at about 20° to 30° N and S. These areas come under the influence of the strong subsidence in the eastern parts of the oceanic subtropical anticyclones. The intensified aridity of the coastal portions of the Sahara Desert in western North Africa, the Kalahari Desert in southwestern Africa, the Chilean-Peruvian Desert in South America, and the Sonoran Desert in northwestern Mexico testify to the drying influence of the eastern margins of the cells.

By contrast, the western side of a subtropical oceanic anticyclone is usually characterized by moist, unstable or neutral air and by fairly abundant rainfall. This condition is the exception in anticyclonic systems. Regions occupying positions coincident with the western ends of the oceanic anticyclones include the lands bordering the Caribbean Sea and Gulf of Mexico in North America, eastern China and southern Japan in Asia, southeastern Brazil in South America, southeastern Africa, and eastern Australia. All of these are rainy places and therefore stand in sharp climatic contrast to the arid regions along the western sides of the continents in similar latitudes, for the dry west-side areas are influenced by the subsident eastern margins of the oceanic anticyclones.

Various causes have been suggested for the marked air-mass and weather contrasts between the eastern and western ends of the oceanic subtropical anticyclones. A group of Norwegian meteorologists views the circulation in the subtropical cells as taking place in such a way that the planes of the ellipses which represent the trajectories of the air particles are tilted upward from east to west. Accordingly, the eastern end of the cell may be considered as tilted downward and the western end upward. So a mass of air in the cellular circulation (Northern Hemisphere) tends to subside as it moves eastward on the northern side of the cell and to be lifted as it moves westward on the southern side. The total vertical displacement of the air as it passes from one end of the cell to another may be $\frac{1}{2}$ mile to a mile. It is to the tilted circulation in the subtropical oceanic cells, with subsidence prevailing at the eastern ends and lifting at the western ends, that these meteorologists would ascribe the greater stability in the east.

Other contributing factors which have been suggested are these: (1) Colder waters at the eastern end tend to chill and stabilize the air masses. (2) The air masses on the west have had a longer oceanic trajectory over warmer waters, so that they are more deeply humidified. (3) On the east the air masses are of more recent polar origin, while those in the west are old tropicalized air. (4) In the east

the atmospheric circulation shows a strong component directed toward the equator, so that decreasing Coriolis force acts to stabilize the air. In the west the circulation may even be directed poleward, with resulting increased instability. (5) In the west where the easterlies come onshore, they are frequently made unstable by orographic lifting (lifting caused by highlands).

When the opposite-moving air currents of two adjacent cells overlap, as they may do in the cols of slightly lower pressure between the cells, the current from the equatorial side of the eastern cell may be warmer than the other coming from the northern side of the western cell. As a consequence the warmer air may be forced to ascend over the cooler along an inclined surface of discontinuity whose slope is approximately 1:200. The cols therefore mark the boundaries between the cells and are characterized by converging air masses separated by discontinuity surfaces along which storms and rainfall may originate. These weak fronts formed in the cols between the cells are sometimes called meridional fronts, or trade fronts.

Middle-latitude westerlies

Moving with the gradient from the subtropical highs to the subpolar lows (roughly 35 or 40° to 60 or 65°) are the middle-latitude winds known as the stormy westerlies. However, the westerly circulation is not just composed of air supplied from the poleward flanks of the subtropical highs. Much genuinely tropical air from farther equatorward enters the westerlies through the extensive longitudinal gaps between the individual high-pressure cells. These invasions are especially conspicuous around the western ends of the oceanic cells and in the form of the summer monsoon in eastern Asia. The poleward boundary of the westerly wind belt is a particularly fluctuating one, shifting with the seasons and over shorter periods of time as well. Both in speed and direction the westerlies are highly variable. "Spells" of weather are one of their distinguishing characteristics. At times, especially in the winter, they blow with gale force; at other times they are

Mean wind directions at Scilly Islands, 49.38° N, 6.16° W (Frequency in percent)

N	5	E	7	S	6	W	11
NNE	5	ESE	5	SSW	5	WNW	10
NE	5	SE	4	SW	6	NW	9
ENE	4	SSE	4	WSW	7	NNW	4
			Calm	3			

Source: After Kendrew.

mild breezes. Most of their winds are moderate to strong, with stormy winds more prevalent than weak winds. Calms are uncommon. Although they are called westerlies, since the most frequent and strongest winds are from that direction, air actually blows from all points of the compass.

The variability of the westerlies in both direction and strength is largely the result of the procession of atmospheric disturbances (cyclones and anticyclones) and their fronts that travel from west to east in these latitudes. Such storms, with their local systems of converging and diverging winds, tend to modify or disrupt the general westerly flow. Moreover, on the eastern side of Asia, and to a lesser degree of North America, continental wind systems called monsoons tend to disturb the westerly flow, especially in summer.

It is in the Southern Hemisphere, which has few land masses in latitudes 40 to 65°, that the stormy westerlies can be observed in their least interrupted development. There over great expanses of ocean, winds of gale strength are common in summer as well as winter. Early mariners called these the "roaring forties," and when later navigators penetrated higher latitudes, they discovered the "furious fifties" and the "shrieking sixties." In the vicinity of Cape Horn, violent winds often make east-west traffic around the Cape not only difficult but dangerous. It is a wild region, where gale follows gale with brief intervening lulls; a place with raw chilly weather, cloudy skies, and mountainous seas.

As this chapter has frequently mentioned, the great Northern Hemisphere land masses with their seasonal pressure reversals cause all wind systems north of the equator to be much more complex. The

westerlies there are considerably less vigorous in summer than in winter. In summer, gentle to fresh breezes prevail, and winds come from a variety of directions with almost equal frequency. But in winter they are like their counterparts in the Southern Hemisphere—strong, boisterous, and westerly more often than anything else.

The poleward margins of the westerlies near the subpolar troughs of low pressure are particularly subject to great equatorward surges of polar air in the colder months. The sinuous line of discontinuity known as the polar front, which separates polar from tropical air, is the zone of origin for a great many middle-latitude cyclones and anticyclones. It follows that the poleward margins of the westerlies are much more subject to stormy, variable weather than the subtropical margins. Since this polar front and the accompanying belt of storms migrate with the sun, retreating poleward in summer and advancing equatorward in winter, it is logical that stormy weather in the middle latitudes is much more pronounced during the winter season.

Convergence and divergence in surface winds

Earlier sections have discussed the climatic significance of horizontal convergence and divergence in airflow and the associated vertical movements. A more integrated representation of horizontal convergence and divergence in the earth's mean surface winds is provided by Figs. 3.36 and 3.37. From them it can be seen that the strongest and longitudinally most continuous convergent zone is the one between the trades—the well-known ITC. As would be expected, Figs. 3.36 and 3.37 also show that divergence is particularly well developed in the latitudes of the subtropical anticyclones. These features have been emphasized throughout the chapter.

But an almost equally striking fact is that the distribution of surface-wind convergence and divergence shown in these maps is not nearly as simple, and certainly not as zonal, as it may appear to be in an idealized atmospheric circulation which accentuates zonal trades, westerlies, horse latitudes, and doldrums. The many nonzonal elements, or

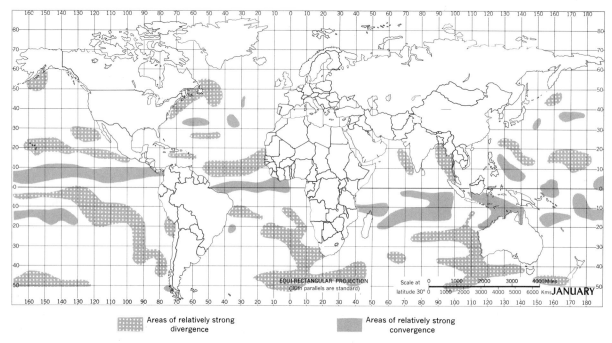

| Areas of relatively strong divergence | Areas of relatively strong convergence |

Figure 3.36 Distribution of areas of strong divergence and convergence of the mean surface wind in January over the oceans. The equatorial latitudes stand out as the main extended zone of convergence. Subtropical latitudes show more consistent divergence, characteristically in centers rather than in belts, and with the centers concentrated on the eastern side of an ocean. (*After Mintz and Dean.*)

Figure 3.37 Distribution of areas of strong divergence and convergence of the mean surface wind in July. Equatorial convergence and subtropical divergence are apparent, but centers are more conspicuous than belts. Note particularly the strong center of divergence in the easternmost North Pacific, off the west coast of North America. (*After Mintz and Dean.*)

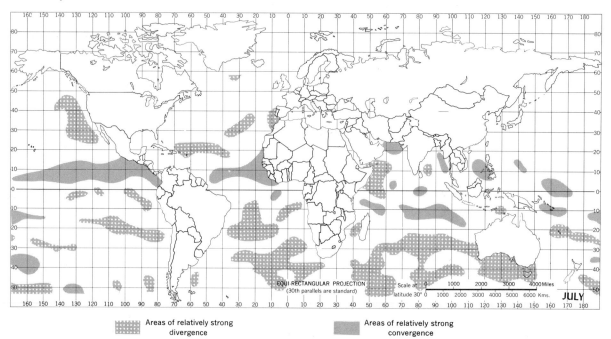

| Areas of relatively strong divergence | Areas of relatively strong convergence |

local areas of convergence and divergence, shown in Figs. 3.36 and 3.37 are just as conspicuous and greatly complicate the general world pattern of climates. This book will not catalogue in detail the numerous nonzonal elements in the distribution patterns of convergences and divergences. The important point to remember is that they are a major factor in world climates.

TERRESTRIAL MODIFICATIONS OF SURFACE WINDS

Among the terrestrial modifications of surface winds are several which were mentioned earlier, such as seasonal reversal of wind direction (monsoon systems), and the latitudinal shifting of wind belts with the seasons. Some terrestrial modifications are planetary in magnitude, others are of subcontinental size, and still others are essentially local. They result from (1) the inclination and parallelism of the earth's axis, which causes a seasonal north-south shifting of the belts of solar energy, (2) the earth's nonhomogeneous surface, on which land and water areas have contrasting temperature, pressure, and wind characteristics, and (3) the variable configurations and altitudes of land areas.

Latitudinal shifting of wind belts

It was explained in Chapter 1 that during half the yearly period of the earth's revolution about the sun, the sun's vertical noon rays shift from $23\frac{1}{2}°$N (summer solstice) to $23\frac{1}{2}°$S (winter solstice)—a total of $47°$. The belt of maximum solar energy actually shifts as much as $70°$, and temperature belts, which are largely sun-controlled, follow the latitudinal migration of solar energy. Pressure and wind belts, which are in part thermally controlled, also shift north and south with the sun (Figs. 3.8 and 3.29).

This north-south shifting of the wind belts is not a simple zonal phenomenon, however; it varies in the amount and rapidity of the shift from one part of the earth to another. In general it lags 1 month, or possibly 2, behind the sun. Over the oceans and along coasts, where the migration is more readily observable, it is fairly small—usually not much over 10 to $15°$. But over continents, where seasonal temperature changes are greater, the total latitudinal shift is also greater. In addition, the time lag is considerably less on land than over oceans. Surface-wind systems are more confused over land masses, however, owing to the effects of terrain irregularities and strong seasonal and diurnal temperature contrasts. Consequently an orderly migration of wind belts is less evident over continents.

Latitudes affected by more than one wind belt. Latitudinal shifting of the wind belts is climatically most important in regions occupying an intermediate position between two unlike wind systems. Such a region is encroached upon at the opposite seasons of the year by contrasting air masses and their strikingly different weather conditions. Theoretically, three such transition zones should be present in each hemisphere; and there is evidence that these actually do exist, although in imperfect form and certainly not as continuous zonal belts (Fig. 4.29).

Latitudes about 5 to $15°$ lie between the wet equatorial convergence zone (the ITC and the equatorial westerlies) on the one hand, and the dry subsidence-divergence zone of the trades and the subtropical anticyclones on the other. With the north-south seasonal shifts of pressure and wind belts, these latitudes mainly get the effects of the ITC and its rainbringing disturbances at the time of high sun (summer), and the effects of subsidence in the subtropical anticyclones and the dry trades at the season of low sun (winter). One wet and one dry season are the result. This seasonal pattern usually is muted along the eastern side of a land mass, where the subtropical anticyclone is ordinarily weak (Fig. 3.35). See also Fig. 4.29.

Latitudes about 30 to $40°$ fall between the fair-weather subtropical anticyclones and the middle-latitude stormy westerlies. Drought associated with subsidence and divergence should therefore be characteristic of summer, while the winter season should have adequate precipitation from traveling cyclonic storms and fronts in the westerlies. Actually, however, these dry summers and wet winters are found only in certain restricted longitudes, mainly on the eastern sides of oceans and the adjacent western margins of the continents. Such a location is dominated by the stable eastern flanks of an oceanic subtropical anticyclone in summer, so that subsidence is strong and the temperature inversion low. But the anticyclone is weaker in the western parts of subtropical oceans and the adjacent eastern sides of continents, as well as in their interiors. During summer in these regions atmospheric disturbances are numerous and any inversions are high or weak, so that it may be actually the wettest season.

Latitudes 60 to 70°, which are the approximate positions of the subpolar lows, are located between the stormy westerlies and winds of polar origin, so that latitudinal shifting of winds should allow this region to experience both during the course of a year. However, the numerous cyclones and anticyclones which infest these latitudes tend to complicate and obscure any simple migration of wind belts. This is much more a region of alternating thrusts of cold polar and warm tropical air. Nevertheless, there is a greater prevalence of cold polar air in winter and of warmer southwesterly currents in summer, a fact which suggests a semblance of wind-belt and storm-belt migration (Fig. 4.29).

Monsoons

Concepts of a monsoon wind system.   Unfortunately, "monsoon" is a term which has come to have a variety of meanings among geographers and meteorologists. It seems to have been derived either from the Arabic "mausin" or from the Malayan "monsin." As first used it was applied to southern Asia and the adjacent waters, and it referred to the seasonal surface airstreams there which reverse their directions between winter and summer. In the original meaning of monsoon, cause was not implied. With such a simple descriptive definition involving only a seasonal wind reversal approaching 180° in magnitude, quite a few regions of the earth actually qualify as having monsoon wind systems. As described in the previous section, seasonal wind reversal is to be expected in the transition zones between unlike wind belts.

But in 1686 Halley of England burdened the original descriptive concept of monsoon with a theory concerning the origin of the Asiatic monsoon, a theory which subsequently was applied to other continental areas as well. He proposed that monsoons are more than just seasonal winds—that they are also directly thermally induced, and so are gigantic convectional systems stemming from differential seasonal heating of continental and oceanic areas. The chain of events is from temperature through pressure and winds to rainfall. In summer, according to Halley, the land surface becomes warmer than that of the surrounding seas. This thermal contrast generates surface pressure differences, resulting in a low center over the warm land and higher pressure over adjacent seas. As a consequence the summer monsoon is a sea-to-land wind, with the tropical maritime air normally bringing to the land an abundance of moisture and warmth.

Conversely, the winter monsoon is a wind of land origin. Because the land is colder than the sea then, a shallow, thermally induced high-pressure cell develops over the land, with lower pressure over the adjacent ocean. The result is a land-to-sea pressure gradient, which causes cold, dry continental air masses to flow seaward.

It is debatable whether or not Halley's definition of monsoons, which involved origin and explanation as well as description, was an improvement. However this may be, throughout geographic and meteorological literature the most common definition of a monsoon involves not only the fact of a seasonal wind reversal, but also the idea of thermal origin arising from differential heating of extensive land and water surfaces. According to this more restricted point of view, monsoons develop because the earth's surface is not homogeneous, for they could not arise if the earth were composed of all land or all water.

Still, authorities use this somewhat standard definition in different ways. To some authors, monsoon is always singular, and the term applies only to the sea-to-land surface circulation in summer. Also, some insist that a genuine monsoon must have a complete 180° reversal of wind direction between winter and summer, while others are satisfied with a smaller directional variation. A number of meteorologists apply the term monsoon to seasonal variations in winds aloft as well as at the surface. As noted in the previous section, it can be that monsoonal wind reversals, both at the surface and aloft, will originate from the normal latitudinal migration of the planetary wind zones. Some authors, therefore, have applied the term monsoon to what appear to be trade winds which are deflected as they cross the equator into the summer hemisphere so that they become equatorial westerlies.

Modifications of the classical concept. There is some doubt whether monsoons as purely thermal systems of winds actually are common and widespread. What seems probable is that the recognized monsoon winds are far more complex than was previously supposed. For example, monsoon lows over the summer continents are not always persistent features on the daily weather charts, even though they are conspicuous on mean summer charts of surface pressure. On daily weather maps, the monsoon lows show great variations in position and intensity from day to day, variations which may be attributed to different cyclonic systems moving through the area. Many of these moving cyclonic storms seem to come in from the sea fully formed, so that they cannot be described as heat lows. Such local disturbances are characteristic of the summer season of monsoon areas like India, China, and northern Australia.

Certainly also, the winter anticyclones over cold continents, which are conspicuous on average sea-level charts, are only partly a consequence of radiation cooling from the cold land surface. Even the thermal winter anticyclone over Siberia, for example, does not have great depth except on certain occasions. Significantly also, the seaward movement of cold continental air is not at all continuous. It occurs in intermittent surges of considerable vertical depth, which must originate in part from great outpourings of Arctic air drawn toward lower latitudes on the rear of eastward-moving upper troughs. These invasions also feed the surface anticyclone.

As it happens, most of the land areas that show a seasonal reversal of wind direction are not in latitudes with sufficiently severe winters to develop thermal anticyclones on the continents. Therefore the offshore land winds of the low-sun season in tropical regions must result directly from nonthermal causes. The fact is that the monsoons of the constantly warm low latitudes, such as those of southern Asia, West Africa, and Northern Australia, are not a consequence of seasonal temperature extremes. Instead, they come from a normal latitudinal migration of wind belts following the course of the sun. As described in the preceding section, tropical easterlies, or trades, prevail at the time of low sun, and equatorial westerlies at the period of high sun.

To a greater extent than was formerly thought, monsoons appear to be modifications of the general planetary wind system. Any thermally induced monsoon circulation is always superimposed upon the original planetary winds, which usually form the dominant framework. If the monsoon were a convectional system of gigantic proportions, the direction of airflow aloft above the surface current should be opposite to that at low levels, and in many instances this is not the case.

Active discussion of monsoons has developed in recent years. Not only have many of the widely held opinions regarding their origins and wind systems been questioned, but some authors have also disputed the efficacy of the summer monsoon itself as an originator of precipitation. Undoubtedly the summer monsoon does transport great quantities of evaporated moisture from sea to land, and hence creates an atmospheric environment favoring the rainmaking processes. However, this is not sufficient to guarantee precipitation. The weather in the summer monsoon is actually much more variable than most textbook accounts would lead one to assume. It does not rain continuously throughout the season of general onshore winds; there are frequent spells of fair weather, some of them lasting several days, during which the skies may be relatively clear and no rain falls. Except in highlands, most spells of cloud and showers during the summer monsoon appear to come with atmospheric disturbances in the form of waves, depressions, or cyclones.

Climatic implications of monsoons. Since a seasonal wind reversal usually involves a change in air masses, it naturally has important effects on precipitation and temperature. Most monsoon regions, tropical as well as middle-latitude, have more rainfall in summer than in winter; in fact, winter is often quite dry. Summer wetness reflects the abundance of moisture in the tropical-equatorial air masses which invade the land at that season. Winter's lesser precipitation, in some parts even drought, is associated in middle latitudes with the dominance of dry, cold, stable air of continental origin. In the tropics the winter circulation obviously cannot be composed of cold air, but it is derived from a subtropical anticyclone, usually of land origin, so that

it is stable and dry. However, if the winter monsoon air crosses a large expanse of ocean before coming onshore, as it does in western Japan and the eastern Philippines, winter precipitation may also be plentiful.

Important temperature effects of monsoons are mainly confined to the middle latitudes, where genuine cold sources exist over the large continents in winter. There the monsoon circulation advects tropical heat in summer and subarctic continental cold in winter. The consequence is abnormally cold winters, sultry heat in summer, and large annual ranges of temperature. No such cold sources exist in the tropics to produce cold winters and large ranges.

Asiatic monsoons. Eastern and southern Asia together have the earth's largest and most perfectly developed monsoon circulation (Figs. 3.30, 3.31). In most parts of this region, the general direction of the seasonal airflow is from the continent in winter and from the sea in summer (Fig. 3.38). The magnitude and full development of the monsoon are largely a consequence of Asia's size and arrangement of mountains, two factors which combine to

Figure 3.38 Principal elements of the low-level circulation patterns over eastern and southern Asia in the cold and the warm seasons. (*After Thompson, Watts, Flohn, and others. From Trewartha, The Earth's Problem Climates, University of Wisconsin Press.*)

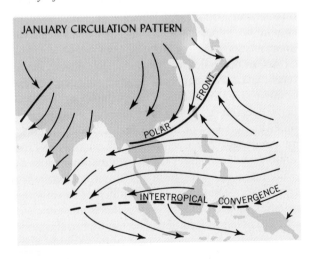
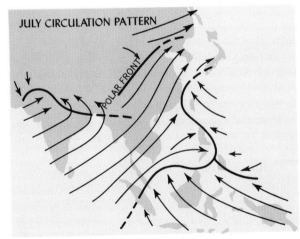

accentuate the winter and summer temperature extremes. These in turn magnify the latitudinal migration of winds as well as their seasonal reversal.

The huge land mass which is the Asian continent naturally intensifies all weather effects associated with continentality. And because of Asia's high east-west cordillera, the grain of the continent is hostile to a meridional circulation of air. This makes the seasonal contrasts in temperature and pressure even more dramatic. Consequently, the winter anticyclone is unusually strong and is positioned well to the east of the continent's center. In summer, the intertropical convergence reaches its maximum northern migration in the hot lowlands of northern India-Pakistan where, because of the barrier of high mountains, air from the north cannot penetrate. By comparison North America, with its smaller size and triangular shape, as well as its mountain system extending north-south, has no such seasonal contrasts in pressure centers, for a meridional exchange of air masses is relatively easy.

East Asia monsoon. This circulation mainly affects China, Taiwan, Japan, and Korea. Since it is located in middle latitudes, seasonal temperature contrasts between continent and ocean play a significant role in producing the wind reversal between winter and summer. In both seasons, local cyclones and anticyclones produce numerous interruptions in the prevailing wind direction, though it is somewhat more constant in winter than in summer. The winter monsoon of East Asia is also much stronger than that of summer, the velocities of the mean resultant surface wind along the coasts being several times greater in January than in July.

Percentage of wind frequency in North China

	N	NE	E	SE	S	SW	W	NW
Winter	17	8	5	6	6	8	18	32
Summer	10	9	12	26	16	10	7	10

During the *warm season,* a weak continental low, at least partly of thermal origin, is positioned over eastern Asia. Three basic air currents dominate the region (Fig. 3.38, July).

1. North of about 40° are the deep zonal westerlies, with a widely fluctuating jet stream aloft whose average position is about 40 or 45°N. Locally over northern Japan this circulation may be from the north.

2. South and west of the zonal westerlies and dominating most of central and southern China and Korea is a deep and humid southwesterly current, which is a poleward extension of the same equatorial westerlies (called the southwest monsoon) that prevail over tropical South Asia in summer. It is this current which supplies much of the moisture for the abundant summer rainfall of East Asia, since during the warm season the mean flux of water vapor over most of that region appears to be from west to east. Separating the zonal westerlies to the north from the equatorial southwesterlies farther south is the fluctuating polar front convergence. Its disturbances generate much of the copious summer rainfall of North China, including the Northeast (Manchuria).

3. The third basic current is the tropical easterlies, whose circulation around the western end of the North Pacific High causes them to arrive in East Asia as a southeasterly, southerly, or even southwesterly current. Its moisture is mainly of Pacific origin. Being somewhat more stable and less deeply humidified than the equatorial southwesterly current, this air from the Pacific does not provide as favorable an environment for the rainmaking processes. Moreover, since the Pacific air normally does not enter deeply into the continent, it is not such an important moisture source in summer, except in eastern subtropical China and in Japan. Significantly, rainfall declines in these regions in mid- and late-summer, at the time when Pacific air reaches its greatest dominance and the polar front is positioned farthest north.

The summer rainfall of eastern Asia does not appear to be directly a result of the warm continent being flooded by humid tropical air, in which surface heating produces numerous random convective showers and thunderstorms. Actually, eastern Asia has many fewer thunderstorms than the southeastern United States in similar latitudes, even though the much rougher East Asian terrain should act to trigger convective systems. Most of the lowland summer rainfall of eastern Asia appears to be associated with extensive atmospheric disturbances, some of which develop along fronts. There are other nonfrontal disturbances which are in the nature of pressure waves, speed convergences, and typhoons.

A Chinese climatologist has pointed out that the stronger and steadier the summer monsoon, in South China at least, the less the precipitation is in that region. This again suggests that the rainfall is not directly monsoonal, but rather is caused by disturbances many of which are embedded in the southerly flow. In this respect, it is highly significant that the probability of rainfall in subtropical China is least with southerly winds and highest with northerly winds—a fact which tends to link rainfall with a disturbed monsoon flow. As noted previously, the migration northward of the polar front and its disturbances to a mean position in North China–Manchuria in midsummer brings those regions a brief but heavy rainfall. Since North China–Manchuria is about the northern limit of penetration of the summer monsoon, and since its northern frontier is a pulsating, migrating border, it is logical that these northern parts of East Asia should have a precarious and variable rainfall.

The surface *winter monsoon* of East Asia is a wind which appears to originate in a cold anticyclone centered in the Baikal area of Siberia. The seaward flow is not a steady one, but occurs in the form of great nonperiodic surges, a fact which suggests that the anticyclone is fed at higher levels by huge expulsions of Arctic air which move southward on the rear of long troughs in the upper atmosphere. At its source in Siberia the northwest winter monsoon is very cold, dry, and stable, with a well-developed inversion, so that it provides a poor environment for precipitation. Over eastern Asia the winter monsoon's temperature varies considerably, depending on whether it has had a land or a sea trajectory, and also on the nature of the terrain over which

it has traveled. Terrain-induced turbulence tends to disrupt the surface inversion and bring down warmer air from above.

Normally the winter monsoon prevails over all eastern Asia, including China, Korea, and Japan, and extends at times into the northern part of the Indochina Peninsula. A widely fluctuating polar front separating cold monsoon air from that of the maritime trades is positioned along the eastern margins of Asia and the adjacent seas (Fig. 3.38, January). Along this front pass many weather disturbances. Zonal westerlies prevail above the not-so-deep monsoon current. The westerlies have two branches, the main one to the north of the central Asian highlands and the other to the south. Each branch is overlain by a jet stream, and these tend to steer cyclonic storms along their routes.

As a result of its well-developed winter monsoon, eastern Asia has the lowest sea-level winter temperatures for its latitude anywhere on the earth. The dry, stable air is not conducive to precipitation. Where the winter monsoon has had a land trajectory and is especially cold and dry, weather disturbances are weak and winter precipitation is meager, as it is in North China–Manchuria. But where it has been humidified by traveling some distance over water, as is the case in Japan and parts of southern China, winter precipitation may be considerable. Over the North Atlantic, for example, studies have shown that polar continental air becomes relatively mild and wet through a thickness of about 4 km (2.5 miles) after a sea trajectory of 600 km (375 miles). Except where highlands cause forced ascent of the air, almost all winter precipitation in the winter monsoon is generated by cyclonic storms, many of them frontal in origin.

Monsoons of tropical southern Asia. The tropical monsoon circulation of southern Asia, including India-Pakistan and Southeast Asia, differs significantly from that of East Asia. The Indian monsoon is effectively separated from that of China by the highlands of the Himalaya-Tibet system (Fig. 3.38). In Southeast Asia, however, this separation of tropical and middle-latitude monsoons is less complete. Among the elements in which the monsoons of

India and China differ is that of the strength and constancy of the seasonal winds. While the winter monsoon in eastern Asia is stronger and more constant in direction than the summer monsoon, the opposite is true in South Asia. There the winter monsoon is frequently only a gentle drift of air (2 or 3 miles an hour). But the average velocity of the summer monsoon at Bombay is 14 miles an hour, and it is even stronger over the sea.

A further difference between the two Asiatic monsoons is in the locations of their centers of action. In *summer* a deep and widespread surface pressure trough, to some degree thermal in origin, extends across northern India–Pakistan into Southeast Asia. This is part of the planetary intertropical convergence zone, which here reaches its maximum poleward displacement on the earth. To the south of the trough is a deep, humid, unstable current of equatorial maritime air, called the southwest monsoon (equatorial westerlies). This unstable southwesterly current crosses India, continues eastward over the Indochina Peninsula, and then moves northward over much of eastern Asia (Fig. 3.38, July). It is the great humidity source for most of southern Asia.

In *winter* much of southern Asia is dominated by weak subtropical anticyclones, so that the northerly winds of that season are essentially variable subtropical winds and trades (Fig. 3.38, January). In the far northwest of the Indian subcontinent, some modified polar air enters from the northwest, while in northeastern Indochina there are also modest invasions of greatly modified polar air from China. But except at these two extremities, the high mountains effectively separate the winter monsoon of South Asia from that farther north. A southern branch of the zonal westerlies, together with a subtropical jet stream, is positioned just south of the Himalayas in winter, and at times this westerly flow may reach down to the surface in the northern lowlands of the subcontinent. In summary, the seasonal reversal of winds in South Asia represents only a latitudinal migration of planetary winds, with northeast trades prevailing in winter and equatorial westerlies in summer.

The summer period of southwest monsoon (equatorial westerlies) dominance is, of course, the rainy season for the region as a whole. Where these warm, humid, unstable air masses of equatorial origin are forced upward over highlands, copious rains result. Over lowlands, most of the showery summer rainfall accompanies the passage of extensive atmospheric disturbances, a great majority of which have weakly developed wind systems. A steady and uninterrupted southwesterly flow is usually associated with fair weather over lowlands. The typical weather sequence during the summer months is one of spells of disturbed weather with organized cloud and rain areas, alternating with intervals of relatively fair weather. In the Indian subcontinent, the advance northward of the ITC and southwest monsoon in late May and June is accompanied by particularly turbulent weather. This is known as "the burst of the monsoon."

During the period of the winter monsoon, the weather element is relatively feeble because of the prevailing anticyclones, and the air is stable, nonbuoyant, and disinclined to rise. Precipitation is meager except along elevated windward coasts and in highlands, and clear skies and fair weather are the rule. The very modest winter rainfall in northern India–Pakistan is associated with weak cyclonic disturbances, which take an easterly course approximating that of a southerly jet stream across the northern part of the subcontinent, across Southeast Asia, and even into southern China.

Other monsoon-like areas. Nowhere else in the world is such an extensive land area affected by seasonal wind reversal as the eastern and southern rimlands of Asia. Yet as the previous section showed, even Asia's monsoons depart from the textbook model in a number of respects. And there are other regions of the earth whose wind systems and consequent weather bear a degree of resemblance to those associated with monsoons.

One such area is tropical West Africa, which fronts on the Gulf of Guinea and the Atlantic Ocean from Nigeria to Sierra Leone. Here during the Northern Hemisphere summer a southwesterly flow of equatorial maritime air prevails, while during the season of low sun it is replaced by northeast trades (Figs. 3.30 and 3.31). This resembles the situation in South Asia, except that along a narrow coastal belt in West Africa the southwesterlies persist in greatly weakened form even in winter, with northeasterly winds on the average not quite reaching to the littoral. The West African wind reversal, like that of South Asia, functions indirectly to produce wet summers and dry winters.

Northern Australia also has an onshore northwesterly flow of humid equatorial maritime air in summer and offshore dry southeast trades in winter, so that the wind reversal is nearly 180° (Figs. 3.30 and 3.31). In most ways it resembles the monsoons of South Asia and West Africa. A wet summer and

Percentage of wind frequency in North Australia

	N	NE	E	SE	S	SW	W	NW
Winter	4	4	14	62	11	2	1	2
Summer	17	9	10	9	3	5	8	39

dry winter result. A similar wind reversal in equatorial East Africa is likewise referred to as monsoonal by the local meteorologists. Keep in mind, however, that seasonal wind reversals in the tropics are rarely induced by the differential heating of land and water, for the winter circulation, the trade wind, is not derived from a cold anticyclone but from a warm subtropical anticyclone.

In middle latitudes, where a convective type of seasonal wind reversal is more likely, North America is the only continent other than Asia whose size might permit the development of a thermally induced monsoon circulation along its eastern and southern margins. South America is too narrow in its middle-latitude parts to produce such a continental system of winds. And even North America, because of its smaller size and meridional mountain systems, cannot compare with Asia in the creation of a thermally induced wind system. Still there are semblances of a monsoon pattern, for the central and eastern United States show an average

Percentage of wind frequency in the eastern United States

	N	NE	E	SE	S	SW	W	NW
Winter	11	15	6	6	7	18	14	23
Summer	8	12	6	11	13	28	9	13

winter circulation of cold northerly surface winds which is fairly anticyclonic. Along the Atlantic and Gulf Coasts, prevailing winter winds are definitely offshore. In summer, by contrast, this same region is fed by a southerly circulation of warm tropical-subtropical air (Figs. 3.30, 3.31). This southerly flow of tropical Gulf air is probably not drawn to the interior by a thermal low, however; rather, it mainly represents the normal circulation around the western end of a subtropical anticyclone. An average onshore-wind component is not characteristic of the Atlantic Coast in summer. Nor does the seasonal march of rainfall everywhere in central and eastern North America have a strong monsoonal character. A wet summer and drier winter are mainly features of stations well inland, especially west of the Mississippi. Much of New England and Maritime Canada have no important seasonal accent in precipitation; parts even show a slight winter maximum, and an extensive region in the subtropical southeastern United States receives more precipitation in the winter half-year than in the summer half.

Minor terrestrial winds

Land and sea breezes.   Just as there are seasonal wind reversals (monsoons) caused at least in part by seasonal temperature contrasts between land and water, so there are diurnal, or daily, monsoons resulting from similar temperature contrasts within the 24-hr period. These are called land and sea breezes. Along coasts, there is often a drift of cool air from land to water at night (corresponding to winter) and a wind from sea to land during the heat of the day (corresponding to summer). These diurnal monsoons represent a convectional circulation (Fig. 3.39).

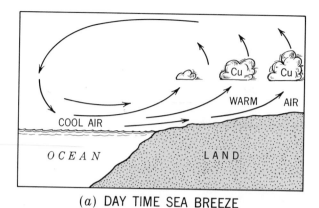

(a) DAY TIME SEA BREEZE

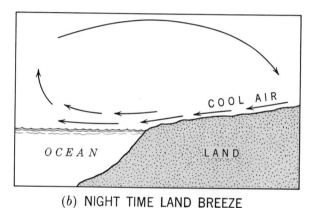

(b) NIGHT TIME LAND BREEZE

Figure 3.39 One type of diurnal wind change.

Usually the sea breeze begins between 10 and 11 A.M., reaches its maximum speed between 1 and 3, and gradually subsides between 3 and 8, after which it is replaced by the weaker land breeze. The height to which the sea breeze extends varies with different climates and with local conditions. Sea breezes off large lakes may reach a depth of 200 to 500 m. Along coasts in the subtropics and tropics this may increase to 1,000 to 2,000 m. The land breeze is much shallower.

The distance on land to which the sea breeze penetrates also varies greatly. Distances of 15 to 50 km are typical of the middle latitudes; in the tropics 50 to 65 km are more characteristic, and maximum distances of over 100 km have been recorded. The land breeze has a much smaller seaward range.

Velocities of the sea breeze also show great variations. In the middle latitudes, normal speeds do not exceed 8 to 12 miles per hour, and maximum values go up to 15 to 25 miles per hour. But along some tropical coasts, the sea breeze may reach storm intensity. It is particularly strong along dry tropical coasts which are paralleled by cool ocean currents, for there the afternoon temperature contrasts between land and water are unusually strong.

The maximum development of strong and regular sea breezes occurs on tropical coasts; the climatic importance of these winds normally decreases in middle latitudes. It is particularly in tropical areas where skies are clear that the sea breeze is a full-grown phenomenon, for such conditions favor large daily temperature contrasts between land and sea. The generally weaker prevailing winds in the low latitudes likewise interfere less with the development of the sea breeze than the winds in stormier regions farther poleward. In the middle and higher latitudes, the sea breeze is more or less confined to the warmer seasons. In the Baltic Sea region, land and sea breezes are characteristic of only about 20 percent of the days even in summer. In Jakarta, Java, on the other hand, they are a year-round phenomenon and occur on 70 to 80 percent of the days. Along a dry coast at Karachi, Pakistan, they blow on 100 percent of the days from May through September.

The sea breeze creates a more livable and healthy climate along tropical littorals than they otherwise would have. When it begins to blow, it may cause a drop in temperature 15 to 20° within $\frac{1}{4}$ to $\frac{1}{2}$ hr. At a coastal station in Senegal, the temperature at 12:30 P.M. on one April 14 was 100°, with a land wind from the northeast and a relative humidity of 3 percent. But at 12:45 the wind direction was northwest from the sea, temperature had dropped to 82°, and the relative humidity had risen to 45 percent (Hann). Frequently the most uncomfortable part of the day on a tropical coast is in the forenoon before the arrival of the sea breeze. Coasts with well-developed sea breezes are inclined to have modified marine climates, with the daily temperature maxima much reduced. In cities like Milwaukee and Chicago, the residents recognize two distinct belts of summer climate: a cooler marine type lying within a mile or so of Lake Michigan, and a markedly warmer one farther in the interior.

Rainfall effects of the sea breeze are less obvious than its thermal effects and do not seem to occur everywhere. But along certain coasts in the tropics and subtropics, the sea breeze appears to produce speed or directional wind convergence which causes lifting. Such lifting results in increased shower activity, particularly in the warm seasons and in the warmer hours of the day, when the sea breeze is at its maximum. The strong summer maximum of precipitation in peninsular Florida and along the Gulf Coast in the United States is believed to be partly due to sea breeze convergence. This summer maximum is especially prominent in peninsular Florida, where there is a convergence of two sea breezes—an easterly one from the Atlantic and a westerly one from the Gulf.

Mountain and valley winds.[7] Like land and sea breezes, mountain and valley winds have a distinct diurnal periodicity. Local thermal differences in mountain areas tend to create a convectional circulation which in the daytime consists of a lower current of air directed toward and up the mountain, and an upper current in the opposite direction. This circulation pattern reverses at night (Fig. 3.40).

The daytime surface current directed toward the mountains and upslope is composed of two elements: the thermal upslope wind and the valley wind. The *thermal upslope wind* is the result of temperature differences between the air over the intensely heated exposed slopes and that over the center of the valley at the same altitude. The result is a strong rising of air along the mountain slopes. The upslope

[7] The foehn or chinook wind is discussed in Chapter 11 on highland climates.

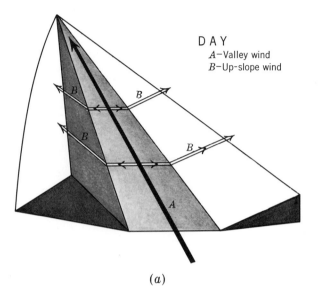

DAY
A—Valley wind
B—Up-slope wind

(a)

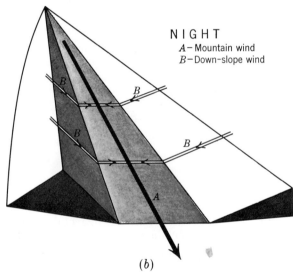

NIGHT
A—Mountain wind
B—Down-slope wind

(b)

Figure 3.40 Another type of diurnal wind change.

winds start shortly after sunrise, reach their maximum at midday, and reverse their direction shortly after sunset. As a result of the stronger solar radiation, they are particularly well developed on southern slopes (in the Northern Hemisphere) and are weak or absent on northern slopes. A consequence of upslope winds is the development of daytime cumulus clouds over peaks and summits. These are the "visible tops of invisible ascending air currents." Daily afternoon cloudiness and showers are therefore common in mountains, and visibility is restricted during the warm hours of the day because of the cloud masses and rain.

Closely associated with slope winds are the *valley winds,* which blow along the axes of the larger valleys. They are especially well known in the wide and deep valleys of the Alps, where they have been studied in detail. They are best developed and most frequent during clear anticyclonic weather in summer. During the day, an up-valley or valley wind blows from about 9 or 10 A.M. until sunset, after which an opposite down-valley or mountain wind blows (Fig. 3.40). Within large mountain valleys, the diurnal temperature variations are more than twice as large as those in a similar air layer over the adjacent plains. This results in a pressure gradient from plains to mountain valleys during the day, and from valleys to plains at night. Weather and climate in mountainous regions are of course greatly influenced by these local winds.

Diurnal variation in wind velocity.   This is another common terrestrial modification of surface winds. It often happens that calm nights and early mornings in the warmer months are followed by windy middays, the maximum surface wind velocity corresponding with the time of greatest heat (Fig. 3.41). By sunset the atmosphere usually becomes calm again. The boisterous midday winds are associated with convectional overturning, which effects an interchange of air between upper and lower strata, at the time of greatest surface heating. Under those conditions the surface air, which becomes linked with the faster-moving air aloft as a result of the ascending and descending currents, is dragged along at a rapid rate. Cumulus clouds are often numerous during the windiest hours when convection is at a maximum, a coincidence that has gained them the name of "wind clouds." During the night, when the

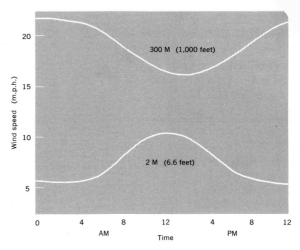

Figure 3.41 Typical variation in wind speed near the ground and at about 1,000 ft (300 m). (*After Riehl.*)

lower air is colder and heavier, there is no tendency for it to rise. The interchange between the upper and lower air is then at a minimum, so that the surface air is relatively undisturbed by the fast-moving currents aloft.

Gravity winds.   Along the coasts of Greenland and Antarctica, which are backed by ice plateaus, unusually strong winds are caused by the descent of the cold, dense air from the seaward-sloping icecap plateau to the shore below. On the edge of the Antarctic Continent, Mawson reported an average wind velocity of 50 miles per hour, while velocities of over 100 miles an hour were frequent. Similar gravity winds on a smaller scale are characteristic of all regions where cold air develops on uplands and along slopes at higher elevations and drains downslope to lower elevations. Such a wind is the *bora* type, characteristic of the Yugoslav coast. Here a narrow coastal plain is backed by a plateau where, under anticyclonic conditions in winter, the air becomes very cold. Because of its density, this plateau air slips through the passes and down the slopes of the plateau as a cold, gusty wind whose temperatures, even after warming by descent, are markedly colder than those along the coast below.

ULATION AND ITS CLIMATIC EFFECTS

e said that the atmosphere directly ...ay controls the oceanic circulation, and ...at the movements of ocean waters in turn have a significant influence upon world climates. The interaction between atmospheric and oceanic circulation is so complicated, however, that it is often impossible to separate cause and effect.

Drifts and currents

Although the oceanic circulation is three-dimensional, it is mainly the surface parts of the system, or those in contact with the atmosphere, that will be considered here. Much the larger part of the surface movement of ocean waters is a slow, relatively inconspicuous transfer (at an average rate of $2\frac{1}{4}$ miles per hour) that affects only shallow depths. This movement is more correctly spoken of as a drift, in contrast to the deeper and more rapidly flowing currents that attain velocities two to three times that of drifts. Currents are much less common than drifts and are usually confined to localities where discharge takes place through restricted channels—as, for instance, the Florida Strait, through which a portion of the Gulf Stream, or Florida Current, emerges from the Gulf of Mexico.

Origin of ocean-water movements. The atmosphere and the oceans are unlike in the nature of their energies. Since the atmosphere is heated chiefly from below, a great amount of kinetic energy (energy of motion) is generated, as is shown by winds and by the general atmospheric circulation. But an ocean is heated from above, so that only about 2 percent as much kinetic energy is imparted to it as the atmosphere possesses. Hence the ocean circulation depends for its driving energy upon the atmosphere.

There are two primary causes for the general circulation of ocean waters. (1) Owing to the frictional effect of winds on the ocean surface, a relatively thin layer of top water about 100 m deep is driven slowly in the general direction of the air movement. If the winds prevailingly are from one direction, a steady drift of surface ocean water, moving in the same general direction, is usually the result. This fairly close correspondence between the great surface drifts of ocean water and the prevailing winds immediately suggests a causal connection and has led some authors to conclude that winds are almost the sole cause of sea drift. (2) The second basic reason for ocean-water circulation lies in contrasts of density within the water itself—contrasts which are due to differences both in temperature and in salinity. Since atmospheric circulation is associated with differences in density, it would seem logical to believe that oceanic circulation is also.

In all probability, the system of water movement as we know it is largely the result of the combined forces of wind friction and contrasting densities. Density differences are responsible chiefly for the great primary circulations, both vertical and horizontal, that take place throughout the entire hydrosphere. Winds largely determine the more readily observable features of surface currents and drifts. But although there is a general agreement between atmospheric and oceanic circulations, the flow patterns of the two fluids are not identical. Modifying agencies affecting the general water circulation are depth, degree of enclosure, shapes of coastlines, and the deflective force of earth rotation.

Mechanics of ocean-water circulation. Observational data on oceanic circulation, especially on the differences of temperature and salinity at various depths in all the seas, has not yet been accumulated in enough detail for a complete understanding of this subject. In general it appears that temperature has more to do with the circulation than salinity.

Temperature. The ocean waters in high latitudes are colder and therefore denser than those in the tropics, which makes for a constant exchange of water between polar and equatorial regions. This exchange is one part of the mechanism, involving

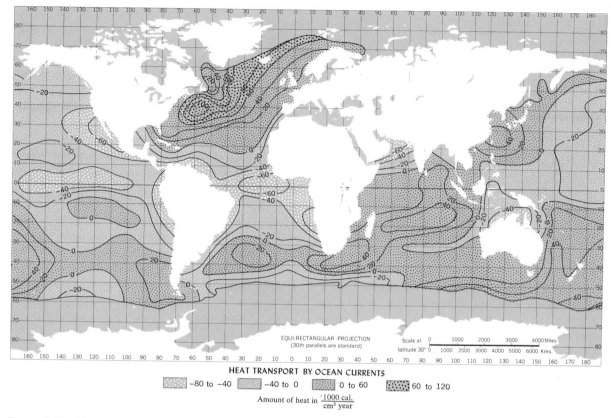

HEAT TRANSPORT BY OCEAN CURRENTS

| | −80 to −40 | | −40 to 0 | | 0 to 60 | | 60 to 120 |

Amount of heat in $\frac{1000\ \text{cal.}}{\text{cm}^2\ \text{year}}$

Figure 3.42 Heat transfer by ocean currents. Shadings indicate the annual amount of heat gained or lost by the atmosphere in contact with the ocean surface. Compare this with Fig. 3.44 showing the general scheme of ocean currents. Note the remarkable heat gain in the northern North Atlantic from the powerful Florida–North Atlantic Current. (*After map by Rudolph Geiger, Justes Perthes, Publishers.*)

circulations of both atmosphere and oceans, for maintaining the earth's latitudinal heat balance (Fig. 3.42). The Antarctic Ocean, having much wider connections with warmer seas than the more enclosed Arctic, no doubt provides more cold water for the general circulation. The principal southern connection between the Arctic and warmer seas to the south is the route through the North Atlantic between Greenland and Eurasia. Here the warm surface waters flow poleward on the eastern side of the basin, and cold return currents move equatorward in the western North Atlantic, passing both to the east and to the west of Greenland (Fig. 3.44). In the North Pacific there is no such free connection

with the Arctic Ocean. As a result the circulation in the North Pacific is less vigorous, and both the warm and cool currents are much smaller than they are in the North Atlantic. In the Atlantic, the easternmost projection of Brazil so divides the equatorial current that much the larger part of its warm water is shunted northward to form the extraordinarily powerful Florida Current (Gulf Stream) and the North Atlantic Drift (Figs. 3.42, 3.44).

Salinity. Differences in salinity tend to complicate the thermally induced circulation further. In the latitudes of the trades and the great permanent subtropical high-pressure centers, where rainfall is meager and evaporation great, salinity of the surface water is relatively high, and accordingly its density is greater. A constant sinking of the denser, saltier surface water of these latitudes is the result. On the other hand, both to the south and to the north of these dry belts with high evaporation are regions of relatively abundant rainfall and decreased evaporation—the wet tropics and the belts of westerlies. In these latitudes the surface waters are constantly being freshened, by direct precipitation as well as by runoff from the lands. The less salty and less dense surface waters have little tendency to sink.

General pattern of surface drifts and currents

Except for the polar seas, all the great oceans have broadly similar general circulations of surface drifts and currents (Fig. 3.43). This follows naturally from the general similarity of atmospheric circulation patterns. The scheme of ocean currents as developed in the North Atlantic ocean will be taken here as an example (Fig. 3.44).

Figure 3.43 Surface currents of the oceans in the Northern Hemisphere winter. (*After Schott and Dietrich.*)

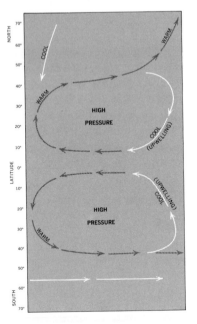

The most conspicuous element of the North Atlantic circulation is the great closed elliptical whirl about the subtropical Azores High. The trade winds on the equatorward sides of the subtropical anticyclones in both hemispheres tend to drift the surface waters before them across the ocean. The deflective force of earth rotation (right in the Northern and left in the Southern Hemisphere) acts to make this a westward-flowing current, moving somewhat at an angle to the direction of the trades. This is the Atlantic Equatorial Current. (In fact, there are really two equatorial currents, separated in the eastern part of the ocean by a minor countercurrent setting toward the east.)

Checked in its westward progress by the eastward thrust of the South American continent, the Equatorial Current is divided so that the larger part of it flows northwestward and the smaller part southwestward. Partly because of the deflective force of earth rotation and the trend of the coastline, and partly because of the wind direction around the western end of the subtropical Azores High (Fig. 3.43), the warm northward-moving current gradually is bent more and more to the east. A part of it enters the Caribbean Sea and passes through the Straits of Yucatán into the Gulf of Mexico. This water returns to the Atlantic through the Florida Strait, where it joins the major part of the warm-water drift, which has kept eastward of the West Indies. Together they form the Gulf Stream (more appropriately called the Florida or Caribbean Current), which parallels the American Atlantic seaboard.

At about latitude 40°N, westerly winds and deflection cause the warm surface waters of this current to turn slowly eastward across the ocean in the form of a west-wind drift. In the eastern Atlantic the drift divides. A part of it is carried by the subtropical anticyclone's northerly and northwesterly winds southward along the coast of southwestern Europe and northwestern Africa, until it again joins the Equatorial Current and thus completes the low-latitude circuit. This is the relatively cool Canaries Current (Fig. 3.43).

A large portion of the west-wind drift, however,

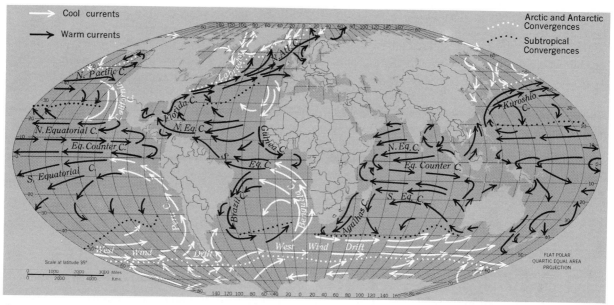

Figure 3.44 Generalized scheme of ocean currents.

is carried northeastward by the stormy southwest-erlies toward Europe to form the mighty North Atlantic Drift, which eventually enters the Arctic Ocean. Nowhere else in the Northern Hemisphere is there a comparably large heat transport by an ocean current. The Arctic, compensating for this receipt of warm water from the eastern Atlantic, produces an outward flow of cold water in the western Atlantic on either side of Greenland. The western branch, called the Labrador Current, may reach as far south as New England.

The circulation pattern sketched above is a greatly simplified one, of course. Superimposed upon this generalized average flow are numerous eddies and surges, together with changes in direction and strength of currents following the seasonal shifting and reversals of winds.

Convergences, divergences, and vertical movements. For both hemispheres oceanographers recognize three general contrasting water masses separated by relatively distinct lines of discontinuity. In the high latitudes are the polar waters, which are characterized by low temperatures, low salt content,

a greenish color, and high plankton content. In the low latitudes are the contrasting tropical or subtropical waters, high in temperature and salt, low in organic forms, and blue in color. Between the two extremes are the "mixed waters" of the middle latitudes. Therefore both hemispheres must have two principal lines of discontinuity where waters differing in temperature, life forms, saltiness, and color are in contact. Those two lines, which separate the westward-drifting tropical waters from the eastward-moving drifts of the middle latitudes, are called the subtropical convergences, sometimes spoken of as the "polar fronts" of the oceans.

The simple schematic diagram of ocean currents and drifts (Fig. 3.44) discloses a number of locations where there is typically a divergence or convergence of flow. For example, convergence occurs in the eastern equatorial oceans and in the western parts of middle-latitude oceans, for in both locations poleward-moving warm currents from the tropics meet equatorward-moving cold currents from the polar seas. Slow convergence also occurs near the centers of the subtropical anticyclones. Divergent flow characterizes the western parts of tropical oceans, where the bifurcated equatorial current spreads to the north and south. Divergence is also typical of the eastern parts of middle-latitude oceans, where the west-wind drift divides the waters.

Where surface drifts converge, surface water must sink. If the converging waters are significantly unlike in temperature and density, the colder, denser water sinks beneath the less dense in a manner similar to that which occurs between unlike air masses along an atmospheric front. If density differences are slight, the sinking is slow and diffuse. Surface divergence is accompanied by a slow rising of waters from below. The climatic effects of surface convergence and divergence are discussed in a later section.

Warm and cool currents.   In general poleward-drifting surface waters, since they come from lower latitudes, are inclined to be relatively warm, while those from higher latitudes are likely to be cooler than the surrounding waters. In the lower latitudes (equatorward from about 40°) warm ocean currents typically parallel the eastern sides of continents, while cool ocean currents parallel their western sides (Figs. 3.42, 3.43, and 3.44). For example, along the west coast of the United States at about 40°N, the average surface-water temperature near the coast is on occasions as low as 50°, while in the same latitude off the east coast of Japan the sea temperature is 70° or higher. At 2°S along the Peruvian coast the water temperature is as low as 62°, whereas in a corresponding latitude on the coast of New Guinea the surface temperature is about 83°. In the middle and higher latitudes this pattern is usually reversed; warm ocean currents parallel the western sides of land masses, and cool ones the eastern sides. Along east coasts (western sides of oceans), therefore, there is likely to be a convergence of contrasting currents, while along west coasts such currents tend to diverge.

Upwelling.   It should be added that a part of the cool water along west coasts in lower latitudes (Peru and northern Chile, northwest and southwest Africa, southern California and adjacent northwestern Mexico, among others) is the result of coastal divergence and a consequent upwelling from somewhat greater depths along the coast. Such regions of upwelling occupy positions along the eastern margins of oceanic subtropical anticyclones. There, paralleling equatorward-moving winds of the subtropical whirls drive the surface waters toward lower latitudes. Owing to the deflective force of earth rotation, the ocean currents along these cool-water coasts have a component of movement away from the land. Colder water from below, therefore, rises to replace the diverging surface water. Usually this overturn takes place within the upper 500 to 600 ft, so that upwelled water does not represent Arctic or Antarctic deep water.

Climatic influences of ocean drifts and currents

It is difficult to formulate simple principles concerning the effects of ocean drifts and currents upon the climate of adjacent land areas. Obviously the temperature effects of a cool current will differ from those of a warm. But whether a current actually has much of an influence in chilling or warming a land also depends on the comparative temperatures of the land and water surfaces. Clearly the same current may affect land temperatures quite differently in winter, when the land is cold, than in summer. The warm North Atlantic Drift makes a much greater contribution to tempering western Europe's winter cold than it does to moderating its summer heat. By contrast, the cold California Current is much more effective in mitigating subtropical coastal California's summer heat than in tempering its mild winter chilliness.

The influence of the water offshore also depends on how consistently the temperatures it generates are carried landward by winds. On windward coasts the temperature influences are far stronger and are carried inland a greater distance than on leeward coasts. Climatic effects become more complicated when, as a result of seasonal wind reversal, a coast that is windward in one season becomes leeward at the opposite time.

When cool currents border tropical coasts, they

greatly moderate the tropical heat. The coast of Peru, which is paralleled by the cold Peru Current, is 10° or more cooler than the coast of Brazil in similar latitudes, where a warm current prevails. In subtropical and middle latitudes, the effects of cool currents are chiefly restricted to the warmer months. Santa Monica on the California coast, where cold water lies offshore, has a cool July temperature of only 66°. This is 10° or more lower than east-coast stations in the subtropical United States, where warm water prevails. Kushiro in eastern Hokkaido (Japan), which is paralleled by the cool Okhotsk Current, has a chilly August temperature of only 63.7°. But the same month in Sapporo on the west side of the island averages about 70°.

Warm ocean currents are particularly effective in moderating the winter temperatures of windward littorals in middle and high latitudes. A most remarkable example is the case of western Europe, parts of which are 30 to 40° warmer in January than the world average for the latitude. This represents the combined effects of the unusually large and warm North Atlantic Drift, and an atmospheric circulation whose westerly winds persistently advect this warmth to the continent (Fig. 3.44). Warm waters also wash the shores of much of the eastern United States and Asia, but they are much less important in tempering the winter cold, for the prevailing winter winds are offshore.

As the previous section said, there is a tendency for cool and warm ocean currents to converge along the western sides of middle-latitude oceans and to diverge along the eastern sides. Where contrasting currents converge, the general effect is to squeeze the isotherms of both sea and air closer together. This makes for marked latitudinal contrasts in ocean temperatures, steep thermal atmospheric gradients, and advection fogs—all of which are found, for instance, along parts of the east coasts of Asia and North America. Where contrasting currents diverge, they tend to spread the isotherms, creating milder temperature gradients in both water and air, as are found in the eastern Atlantic and western Europe. This does not mean, however, that ocean currents are the principal cause of these temperature-gradi-

ent phenomena on the opposite sides of oceans; at best they are only auxiliary to the more powerful overall oceanic and continental influences.

Cool-water coasts in low latitudes are often characterized by both fog and aridity—on first thought an apparently contradictory combination. The surface fog is the result of warm air from over the open ocean being chilled by blowing over the cool current lying alongshore and mixing with the cool air above it. Fog may then be drifted in over the land, though usually it is confined to a narrow coastal fringe. During daytime hours the sea fog over land may be prevented by turbulence from reaching down to the surface. Frequent high fog or stratus cloud is also a consequence of subsidence and a low-level inversion in the strong anticyclonic circulation that prevails. The intense aridity of cool-water tropical coasts with their stable air masses is well known. To what extent the stability of the air is the result of the cool water is controversial. At the present time the stabilizing influence of the water seems to be viewed as an auxiliary process rather than as the primary one. The more effective of the two aridifying agents is probably the strong above-surface subsidence in the subtropical anticyclonic cell, whose eastern margins are located over these tropical and subtropical west coasts.

In summary, the following generalizations may be made concerning the climatic characteristics of coasts paralleled by warm and cold currents (Fig. 3.45).

1. West coasts in subtropical and tropical latitudes which are bordered by cool waters have relatively low average temperatures and small annual and diurnal ranges. They are foggy even though arid.

2. West coasts in the middle and higher latitudes which are bordered by warm waters have strikingly marine climates. Unusually mild winters and small annual ranges of temperature are the rule.

3. East (and therefore leeward) coasts in the lower middle latitudes, even though bordered by warm waters, have modified continental climates with relatively cold winters and warm-to-hot summers.

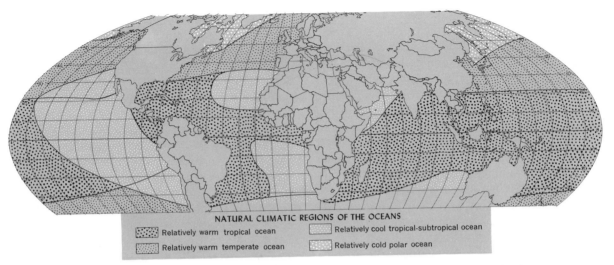

NATURAL CLIMATIC REGIONS OF THE OCEANS

Relatively warm tropical ocean		Relatively cool tropical-subtropical ocean	
Relatively warm temperate ocean		Relatively cold polar ocean	

Figure 3.45   Classification of oceanic regions relative to their surface temperature. (*After Markus.*)

4. East coasts in the higher middle latitudes which are paralleled by cool ocean currents are noteworthy for their cool summers.

Indirect climatic effects of ocean currents.   Indirectly, ocean currents may affect the general climatic and weather conditions of a region by their influence upon the locations of the great frontal zones, and consequently upon the tracks of cyclonic storms. Two of the main frontal zones and associated regions of cyclone formation in winter are situated off the eastern coasts of North America and Asia, roughly between latitudes 25 and 50°. In both places, an abundance of tropical water is being transported into the middle latitudes, and as a result energy is being supplied to the atmosphere in great amounts. It is in these same locations that temperature gradients are unusually steep, for the cold eastern sides of the great continents and the warm waters offshore create marked thermal contrasts. The fact that frontal zones appear to occur where unusual amounts of energy are being supplied to the atmosphere suggests that the cyclones which develop along these fronts are at least partly of thermodynamic origin. It has been pointed out also that the two principal hurricane paths in the Caribbean region coincide with warm waters. One follows the route into the Gulf of Mexico, and the other the route of the warm waters (Caribbean or Florida Current) off the northern and eastern coasts of the Greater Antilles and Florida (Fig. 3.42).

SELECTED REFERENCES FOR FURTHER STUDY OF TOPICS IN CHAPTER THREE

1. **Atmospheric pressure: relation of winds to pressure.**   Blair and Fite, pp. 21–36, 122–128; Petterssen, pp. 145–163, 174–181; Hare, pp. 44–56; Blüthgen, pp. 213–225; Riehl, *Tropical Meteorology;* Riehl, *Introduction to the Atmosphere*, pp. 18–20, 117–136; *Aviation Weather*, pp. 19–25; Critchfield, pp. 70–88.

2. **General circulation of the atmosphere.**   Blair and Fite, pp. 135–150; Blüthgen, pp. 338–378; Byers, pp. 260–286; Critchfield, pp. 88–92; Gentilli, pp. 37–65; Hare, pp. 91–103; Jerome Namias, "The Jet Stream," *Scientific American*, Vol. 187, pp. 27–31, October, 1952; Willett and Saunders, pp. 118–151;

Compendium of Meteorology, pp. 541–567; H. Flohn, "Studien zur allgemeine Zirkulation der Atmosphäre," *Ber. Deut. Wetterdienstes in der U.S. Zone,* no. 18, 1950; H. Flohn, "Neue Anschauungen über allgemeine Zirkulation der Atmosphäre und ihre klimatische Bedeutung," *Erdkunde,* Vol. 4, pp. 141–162, 1950; Hermann Flohn, "Die Revision der Lehre von Passatkreislauf," *Meteorologische Rundschau,* Vol. 1, pp. 1–60, 1953; Riehl, *Tropical Meteorology,* pp. 358–382; H. Riehl, M. A. Aeaka, C. L. Jordan, and R. J. Renard, "The Jet Stream," *Meteorological Monographs,* Vol. 2, No. 7, 1954; Reiter, *Jet-Stream Meteorology,* pp. 324–409; Reiter, *Jet Streams,* 55–178; Riehl, *Introduction to the Atmosphere,* pp. 203–214; Willett and Saunders, pp. 152–195.

3. **Surface winds and their characteristics.**   Conrad, pp. 252–277; Haurwitz and Austin, pp. 44–63; Yale Mintz and Gordon Dean, "The Observed Mean Field of Motion of the Atmosphere," *Geophysical Research Papers,* No. 17, Air Force Cambridge Research Center, Cambridge, Mass., 1952; *Atlas of Climatic Charts of the Oceans,* U.S. Weather Bureau, 1938; J. S. Sawyer, "Memorandum on the Intertropical Front," *Meteorol. Repts.,* No. 10, British Meteorological Office, 1952; *Compendium of Meteorology,* pp. 859–887; Hare, 104–115; Petterssen, 169–189; Blüthgen, 227–232; Riehl, *Introduction to the Atmosphere,* pp. 229–232.

4. **Monsoons.**   Blüthgen, pp. 354–365; Hare, pp. 139–154; "Monsoons of the World," *Symposium on Monsoons of the World,* New Delhi, 1960; P. Pédelaborde, *The Monsoon* (translated by M. J. Clegg), Methuen & Co., Ltd., London, 1963.

5. **Local winds.**   *Compendium of Meteorology,* pp. 655–672; Blüthgen, pp. 232–248; Petterssen, pp. 164–168.

6. **Ocean drifts and currents.**   William S. von Arx, *An Introduction to Physical Oceanography,* Addison-Wesley Pub. Co., Reading, Mass., 1962; Cuchlaine A. King, *Oceanography for Geographers,* E. Arnold, London, 1962.

7. **General references on wind and pressure systems.**   Jen-Hu Chang, "The Indian Summer Monsoon," *Geog. Rev.,* Vol. 57, no. 3, pp. 372–396, July, 1967; F. K. Hare, "The Westerlies," *Geog. Rev.,* Vol. 50, pp. 345–367, 1960; "Energy Exchanges and the General Circulation," *Geography,* Vol. 50, pp. 229–241, 1965; H. H. Lamb, "Representation of the General Atmospheric Circulation," *Met. Mag.,* Vol. 89, pp. 319–330, 1960; P. Koteswaram and N. S. Bhaskara Rao, "The Structure of the Asian Summer Monsoon," *Australian Met. Mag.,* Vol. 42, pp. 35–56, 1963; J. E. McDonald, "The Coriolis Effect," *Scientific American,* Vol. 186, pp. 72–78, 1952; Jerome, Namias, "Interactions of Circulation and Weather between Hemispheres," *Monthly Weather Rev.,* Vol. 91, No. 10–12, pp. 482–486, 1963; E. Palmén, "The Role of the Atmospheric Disturbance in the General Circulation," *Quar. Jour. Roy. Met. Soc.,* Vol. 77, pp. 337–354, 1951; Herbert Riehl, "General Atmospheric Circulation of the Tropics," *Science,* Vol. 135, pp. 13–22, 1962; "Jet Streams of the Atmosphere," *Tech. Paper No. 32,* Colorado State University, 117 pp., 1962; V. P. Starr, "The General Circulation of the Atmosphere," *Scientific American,* Vol. 195, pp. 40–45, 1956; G. B. Tucher, "The General Circulation of the Atmosphere," *Weather,* Vol. 17, pp. 320–340, 1962; E. W. Wahl, "Singularities and the General Circulation," *J. Meteorology,* Vol. 10, pp. 42–45, 1953.

CHAPTER FOUR

ATMOSPHERIC MOISTURE AND PRECIPITATION

HUMIDITY

Humidity refers to the water in gas form, or water vapor, in the atmosphere—but not to liquid droplets of cloud, fog, or rain. Water vapor has nothing to do with wetness, for it is dry like any other gas. Also like the other atmospheric gases, it exerts a pressure, which is known as the *vapor pressure* of the air. Air is saturated when its vapor pressure equals that over a smooth water surface.

Although water vapor comprises less than 2 percent of the atmosphere's total volume, it is the single most important component of the air from the standpoint of weather and climate. As noted in the Introduction, the proportions of most of the atmosphere's gases are relatively constant from place to place. It is chiefly water vapor that is highly inconstant, varying from nearly zero up to a maximum of about 3 percent in the middle latitudes and 4 percent in the humid tropics. This variability, in both place and time, is of outstanding importance for several reasons:

1. Water vapor is the source of all forms of condensation and precipitation. The amount of water vapor in a given mass of air is one indicator

of the atmosphere's potential for precipitation.

2. As the air's principal absorber of solar energy, and of radiant earth energy as well, water vapor operates as a heat regulator and so has a great effect on air temperature.

3. The latent heat contained in water vapor is an important energy source both for the circulation of the atmosphere and for the development of many atmospheric disturbances, especially those in tropical latitudes.

4. Also because of its latent heat, the amount and vertical distribution of water vapor in the atmosphere indirectly affects the buoyancy of air and hence its tendency to ascend. This in turn is closely related to the formation of cloud and precipitation.

5. Humidity is an important factor in the rate of evaporation, a process that greatly influences plant and animal life. By affecting the human body's rate of cooling, evaporation is one determinant of its sensible temperature, or feeling of heat and cold.

6. Unlike other gases comprising the air ocean, water vapor can be changed to liquid and solid forms well within the range of atmospheric temperatures.

Evaporation

The process by which water in its liquid or solid form is converted into water vapor, a gas, is called evaporation.[1] Water vapor enters the atmosphere by evaporation, chiefly from the ocean surfaces, but also from smaller bodies of water, from the moist ground, from the transpiring leaves of plants, and from raindrops falling through the air.

Evaporation takes place when the vapor pressure at the earth's surface exceeds that in the air above. At an open water surface, molecules escape from the liquid water into the air, while at the same time

some gaseous molecules return to the liquid. If the temperature of the liquid is higher than that of the air, more molecules escape from the water than return to it, and evaporation occurs. But as the number of water vapor molecules in the air increases, so also does the partial vapor pressure, and consequently a larger number of molecules returns to the liquid. Eventually equilibrium is reached, with the number of escaping molecules equaling those returning. Evaporation then ceases; the air is saturated. Under existing temperature conditions it can hold no more water vapor. But saturation pressure changes rapidly with temperature. Over the earth's range of temperature, it varies from under $\frac{1}{10}$ mb to over 100 mb.

There must be an expenditure of energy to change liquid water into the vapor state. This energy is usually supplied from the evaporating surface, which as a consequence is cooled. Thus one experiences the chilling effect of evaporation upon stepping out of a bath. Evaporation from falling raindrops chills the air, since the air provides most of the energy for evaporating the water.

The cooling effect of evaporation is involved in the functioning of a wet-bulb thermometer. As Chapter 2 described, the instrument consists of an ordinary thermometer whose bulb is covered by gauze saturated with water. Evaporation from the wet gauze causes the wet-bulb thermometer to record a lower temperature than the ordinary dry-bulb thermometer does. The amount of cooling is directly proportional to the dryness of the air. From the differential temperature readings of the wet- and dry-bulb thermometer, one can determine from prepared tables the dew point, vapor pressure, and relative humidity of the air.

The rate of evaporation depends mainly upon the temperature of the evaporating surface compared with that of the air, but also upon the relative humidity of the air or its degree of saturation, and the speed of the wind. Evaporation is highest when the evaporating surface is warmest, when the air is relatively dry, and when the winds are strongest. Consequently evaporation is greater in summer than in winter, and at midday than at night. When frigid air with low humidity is advected over a rela-

---

[1]As used here, evaporation includes transpiration from plants, sometimes called evapotranspiration. Water loss from plant surfaces (mainly the leaves) by transpiration is a complex process. It occurs when the vapor pressure in the leaf cells is greater than the atmospheric vapor pressure. Evapotranspiration losses from natural surfaces cannot be measured directly. Only indirect methods and theoretical formulas are available (see Chapter 12, Dry Climates).

tively warm water surface, evaporation is rapid, since the vapor pressure of the cold atmosphere is always less than that over the warmer water. Moreover, under these circumstances the air is heated from below by contact with the warm water so that it becomes unstable. This increases turbulence and therefore evaporation.

Moisture entering the air as water vapor is widely distributed by winds and vertical air currents. Often it is carried great distances before being eventually removed as liquid or solid condensation and precipitation.

Distribution of evaporation. Since the rate of evaporation depends mainly on temperature, obviously evaporating power, or *potential evaporation,* will decline from tropical to polar latitudes, given the presence of unlimited amounts of water (see the following table and Fig. 4.1).

Variation of average annual *potential* evaporation by latitude zones*

Latitude	North		South	
	cm	in.	cm	in.
70–60°	18	7	?	?
60–50°	40	16	30	12
50–40°	70	27	60	24
40–30°	110	43	100	40
30–20°	130	51	130	51
20–10°	140	55	130	51
10–0°	120	47	120	47

* Evaporating power given in height of evaporated water column.

Source: After Landsberg.

Figure 4.1 World distribution of average annual effective evapotranspiration. (*After Rudolph Geiger, Die Atmosphäre der Erde, Justus Perthes, Darmstadt, Germany.*)

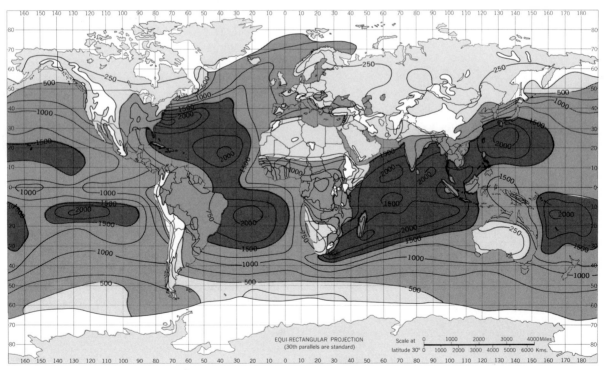

ANNUAL EFFECTIVE EVAPOTRANSPIRATION

0 to 500   500 to 1500   1500 to 2500 mm

The *actual* evaporation (as distinguished from *potential*), however, depends not only upon air and surface temperatures, air motion, and degree of air saturation, but also on the available supply of moisture. On nonliquid surfaces, the evaporating power of the air may be several times greater than the amount of water available.

Available data on measured evaporation are scanty and often unreliable. They are usually supplemented by estimates for actual evaporation from various natural surfaces, compared with amounts measured from evaporating pans, or calculated by the use of various formulas. Evaporation from large water surfaces is estimated to be about 70 to 75 percent of that from a pan exposed to the same temperature and wind conditions. Evaporation from a wet bare soil may be about 90 percent of that from an open water surface.

The following table illustrates two main points concerning the distribution of actual evaporation.

1. In most latitudes, actual evaporation is greater over oceans than over continents. This reflects the facts that the supply of water is unlimited at the ocean surface, while over many land areas water is scarce. But in the very low latitudes, between about 10° N and S, there is more evaporation over land than over water, because of the abundant supply of water available in these rainy regions and the unusually great transpiration from the dense equatorial forests.

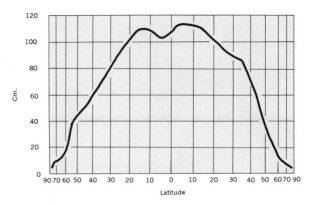

Figure 4.2 Distribution of average annual effective evaporation by latitude zones. Since evaporation is mainly a function of temperature, highest values are in the low latitudes, and there is a decline toward either pole. (*Data from G. Wüst.*)

2. The mean zonal or meridional pattern of actual-evaporation distribution is chiefly a function of air temperature, since there is a maximum in low latitudes and a steady decline toward either pole (Fig. 4.2). Perhaps as much as 60 percent of the earth's evaporation is furnished by the belt 25°S to 25°N, and 80 percent occurs in the zone bounded by the 35° parallels.

Latent energy in water vapor

It is common knowledge that energy is required in the form of heat to melt the solid, ice, into the liquid,

Zonal distribution of actual mean annual evaporation (Inches)

	Latitude					
	60–50°	50–40°	40–30°	30–20°	20–10°	10–0°
Northern Hemisphere						
Continents	14.2	13.0	15.0	19.7	31.1	45.3
Oceans	15.7	27.6	37.8	45.3	47.2	39.4
Mean	15.0	20.1	28.0	35.8	42.9	40.6
Southern Hemisphere						
Continents	(7.9)	(19.7)	20.1	16.1	35.4	48.0
Oceans	9.1	22.8	35.0	44.1	47.2	44.9
Mean	8.8	22.8	35.5	39.0	44.5	45.7

Source: After Wüst.

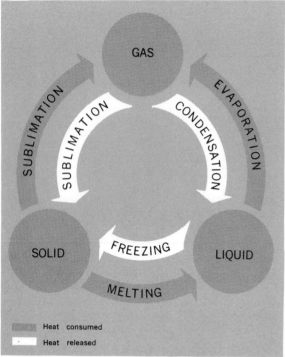

Figure 4.3 Changes of state as applied to water.

it is used only in producing a change in state from liquid to gas. One reason why the sea surface or a vegetation cover never becomes really hot on a sunny day—as a dry, sandy beach does, for example—is that so much energy is consumed in evaporation at their surfaces.

If energy is consumed in the process of evaporation, then conversely, energy will be released during condensation, when water vapor returns to a solid or liquid state. This released heat, known as the latent heat of condensation, is an important source of atmospheric energy. On a night when large-scale cloud condensation and precipitation take place, cooling is retarded by the liberation of so much latent heat. Condensation, then, is the mechanism for releasing latent heat gained during evaporation. Through cloud formation, heat of condensation is mixed through the troposphere—in the tropics, up to a height of 50,000 ft. Evaporation-condensation probably account for about two-thirds of the heat exchange between the land-water surface and the atmosphere. To maintain the heat balance, it is estimated that on the average, 30 to 40 in. of water a year must be evaporated at the land-water surface into the atmosphere and subsequently precipitated.

The hydrologic cycle

A never-ending round of evaporation from sea and land creates the air's reservoir of water vapor, which then condenses to form clouds and subsequently returns to land and sea as precipitation. This hydrologic cycle involving evaporation → condensation → precipitation has two main subdivisions: a meridional cycle which involves a transfer of moisture between different latitude belts, and another which involves an exchange between land and sea. From the previous section on latent heat, it must be clear that any exchange of water vapor must also involve a transfer of energy (Fig. 4.4).

Meridional moisture exchange. As the following table indicates, some latitude zones have a surplus of precipitation over evaporation, while in others the reverse is true. Such an arrangement requires

water, and to evaporate water into vapor, a gas (Fig. 4.3). The unit of heat energy, the calorie, is the amount of heat required to raise the temperature of a gram of water 1° centigrade. But it takes 79 calories to convert a gram of ice into a gram of water at freezing temperature, and 607 calories to evaporate the gram of water at freezing temperature and convert it into water vapor at the same temperature.

Since energy is required to change the solid into a liquid, and likewise the liquid into a gas, it follows that water vapor contains more potential energy than liquid water, and water in turn more than ice. This stored-up energy in water vapor is known as latent heat, or latent energy. It is transformed sun energy, which has been employed in evaporating water or ice and converting them into water vapor. The energy which the evaporating surface loses during evaporation does not warm the water vapor gas;

Precipitation excess and deficiency by zones (In 1,000 cu km)

North latitude		Precipitation—evaporation	South latitude		Precipitation—evaporation
90–80°		+ 0.4	90–80°		+ 1.0
80–70°	Precipitation excess	+ 2.3	80–70°	Precipitation excess	+ 2.5
70–60°		+ 5.0	70–60°		+ 3.6
60–50°		+ 8.1	60–50°		+12.0
50–40°		+10.1	50–40°		+10.7
40–30°		− 7.1	40–30°		+ 0.1
30–20°	Precipitation deficiency	−19.0	30–20°	Precipitation deficiency	−16.5
20–10°		−16.2	20–10°		−16.0
10–0°	Precipitation excess	+19.3	10–0°		− 0.2

Source: After Wüst, Gentilli, and others.

a meridional exchange of moisture, and hence energy, between zones of surplus and deficiency.

The table shows that there are three main belts of precipitation excess, and hence of net moisture and energy gain: the two middle-latitude zones (40° to 70° in each hemisphere), and the equatorial zone, especially 0° to 10°N. Winds advect vast amounts of moisture, and consequently of latent heat of condensation, to these regions. In contrast, there are two extensive belts of precipitation deficiency, located at about 10° to 40° in each hemisphere where evaporation exceeds rainfall. These are the zones of the subtropical anticyclones and the trade winds. In them there is an enormous energy loss by evaporation. This energy, in the form of latent heat in water vapor, is advected by winds to the equatorial and middle latitudes, where precipitation exceeds evaporation.

Within the high-evaporation trade-wind belt, the moist convective layer gradually deepens in the direction of the airflow (equatorward and to the west). In the trades, most of the moisture is retained in vapor form rather than rained back to the ocean. The trades' accumulated water vapor is transported toward the equatorial trough, where much of it is condensed, releasing latent heat that is carried to great heights in cumulonimbus clouds. Such large clouds are concentrated in atmospheric disturbances, which are relatively numerous within the equatorial trough. Thus the upward transfer of energy, both latent and sensible heat, from the land-sea surface to the atmosphere is significantly increased by synoptic disturbances. Such traveling disturbances form a vital link in the moisture transfer between the tropical land-sea surface and the atmosphere.

Land-sea moisture exchange. A moisture exchange between land and sea is required because continents have more precipitation than evaporation, and oceans more evaporation than precipitation.

	Cu km per year
Precipitation on continents	122,000
Evaporation from continents	97,000
Surplus on continents	25,000
Precipitation on oceans	259,000
Evaporation from oceans	384,000
Deficiency on oceans	25,000
Transferred from continents to oceans	25,000

Some of the water vapor added to the atmosphere by evaporation over the sea is transported by winds to the continents where, together with land-evaporated moisture, it condenses and falls as precipitation. A part of this land precipitation enters the ground to form an important groundwater resource. A part is returned to the sea by runoff

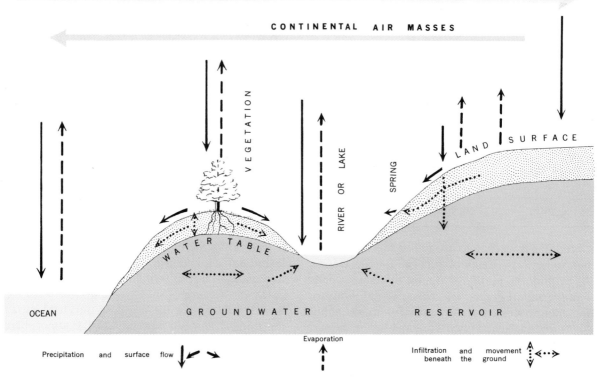

Figure 4.4 Some of the major relationships between the hydrologic cycle, waters on the land, and the air-mass cycle.

in the form of streams and glaciers. And still another part is transported back to the oceans by land winds containing land-evaporated moisture (Fig. 4.4). Water evaporated in one locality is usually precipitated hundreds or even thousands of miles distant; the hydrologic cycle is rarely completed locally. Of course, much of the sea-evaporated moisture is returned directly to the ocean by rains over the sea.

Through careful observation it has been discovered that the amount of water precipitated upon the continents is well in excess of the runoff from those same areas in the form of rivers and glaciers. Since only roughly 20 percent of the land precipitation is removed by runoff, it follows that close to 80 percent must be returned to the atmosphere by evaporation from the ground, inland bodies of water, and the vegetation cover. From these data

it might be concluded that the oceans contribute to continental precipitation only that proportion included in the runoff, while local continental evaporation must provide the other 80 percent. But this reasoning neglects a fundamental consideration—that if sea winds can transport water vapor from the oceans to the land, then land winds can also transport it from land to the oceans (Fig. 4.4).

In the general circulation of the atmosphere in the middle latitudes, and in the cycle of atmospheric exchange between land and sea, humid tropical maritime air masses traveling poleward become cooled, precipitate much of their moisture, and are ultimately converted into polar continental and polar maritime air masses. Conversely, polar continental air masses in moving equatorward over land areas become warmed, absorb much land-evaporated moisture, and eventually are transformed into warm, moist, tropical maritime air masses over the oceans. Thus it is not only rivers and glaciers that carry land-precipitated moisture back to the oceans, but also these dry polar continental air masses, which may pass entirely across the continent from north to south without any re-precipitation.

The amount of evaporation by North American polar continental air masses has been calculated by measuring their mosisture content when they cross the Canadian border and when they arrive at the Gulf of Mexico. It was found that the water content of southward-moving polar continental air at Ellendale, North Dakota, was equivalent to 0.44 in. of rainfall, and at Pensacola, Florida, to 0.97 in.—a gain of 0.53 in. If these figures are representative, the water removed by polar continental evaporation from the Mississippi drainage basin reaches the astounding figure of 5,909,000 cu ft per sec, which is nine times the average discharge of the Mississippi River. Air masses and their various characteristics will be treated in more detail in Chapter 5. The important point here is that polar continental air masses moving southward across a continent resemble great invisible rivers transporting vast amounts of water vapor from the land to the ocean. There it is precipitated, later to be evaporated from the sea and returned to the continents by tropical maritime air masses.

Water balance of individual continents.   From the accompanying table, it can be seen that the greatest amounts of precipitation, evaporation, and runoff are in South America, which contains large regions

with tropical humid climates and few areas with dry climates. Runoff is least in Australia, which is predominantly a continent of dry climates.

Distribution of humidity

The actual moisture content of the atmosphere in any locality may be expressed in various ways. As noted earlier, *vapor pressure* is that part of the whole atmospheric pressure which is due to the water vapor. It is expressed in the same units as total air pressure—i.e., either in millibars, or in inches or millimeters of mercury. *Specific humidity* is defined as the weight of water vapor per unit weight of air. It is usually expressed as the number of grams of water vapor contained in 1 kg of air. Specific humidity is nearly proportional to the water vapor pressure, so that the two terms are used interchangeably in the following discussion on distribution of humidity. *Absolute humidity* refers to the weight of water vapor per unit volume of air—as, for example, grains per cubic foot or grams per cubic meter. This concept is less frequently used by meteorologists because, since volume changes as an air mass is elevated or subsides, absolute humidity varies with contraction or expansion of the air.

The capacity of the air for water vapor, expressed in any of the three ways mentioned above, depends upon its temperature. Not only does the capacity increase at higher temperatures, but it increases at an increasing rate (see the following table and Fig. 4.5). Thus a 10°C increase from 0° to 10° advances the capacity only 4.6 g, but an equivalent increase of

Water balance of the continents (In mm per year)

Continent	Precipitation	Evaporation	Runoff
Europe	600	360	240
Asia	610	390	220
North America	670	400	270
South America	1,350	860	490
Africa	670	510	160
Australia	470	410	60

Source: After Budyko.

Maximum water vapor capacity of a cubic meter of air at different temperatures

Temperature			Temperature		
°C	°F	Grams	°C	°F	Grams
−5	23	3.261	20	68	17.300
0	32	4.847	25	77	23.049
5	41	6.797	30	86	30.371
10	50	9.401	35	95	39.599
15	59	12.832	40	104	51.117

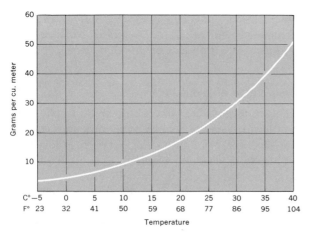

Figure 4.5 Variations in the capacity of air at different temperatures for water vapor. Not only does the capacity increase as the air temperature rises, but equally important, it increases at an accelerating rate.

10°C from 25° to 35° results in an increased capacity of 16.6 g, or three to four times as much. Obviously warm summer air is able to contain much more moisture than cold winter air, and it therefore has greater potentialities for precipitation. When air contains all the water vapor it can hold at a given temperature and pressure, it is said to be *saturated*. It has reached its *dew-point* temperature and also its *saturation vapor pressure*.

Average vertical distribution of water vapor in middle latitudes

Height (km)	Water vapor (vol. in %)
0.0	1.3
0.5	1.16
1.0	1.01
1.5	0.81
2.0	0.69
2.5	0.61
3.0	0.49
3.5	0.41
4.0	0.37
5.0	0.27
6.0	0.15
7.0	0.09
8.0	0.05

Source: From Landsberg.

Because the main source of atmospheric humidity is the earth's land-sea surface, much of the water vapor in the air is concentrated in the lower troposphere, and there is a rapid decrease with height. Half the total water vapor is below 6,500 ft. Above about 6 miles (10 km), the atmosphere contains almost none. (See preceding table.)

The zonal distribution of water vapor in the air is shown in Fig. 4.6, where the scale has been adjusted to indicate the relative size of the latitude belts. The atmosphere's water vapor content, expressed as specific humidity or vapor pressure, is highest near the equator and lowest in high latitudes. This reflects the distribution of air temperature, since temperature largely determines the air's capacity for water vapor. It is temperature also which causes the specific humidity of any latitude to be higher in summer than in winter, so that the values shown in Fig. 4.6 are displaced northward in July and southward in January. But distribution of water vapor is not simply zonal in character. Along the same parallel, a dry continental area is likely to have a lower specific humidity than the oceans. It is these contrasts which cause the minor irregularities in the relatively symmetrical zonal curve of Fig. 4.6. However, the water vapor content

Figure 4.6 Distribution by latitude zones of the water vapor content of the air. Specific humidity is highest in equatorial latitudes and decreases toward the poles. (*After Haurwitz and Austin.*)

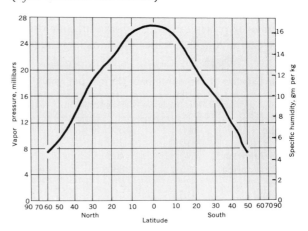

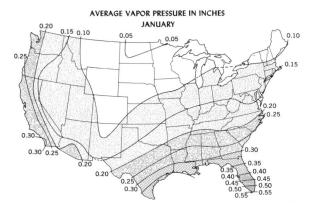

Figure 4.7

of desert air is not necessarily low in an absolute sense; the superheated air of the Sahara in summer may contain more moisture than cold maritime air farther poleward.

For most regions of the earth, the *annual* variation of specific humidity closely parallels that of temperature, being highest in summer and lowest in winter. Over the north central United States, July air contains three to six times as much water vapor as January air (Figs. 4.7 and 4.8). The *diurnal* variation of specific humidity is more complicated, for while over the oceans it follows the temperature march, over land there are two maxima and two minima within the 24-hr period. This is because a secondary minimum occurs at midday. It is the

result of convective turbulence, which transports enough water vapor upward away from the earth's surface to offset the effect of the high afternoon temperatures.

Relative humidity differs from the parameters of humidity described earlier, for it represents the amount of water vapor actually present in the air compared with the maximum that could be contained under conditions of saturation at a given

Figure 4.9   Each cube represents 1 cu ft of air. The top row shows the changing capacity for water vapor of a saturated cubic foot of air under three different temperature conditions. The cubic-foot samples in the bottom row have the same temperatures as those in the top, but they are unsaturated—they do not contain all the water vapor possible at those temperatures. The different amounts of water vapor which they hold at the different temperatures cause them to have different relative humidities, as represented by the variations in shading.

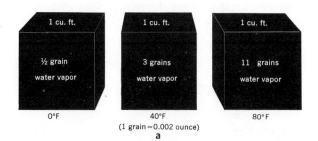

SATURATED CONDITIONS
(RELATIVE HUMIDITIES 100%)

(1 grain = 0.002 ounce)

a

Figure 4.8

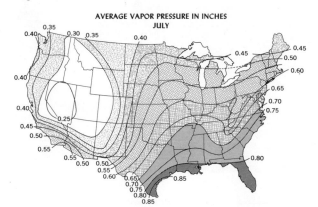

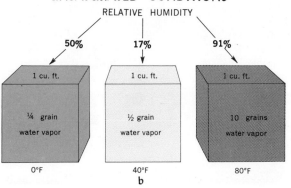

UNSATURATED CONDITIONS
RELATIVE HUMIDITY

b

temperature and pressure. It is always expressed in the form of a ratio, fraction, or percentage. When relative humidity reaches 100 percent, the air is, of course, saturated. For example, if at constant pressure and a given temperature, 1 kg of air can hold 12 g of water vapor, but actually contains only 6 g, it has a relative humidity of 50 percent. Relative humidity can be altered either by changing the amount of water vapor or by varying the capacity of the air, i.e., changing its temperature.

Relative humidity is an important determinant of the amount and rate of evaporation. Consequently it is a critical climatic factor in the rate of moisture and temperature loss by plants and animals, including human beings. Various humidity relationships are illustrated by Fig. 4.9.

Comparison of Figs. 4.10 and 4.6 indicates that the zonal distribution of relative humidity is quite different from that of specific humidity. Relative humidity has its highest maximum at the equator

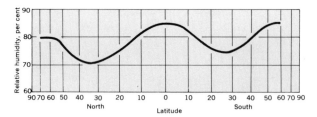

Figure 4.10   Distribution of relative humidity by latitude zones. Note that zonal distribution of relative humidity is quite different from distribution of specific humidity (see Fig. 4.6).

and decreases poleward toward the latitudes of the subtropical anticyclones. It is in these subsiding and diverging air masses that the lowest values occur. From about 30° poleward, relative humidity increases as a result of the decreasing temperature. The belts of highest and lowest relative humidity shift northward in July and southward in January, following the course of the sun (also see Fig. 4.11).

Figure 4.11   World distribution of average relative humidity in July. Two zones of low values approximately coincide with the latitudes of the subtropical highs. Higher values are characteristic of the oceanic parts of the middle-latitude westerlies, the equatorial latitudes, and the monsoon coasts of southern and eastern Asia. (*After J. Száva-Kováts.*)

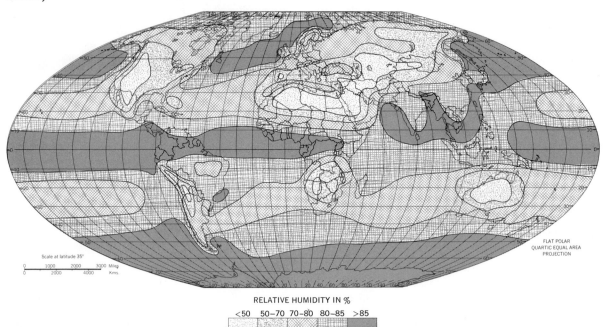

RELATIVE HUMIDITY IN %

<50   50–70   70–80   80–85   >85

The seasonal distribution of relative humidity differs with latitude. In the low latitudes from about 30°N to 30°S, where seasonal temperature variations are small, average relative humidity is higher in the wet summer than in the drier winter. But in higher latitudes the highest humidities coincide with the cold winters, especially over the frigid continents. The diurnal variation in relative humidity is generally the reverse of the march of temperature; relative humidity declines from a maximum in the early morning to a minimum around mid-afternoon.

CONDENSATION

If air that is not saturated is sufficiently cooled, so that its capacity for moisture is reduced, it eventually reaches a temperature at which its relative humidity is 100 percent, even though the amount of water vapor has not been altered. As noted earlier, this critical temperature at which saturation is reached is called the dew point. If air is cooled below the dew point, then the excess of water vapor over what the air can contain at that temperature is given off in the form of minute droplets of water or particles of ice. Thus condensation has taken place.

The only method known whereby significant amounts of water vapor in the atmosphere can be converted into the liquid (condensation) or solid (sublimation) state is to reduce the temperature of the air close to or below the dew point. When the air is cooled, its capacity for water vapor is lowered, and if this capacity is sufficiently reduced, condensation must result. The dew point of any mass of air is closely related to its relative humidity. When the relative humidity is high, the air is close to the saturation point. Only a slight amount of cooling will be required before the dew point is reached and condensation begins. On the other hand, when relative humidity is low, as it usually is over the hot deserts, an astonishingly large amount of cooling is required before the dew point is reached. Condensation therefore depends upon two variables: the amount of cooling, and the relative humidity of the air. If the dew point is not reached until the temperature falls below 32°, some of the condensed water vapor may be in the form of tiny ice crystals (white frost, snow, and some clouds). If condensation occurs above the freezing point, it will be in the liquid state (dew, fog, and cloud). Observations seem to indicate that while solid condensation may occur at any temperature below 32°, actually much cloud condensation down to about 5°F (−15°C) is still in the form of supercooled liquid droplets.

Enough cooling of the atmosphere to cause condensation may occur in several ways. Such processes as radiation and conduction from the overlying air to the cold earth, and the mixing of two unlike air masses of contrasting temperatures and humidities, can lower the temperature of relatively shallow layers of air below condensation level. But the condensation forms (dew, white frost, and fog) resulting from these methods of cooling usually represent small-scale condensation which is confined to air layers close to the earth's surface. Appreciable rainfall probably never develops from such cooling. The one process that can reduce the temperature of deep and extensive masses of air enough to bring about cloud condensation which results in abundant precipitation is the expansion associated with rising air currents—adiabatic cooling.

Condensation apparently is a continuous process, for strongly hygroscopic particles begin to attract water around them even at humidities as low as 75 percent. Haze is the first evidence of such subsaturation condensation. Visibility then decreases, and the landscape takes on a soft blue-gray appearance. As the relative humidity approaches 100 percent, the condensation droplets rapidly grow larger, so that the haze thickens and gradually develops into fog. Thus haze (with the exception of the ordinary dust haze of dry weather) is often the forerunner of fog. Each cloud and fog droplet forms around a condensation nucleus consisting of a water-attracting substance such as common salt, derived from evaporated sea spray, or sulphuric acid, a product of city smoke and motorcar exhausts.

Minor condensation: dew, white frost, rime, fog

Dew, white frost, and rime are relatively unimportant forms of condensation which develop at or near the ground. Dew and white frost result from radiational cooling at night, usually with clear skies and little or no wind. Rime consists of ice crystals formed when droplets of supercooled fog or cloud touch cold objects. Dew is unimportant in humid climates, but in dry and subhumid climates frequent night dews may significantly contribute to the meager water supply for plant life. In subhumid Palestine, the maximum annual dew water amounts to as much as 55 mm (2.17 in.), and most of it occurs in the dry summer. Since plants are able to absorb dew water on their leaves, this moisture source has considerable agricultural usefulness.

Fog, although far less important than cloud and precipitation, is more prominent in human affairs than the other forms of surface condensation. For the most part its consequences are negative. For example, fog at sea makes navigation difficult or hazardous; fogged-in airports are temporarily put out of use; and fog slows highway motor traffic and can cause serious accidents. On the other hand, through its retarding effects on radiational cooling, a night fog may save a region from killing frost in fall or spring.

Unlike thick, rain-producing clouds, which are characteristically formed by the expansional cooling of rising air masses, fog is usually caused by the cooling of humid surface air below the dew point. This cooling can result from radiational processes or from the mixing of warm and cool air masses.

Radiation fogs.   A very common type of land fog, known as *radiation* or *ground-inversion* fog, is produced by radiation cooling of relatively shallow layers of quiet, humid air overlying a chilled land surface. Nighttime conditions which favor radiation fogs are a surface inversion of temperature, a cloudless sky, and slight air movement (but not an absolute calm). The inversion is necessary to prevent the fog from rising. Cloudless skies promote fog because a low cloud cover absorbs a large part of the earth radiation and reradiates it back to the earth's surface, where it is absorbed and consequently acts to reduce the net loss of heat. Slight air movement is a requirement because fogs of the radiation type cannot form when the wind velocity is greater than 6 to 10 miles an hour; at higher speeds, the turbulence associated with the wind carries heat downward and thus prevents formation of an inversion. Some slight turbulence and mixing appear to be necessary, however, in order to develop a fog of moderate density.

Radiation fogs build up by gravitation. For this reason they are most prevalent in valleys and depressions, where air drainage causes the colder, heavier air to collect. Often the slopes and uplands of a region are clear while the adjacent lowlands are fogged in, so that from an elevation one sees many "lakes" of fog occupying the surrounding depressions. On a convex land surface, air drainage reduces the likelihood of temperature inversion and radiation-fog formation.

Radiation ground fog has a distinct diurnal periodicity and is usually short-lived. It grows and deepens from the ground upward as the night progresses, only to burn off and disappear as the temperature inversion is dissipated and the fog droplets are evaporated by the warming air during the following morning. Radiation fog is at its worst in the vicinity of large cities, where the air is rich in hygroscopic particles derived from coal and oil smoke and the exhaust fumes from cars. These abundant condensation nuclei result in tinier fog particles, which make for greater density of the fog, or smog.

Another variety of radiation fog is known as high-inversion fog. In this type not only is the inversion layer much deeper than in the radiation ground fog, but in addition the inversion commonly is located 400 to 2,000 ft above the earth's surface. With warmer, drier air overlying cooler air at the surface, upward movement of air is suppressed. Continued cooling of the surface air for a succession of nights results in a fogging of the surface strata. Turbulence and convective overturning by day usually lift the fog layer above the surface, so that it appears as a deck of low stratus at the inversion base.

Ideal conditions for high-inversion fogs are similar to those for a ground fog except that they are caused by cooling which results not from one night's radiation, but from a cumulative net loss of heat by radiation. Polar maritime air that has become stagnant over a continent provides ideal temperature and moisture conditions for such fogs. Thus western Europe, which is open to direct invasion of polar maritime air, has many high-inversion fogs in winter. The stratus deck formed at the inversion level is an excellent reflector of solar radiation by day and an equally good radiator of earth radiation at night. This tends to intensify the inversion, so that the high fog, which descends to ground level at night, may persist for days or even weeks. Under such conditions airports may be closed for days at a time.

Advection-radiation fogs.   Formation of an advection fog always involves the movement of air, and usually warm moist air, over a cold surface, with a consequent loss of heat by radiation. Here the emphasis is upon *moving* air, rather than quiet air. Favored locations for such fogs are along seacoasts and the shores of large inland bodies of water such as the Great Lakes, where temperature contrasts are great. Advection fogs are most common over oceans and large inland bodies of water in summer, and over lands in winter. This is because the horizontal contrasts in temperature are more marked over continents in winter. Over oceans, on the other hand, temperature contrasts are greater in summer, since the northern waters are kept cool by melting ice. The diurnal periodicity so conspicuous in most types of radiation fogs is not characteristic of the advection fog as a class.

A common variety of advection fog is the sea fog, which forms when warm, moist air moves over colder waters. It is especially prevalent in the vicinity of cool ocean currents. Another form of advection-radiation fog results when a moist tropical air mass is transported poleward over a progressively cooler surface. This type is most frequent in the middle latitudes, where latitudinal temperature contrasts are most marked. Such fogs are common over both sea and land, and since they are related to an extensive air mass, they usually cover large areas. Mist or even drizzle often accompanies them. They occur frequently in the north central United States in winter when a cyclone traveling on a northern track draws tropical air northward over a snow-covered surface.

Frontal fogs.   These fogs are associated with the passage of the boundaries separating unlike air masses. Such boundaries are known as fronts. Frontal fog is formed chiefly through saturation of the cold surface layer of air by rainfall from the overrunning warm air aloft.

Distribution of fog.   For the earth as a whole, fogs are much more common over the ocean than over land. A study of fog distribution over oceans obviously also involves a study of ocean temperatures and the system of ocean currents. In the low latitudes, including the subtropics, cool ocean currents are concentrated along the eastern sides of oceans (west sides of continents), making these regions some of the foggiest of the earth. In the middle latitudes, much ocean fog develops as a result of warm tropical air moving poleward in the warm sectors of cyclonic storms. Such fogs are common in the North Atlantic, especially its eastern parts, and in the North Pacific near the Aleutian Islands and the Gulf of Alaska. In the Newfoundland area of the North Atlantic and in the region northeast of Japan in the North Pacific, summer fogs are prevalent because of the convergence of warm and cool ocean currents (Fig. 4.12).

For the continents, as might be expected, fog is strongly concentrated on the coastal margins. In the United States there is a definite regional pattern of

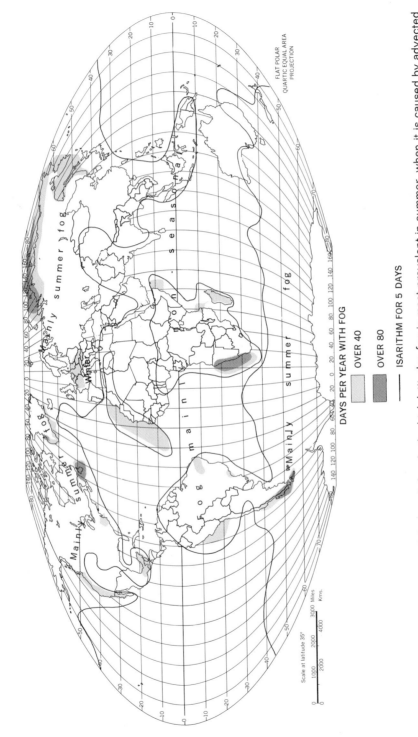

Figure 4.12 World distribution of days with fog. In the high latitudes fog is most prevalent in summer, when it is caused by advected warmer air being cooled over ice surfaces and cold seas. In tropical latitudes fog is less seasonal. It is most frequent in the vicinity of cool currents and their upwelled waters. (*After J. Blüthgen in Allgemeine Klimageographie.*)

DAYS PER YEAR WITH FOG

OVER 40

OVER 80

ISARITHM FOR 5 DAYS

FLAT POLAR
QUARTIC EQUAL AREA
PROJECTION

Scale at latitude 35°

0   1000   2000   3000 Miles
0   2000   4000 Kms.

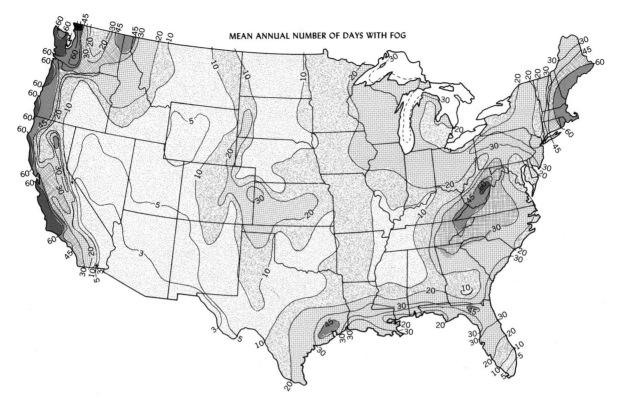

Figure 4.13 Fog frequency in the United States. (*After Arnold Court and Richard D. Gerston in Geog. Rev., vol. 56, October, 1966.*)

fog frequency. Three regions have the most days with heavy fog: the coast and west-facing slopes of the Pacific states; eastern New England; and sections of the Appalachian Highlands (Fig. 4.13). Secondary concentrations are found in parts of the Rocky Mountains, the Gulf Coastal Plain, and restricted coastal sections of the upper Great Lakes. The dry West and southernmost Florida are areas of minimum fog.[2]

Seasonal variations in fog frequency differ for continental and marine locations. Continental stations usually have a maximum of fog in winter and a minimum in summer, while marine stations have the opposite. Radiation ground fogs tend to develop

[2]Arnold Court and Richard Gerston. "Fog Frequency in the United States." *Geog. Rev.*, Vol. 56, pp. 543–550, 1966.

over land areas in winter because of the greater frequency of large anticyclones then. The clear, calm air of the anticyclone and the long winter nights provide ideal conditions for strong radiational cooling and hence for fog formation. Advection fogs also are more frequent over land in winter because moist maritime air masses entering a continent are chilled at the base from moving over the relatively cold land surface. Over oceans, radiation fog is infrequent, and advection fog is at a maximum in summer since the water surface is cooler than the land at that season.

In both continental and marine locations, the low latitudes have less fog than the middle and high latitudes. Moreover, fog in the tropics is not seasonally concentrated, while in the middle and high latitudes it is most prevalent in summer.

Formation of clouds in ascending air currents

Adiabatic temperature changes.   As air is moved upward away from the land-water surface or downward toward it, very important changes occur in the air temperature. Air moving upward away from the surface comes under lower pressures because there is less weight of atmosphere upon it, so it stretches or expands. Air moving downward toward the surface from higher elevations encounters higher pressures and shrinks in volume. Even when there is no addition or withdrawal of heat from surrounding sources, the temperature of the upward- or downward-moving air changes because of its expansion or contraction. This type of temperature change which results from internal processes alone is called adiabatic change.

According to kinetic theory, a gas such as air is composed of molecules which are in a state of constant motion. Individual molecules are continually colliding, and the impact of these collisions produces the pressure of the gas. The pressure therefore depends upon the number and mass of the molecules and the speed at which they are moving, and the speed in turn is determined by temperature. If the temperature is high, the molecular velocity is greater and the number of collisions more frequent. Consequently the gas pressure is greater at high temperatures than at low temperatures, when the volume remains constant.

Some principles indicating the relationship between pressure and volume (hence also density) in gases may be expressed in the form of physical laws as follows:

1. In a gas kept at constant temperature, the volume is inversely proportional to the pressure. If pressure on the gas is doubled, its volume is reduced by one-half.

2. In a gas kept at constant pressure, the volume varies directly with the absolute temperature. Therefore, as the temperature of a gas increases, its volume also increases, and as its temperature is lowered, its volume is decreased.

When a mass of air is lifted, it comes under decreased pressure, so that its volume is increased.

The rising and expanding air does work in making room for its increased volume. This requires an expenditure of energy by the expanding air, with a consequent lowering of its temperature. Stated in a different way, the increased volume of rising air results in fewer molecular collisions. Conversely, when air descends, its volume is decreased by the greater air pressure, molecular collisions increase, and its temperature and density are increased.

The rate of adiabatic heating and cooling of dry or nonsaturated air masses through vertical movement is constant, no matter what the temperature of the air (Fig. 4.14). It is approximately 5.5°F per 1,000-ft change in altitude, or 10°C per 1,000 m. This is known as the dry adiabatic rate, for it applies only to air which is not saturated. The rate of cooling of ascending air, therefore, is considerably more rapid than the normal vertical decrease in temperature (lapse rate), which averages about 3.5°F per 1,000 ft, or 6.5°C per 1,000 m.

These two rates should be clearly differentiated. The lapse rate, which is variable as to time and place, is simply a record of vertical temperature distribution in the atmospheric environment and has nothing to do with rising or subsiding air and associated temperature changes. It can be measured by thermometer readings at fixed levels in the atmosphere. By contrast, the adiabatic rate in nonsaturated air is a fixed rate, and it expresses the temperature changes occurring within unsaturated air which is itself moving upward or downward.

The moist or retarded adiabatic rate.   Since the adiabatic rate of cooling for unsaturated air is the same no matter what the temperature, the three dry adiabats in Fig. 4.14 are all parallel. But as the unsaturated air continues to rise and cool, it is likely to reach a temperature at which condensation begins. This is called the condensation level. In Fig. 4.14 the condensation levels represented for the three rising air masses, each of which has a different temperature, are not the same, because their relative humidities probably are not the same. Thus the cooler air C, which normally would have the highest relative humidity, is shown reaching condensation level first, or at the lowest elevation. The

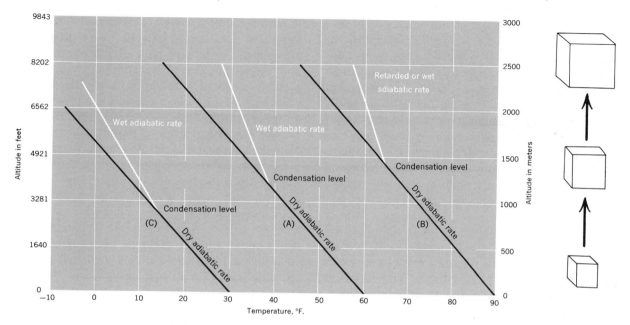

Figure 4.14 Adiabatic cooling in rising air of different temperatures.

warmest air *B*, which normally would be the lowest in relative humidity, is represented as having to rise higher and undergo a greater drop in temperature before the saturation point is reached and condensation begins.

After the rising air reaches the condensation level, where clouds begin to form, the now-saturated air as it continues to rise no longer cools at the previous dry adiabatic rate, but at one which is somewhat slower. This is called the retarded, or moist adiabatic, rate. Above the condensation level, water vapor is being converted into clouds composed of liquid and ice particles, and heat of condensation is released into the atmosphere. It is this added source of energy which slows up the rate of cooling in the rising air. Thus two counteracting processes, one resulting in cooling and the other in heating, are proceeding simultaneously; for while the saturated air continues to cool by expansion, the heat liberated as a result of condensation acts as a brake on the cooling action. Of the two processes, the cooling due to stretching is the primary one, so that the rising saturated air continues to cool but at a slower rate.

It may be observed from Fig. 4.14 that the retarded, or moist adiabatic, rates are not identical for the three air masses, but vary with the temperature of the air. The same amount of cooling will lead to the condensation of a greater amount of moisture when air temperature is high, because the specific humidity of warm air is higher than that of cool air. As a result, the amount of liberated heat of condensation usually is much greater at high temperatures, so that the moist adiabatic rate of cooling is slower in 90° air than in 30° air. In very cold air, the moisture content is so low that the moist adiabatic rate is similar to the dry adiabatic rate. With increasing altitude there is less and less moisture to condense, and the rate of cooling in saturated air approaches the dry adiabatic. In the wet tropics, the rising warm humid air cools more slowly than that farther poleward and hence ascends to greater heights. At high temperatures the moist (or wet) adiabatic rate may be about half the dry adiabatic rate, or about 3° per 1,000 ft (0.5°C per 100 m).

Adiabatic cooling and precipitation. Air which rises voluntarily because of its instability and buoyancy will continue to rise until it reaches an atmospheric environment of its own temperature or density. At this point buoyancy vanishes, and upward movement decelerates. To repeat a statement made earlier, this process of cooling by expansion in rising air is the only one capable of reducing the temperature of extensive and thick masses of air below the dew point. Therefore it is the only one capable of producing condensation on such a large scale that abundant precipitation results. Nearly all the earth's precipitation is the consequence of this expansion and cooling in rising air. The direct outcome of cooling due to ascent is clouds, a form of condensation characteristic of air at altitudes usually well above the earth's surface—just as dew, white frost, rime, and fog are forms characteristic of the surface air. Though all precipitation has its origin in clouds, not all clouds generate precipitation, which is the result of additional processes beyond those causing condensation.

Stable and unstable atmospheric conditions

Since practically all precipitation is caused by the upward movement of air, the conditions that tend to promote or hinder such movement are extremely important. Air is said to be stable, and consequently antagonistic to precipitation, if it is nonbuoyant and resists vertical displacement. Voluntary vertical motions are largely absent in stable air. On the other hand, if displacement results in buoyancy and a tendency for further movement away from the original position, the air is unstable. Under such conditions vertical movement is prevalent. Whether an air mass is stable or unstable can be determined by comparing its lapse rate, a variable, with the dry adiabatic rate, which is fixed. When the dry adiabatic rate (about 5.5°F per 1,000 ft) is exceeded by the lapse rate—as may possibly happen on a hot, sunny afternoon, for example—the surface air is buoyant, unstable, and inclined to rise. But when the lapse rate is lower than the adiabatic rate—as it may be, for example, over a cold middle-latitude continent in winter—the air is nonbuoyant and stable, and it resists vertical displacement. Remember that the lapse rate is the variable one; the dry adiabatic rate is the same at all times and under all conditions.

In Fig. 4.15, the black lines *A* and *X* represent conditions of stability and instability, respectively.

Figure 4.15 Atmospheric stability and instability: When the lapse rate exceeds the adiabatic rate, instability prevails. When the reverse is true, the air is stable.

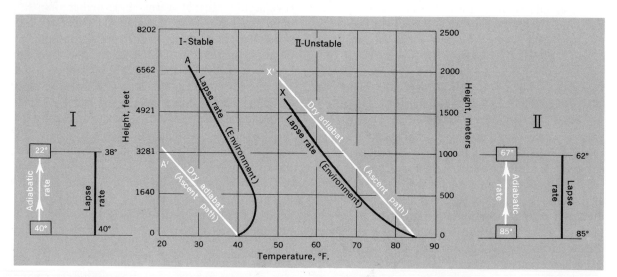

The white lines A' and X' indicate the dry adiabatic rate—which, of course, is the same for unsaturated air, no matter what the temperature. The white lines are therefore parallel.

Instability.   If in Fig. 4.15 a parcel of unsaturated air with a surface temperature of 85° is caused to rise, its rate of cooling will be represented by the white dry adiabat line X'. At any point along this line, the parcel of air will be warmer, and therefore less dense, than the surrounding atmospheric environment, represented by the black-line lapse rate X. The parcel will therefore continue to rise freely because of its buoyancy after an initial upward impetus has been given it.

This condition, where the lapse rate throughout is greater than the dry adiabatic rate of 5.5°F per 1,000 ft, illustrates what is known as absolute instability. Moderately unstable air will not begin to rise voluntarily, but if upward movement is once started, or "triggered," either by convergence or by a highland barrier, the ascent will continue because of the buoyancy forces involved (Fig. 4.16).

Stability.   When an air layer has a lapse rate that is less than the dry adiabatic rate of 5.5° per 1,000 ft, the air is stable and opposed to vertical movement. If in Fig. 4.15 an air parcel with a surface temperature of 40° is forced to ascend, then at any point along dry adiabat A' the parcel will be cooler and hence denser than the surrounding atmospheric environment, whose vertical temperature structure is represented by black line A. Consequently the parcel of air will tend to sink back to its former position. It would never have risen in the first place except under compulsion (Fig. 4.16).

If the lapse rate is less than the *moist* adiabatic rate, which is a variable but on the average is about 2.5°F. per 1,000 ft, the air is said to be absolutely stable. This air resists vertical displacement even when condensation takes place. A common instance of absolute stability is the temperature inversion. An inversion is so stable that it acts as an aerial "lid" to halt ordinary rising currents. Rising columns of smoke or growing clouds are forced to spread

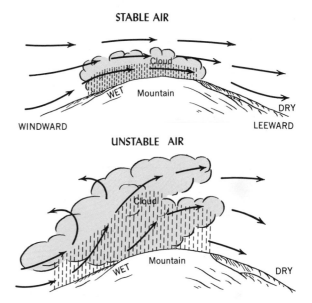

Figure 4.16   When stable or nonbuoyant air is forced upward, as over a terrain obstacle, the resulting clouds are more likely to be of the stratus variety with limited vertical thickness, so that the resulting precipitation may be fairly light. But in unstable or buoyant air, cloud forms are likely to be of the cumulus variety with great vertical thickness, and the resulting showery rainfall will ordinarily be heavier.

out horizontally beneath its base. When nonbuoyant, stable air is forced to ascend—as, for example, over a highland barrier or along a convergence zone or a front—a dense cloud cover without great vertical thickness results. If any rain falls from this cloud cover, it is likely to be light and fairly steady.

Conditional instability.   The information on stability and instability discussed in the previous sections leads to the conclusion that a lapse rate greater than 5.5°F per 1,000 ft represents instability, while a lapse rate of less than about 2.5°F indicates absolute stability. If an air mass has a lapse rate between the dry adiabatic (5.5° per 1,000 ft) and the moist adiabatic (over 2.5° per 1,000 ft) rates of cooling, its instability is conditional upon the saturation of the air at all levels. The lapse rate shown in Fig. 4.17 represents a state of conditional instability.

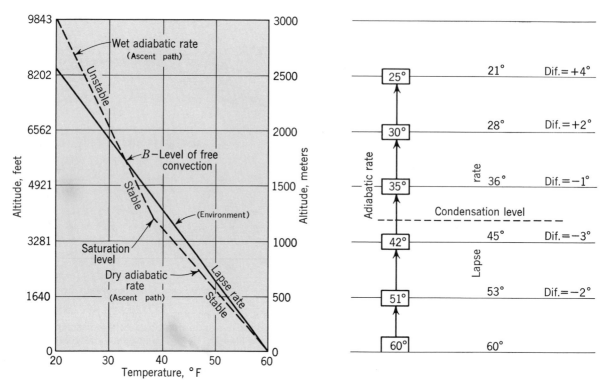

Figure 4.17 Conditional instability: Air that was originally stable is made unstable by forced ascent, during which heat of condensation is added.

While still unsaturated, the rising air parcel follows the dry adiabatic rate of cooling. The lapse rate is less than the dry adiabatic rate, so that during this early phase the rising air is cooler than its environment. It is therefore stable and resists lifting, and any rise is the result of forced ascent. But when the rising air reaches condensation level and latent heat is added, any further cooling takes place at the retarded, or moist adiabatic, rate, which is less than the lapse rate. As a result of the lapse rate being greater than the wet adiabatic rate, from point *B* upward the rising air is warmer than its atmospheric environment. Consequently it is buoyant and unstable, so that it rises freely of its own accord. In other words, conditionally unstable air performs like stable air until it rises somewhat above condensation level, whereupon it behaves like unstable air.

Summary. The concepts of atmospheric stability, instability, and conditional instability are fundamental to an understanding of the origin of precipitation and the relationship between air masses and precipitation. The following points summarize the basic temperature data connected with these concepts (Fig. 4.18).

1. Absolute stability prevails when the temperature lapse rate is less than about 2.5°F per 1,000 ft.

2. Stability prevails in a relatively dry air mass when its lapse rate is less than the dry adiabatic rate (lapse rate between about 2.5° and 5.5° per 1,000 ft).

3. Conditional instability prevails in a relatively moist air mass when its lapse rate lies between the dry and the wet adiabatic rates (lapse rate between about 2.5° and 5.5° per 1,000 ft).

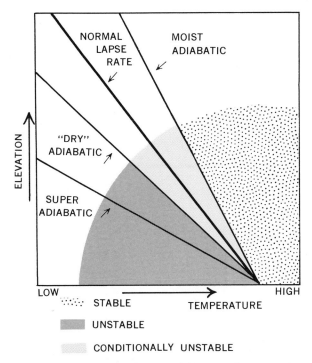

Figure 4.18 Degree of air stability in relation to the rate at which temperature changes with height.

4. Absolute instability prevails in an air mass when its lapse rate is greater than the dry adiabatic rate (lapse rate greater than 5.5° per 1,000 ft).

Vertical displacements of deep and extensive air masses. For the sake of simplicity, the previous discussion dealt with the rising or subsidence of isolated parcels or currents of air. But the lifting or sinking of an entire air mass several thousand feet thick, and covering hundreds of thousands of square miles, is a different story. It involves vertical stretching or contraction of the air mass as a whole, and there are consequent changes in the vertical thickness of the mass which greatly affect condensation processes. In addition to the general cooling of the air mass with ascent and heating with descent, there are differential rates of cooling and heating at different levels within the thick layer.

In the lifting process, accompanied by vertical stretching, the upper layers of a thick air mass expand and stretch more than the lower ones and as a result are cooled more. This differential cooling tends to steepen the lapse rate within the air mass. Conversely, during subsidence the lower strata are less involved in the vertical shrinking than those aloft, so that adiabatic heating is not so marked at the lower levels. The result of this differential heating at the different levels is to decrease the lapse rate of an air mass and make it more stable. These effects upon the lapse rate of lifting and subsidence are illustrated by Fig. 4.19. When the layer of air lying between the 1,000- and 900-mb surfaces is lifted sufficiently so that pressure decreases by 300 mb and its bounding isobaric surfaces are 700 and 600 mb, the vertical thickness of the air mass has increased and stretching has taken place. This is because the density of air is less at higher altitudes, and consequently the isobaric surfaces are farther apart. In the lifting process graphed in Fig. 4.19, the lower part of the layer at *A* will cool to *A'*; the upper part with the temperature *B* will cool to *B'*. The result is that the lapse rate has been steepened

Figure 4.19 Effects upon lapse rates of the lifting and subsidence of a thick air mass.

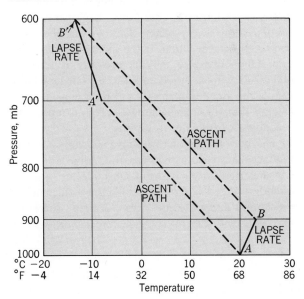

from *AB* to *A'B'*, and the air mass is less stable. If the layer shown at *A'B'* is caused to sink, the reverse process occurs, and the lapse rate is made more stable (*AB*). Actually, the lapse rate *AB* indicates an inversion condition, so that absolute stability prevails. As a general rule, then, lifting and stretching of a thick air mass steepens its lapse rate and therefore increases instability. Conversely, subsidence or sinking, accompanied by horizontal spreading, decreases the lapse rate and so increases stability.

Convective instability.   It frequently happens that the lower layers of an air mass have a much higher relative humidity than those aloft. When lifting takes place in an air mass in which relative humidity decreases rapidly with elevation, the lower strata reach condensation level first. Added heat of condensation then causes them to cool more slowly than the drier upper layers, which continue to follow the dry rather than the wet adiabatic rate of cooling. A greatly steepened lapse rate thus develops within the air mass, and it becomes unstable. Such an air mass is said to be convectively unstable.

In Fig. 4.20, the air mass lying between the 1,000- and 900-mb levels has a lapse rate indicated by line *AB*. Because the air at *A* has a higher relative humidity than that at *B*, after ascent begins it reaches condensation level sooner than *B* and therefore cools at a retarded rate. If the air mass with lapse rate *AB* is lifted so that its pressure is reduced 300 mb, *A* will cool to *A'* and *B* to *B'*. The new lapse rate of the ascending air layer, *A'B'*, is considerably steeper than the old lapse rate *AB* and represents a condition of greater instability.

The importance of convective instability lies in the fact that even air that was originally stable may be converted into a buoyant, unstable air mass by a modest forced ascent—provided the surface layers are humid and the water vapor content decreases markedly with elevation. Such forced vertical dis-

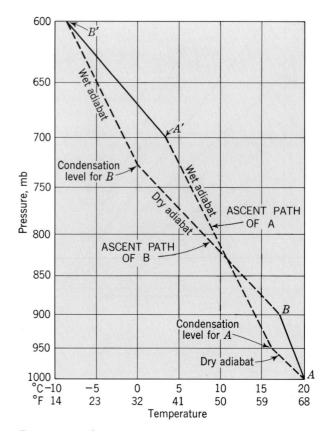

Figure 4.20   Convective instability.

placement of extensive air masses takes place along the windward sides of mountain ranges, and also along frontal surfaces in cyclonic storms where cold and stable air masses act as the obstacle to produce forced ascent. When potentially unstable (convective or conditional) air is lifted, the resulting clouds are usually a mixture of the layer clouds and convective cumulonimbus forms. The cumulonimbus types are associated with the buoyant unstable later stages of the ascent. Rainfall is likely to be heavier than is the case with stable air, as well as more showery and localized.

CLOUD TYPES

Classification of clouds. Since clouds clearly reflect the physical processes taking place in the atmosphere, they are good indicators of weather conditions and so are studied intensively by weather analysts. They are also very important to geographers for a number of reasons. As described in the previous sections, they are the originators of the earth's precipitation. Chapters 1 and 2 discussed them in connection with the earth's heat budget, since clouds greatly influence air temperature by their reflection and scattering of solar radiation and their absorption of earth radiation. In addition, clouds account for a large part of the upward heat transport at heights above the shallow turbulent layer. And of course, cloud forms and illumination are important features of the natural landscape.

The detailed study of cloud types which is useful to the weather forecaster lies outside the province of this book. Below are brief descriptions of the 10 principal types recognized in the international classification of clouds that has been adopted by most countries, including the United States (Fig. 4.21).

Family A. High Clouds. (Mean lower level, 20,000 ft)

1. Cirrus (Ci)—thin featherlike clouds with a fibrous structure and a delicate, silky appearance. When detached and arranged irregularly in the sky, they are harbingers of fair weather. On the other hand, when they are systematically arranged, as in bands, or connected with cirrostratus or altostratus, they usually foretell bad weather. They are always composed of ice crystals.

2. Cirrostratus (Cs)—a thin whitish sheet of cloud covering the whole sky and giving it a milky appearance. These clouds commonly produce a halo around the sun and moon and usually are the sign of approaching storm.

3. Cirrocumulus (Cc)—small white flakes or small globular masses, usually without shadows. They are usually arranged in groups, lines, or ripples resulting from undulation of the cloud sheet. Called a mackerel sky.

Family B. Middle Clouds. (Mean upper level, 20,000 ft; mean lower level, 6,500 ft)

4. Altostratus (As)—a uniform sheet cloud of gray or bluish color, frequently showing a fibrous structure. It is like thick cirrostratus and often merges gradually with it. Through it the sun and moon shine wanly, with a faint gleam. Altostratus commonly is followed by widespread and relatively continuous precipitation.

5. Altocumulus (Ac)—flattened globular masses of cloud, arranged in lines or waves. Differs from cirrocumulus in that it has larger globules, often with shadows.

Family C. Low Clouds. Such clouds commonly cover the whole sky, causing a gray overcast. (Mean upper level, 6,500 ft; mean lower level close to earth's surface)

6. Stratocumulus (Sc)—large globular masses or rolls of soft gray clouds with brighter interstices. The masses are commonly arranged in a regular pattern.

7. Stratus (St)—a low uniform layer of cloud resembling fog, but not resting on the ground.

8. Nimbostratus (Ns)—a dense, shapeless, and often ragged layer of low clouds from which continuous precipitation commonly falls.

Family D. Clouds with Vertical Development. Such clouds usually create a broken sky with clear areas between individual clouds. (Mean upper level, that of cirrus; mean lower level, 1,600 ft)

9. Cumulus (Cu)—a thick, dense cloud with vertical development. The upper surface is dome-shaped with a cauliflower structure, while the base is nearly horizontal. Much cumulus cloud is of the fair-weather type, although towering cumulus may develop into cumulonimbus or thunderheads.

10. Cumulonimbus (Cb)—heavy masses of cloud with great vertical development whose summits rise like mountains, towers, or anvils. They are accompanied by sharp showers, squalls, thunderstorms, and sometimes hail (Fig. 4.22).

Distribution of cloudiness. Cloudiness is expressed in terms of the total area of sky covered by clouds and is given in either tenths or percent. A cloudiness of 0 indicates a cloudless sky; a cloudiness of 10 represents a sky completely overcast, and so does a cloudiness of 100 percent.

The zonal distribution of cloudiness parallels that of rainfall fairly closely. Thus in equatorial latitudes, where horizontal convergence is strong, there is a modest secondary maximum of cloudiness (see the table on page 146 and Fig. 4.23). It is not as strong as the equatorial primary maximum in rainfall,

Figure 4.21 A very generalized vertical arrangement of cloud types. (*From Atmosphere and Weather Charts, published by A. J. Nystrom and Company.*)

Figure 4.22   A cumulonimbus cloud, a type in which convective showers originate. Photographed from an airplane. (*Courtesy of T. Fujita.*)

however, because the tropics have a predominance of convective clouds of the cumulus type. While vertically deep, these are localized clouds which usually cover only a part of the sky, even though

Figure 4.23   Distribution by latitude zones of the annual means of cloudiness, in percent. Note that the greatest cloudiness is not in equatorial latitudes, where rainfall is heaviest, but in the middle and higher latitudes, where stratus clouds associated with cyclonic storms and their fronts reach a maximum development. Cloudiness is least in the latitudes of the subtropical anticyclones and the trade winds. Compare with Fig. 4.27. (*Data from C. E. P. Brooks.*)

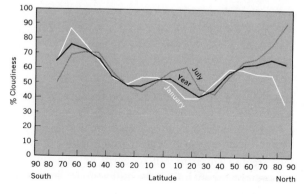

they yield heavy showery precipitation. In the latitudes of the subtropical anticyclones and dry trades (20°–30° N and S), there are minima of cloudiness, as there are of rainfall. The subtropical minima are much more striking on the continents, with their extensive low-latitude deserts, than on the oceans. Poleward from the subtropics, both cloudiness and rainfall increase. But while rainfall shows only secondary maxima in the middle latitudes of both hemispheres (Fig. 4.22), cloudiness reaches its primary maxima there. This is because much of the middle-latitude cloudiness and rainfall is associated with cyclones and fronts. In these weather disturbances, clouds tend to be of the stratus type which covers the whole sky, but a good part of the precipitation that falls is only light or moderate.

The *annual variation* in cloudiness is likely to roughly parallel that of rainfall. Close to the equator, the difference in cloudiness between individual months may be small. In the tropical belts located between 10° and 20°, the cloud maximum coincides with the summer rainfall maximum (see table on page 146). But toward the western sides of continents in the subtropical latitudes (between 30° and 40°),

Average monthly cloudiness (Percent)

Latitude	J	F	M	A	M	J	J	A	S	O	N	D	Yr	Continents	Oceans
90–80°N	36	47	56	46	76	87	90	85	84	64	45	41	63		63
80–70°N	56	56	55	63	70	74	75	76	78	75	63	50	66	63	70
70–60°N	57	56	54	59	65	66	66	68	71	72	67	60	63	62	72
60–50°N	59	57	57	59	64	63	63	62	62	67	67	64	62	60	67
50–40°N	59	57	57	57	56	56	54	49	49	54	58	61	56	50	66
40–30°N	50	49	49	48	48	43	42	39	39	43	45	48	45	40	52
30–20°N	41	41	41	39	41	43	45	44	40	39	38	40	41	34	49
20–10°N	40	39	39	40	47	53	59	58	54	46	44	44	47	40	53
10– 0°N	50	48	49	53	54	56	57	55	53	53	53	53	53	52	53
0–10°S	54	53	53	52	50	50	50	52	53	53	53	55	52	56	50
10–20°S	54	52	52	49	46	45	43	44	43	47	49	54	48	46	49
20–30°S	49	50	50	47	48	48	47	45	48	47	49	50	48	38	53
30–40°S	53	52	54	53	55	56	56	54	55	56	55	52	54	48	57
40–50°S	64	65	63	64	64	67	69	64	66	67	67	66	66	58	67
50–60°S	76	69	71	74	83	82	70	69	68	71	71	75	72	70	72
60–70°S	86	80	80	72	72	66	68	74	75	77	83	80	76		76
70–80°S	64	80	69	69	64	47	49	59	65	74	62	63	64		64
Continents	47	47	47	48	49	50	49	48	48	49	49	50	49		
Oceans	59	58	58	57	58	58	59	58	58	59	58	59	58		

Source: After C. E. P. Brooks.

it is the cool season that has the most cloud and also the most rainfall. Poleward from about 50°, summer is cloudier than winter, especially in the Northern Hemisphere. This contrast between summer and winter strengthens in the higher latitudes as the winter continental anticyclones become increasingly dominant. The interiors of large middle-latitude continents not uncommonly show annual variations of cloud and precipitation that are out of phase with each other—a summer minimum of cloudiness, but a maximum of rainfall. This situation reflects the greater amounts of local convective cloud in the warm season and of stratiform frontal cloud in winter.

The *daily variation* in cloudiness is complicated because of the contrasts in the origin of cumulus and stratiform cloud types. Since surface heating tends to produce cumulus clouds, they often reach a maximum in the early and middle afternoon. Stratiform clouds, on the other hand, are usually created by stable atmospheric conditions, so that their maximum occurs in the early morning hours and their minimum in midafternoon.

PRECIPITATION

Precipitation processes.   It is possible for ascending air which reaches and passes beyond the condensation level to form cloud but still yield no precipitation. Cloudy condensation probably does not take place without at least a slight degree of supersaturation. As relative humidity exceeds 100 percent, condensation first occurs on the largest hygroscopic nuclei. But if it continues, condensation collects on almost innumerable smaller nuclei as well, with the result that the individual cloud droplets are too small to fall to earth as rain. Even a very slight ascent of air is sufficient to keep such minute droplets in suspension. And even if they did succeed in falling below condensation level, probably they would be evaporated before reaching the earth. It is understandable, then, why there can be so many days with cloud on which no precipitation occurs.

Thus rainfall is not the result of a simple continuation of the condensation processes which produce clouds. The essential feature of the precipitation process is the combining of myriads of small cloud droplets into fewer larger drops capable of falling to earth. Two precipitation mechanisms are believed to cause most of this combining that forms raindrops.

The first mechanism is the result of cloud instability brought about by the coexistence of water droplets and ice particles in a cloud at temperatures below 32°F. For an appreciable amount of precipitation to occur in this instance, the ascending air must rise above the freezing level, where some of the liquid droplets will be changed into ice, and where direct sublimation (water vapor to ice) may also take place. The difference in vapor pressure around the liquid droplets and around the ice particles leads to evaporation of the liquid droplets and then to condensation around the ice particles. As water continues to accumulate around an ice nucleus, the drop eventually reaches such a size that it can no longer be held up by the ascending currents. It begins to fall, first within the cloud, and then through the lower air to the land-water surface. Unless it is broken up by the speed of its descent, the drop continues to grow by accretion until it leaves the cloud. The best evidence that this mechanism operates as described here is the sudden release of precipitation when a cumulus cloud grows into a cumulonimbus after it reaches the glaciation, or ice-nuclei, level. Glaciation of the upper part of the cloud changes its form from the typical boiling, cauliflower top to one that is anvil-shaped.

The second mechanism believed to cause precipitation occurs without the presence of ice particles. It involves simply the coalescence of droplets of various sizes as they collide because they are falling at different rates within the cloud. Thus the rate of growth by this process depends upon the size, size distribution, and concentration of the drops.

A good-sized raindrop contains as much water as 5 to 10 million cloud particles and falls 200 times as fast. The maximum size to which a raindrop can grow is about $\frac{1}{5}$ in. (5 mm) in diameter, for at that size its rate of fall is about 18 miles per hr. Above that size and speed, drops begin to break up. In gently ascending air currents condensation is relatively slow. Even small drops can fall to earth through the slowly rising air, so that light rain or drizzle results. On the other hand, the strong upward surges in a violent thunderstorm produce vigorous condensation and are able to support drops of great size. Consequently the first few isolated drops that fall preceding a general downpour make sizable splashes. Raindrops are usually larger than $\frac{1}{50}$ in. in diameter, and in still air they fall faster than 10 ft per sec. Drizzle droplets are less than $\frac{1}{50}$ in. in diameter.

Solid forms of condensation and precipitation. In rising air, solid condensation forms may appear in the atmosphere as a result of either the freezing of liquid condensation, or the direct condensation from the vapor to the solid state. Liquid condensation is possible at temperatures well below freezing. Down to 15°F, clouds composed of supercooled water droplets are much more common than ice clouds, and they have been observed at far lower temperatures.

Snow condensation is in the form of intricately branched, flat hexagonal crystals in an almost infinite variety of patterns. A snowflake is simply an agglomeration of snow crystals matted together because of a film of water on the individual crystals. Since very cold air contains little moisture, heavy snowfalls are usually associated with surface temperatures not much below freezing. Large wet flakes fall when temperatures are comparatively high, while fine hard snow is characteristic of very cold regions and periods. As a rough approximation, it requires about 12 in. of snow to equal 1 in. of rain, although the ratio may vary from 5 to 1 to 50 to

1, depending on the density of the snow. If snow forms at fairly high levels in the atmosphere while surface temperatures are well above freezing, it will melt before reaching the ground and therefore will arrive at the surface as rain. A considerable proportion of the rainfall reaching the ground in middle latitudes originated as snow.

Data on the amount of snowfall and the duration of the snow cover are scanty and fragmentary for much of the earth, so that a satisfactory description of the distribution of snow is difficult to provide. Snow falls occasionally near sea level even in subtropical latitudes, but it does not remain on the ground long. At low elevations a durable snow cover in winter lasting for a month or more is characteristic only of the interior and eastern parts of Eurasia and North America poleward of about 40°. Köppen indicates that a snow cover of appreciable duration is typical of regions where the temperature of the cold month is 27°F (-2.8°C) or below. A permanent snow cover exists at very high altitudes even in the tropics. The height of the snow line declines poleward. Thus at 68°N in Norway, permanent snow is found at an elevation of about 3,500 ft, while on Mount Kilimanjaro in equatorial East Africa at 3°S, the snow line is at about 18,400 ft. Obviously the height of the snow line depends not only on temperature, but also on the amount of snowfall, for if the snowfall is sufficiently heavy a permanent snow cover may exist even where the average summer temperatures are somewhat above freezing (Fig. 4.24).

Sleet is frozen, or partly frozen, rain and appears as particles of clear ice. Glazed frost is actually not a form of precipitation but is the accumulation of a coating of ice on surface objects. Fortunately it is not of common occurrence, for the so-called ice storm that produces glazed frost is one of the most destructive of the cool-season weather types. It occurs when supercooled rain or drizzle strikes surface objects and is immediately converted into ice. The weight of the ice accumulation may become so great that trees are often damaged; telephone, telegraph, and electric wires are broken and their poles snapped off. Rime is composed of white layers of ice crystals deposited on windward edges or points of objects, generally in supercooled fog or mist. Hail, although the heaviest and largest unit form of solid precipitation, is exclusively the product of vigorous convection such as characterizes thunderstorms. These in turn are mainly features of the warm regions and warm seasons.

Precipitation types

Since most precipitation results from expansion and cooling in ascending air, it is important to analyze the conditions under which large masses of air may be caused to rise. Three common types of ascent and the precipitation characteristics associated with each are described below. The three are not mutually exclusive, however, and any particular rainfall is not necessarily the result of only one. In reality, most of the earth's precipitation is caused by the joint action of several types of atmospheric lifting.

Convectional precipitation. This type of precipitation originates with the adiabatic cooling of buoyant air currents whose ascent is truly vertical with respect to the land-water surface. It is not an oblique upgliding of air such as occurs along a hill slope or an atmospheric front. Convection currents, usually of limited diameter, may attain considerable speed. The whole convective system consists of numerous cells of local up currents and down currents, with the rapid vertical chimneys of updraft separated by broader, slower, down currents. When the chimneys of buoyant rising air reach condensation level, they are capped by the dramatic cauliflower-topped cumulus cloud. Such a cloud is the visible top of an invisible ascending convectional current. If the air is deeply humidified and unstable, the released heat of condensation may be so great as to cause some of the cumuli to burgeon into vertically deep cumulonimbus clouds. These are capable of producing heavy showery precipitation, lightning and thunder, and perhaps even hail.

But even in conditionally and convectively unstable air, some initial upward displacement of the surface air is usually required in order to trigger

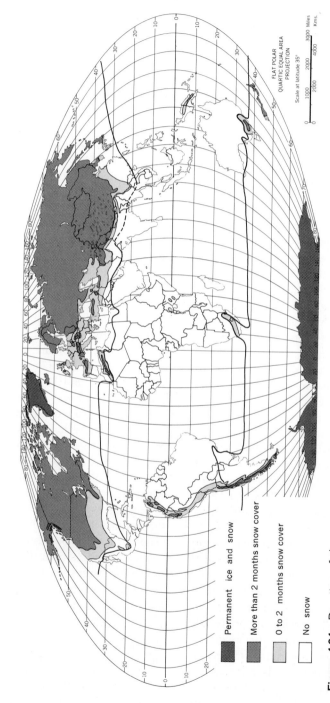

Figure 4.24 Duration of the snow cover and equatorial limits of snowfall. (*After Sekiguchi and Blütgen.*)

Permanent ice and snow

More than 2 months snow cover

0 to 2 months snow cover

No snow

FLAT POLAR
QUARTIC EQUAL AREA
PROJECTION

Scale at latitude 35°

the buoyant convectional currents. This trigger action may be supplied in several ways—by uplift over a terrain obstacle such as a mass of hills; by mechanical turbulence resulting from ground friction or from internal eddies, which are always present in moving air; by lifting along fronts where less dense air glides up over colder denser air; and by directional convergence in the airflow. Some authorities would add that trigger action can be supplied by a warming effect from below, as when land surfaces heat up in the daytime, or when cold air is advected over warm water. This is controversial, however. There can be no doubt that heating from below makes an air mass more buoyant and unstable. But it is uncertain whether surface heating in itself is sufficient to trigger ascent.

In fact, weather specialists appear to be increasingly skeptical of the notion that widespread thermal convection is random in occurrence and stems from surface heating of air. If heating from below were a main trigger for convectional activity, then convective showers should develop every afternoon over land surfaces in the tropics, which they do not. Convection and its associated shower activity appear to occur in organized (not random) regional patterns, with the shower regions related to one or more of the types of trigger action mentioned above. And since many of the shower regions change their shapes and locations from day to day, the evidence suggests that intensified convection is often connected with extensive moving atmospheric disturbances in which convergence in airflow is present. Thus it is clear that much convectional precipitation is complex in origin.

Rainfall associated with convective overturning has certain distinctive characteristics. Since a single convective unit is composed of several columns or cells of rapidly ascending air, each often capped by a cumulus or towering cumulonimbus cloud, cooling is rapid, and the resulting rain commonly falls as a pelting downpour. But since the ascending chimneys of air and their cumulonimbus clouds are not horizonally extensive, the rain is often spotty, local, and brief, for the raincloud quickly drifts by.

We usually speak of convective *showers* (or thundershowers) rather than of convective *rains*.

Much convective shower activity has a seasonal and diurnal periodicity reflecting the influence of solar heating. It tends to follow the sun and occurs at the time of greatest heat and greatest atmospheric instability. In the middle latitudes this means the warmer months, when the daily forecasts refer much more frequently to showers than to general rains. In the low latitudes, also, convective shower activity follows the sun and coincides with the meridional shifting of wind belts. Over the 24-hr period, shower activity generally reaches a maximum in afternoon and early evening, when the surface air is warmest and most unstable.

It has been discovered recently that within the tropics (and probably middle latitudes as well), half the total rainfall falls within 10 percent of the time intervals, where the latter range from 24 hr to $\frac{1}{10}$ hr.[3] Obviously this demonstrates the importance of convective-scale motions in the origin of tropical rainfall. Three scales of circulation or disturbance are recognized: (1) the synoptic or cyclonic scale (time scale, 24 hr), (2) the convective scale (time scale, hours), and (3) individual convective cells (time scale, tenths of hours). The essential point is that synoptic-scale disturbances provide a favorable environment for the development and organization of convective-scale motions, within which the smaller individual convective cells originate; and it is the latter that are responsible for producing most of the precipitation. Thus synoptic-scale disturbances are just as essential for rainfall in the tropics as in the middle latitudes, but precipitation occurs in synoptic systems as a consequence of enhanced convection, characteristically in organized patterns. Some authorities are of the opinion that all tropical rainfall has its immediate origin in convective cells. But towering cumuli require convergence in the

[3]N. E. La Seur. *Proc. 1964 Army Conference on Tropical Meteorology.* Fort Monmouth, N.J. May 14–15, 1964. Pp. 20–25. Michael Garstang. "Atmospheric Scales of Motion and Rainfall Distribution." *Proc. 1966 Army Conference on Tropical Meteorology.* Miami Beach, Fla., May 26–27, 1966. Pp. 24–35.

large-scale flow such as is provided by macro-scale disturbances.

Because it comes frequently in the form of heavy showers, convectional precipitation is less effective for crop growth than steady rain, since much of it runs off in the form of surface drainage instead of entering the soil. This is a menace to plowed fields, where soil removal through slope wash and gullying is likely to be serious. On the other hand, for the middle and higher latitudes convectional precipitation comes at the time when it is most effective: in the warm season of the year when vegetation is active and crops are growing. Moreover, it provides the maximum rainfall with the minimum duration of cloudiness.

Orographic precipitation. This may be defined as precipitation which is caused or intensified by the upthrust effects on air of highlands. Total annual precipitation in highlands is strikingly larger than that normal to the surrounding lowlands, so that highlands stand out on a rainfall map as centers of precipitation. One of the commonest effects of a mountain chain is the upslope motion given to broad and deep currents of air which lie athwart its course. This motion is called forced ascent, because an airstream can only reluctantly be made to surmount a highland barrier.

Since water vapor is largely confined to the lower layers of atmosphere and rapidly decreases upward, heavy orographic rainfall is often the result of such forced ascent of air associated with the blocking effect of terrain obstacles. Examples include the very abundant precipitation along the western, or windward, flanks of the Cascade Mountains in Washington and Oregon; along parts of the mountainous east side of Madagascar, which lies in the trades; and bordering the abrupt west coast of India, where the westerly currents of the summer monsoon meet the escarpment of the Western Ghats practically at right angles. The leeward sides of such mountain barriers, where the air is descending, warming, and becoming more stable, are characteristically drier (Fig. 4.25). This is called the rain

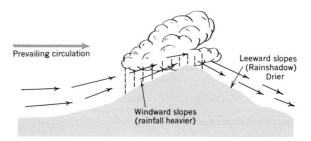

Figure 4.25 Rainfall contrasts on windward and leeward slopes.

shadow. The blocking effect of a mountain upon an airstream is normally felt at some distance out in front of the abrupt change in slope. Heaviest orographic rainfall along a mountain front usually is not far above the point where precipitation begins, although its elevation varies with the season, exposure, and latitude.

It seems likely, though, that a considerable part of the increased precipitation associated with highlands is not solely the result of the forced upslope ascent of prevailing winds, but is complex in origin. Other indirect effects of highlands are also important: (1) their production of strong turbulence of both a mechanical and a convective nature; (2) their obstructing and slowing effect upon the progress of cyclonic storms; (3) orographically conditioned convergence in horizontal currents; and (4) the trigger effect of highlands that gives the initial upthrust to conditionally or convectively unstable air masses. Sometimes only a slight amount of lifting is necessary to bring unstable air masses to the condensation level. After that, added heat of condensation makes them unstable and buoyant and causes them to continue rising, yielding abundant showery convective rainfall. Thus highlands less than 3,000 ft in elevation, although they probably induce no great amount of rain through simple blocking action, may by these indirect means become distinctly wetter than adjacent lowlands.

As might be expected, orographic rain has less seasonal and daily periodicity than that of convectional origin, and it varies from region to region.

Such features as the strength of the winds, the angle at which they meet the mountain barrier, and the degree of contrast between land and water temperatures may determine the season of maximum orographic rainfall. The effects of highlands upon precipitation cannot be judged exclusively by their height, for factors such as temperature and humidity of the upslope air, as well as speed and direction of the wind, are also involved. The cloud types and the rainfall intensity and extensiveness associated with orographic effects are highly variable in character. Upslope movement of stable air favors the development of sheet clouds with accompanying light and long-continued precipitation. But in potentially convective air, cumulus cloud forms and showery rainfall will also be present.

Disturbance precipitation.   Whenever surface airstream convergence occurs, lifting of the opposing air masses results, and atmospheric instability increases. Extensive, mobile atmospheric disturbances of many types are one of the most common situations where widespread convergence and upward movement of air masses occur. Lifting of the air in such a convergent system is often rather general and slow, so that widespread instability is attained gradually and pervasively. In warm latitudes and warm seasons, areas of organized convection and associated shower activity commonly develop within the convergent air of these extensive atmospheric disturbances. Obviously such rainfall is a combination perturbation-convection type.

In contrast with the tropics, middle-latitude air masses differ in temperature and density, so that much lifting of air within extensive atmospheric disturbances results from a slow and gradual upglide of warm and less dense air over colder air (Fig. 4.26). Such lines or zones of convergence between contrasting air masses are known as fronts. Frontal precipitation is very common in the middle latitudes, and since fronts are a characteristic feature of cyclonic vortex disturbances, most frontal rainfall is also cyclonic in origin.

Frontal and cyclonic clouds and precipitation

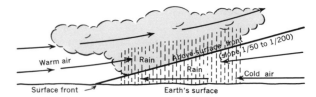

Figure 4.26   The origin of precipitation along an atmospheric front. Here the warmer and less dense air is forced upward over a mildly inclined wedge of cooler and denser air, with the consequence that the rising air is cooled by expansion.

have no fixed character. Because a considerable amount of the upward movement of air is a slow upglide, cooling may be slow and the resulting clouds may be the stratus type providing a gray overcast and steady long-continued precipitation. But in conditionally and convectively unstable air, a slight amount of uplift along a front may provide the trigger effect necessary to start vigorous convective overturning, especially in the warmer months. Cumulus clouds and showery precipitation result.

Distribution of precipitation

Salient features.   Among the data concerning precipitation which are of special importance in describing regional climates are the average annual amount or depth, the average number of rain-days, the seasonal distribution or annual march of precipitation, its dependability or reliability, and its probability.

It is estimated that if the *total average precipitation for the year* were spread evenly over the earth's surface, it would form a layer about 39 in. deep. In reality, the annual precipitation is spread very unevenly, for there are great desert areas that receive less than 5 in., while a few spots receive over 400 in. (33 ft). Since continental air is lower in humidity than oceanic air, the average yearly precipitation over land is estimated to be only about 60 percent of that over the oceans.

The number of rain-days, or days on which 0.01 in. or more of precipitation falls, can be compared with the total annual or monthly amount to give some indication of the rate of fall or *intensity* of rain in a region. This measure also provides a general impression of the dampness or dryness of a climate (see the following table). For example, Marquette, Michigan, receives about 32.5 in. annually which, since there are 165 rain-days, is 0.20 in. per rain-day. By contrast, Pensacola, Florida, has nearly 58 in. of precipitation, which falls in 114 rain-days, making 0.51 in. per rain-day. In the United States the number of rain-days is especially large along the North Pacific Coast and in the Great Lakes–New England region. It is particularly small in the dry Southwest. Figures on the *probability* of rain-days for an area are valuable for such people as farmers and resort owners. Probability may be computed by dividing the number of rainy days in a month or year by the total number of days.

The *seasonal distribution* of precipitation is as important as the total amount. From a geographer's standpoint, the fact that Los Angeles, California, annually receives about 15 in. of precipitation must be evaluated in the light of the fact that 60 percent of this falls in the three winter months and almost none in the three summer months. Seasonal distribution of precipitation becomes especially significant in latitudes which have a dormant season for plant growth imposed by low temperatures, i.e., the winter season. In the tropics, where frost is practically unknown except at higher elevations, rainfall

is effective for plant growth no matter at what time of year it falls. In the middle latitudes, however, only the part of the annual precipitation which falls during the freeze-free season may be effective. In the more severe climates, a strong concentration of rainfall in the warmer months when plants can use it is desirable.

The *dependability,* or *reliability,* of the annual or seasonal precipitation is an expression of its variability (Fig. 4.35). Variability may be defined as the deviation from the mean computed from 35 years or more of observations. In humid climates the annual variability is usually not greater than 50 percent on either side of the mean; i.e., the driest year may have about 50 percent of the normal value, while the wettest year may have 150 percent. In dry climates these values vary between about 30 and 250 percent. Thus it is a general rule that variability increases as the annual amount of rainfall decreases: an inverse ratio prevails.

Precipitation variability must be taken into consideration by the farmer, for he must expect that there will be years when the precipitation is less than average. In semiarid and subhumid climates, where crop raising ordinarily depends on a small margin of safety in rainfall, variability is crucial. Moreover, the agriculturist in such regions must bear in mind that negative deviations from the mean are more frequent than positive ones. This means that a greater number of dry years are com-

Rain-day information for Philadelphia, Pennsylvania, and Cherrapunji, India

	J	F	M	A	M	J	J	A	S	O	N	D	Yr
Precipitation, mm
Philadelphia	86	88	88	85	85	88	112	118	87	75	77	84	1,078
Cherrapunji	17	59	268	809	1,495	2,632	2,729	2,069	1,255	426	58	7	11,824
Rain-days
Philadelphia	12	11	12	11	11	10	11	11	8	8	9	10	124
Cherrapunji	1.4	3.3	8.4	17.3	21.0	24.8	27.2	26.0	18.7	8.4	1.4	0.6	158.5
Mm per rain-day
Philadelphia	7.1	8.0	7.4	7.7	7.7	8.8	10.2	10.8	10.9	9.5	8.6	8.4	8.7
Cherrapunji	12.1	17.9	31.9	46.7	70.7	100.0	101.0	79.5	67.0	50.6	41.4	11.6	69.5

Source: After Landsberg.

pensated for by a few excessively wet ones. Variability of seasonal and monthly rainfall amounts is characteristically greater than that of annual values.

Average annual amounts. Even a glance at the rear endpaper shows that precipitation is distributed very unevenly over the earth's surface and that the patterns of distribution are complex. No single explanation is widely applicable. Basically, the amount of precipitation which falls in a region depends on two groups of factors—those which influence the vertical motions of the atmosphere, and those relating to the nature of the air itself, particularly whether it is dry or moist, warm or cold, stable or unstable. The first of these, which emphasizes lifting and subsidence, is closely related to the distribution of (*a*) the principal zones of horizontal convergence and divergence, (*b*) atmospheric disturbances, and (*c*) highland barriers. The second group of factors, the nature of the air, chiefly depends on its place of origin and its subsequent trajectory, both of which determine whether it is maritime or continental, tropical or high-latitude, in its characteristics.

Some of these controls of precipitation—for example, certain belts of horizontal convergence and divergence—are fairly zonal in arrangement. Others—such as the distribution of land and water, and the arrangement of highlands and lowlands—are nonzonal and hence operate to produce a modification of the zonal patterns. Certainly the complicated character of annual rainfall distribution on the individual continents (see rear endpaper) makes generalizations difficult to perceive. In order to simplify the situation, some of the more significant facts of world distribution are portrayed by a graph of a meridional profile of average annual precipitation in Fig. 4.27, and by a diagram of the main rainfall type-regions on a hypothetical continent in Fig. 4.28. Other features of distribution unique to individual continents will be discussed in Part Two, which deals with climatic types and regions.

Figure 4.27 Distribution of average annual precipitation by latitude zones. (*Data from Meinardus, Brooks, and Hunt.*)

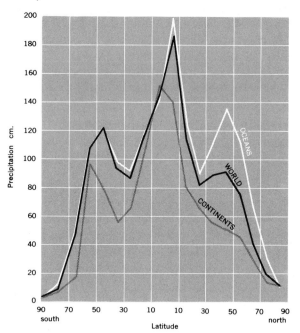

Zonal features of annual averages. A meridional profile of average annual rainfall amounts, showing the means for different parallels around the entire earth, suggests some of the most fundamental facts of rainfall distribution (Fig. 4.27). Of course, much is omitted in such a profile, for it indicates none of the variations in amount of rainfall in an east-west direction, i.e., along a parallel.

As seen in Fig. 4.27, there is a strong primary maximum of precipitation (±1,600 mm) in a belt about 10 to 20° wide in the vicinity of the equator. In this belt, directional convergence (ITC) of surface winds results in large-scale lifting of warm, humid, unstable air. Numerous weak, rain-generating disturbances develop along the ITC. (The main exception within the equatorial belt of heavy rainfall is the narrow dry zone along the equator in the eastern central Pacific Ocean, as will be discussed in Chapter 8. Recent satellite photographs confirm this dramatic climatic anomaly.) From the equator, annual amounts of precipitation decline poleward in each hemisphere. Belts of lower rainfall, providing secondary minima, exist at latitudes about 20 to 35° N and S. Here the average rainfall is only 800 to 900 mm. These are the latitudes of the great subtropical anticyclones, with their diverging wind systems and associated vertical subsidence. Since some of the earth's great deserts are located here, it may seem odd that the average zonal rainfall is not lower than Fig. 4.27 indicates. It must be kept in mind, however, that the western sides of the subtropical highs are rainier, and these heavier rainfalls tend to raise the average for the subtropical latitudes as a whole.

Poleward from the subtropics, rainfall again increases. Secondary maxima with an average annual precipitation of 1,000 to 1,200 mm are indicated for latitudes about 40 to 55° N and S. These are the zones of the middle-latitude convergences (polar front), with which the belts of maximum cyclonic activity are associated. The average zonal rainfall of these belts is lower in the Northern Hemisphere than in the Southern, because of the extensive interior middle-latitude deserts in Eurasia and North America. (If rainfall over land alone is considered, there is no middle-latitude maximum in the Northern Hemisphere.) Poleward from about latitude 50 to 55° in both hemispheres precipitation declines sharply, so that primary zonal minima of less than 150 mm are reached in the cold regions of the high latitudes beyond about the 75° parallel.

Although the total annual precipitation is about the same in the Northern and Southern Hemispheres, some contrasts in zonal distribution may be observed. The most conspicuous difference is that latitudes 0 to 10° N have more precipitation than latitudes 0 to 10° S. This reflects the fact that the intertropical convergence is positioned north of the equator over more extensive longitudes and for a greater part of the year than it is to the south. Another difference is that the secondary maximum of precipitation at about latitudes 40 to 60° is considerably higher in the Southern Hemisphere than in the Northern, because of the larger proportion of ocean in these latitudes in the Southern Hemisphere.

Another principal factor affecting zonal rainfall

amounts is the distribution of oceans and continents. For the earth as a whole, the average amount of precipitation is much higher over the oceans than over the continents: about 44 in. for the oceans, compared with 26 in. for the land. Taking into consideration the fact that 71 percent of the earth's surface is water and only 29 percent land, it has been computed that 19 percent of the earth's total annual precipitation by weight falls on land surfaces and 81 percent on water. It is in the Northern Hemisphere, where there is a more equitable distribution of land and water areas, that the zonal patterns of rainfall over oceans and continents are most in contrast. Continental rainfall, for example, shows no secondary middle-latitude maximum north of the equator, while this zonal maximum is very definite over the oceans (Fig. 4.27).

Precipitation regions on a hypothetical continent. Figure 4.28 is a highly generalized representation of rainfall distribution, in both its zonal and its nonzonal aspects, on a hypothetical continent which is broad in the Northern Hemisphere and tapers southward. In equatorial latitudes in the vicinity of the intertropical convergence zone, wet climates with abundant rainfall extend across the entire breadth of the continent. Explanations for this equatorial rain belt have been provided in the preceding section on zonal distribution of rainfall. The wet belt is broader along the eastern side of the continent, for this is the windward side, which is paralleled by warm ocean currents and lies adjacent to the more unstable western margins of the subtropical anticyclones. Here inversions are high or absent. The wet belt is narrower along the west side, which is dominated by the stable eastern sides of subtropical anticyclones and by cold currents with upwelling. Wet regions are also found along the elevated windward western margins in middle latitudes, both north and south of the equator. These wet areas are far smaller than the equatorial rain belt.

Figure 4.28 shows that areas characterized by below-average precipitation, including both dry and subhumid types, are to be found in continuous

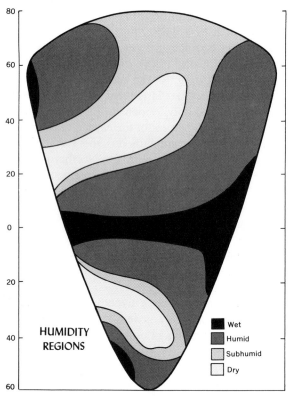

Figure 4.28 Very generalized patterns of distribution for four levels of average annual rainfall, as they might appear on a hypothetical continent.

bands in both hemispheres, reaching from low into middle latitudes. In the low latitudes the dry regions are asymmetrically developed, for they are concentrated in the western and central parts of a large land mass. Such locations are under the influence of the stable eastern ends of subtropical anticyclones, where subsidence and horizontal divergence prevail. Cool ocean currents and upwelling along the subtropical and tropical west coasts may intensify the aridity. In the middle latitudes the dry-subhumid areas are located toward the center of the continent, since this region is farthest removed from the oceanic sources of moisture. Among the actual continents in the Southern Hemisphere (see rear endpaper), only South America extends far into the middle latitudes, and there the land mass is so narrow that dry climates reach to the east coast.

As diagrammed in Fig. 4.28, humid conditions, reflecting moderate rainfall, prevail in two locations in each hemisphere. Both are situated between the wet and the dry-subhumid types. One occupies a zonal belt lying just poleward of the equatorial wet region and then continues into the middle latitudes along the eastern side of the continent, so that the whole has roughly the form of a boomerang. The low-latitude part of this boomerang-shaped area lies in the region of alternating ITC and trades. The part which continues into the middle latitudes is affected both by frequent cyclonic storms and by tendencies toward monsoon systems. The other location of humid conditions, or moderate rainfall, is in middle latitudes along the western side of the continent, inland from the wetter oceanic margins. Here cyclonic activity accounts for much of the precipitation.

These patterns of rainfall distribution represented on the hypothetical continent in Fig. 4.28 should be compared with rainfall patterns of actual continents on the rear endpaper and with the index-of-humidity map, Fig. 4.29.

Seasonal rainfall variations. One factor which greatly influences the seasonal march of precipitation, especially in the tropics and subtropics, is the north-south migration of the wind belts. As explained in Chapter 3, these, together with their associated zones of convergence and divergence, follow the course of the sun. In the low latitudes, evidences of a zonal pattern of seasonal rainfall distribution are moderately conspicuous. By contrast, the middle latitudes show more evidence of a nonzonal pattern, imposed in considerable degree by the effects of continents and oceans. Oceanic areas not only have a greater total depth of annual precipitation than the lands do, but their precipitation is also less seasonal in its fall. Large continents in middle latitudes are likely to have more of their annual precipitation concentrated in the warmer months, both because of their cold winters and warm summers, which greatly influence the stability and moisture content of seasonal air masses, and because of their tendency to develop a monsoonal wind system.

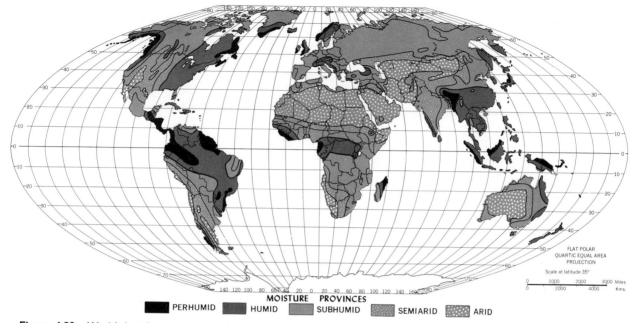

MOISTURE PROVINCES

■ PERHUMID   ▨ HUMID   ▨ SUBHUMID   ▨ SEMIARID   ▨ ARID

Figure 4.29   World distribution of the index of humidity. The five humidity-index subdivisions are defined as follows:

A Perhumid $\geqq$ 16.2
B Humid   8.7–16.1
C Subhumid   4.7–8.6
D Semiarid   2.5–4.6
E Arid $<$ 2.5

The humidity index EP (effective precipitation) is calculated after the following formula: $EP = P/1.025\ T + X$, where P is annual rainfall in inches, T is the annual temperature in °F, and X is the correction supplied by a nomogram. (*After Harry P. Bailey, Geog. Ann., Vol. 40, pp. 196–215, 1958. For the formula, see his Fig. 2, p. 200.*)

Zonal variations in seasonal rainfall.   Figure 4.30 is a diagram of the principal zones of convergence and divergence associated with the entire atmospheric circulation. Parts A and B indicate the maximum latitudinal displacement in the extreme seasons. Part C provides a general description of the zonal belts of seasonal rainfall that would result from a regular north-south migration of the zones of convergence and divergence. This diagram does not show the important seasonal variations in precipitation which are the result of nonzonal factors: longitudinal differences in the atmospheric circulation pattern, and terrestrial influences such as land-water distribution and the arrangement of highlands. Consequently Fig. 4.30 should be studied together with Fig. 4.31, which illustrates the general arrange-

ment of the types of seasonal rainfall concentration that might appear on a hypothetical composite continent. Here zonal and nonzonal features are combined (see also Fig. 4.32).

Tropics.   In the very low latitudes near the equator, where the trades converge and weak disturbances are numerous, rainfall is abundant and falls throughout most of the year, so that there is either no dry season or only a very short one (Fig. 4.30, zone 1). Farther away from the equator, from about 5 or 10° out to 15 or 20°, rainfall becomes more seasonal as it decreases in amount. There is a marked dry season in low sun, or winter, while summer, or the high-sun period, is wet (zone 2). This feature of high-sun rainfall and low-sun drought is related to the north-south shifting of the

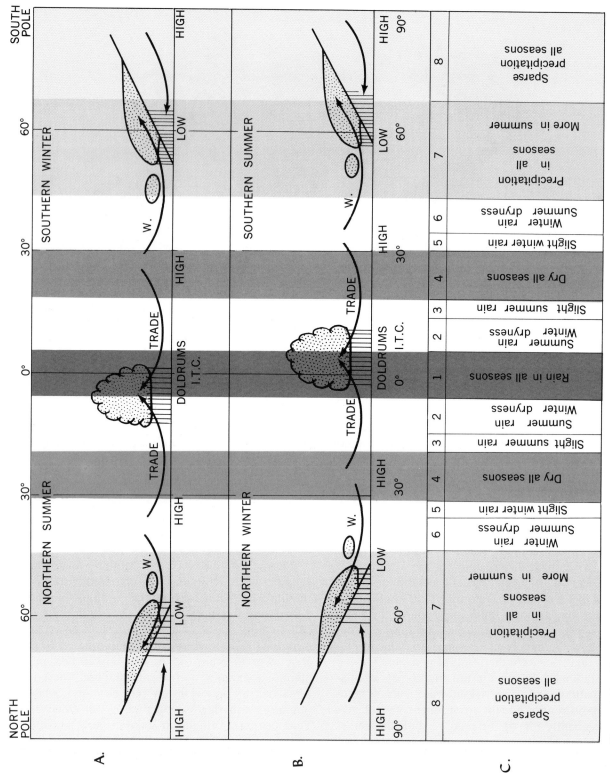

Figure 4.30 Main zones of atmospheric horizontal convergence and ascent, and of divergence and subsidence, together with associated seasonal characteristics of precipitation; *A*, during the Northern Hemisphere summer; *B*, during the Northern Hemisphere winter; *C*, zones of seasonal precipitation. But remember that many nonzonal features of precipitation distribution cannot be adequately represented on this type of schematic latitudinal cross section. (*From Petterssen, Introduction to Meteorology, McGraw-Hill Book Company, New York.*)

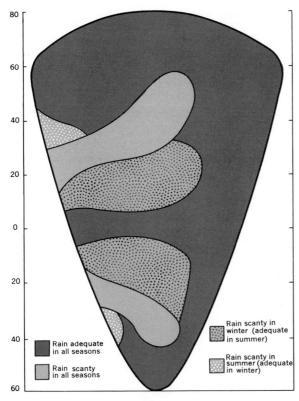

Figure 4.31 Very generalized patterns of seasonal rainfall concentration as they might appear on a hypothetical continent.

wind belts and zones of convergence following the course of the sun. Such latitudes are influenced by the ITC and its disturbances at the time of high sun, and by the subtropical anticyclone with its subsidence and divergence in the low-sun period. And as Fig. 4.31 shows, the tropical winter-drought regime does not ordinarily extend to the east side of the continent, where the subtropical anticyclone is weaker and prevailing winds are onshore.

Within the area (shown in Fig. 4.30) where rainfall is both meager in annual total and scanty in all seasons, (zone 4) seasonal variation is not of

Figure 4.32 Illustrating seasonal rainfall regimes in the low latitudes by means of a series of stations in Africa north of the equator. The stations are arranged according to latitude, with Nouvelle Anvers closest to the equator and Rabat farthest away from it.

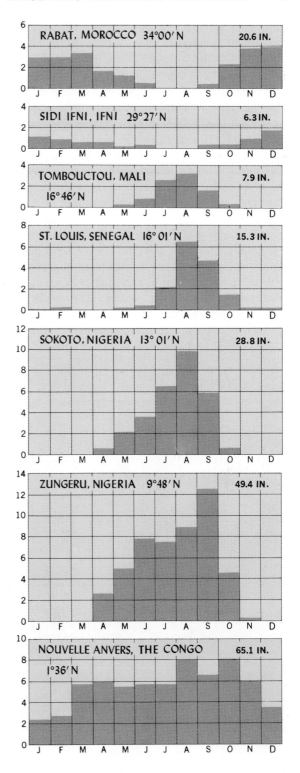

great consequence. In tropical dry climates, the equatorward margins have least rain in winter (zone 3). On the poleward western margins, summer is the driest season (zone 5). Where the dry type extends well poleward into the middle-latitude heart of the hypothetical continent, winter is usually the season of scantiest rainfall (Fig. 4.31).

Subtropics (about 30 to 40° N and S). Located along the subtropical *western* side of the hypothetical continent, in an intermediate position between the middle-latitude convergence zone on its poleward side and the subsident western end of a subtropical anticyclone on its equatorial side, is a restricted area where rain is scanty in summer and moderately abundant in winter (Fig. 4.31). The wet winters coincide with the equatorward migration of middle-latitude westerlies and their cyclonic storms following the sun (Fig. 4.33a). The aridity of summer is associated with the poleward retreat of the storm belt and the reestablishment of anticy-

clonic control with its strong upper-air subsidence (Fig. 4.30, zone 6).

The eastern sides of the continents in these same subtropical latitudes (about 30 to 40°), however, are very different in their precipitation characteristics (Fig. 4.33b). Normally, they have more rainfall than the western side, and in addition the winter maximum and summer drought have entirely disappeared. Here it is the western margin of a subtropical anticyclone with its unstable air masses which is in control, so that rain falls throughout the year, and summers, with their tendency to onshore monsoon winds, are likely to have more precipitation than winters.

Latitudes poleward of about 40°. On the hypothetical continent, most of the middle and higher latitudes are represented as having adequate rain in all seasons (Fig. 4.31). This is the latitude of the cyclonic westerlies, whose disturbances bring precipitation both in winter and in summer. But this

Figure 4.33 Subtropical rainfall regimes: *left*, west side of continent; *right*, east side of continent.

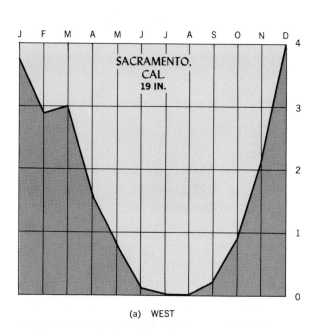

(a) WEST

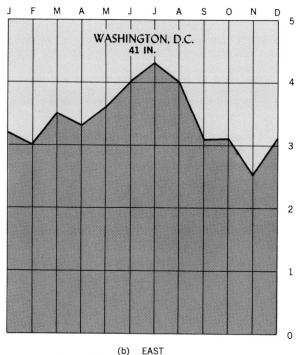

(b) EAST

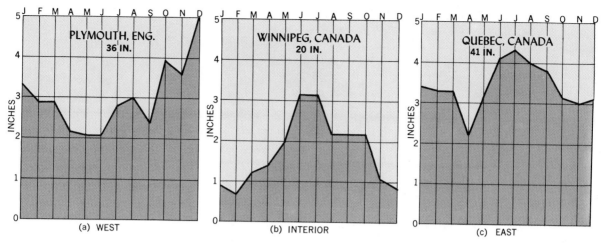

Figure 4.34 Middle-latitude rainfall regimes.

does not mean that seasonal contrasts are entirely absent.

On the *western* or windward side of the continent, it is not uncommon for the most marine locations to show a slight winter maximum (Fig. 4.34*a*). This is probably a widespread feature of oceanic climates in middle latitudes. It is associated with the intensified cyclonic activity in the cooler seasons and the greater temperature contrasts between sea and land at those times.

The *interior* of a large continent in middle latitudes, where total annual rainfall is on the scanty side, is likely to show varying degrees of summer maximum, even though winter is by no means dry (Fig. 4.34*b*). The summer maximum is a distinctive feature of land-controlled climates. This fact is associated with the low winter air temperatures which reduce the possible water vapor capacity, the greater prevalence of anticyclones in winter, and the tendency toward monsoonal outflows of continental air in the winter season. In summer, on the other hand, surface heating causes greater convective activity, the warm air has a higher moisture capacity, strong anticyclones are less pronounced, and there is a tendency toward a monsoonal indraft of warm, humid air from the oceans.

The humid *eastern* side of a large continent in middle latitudes usually shows varying degrees of summer concentration of precipitation. In eastern Asia, where the monsoon circulation is particularly strong, the summer maximum is more pronounced than in eastern Anglo-America, where winter cyclones are more active (Fig. 4.34*c*). Dry Patagonia, in the rain shadow of the Andes, is the exception to humid eastern sides of middle-latitude continents.

In the very high latitudes, the maximum precipitation probably occurs during the season of least cold, since at that time there is more moisture in the air, and cyclonic influence can penetrate deeper (Fig. 4.30, zone 8).

Annual precipitation variability.   Annual precipitation is most variable in dry and subhumid regions. As described earlier, there is usually an inverse ratio between rainfall amount and rainfall variability. In Fig. 4.35 two types of regions stand out: the deserts and steppes of the tropics and middle latitudes, and the cold regions of high latitudes. The highest variability is in the deserts. But the economic consequences of high variability in the earth's sparsely populated dry regions and its cold regions may not be nearly so serious as a smaller variability in more populous humid areas, where agriculture is a major industry.

Small rainfall variability is characteristic of two types of humid regions—those of the wet tropics,

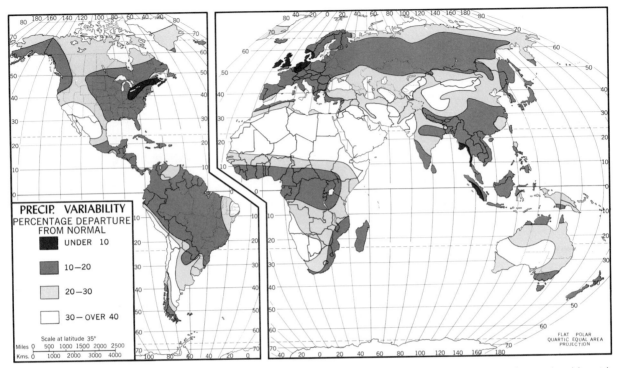

Figure 4.35 Variability or undependability of annual precipitation is usually at a maximum in dry and subhumid climates. (*After Biel, Van Royen, and others.*)

and those of the cyclonic middle latitudes. The least variability is found in maritime western Europe and an east-west belt along the United States–Canadian border in eastern Anglo-America.

Diurnal variation in precipitation. This is a relatively complicated phenomenon, although two gen-

eral types may be recognized; a continental type and a marine one. Over large land masses, more of the rainfall is likely to occur in the warmer hours of the day, when solar heating of the land surface is at a maximum and a steepened lapse rate prevails in the lower air, causing it to be more buoyant. Oceans tend to have a maximum of precipitation

Diurnal variation in precipitation (In thousandths of total amount)

Place	Hours					
	12 P.M.–4 A.M.	4 A.M.–8 A.M.	8 A.M.–12 M.	12 M.–4 P.M.	4 P.M.–8 P.M.	8 P.M.–12 P.M.
Valentia, Ireland, 52°N	181	183	160	149	162	163
Pavlovsk, U.S.S.R., 60°N	148	156	144	201	185	157
San José, Costa Rica, 10°N	13	6	44	342	485	84

Source: After Köppen.

during the night or early morning, when the maritime air is most unstable (Fig. 2.18). The largest midday maximum over land in middle latitudes occurs during the summer season. The surface temperature of oceans, unlike those of continents in summer, changes very little from day to night, and as a result the surface air varies little in temperature. At some distance above the ocean surface, where the air temperature is largely controlled by radiation, the

atmosphere is warmer by day and cooler by night. Consequently the lapse rate is steepest at night and convective activity is greater. These generalizations are illustrated in the table on page 162, which shows the diurnal variation in the amount of precipitation for Valentia, Ireland, a marine station in middle latitudes; Pavlovsk, U.S.S.R., a continental station in middle latitudes; and San José Costa Rica, located in the tropics.

SELECTED REFERENCES FOR FURTHER STUDY OF TOPICS IN CHAPTER FOUR

1. **Atmospheric humidity and condensation.** Riehl, *Tropical Meteorology*, pp. 144–155, 156–192; Riehl, *Introduction to the Atmosphere*, pp. 67–89; Blair and Fite, pp. 36–59, 100–110; Blüthgen, pp. 108–157; Critchfield, pp. 37–46; Hare, pp. 17–25; Gentilli, pp. 80–86, 112–114; Petterssen, pp. 61–69; Haurwitz and Austin, pp. 83–96; *Compendium of Meteorology*, pp. 165–175, 192–197, 199–205, 1179–1189; Willett and Sanders, pp. 82–101.

2. **Precipitation: origin and kinds.** *Compendium of Meteorology*, pp. 175–179; Blair and Fite, pp. 110–120; Blüthgen, pp. 158–186; Riehl, *Tropical Meteorology*, pp. 105–124; Riehl, *Introduction to the Atmosphere*, pp. 91–101; Critchfield, pp. 46–69; Hare, pp. 25–37; Petterssen, pp. 40–60; Willett and Sanders, pp. 101–117.

3. **Precipitation distribution.** Haurwitz and Austin, pp. 64–83; Blüthgen, pp. 186–210; Riehl, *Introduction to the Atmosphere*, pp. 218–244; H. Flohn and J. Huttary, "Zur Kenntnis der Struktur der Niederschlags Verteilung," *Zeitschrift für Meteorol.*, Vol. 6, pp. 304–309, 1952; Gentilli, pp. 87–108; Fritz Möller, "Vierteljahrskarten des Niederschlags für die ganze Erde," *Petermanns Geograph. Mitt.*, Vol. 95, pp. 1–7, 1951.

4. **General references on atmospheric moisture and precipitation.** Harry P. Bailey, "A Simple Moisture Index Based upon a Primary Law of Evaporation,"

Geog. Ann., Vol. 40, pp. 196–215, 1958; C. E. P. Brooks and T. M. Hunt, "The Zonal Distribution of Rainfall over the Earth," *Mem. Roy. Meteorol. Soc. (Great Britain)*, no. 3, pp. 139–158, 1930; M. I. Budyko, *Evaporation Under Natural Conditions* (translated from Russian), Office of Technical Services, Washington, D.C., 1963; J. J. George, "Fog," In *Compendium of Meteorology*, pp. 1179–1189, 1951; International Cloud Atlas (2 vols.), World Meteorological Organization, Geneva, 1956; B. J. Mason, *Clouds, Rain and Rainmaking.* Cambridge University Press, London, 1962; J. E. McDonald, "The Evaporation-Precipitation Fallacy," *Weather*, Vol. 17, pp. 168–177, 216, 1962; W. Meinardus, "Niederschlagsverteilung auf der Erde," *Meteorol. Zeitschrift*, Vol. 51, pp. 345–350, 1934; H. L. Penman, "Weather, Plant, and Soil Factors in Hydrology," *Weather*, Vol. 16, pp. 207–219, 1961; H. L. Penman, "Estimating Evaporation," *Trans. Amer. Geophysical Union*, Vol. 37, pp. 43–50, 1956; R.C. Sutcliffe, "Water Balance and the General Circulation of the Atmosphere," *Quart. Jour. Roy. Meteorol. Soc.*, Vol. 82, no. 354, pp. 385–395, 1956; *Symposium on Monsoons of the World*, Indian Meteorological Department, New Delhi, pp. 177–234, 1960; C. W. Thornthwaite and J. R. Mather, "The Water Balance," *Publications in Climatology*, Vol. 8, no. 1, Drexel Institute of Technology, Centerton, N. J., 1955; R. C. Ward, "Measuring Potential Evapotranspiration," *Geography*, Vol. 48, pp. 49–55, 1963.

CHAPTER FIVE

AIR MASSES AND FRONTS

An air mass is an immense body of air that moves over the earth's land-sea surface as a recognizable entity, with temperature and humidity characteristics which are relatively uniform in a horizontal direction at different levels. Its horizontal homogeneity is not complete, of course, for since an air mass may extend through 20 to 30° of latitude and cover up to several million square miles, it is bound to have some internal differences. But these are always small compared with the much more rapid rates of temperature change across the air-mass boundaries. Air masses show up on weather maps as broad-scale atmospheric currents of polar or tropical origin. As earlier chapters have said, these currents are the vast units of exchange by which the general circulation effects a transfer of energy between tropical and polar latitudes. Weather is likely to be relatively uniform throughout an area covered by the same air mass. It changes rapidly along the air-mass margins.

The air-mass concept is mainly a refinement and amplification of the general circulation and planetary winds described in Chapter 3, for both trades and westerlies have unlike properties at different places and times. The concept of air masses is also related to the discussion of atmospheric disturbances in Chapter 6, since a majority of disturbances in middle latitudes appear to originate along the boundary zones separating unlike air masses. The prevailing weather is determined to a large degree by the nature of the air masses moving over a region. This is especially true in the zones of the disturbed westerlies, where the succession of weather events is intimately related to the passage of cyclones and anticyclones and the sequence of air masses accompanying them. Although the air-mass concept may not provide a very sophisticated tool for the climatologist, it continues to be useful and revealing. It has even served as the basis for a number of climatic classifications.

Weather characteristics of an air mass depend on two basic properties: vertical temperature distribution, and moisture content and its vertical distribution. The first property indicates not only the warmness or coldness of an air mass, as reflected in its surface temperatures, but also its stability, which in turn influences the extent of vertical movement. The moisture content partly determines the presence or absence of condensation forms, while the vertical stratification of moisture also influences vertical movement.

Source regions.   Air masses originate under conditions which promote the development of vast bodies of horizontally uniform air. An ideal air-mass source region has two essential characteristics: an extensive physically homogeneous surface, and a sufficient stagnation of atmospheric circulation so that the air has time to acquire the temperature and moisture properties of the underlying surface. A region with highly uneven terrain, or one composed of both land and water surfaces, is not satisfactory. Nor is one in which there is strong convergent airflow, for in most parts of the earth outside the inner tropics, converging surface winds usually advect unlike temperatures toward the zone of convergence, resulting in steep temperature gradients. It is anticyclonic circulations, with their light winds and calms, and their prevailing subsidence and horizontal divergence, that favor development of the horizontal temperature uniformity required in an air

mass. Examples of good source regions are the snow-covered arctic plains of North America and Eurasia in winter, the extensive subtropical and tropical oceans, and the superheated Sahara in summer.

The depth to which an air mass is affected by its source region depends upon both the length of time it remains in that region, and the kind and degree of temperature differential between the air and the underlying surface. When the air is initially colder than the surface of the source region, it is heated from below. This produces convective ascending currents which carry heat and moisture aloft, so that the air mass is modified up to considerable heights. But when the air is initially warmer than the underlying surface, it is cooled from below and made nonbuoyant. In such stable air convective currents do not develop, and the modification of the air is much slower and shallower. Since the properties of source regions vary from season to season, so also do the temperature and moisture properties of air masses originating in them.

Once having formed over its source region, an air mass does not long remain stationary. The general circulation of the atmosphere, which acts to compensate for the energy imbalance between low and high latitudes, ensures that an air mass will soon move outward from its source region. When this happens, the air itself is slowly modified by its new environment, while it in turn modifies the weather of the region it invades. An extensive and horizontally homogeneous body of air is conservative in character: it can travel for long distances over the earth's surface and still retain many of the properties acquired at its source. Because of its great size and the slowness with which it is modified, the movement of an air mass can be traced from day to day, and any changes which are being induced by its new environment can be measured. Usually such changes are small and gradual compared with those which occur along the boundary zones that separate unlike air masses.

In addition to being influenced by the surfaces over which it moves, and the different amounts of radiation and moisture which it receives, an air mass is also greatly modified by the lifting and sub-sidence of thick air layers within it.

Surfaces of discontinuity and fronts. When air masses with different temperature and moisture properties, and therefore with density contrasts, are brought together, they do not mix freely with each other. They tend to remain separate, with more or less distinct sloping boundary surfaces, called surfaces of discontinuity or fronts, between them (Fig. 5.1). Where such sloping surfaces of discontinuity in the free atmosphere intersect the earth's land-sea surface, surface fronts are formed. It is these intersections which are charted on a surface weather map. Since there is an upward movement of air along fronts, many of them are accompanied by an organized system of clouds and precipitation extending over immense horizontal distances. Fronts are active weather breeders, and their location in the atmosphere and the nature of the contrasting air masses on either side of them are of great significance in weather analysis.

Two conditions are essential for the formation of fronts, and unless both are operating simultaneously, frontogenesis cannot occur. (1) The two adjacent air masses must have contrasting temperatures, so that one is colder and denser than the other. (2) The atmospheric circulation must have a convergent flow strong enough to transport the air masses toward each other at the front line. But even when

these two conditions are present, fronts still would not develop in the absence of Coriolis force. If the earth suddenly stopped rotating, the cold denser air would settle quietly under the warm air, like water under oil in a tank. Then the surface of discontinuity separating the two would be horizontal, not sloping, and there would be no surface front.

The decay and disappearance of fronts, called frontolysis, is caused whenever (1) the temperature contrast between the air masses weakens and eventually disappears or (2) the wind system no longer brings about convergence of the air masses.

Surfaces of discontinuity, or fronts, are not mathematically abrupt features, but rather transition zones of appreciable width, where changes in the weather elements are much more rapid than within the air masses themselves. The width of the frontal transition zone of pronounced temperature gradient separating cold polar from warm tropical air is most commonly between 50 and 150 miles. Marked shifts in temperature, and also in humidity and wind direction, usually can be observed upon crossing an airmass boundary zone. The front represents a temperature discontinuity most of all, for it is chiefly through temperature contrasts that differences in air-mass densities are maintained.

The discontinuity surface separating unlike air masses rarely remains very long in a stationary position. Usually one air mass begins to advance into the domain of the other, so that the front itself begins to move. Two principal types of fronts are recognized: (1) a zone where there is an active upglide of lighter warm air over cold dense air; and (2) a zone where there is a forced ascent of warm air over cold because the cold air is actively underrunning and lifting the warm. These are the well-known warm front and cold front (Fig. 5.2). Chapter 6 on atmospheric disturbances will discuss their characteristics and the types of weather each brings.

It is the middle latitudes, lying as they do between cold polar and warm tropical source regions, that have the greatest air-mass contrasts. Consequently these latitudes also have the best-developed fronts and the most pronounced weather changes associated with them. In fact, the concepts of air masses and

Figure 5.1 Three-dimensional representation of an atmospheric front.

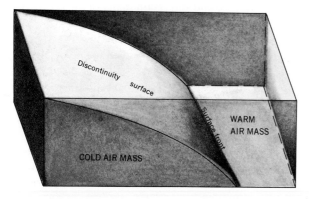

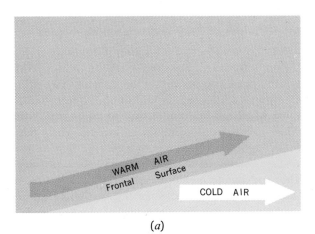

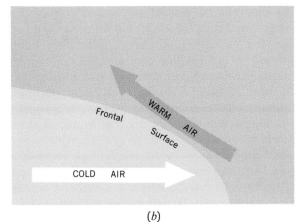

(a)   (b)

Figure 5.2 Arrangement of air masses along a warm front (a) and a cold front (b).

fronts developed out of weather analysis in the middle latitudes and are not very useful when applied to the tropics. Even though a zone of strong wind convergence in the tropics may be accompanied by a wind shift and an organized system of clouds and precipitation, usually the converging air masses do not have significant temperature and density contrasts. Thus a front does not exist. As a result, there is no upgliding of the less dense air along an air-mass surface of discontinuity, but instead sporadic convectional ascent of a vertical nature.

CLASSIFICATION OF AIR MASSES

The attributes of an air mass which determine its characteristic weather features are chiefly acquired from its source region. To a lesser degree, an air mass is also affected by other influences which continue to modify it as it moves away from its source region. Any useful classification of air masses must express their weather characteristics and consequently must be based upon the nature of their source regions and the subsequent modifications which they undergo.

Polar and tropical. The primary air-mass source regions are polar (P) and tropical (T). It is mainly in high latitudes and low latitudes that extensive homogeneous surfaces characterized by light air movement can be found. Since the middle latitudes are the scene of intense interaction between air masses arriving from polar and tropical latitudes, they lack the uniformity of conditions essential to a source region. Nearly all air masses in middle latitudes can be traced back to polar or tropical source regions.

Some authorities differentiate cold air from high latitudes into arctic (A) and polar (P) subgroups, the former originating in the polar areas and the latter over the cold continents of Eurasia and North America. Similarly, warm air from low latitudes is sometimes separated into equatorial (E) and tropical (T), the equatorial air, which originates in the inner tropics, being more unstable and more deeply humidified. Although these refinements have some usefulness, they are not included in the simplified scheme of air-mass classification presented here.

Maritime and continental. Polar and tropical air masses may each be subdivided into *maritime* (*m*) and *continental* (*c*) subgroups, depending upon whether they originated over oceans or over continents. The *m* or *c* symbol indicates whether the air mass left the source region with moist maritime characteristics, so that condensation is likely, or whether it originated as a dry continental air mass in which condensation will be meager. When a dry continental air mass moves out over an ocean surface, moisture evaporates into the dry air and changes it relatively rapidly into a humid maritime air mass. The transformation from maritime to continental air is ordinarily much slower, since there is not necessarily a prompt and large-scale removal of moisture by precipitation from a maritime air mass that moves inland over a continent. This classification, then, includes four principal types of source regions and four corresponding principal air masses—*cP, mP, cT,* and *mT.*

Modifications of polar and tropical air masses

Modifications of an air mass after it leaves its source region may partly determine the nature of the weather which occurs within the air mass. Two principal types of air-mass modification are recognized: those which are thermodynamic in origin and those which arise from mechanical causes. They may occur separately or in combination.

Thermodynamic modifications. These result from the transfer of heat between the bottom of an air mass and the surface over which it moves. The degree of modification depends upon the original character of the air mass, the nature of the underlying surface, the trajectory or path of the air mass as it leaves its source, and the number of days it has traveled in arriving at the observation point.

If the air mass moves over a surface that is warmer than its own ground temperature, the con-

Basic classification of air masses

Major group	Subgroup	Source region	Properties at source
Polar (including arctic)	Polar continental (*cP*)	Arctic Basin; northern Eurasia and northern North America; Antarctica	Cold, dry, very stable
	Polar maritime (*mP*)	Oceans poleward of 40 or 50°	Cool moist, unstable
Tropical (including equatorial)	Tropical continental (*cT*)	Low-latitude deserts, especially Sahara and Australian Deserts	Hot, very dry, stable
	Tropical maritime (*mT*)	Oceans of tropics and subtropics	Warm, moist; greater instability toward west side of ocean

sequent warming of its basal layers will result in an increased lapse rate and added buoyancy and instability. This condition favors ascent of the heated lower air and thus creates the possibility of condensation and precipitation. The maximum vertical change in temperature occurs in the lowest layers. Conversely, when an air mass moves over a surface that is colder than its own ground temperature, the basal air is chilled, and a surface inversion develops which increases the stability of the mass. Such a condition is opposed to the ascent of air and consequently also to the formation of clouds and precipitation. Naturally, polar air masses will most frequently undergo the first type of modification, tropical air masses the second.

These modifications of the source properties of an air mass are represented by the letters *W* (warm) or *K* (*kalt,* or cold). *W* indicates that the air mass is warmer than the underlying surface and so is in the process of being chilled at the base and made stable or nonbuoyant. *K* means that the air is colder than the underlying surface and is therefore being warmed at the base and made unstable and buoyant. Note that these letters do not specify whether the air mass itself is either hot or cold; they only indicate its *relative* temperature with respect to the surface beneath.

A *K* air mass typically has these traits: turbulence up to a height well above the friction layer; an unstable lapse rate; cumuliform clouds; generally good visibility except in rain; showers, thunderstorms, and possibly snow flurries. By contrast, a *W* air mass is more often characterized by these features: little turbulence above the friction layer; a stable lapse rate; poor visibility at lower levels, where dust and smoke are concentrated; stratiform clouds; fog and precipitation, if there is any, in the form of drizzle.

The height to which the surface thermal influence extends up into the air mass depends on whether the air has a *W* or *K* character. Since surface cooling tends to produce stability, vertical turbulence and convective transport are restricted. Thus the *W* character, or chilling of the lower air, is confined

to a fairly shallow layer—usually the first few thousand feet. But the *K* characteristic, signifying an air mass warmed at the surface, is usually carried to a much greater height by convective turbulence. In an air mass which is moderately unstable aloft, there is almost no limit to which the surface convection and its attendant transport of water vapor can extend into the troposphere.

Further thermodynamic modification of an air mass results from the addition of moisture to it by evaporation—either from a moist underlying surface (particularly a water surface), or from raindrops which fall through the air mass out of an overrunning air current. Turbulence and vertical convection act to distribute the moisture through a moderately thick layer of the atmosphere. Thus in addition to a direct increment of sensible heat, evaporation is another way of adding energy to the lower atmosphere and increasing its instability, for the evaporated moisture represents actual or potential energy in the form of latent heat.

Mechanical modifications. Besides thermal modifications of air masses, others of a mechanical nature can affect stability. One of these is turbulence resulting from the frictional effects of the earth's surface. The effect of turbulence is to mix the atmosphere vertically, so that heat and moisture are carried upward from the surface and a layer of atmosphere several thousand feet deep may be modified.

Much more important modifications of an air mass result from large-scale horizontal convergences and divergences that may occur near, as well as above, the earth's land-sea surface. Such circulations, which produce slow upward and downward movements of thick and extensive masses of atmosphere, thereby affect air-mass stratification and possibly cloud and precipitation. An air mass that is part of an anticyclonic circulation undergoes above-surface subsidence and so becomes more stable. Likewise, air which descends on the leeward side of a mountain barrier is made more stable by the subsidence. On the other hand, an air mass which is involved in a cyclonic circulation, where convergence, lifting, and stretching are dominant, is made more unstable. Lifting over highlands has a similar effect (Fig. 4.19).

Also, an air mass moving toward higher latitudes, where the earth's circumference shrinks, tends to undergo horizontal convergence, while increasing divergence characterizes equatorward-moving air. In addition, other things being equal, the relative warmth of a tropical current moving poleward promotes upward movement, while the relative coldness of a polar current moving equatorward favors subsidence. As a consequence the development of stable characteristics is favored in polar air masses reaching low latitudes, and unstable characteristics tend to appear in tropical air attaining higher latitudes.

The mechanical changes described here mainly affect those parts of an air mass above the surface, or friction, layer. They are likely to be independent of the other modifications resulting from surface heating or cooling which were treated in the previous section. In order to represent air-mass qualities associated with stability and instability conditions aloft, a fourth pair of letters may be added to the air-mass classification system: s = stable air aloft; u = unstable air aloft. Under most conditions the s symbol is associated with anticyclonic circulation and the u symbol with cyclonic circulation. Note that the s or u characteristic of an air mass is a feature unrelated to the surface qualities of its source region, or in many instances, to its subsequent trajectory. Instead, this feature is associated with the local or broad-scale circulation pattern in which the air mass originates or subsequently migrates through.

Figure 5.3   Air masses and fronts in January. (*After Willett.*)

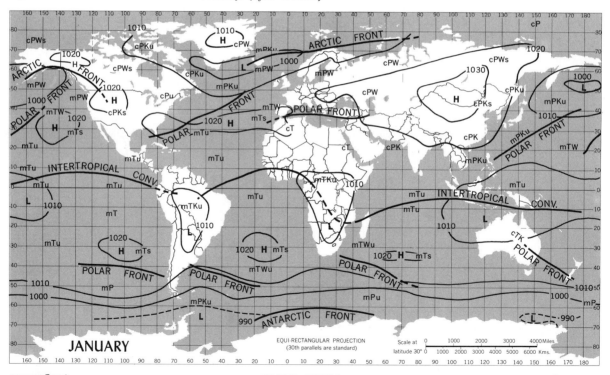

- - - - - Front
—mb— Isobar

AIR MASS SYMBOLS: T = Tropical   P = Polar   m = Maritime   c = Continental

W = Warmer than,   K = Colder than,   underlying surface.   s = Stable aloft   u = Unstable aloft

WORLD PATTERN OF FRONTS AND AIR MASSES

Figures 5.3 and 5.4 offer a generalized picture of the distribution of the principal air masses and the average locations of the major fronts and zones of convergence at the two extreme seasons. (Compare them with Figs. 3.30 and 3.31 showing resultant surface winds, and review the discussion of lines of convergence under the general topic of surface winds in Chapter 3.) At best, of course, these seasonal charts of air masses are a bird's-eye view; only the most conspicuous elements are represented. In addition, they can show only the mean positions of frontal zones, which in reality are constantly shifting. At any particular time, both frontal zones and air masses may occupy positions well removed from those given on the charts. The air-mass symbols and their positioning on the maps represent mean conditions only.

Generalized mean frontal zones

Chapter 3's discussion of the planetary winds said that because of the nature of the general circulation there are bound to be certain extended zones of convergence in wind direction (Fig. 5.5; also Fig. 3.25). And when the converging circulations have distinctly unlike temperatures, and hence densities, a more or less permanent, though fluctuating, frontal zone must develop. For the world's weather, the

Figure 5.4 Air masses and fronts in July. (*After Willett.*)

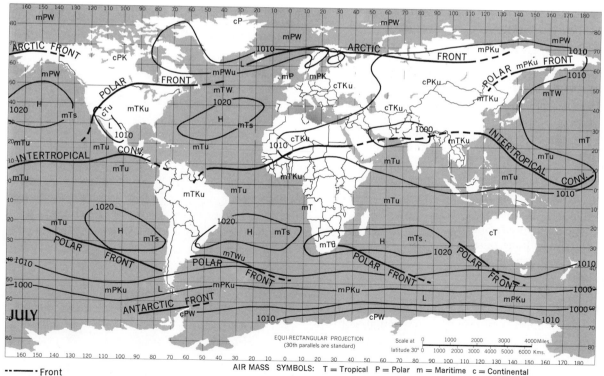

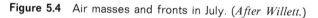

- - - - Front
—mb— Isobar

AIR MASS SYMBOLS: T = Tropical P = Polar m = Maritime c = Continental

W = Warmer than, K = Colder than, underlying surface. s = Stable aloft u = Unstable aloft

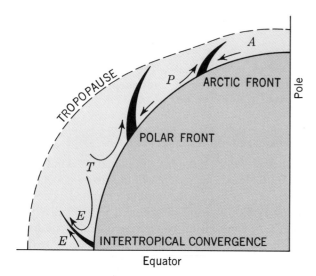

Figure 5.5 Diagrammatic cross section of the atmosphere showing principal frontal zones and air masses in the Northern Hemisphere. (*From Sverre Petterssen, Introduction to Meteorology, McGraw-Hill Book Company, New York.*)

most important of these extended frontal zones of wind and air-mass convergence is the polar front of middle latitudes, which marks the zone of conflict between polar and tropical air masses, either continental or maritime (Fig. 5.6). As would be expected, temperature gradients are steep across the polar front, and it is along certain parts of this convergence zone that numerous cyclonic storms develop. The mean latitudinal position of the polar front shifts periodically following the seasonal course of the sun—poleward in summer and equatorward in winter. But since it also has wide short-time fluctuations of a nonperiodic character, any mean position on the maps is only an average of a feature that is extremely fickle in location. Along certain parts of the polar front, cold air surges equatorward; in other parts, warm air pushes poleward. The total effect is one of alternating tongues of cold and warm air, giving the front a sinuous or wavelike shape. Usually it is not continuous around the earth. At times the polar front and its polar air deeply invade the tropics.

Along the high-latitude Arctic and Antarctic fronts, the converging circulations are both of polar (or arctic) origin. In some sectors polar continental and polar maritime air masses are in conflict; in others it is two continental or two maritime air masses. Normally the temperature contrasts are weaker than along the polar front, and cyclogenesis is also.

As mentioned earlier, zones of wind convergence within the tropics, like the ITC, are rarely density fronts with upgliding air, since the opposing air masses are too similar in temperature. In certain localities the polar front may occasionally break through into the poleward margins of the tropics—as it does, for example, in Caribbean America, northeastern Southeast Asia, and perhaps tropical West Africa—but only rarely do these invasions reach equatorial latitudes.

General properties of the main air masses

cP **air.** Polar continental air originates over the higher latitudes of Eurasia and North America,

Figure 5.6 Hemispheric view of the polar front.

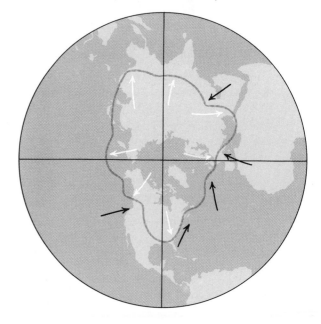

Greenland, and the Arctic Basin in the Northern Hemisphere, and over Antarctica in the Southern Hemisphere.

In *winter* the snow-covered source regions grow bitterly cold because of prolonged earth radiation and because they are remote from warm oceans. The circulation is anticyclonic and divergent, with light air movement. Hence winter *cP* air, a consequence of both intense surface cooling and outpourings of polar air aloft, consists of a layer of extremely cold, dry air reaching at times up to 3,000 m (10,000 ft). There is a persistent strong temperature inversion, with the lowest temperatures at or near the surface. Weather is predominantly clear and frigid; clouds and precipitation are meager. The air-mass symbol at the heart of the source region is *cPWs*, indicating that the air is warmer (*W*) than the surface and therefore is being chilled by it, while anticyclonic subsidence produces above-surface stability (*s*).

As winter *cP* surges outward from its source region, it carries its cold and dryness into the areas which it invades. Simultaneously the *cP* is itself modified—a process that is likely to be slow as long as the air's route is over a cold snow surface. But as soon as the *cP* moves out over extensive warmer surfaces of open water, it is rapidly heated, humidified, and made more unstable. Then it is on its way to being converted into *mP* air.

If the outward-moving *cP* encounters highlands, the resulting turbulence tends to destroy the surface inversion and so causes the low-level temperatures to be less cold. Along the seaward eastern margins of Asia and North America, the modified polar air may warrant the air-mass symbol *cPK*—or even *cPKu*, if the circulation has become cyclonic (Fig. 5.3). Conversion from *cP* to *mP* goes on with greatest speed over the western parts of middle-latitude oceans lying leeward of the great Northern Hemisphere continents, where both heat and moisture are rapidly acquired.

In *summer* the principal northern source regions of *cP* are free of snow, the land surfaces are much warmer, and anticyclonic circulation is less prevalent. Consequently *cP* in July at its continental sources has moderate surface temperatures and so is less stable than in winter. Bright, pleasant weather is characteristic. *cPK*, and even *cPKu*, are the typical air-mass symbols in the vicinity of the source regions. But air from other sources frequently invades the summer *cP* source regions, so that fronts develop, with associated cloud and precipitation. Obviously *cP* source regions are not as ideal for air-mass development in summer as in winter. Thus summer *cP* is much less homogeneous and clearly identifiable than its winter counterpart. Nor does it invade regions surrounding the source region to the same degree.

mP **air.**   Polar maritime air acquires its distinguishing properties over the great oceans of the higher middle latitudes. These are not regions where air can lie stagnant for long, so that *winter mP*, in the Northern Hemisphere at least, is characteristically polar-arctic air which has had a sea route of variable length. During its fairly prolonged period of contact with a *relatively* warm sea surface, the air has been heated and humidified in its lower layers and converted into a milder, relatively moist and, many times, unstable air mass. On the January map (Fig. 5.3) its usual symbol is *mPKu*, the *K* indicating that it often is cold *cP* air in the process of being modified by additions of heat and humidity from below. Its *u* character is acquired because it becomes involved in transient or semipermanent cyclonic circulations over the northern Pacific and Atlantic Oceans. These circulations produce lifting and consequently instability. Toward the eastern side of the oceans, the *K* may be replaced by *W* as a result of the air's long southerly sea trajectory, while the *u* disappears because the air becomes more neutral as regards stability aloft. Weather accompanying *mP* air is variable. Fresh *mPKu* air on the rear of a cyclonic storm is unstable both at the surface and aloft. It is full of cumulus clouds, which often bring rain showers over the sea and over onshore lands as well. But warmer *mPW* air arriving from the southwest may be warmer than the sea or the land. In this case it is stable at low levels, so that in winter it provides only stratus cloud and drizzle.

Summer mP is apt to be more stable at low levels than the same air in winter. If it was originally warm land air, subsequently chilled over a cooler sea, its air-mass symbol is likely to be *mPW*. And since the circulation over the ocean is only weakly cyclonic, or even anticyclonic, the air aloft is usually neutral or actually stable. Such air often provides relatively clear weather (see Fig. 5.4).

cT **air.** Tropical continental air, formed over the tropical and subtropical deserts, does not spread widely beyond its source regions and hence is fairly unimportant except in those locations. In both winter and summer the air is very dry, and in summer it is exceedingly hot. Subsidence and stability aloft are characteristic of a majority of the source regions.

mT **air.** Tropical maritime air, which includes equatorial air, is the world's most extensively developed air mass. It is also the tropical air mass which most frequently and deeply invades the middle latitudes. It has source regions both in the great tropical oceans and in the extensive parts of tropical continents where lush forests yield a bountiful supply of moisture for the atmosphere. Typically, *mT* surface air is humid and fairly hot (though not as hot as summer *cT*), and in the absence of wind it produces a sultry and oppressive environment.

But while *mT* air is characterized by uniformly high temperatures and humidity (so much so that convergence rarely results in density fronts within the low latitudes), the vertical structure often varies so widely that *mT* air masses may show great contrasts in weather and in amounts of precipitation. Two principal contrasting types are (1) tropical maritime in which subsidence and divergence prevail and hence produce stability aloft (*mTs*); (2) tropical maritime in which convergence and upward movement prevail, with resulting instability aloft (*mTu*). In addition there is tropical maritime air which is neither markedly stable (*s*) nor unstable (*u*) aloft, but intermediate or neutral in stability. This neutral condition (*mT*) is very common.

Source regions of stable *mTs* air are found most often in the eastern and central parts of the sub-tropical anticyclones over oceans, and in the poleward and eastern parts of their tropical circulation (trade winds). Here, above-surface subsidence is marked and the inversion level low, so that the air is very stable and rainfall is meager. Such *mTs* air is dry and warm aloft.

Source regions of convergent unstable tropical maritime air (*mTu*) are characteristic of equatorial latitudes over both oceans and continents (Figs. 5.3 and 5.4). In some classification systems this air is designated as equatorial (*E*). Here in the ITC between the trades, the prevailing upward movement of air has two consequences: (1) the moisture evaporated at the surface is carried to great heights, so that a deep layer is charged with humidity, and (2) the inversion is dissipated, and general instability exists aloft. Such air has a high potential for producing abundant cumulonimbus clouds and heavy showery rainfall. In addition to the equatorial latitudes, *mTu* air may develop at the western extremities of the oceanic anticyclones and their trades.

Neutral *mT* air, as its name suggests, forms in regions where neither subsidence nor convergence is marked. It is common in parts of the trades where *mTs* air has had a long journey over warm waters, traveling equatorward and westward in the trade-wind circulation. Hence *mT* air occurs most often along the equatorward and westward flanks of the oceanic subtropical anticyclones. As a consequence of its long trajectory over a warm ocean, the lower air is thoroughly warmed and moistened, and turbulence and convection have carried the heat and humidity upward to considerable heights. In addition, as the air has progressed farther from the poleward and eastern parts of the oceanic anticyclone, subsidence has abated, and the temperature inversion has weakened and lifted. Thus clouds extend up to greater heights, and resulting rainfall is more abundant.

From this description of stable, unstable, and neutral *mT* air, it follows that *mT* air reaching western Europe (east side of ocean) is likely to be more stable than that entering eastern North America and eastern Asia (west side of ocean). *mT* air in Atlantic Europe occurs either in the warm sectors of passing cyclonic storms or as a broad flow on the north and west side of a fairly stationary anticyclone. It is not only fairly stable aloft, but is undergoing low-level stabilization through cooling at the surface. As a result its symbol may well be *mTs*. Stratus clouds and sea fog are common in such air.

The *mT* air affecting the West Coast of the United States is quite similar to that in Atlantic Europe. But the *mT* air which enters the eastern United States and eastern Asia in summer is warmer, moister, and less stable (i.e., either unstable or neutral), for its course has been over warmer waters. The warm land surface then further increases surface instability (*mTK*). In winter, however, the colder land causes the air to take on *mTW* characteristics, so that it becomes stabilized in its lower layers and is not inclined to ascend convectively. But if it is forced to rise along fronts or over highlands, widespread stratus clouds may form and sometimes may yield considerable rain or snow.

NORTH AMERICAN AIR MASSES

Winter

cP **air masses.**   North American *cPWs* air in winter originates over the snow and ice-covered areas of interior Canada north of about latitude 50 or 55°, as well as over Alaska and the frozen Arctic seas (Figs. 5.7 and 5.8). It enters the United States from Canada, usually between the Rocky Mountains and the Great Lakes. On the weather map it commonly takes the form of a rapidly moving polar-outbreak anticyclone. Because the continent has no major highlands between the arctic plains and the Gulf of Mexico, it is relatively easy for these outbreaks of polar air to move rapidly southward, carrying abnormally cold weather to the subtropical latitudes of the east central United States (Fig. 5.9). The first freeze in fall, the last in spring, and the cold waves over most of the country all are associated with *cP* air. The openness of the continent also makes central and eastern North America an ideal location for the clash of polar and tropical air masses. In winter the middle latitudes of North America are the world's most active continental region of cyclogenesis, an area whose winter storminess is proverbial. (See also Fig. 6.15.)

Modified cP air in the southern and eastern United States.   As winter *cP* moves southward from its source, it is modified by the addition of heat and moisture at the surface and by mechanical turbulence. Surface heating becomes more marked after the polar air leaves the snow surface, whose southern boundary, on the average, is about at the latitude of central Illinois. Continuing subsidence aloft serves to maintain the upper-level stability, so that *s* persists in the air-mass symbol. Turbulence acts to weaken the surface inversion and raise the surface temperature. As the wind dies down, however, a nighttime surface inversion is reestablished, and ex-

Figure 5.7   North American air masses and their source regions.

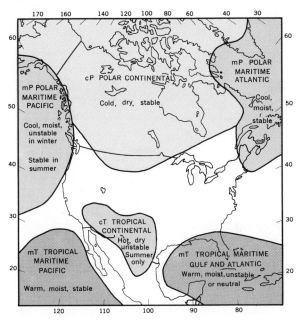

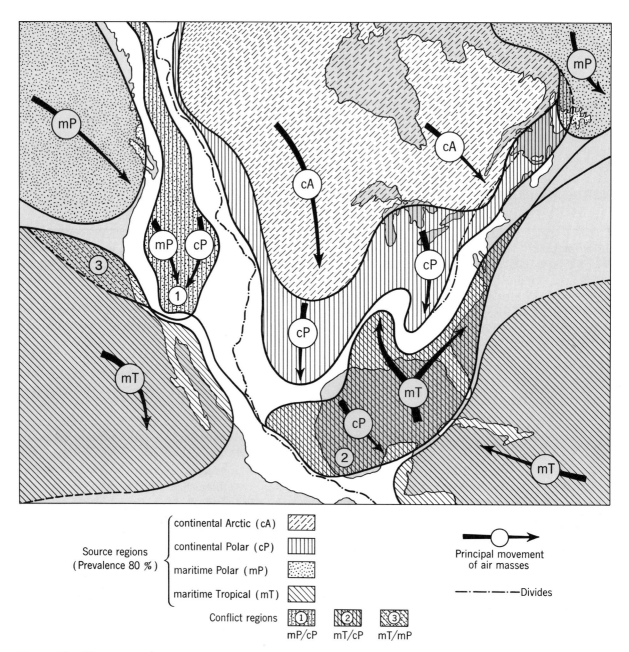

Source regions
(Prevalence 80 %)

continental Arctic (cA)

continental Polar (cP)

maritime Polar (mP)

maritime Tropical (mT)

Conflict regions

① mP/cP   ② mT/cP   ③ mT/mP

Principal movement
of air masses

———·———Divides

Figure 5.8 Winter air masses in North America. (*After Brunnschweiler.*)

Classification of North American air masses

Classification by local source regions				General classification after Bergeron (international)	Local air-mass names
Source by		Local source regions	Season of frequent occurrence		
Latitude	Nature				
Polar	Continental	Alaska, Canada, and the Arctic	Entire year	cP or cPW, winter cPK, summer	Pc, polar continental
		Modified in southern and central United States	Entire year	cPk	
	Maritime	North Pacific Ocean	Entire year	mPK, winter mP or mPK, summer	Pp, polar Pacific
		Modified in western and central United States	Entire year	cPW, winter cPK, summer	
		Colder portions of the North Atlantic Ocean	Entire year	mPK, winter mPW, spring and summer	Pa, Polar Atlantic
		Modified over warmer portions of the North Atlantic Ocean	Spring and summer	mPK	
Tropical	Continental	Southwestern United States and northern Mexico	Warmer half of year	cTK	Tc, tropical continental
	Maritime	Gulf of Mexico and Caribbean Sea	Entire year	mTW, winter mTW or mTK, summer	Tg, tropical Gulf
		Modified in the United States or over the North Atlantic Ocean	Entire year	mTW	
		Sargasso Sea (Middle Atlantic)	Entire year	mTW, winter mTW or mTK, summer	Ta, tropical Atlantic
		Modified in the United States or over the North Atlantic Ocean	Entire year	mTW	
		Middle North Pacific Ocean	Entire year	mTW, winter mTW or mTK, summer	Tp, tropical Pacific
		Modified in the United States or over North Pacific Ocean	Entire year	mTW	

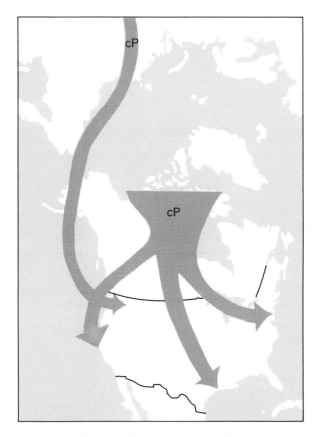

Figure 5.9 Routes of winter *cP* air in North America.

ceptionally low minimum temperatures, associated with clear skies, are the rule. Surface heating and humidification are by no means sufficient to overcome the stability (*s*) aloft, so that the air mass remains stable and largely cloudless (*cPKs*) even over the southern United States.

After crossing the Gulf of Mexico, a polar outbreak may arrive in Central America and Mexico in the form of a strong "norther." By then it has become either cool *mTKu* air accompanied by heavy convective precipitation, or anticyclonic *mTKs* air with drizzle or no rain at all.

If the *cP* air takes a more eastward course, somewhat different modifications occur (Fig. 5.10). One is that the stability aloft weakens as a result of a waning anticyclonic circulation within the polar cur-

rent eastward from the Great Lakes. Consequently upper-level subsidence is diminished, and the *s* element gradually fades from the air-mass symbol. Another modification takes place over the open water of the Great Lakes in winter, where the lower air is humidified and warmed, producing some surface instability. Heavy snow showers are characteristic of this *cPK* air on the lee side of any of the Great Lakes. Still another modification is created by the rough terrain of the Appalachian country, which causes a thorough mixing of the lower few thousand feet of air and so eliminates the surface temperature inversion and raises surface temperatures. On the western slopes of the eastern highlands, the forced ascent of modified *cP* air from over the Great Lakes produces general cloudiness and heavy local snowfall as long as there is a strong flow of cold air. Heat of condensation then acts to warm the air mass, and as it descends the eastern slopes of the highlands, it is further warmed as a result of subsidence (see the data for Boston in the table on page 179). Thus the cloud cover disappears and the snowfall ceases.

Modified cP air west of the Rockies. Because of the Rocky Mountain barrier and the general west-to-east atmospheric circulation in middle latitudes, *cP* air less frequently invades the intermontane region lying between the Rockies and the Pacific Coast mountains. And it is only occasionally that these air masses reach the Pacific Coast lowlands. When *cP* air does arrive at the intermontane plateaus and basins, it has been considerably warmed from turbulent mixing in the lower layers, which has brought

Figure 5.10 Modifications induced in North American winter *cP* air by the Great Lakes and the Appalachian Highlands.

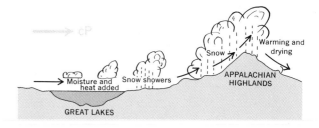

Winter characteristics of some American air masses

Air mass	Station	Weather element	Elevation above sea level				
			Surface	1 km	2 km	3 km	4 km
cP	Ellendale, N.D.	Temp., °F Sp. humid., g/kg Rel. humid., %	−15 0.32 82	−13 0.35 80	−4 0.60 75	−7 0.50 63	−13 0.45 71
	Boston	Temp., °F Sp. humid., g/kg Rel. humid., %	21 0.9 43	6 0.6 50	0 0.5 50	−9 0.3 44	−20 0.2 48
mP	Seattle	Temp., °F Sp. humid., g/kg Rel. humid., %	46 4.4 66	32 2.7 64	18 1.5 64	7 0.8 52	−2 0.4 35
	Ellendale, N.D.	Temp., °F Sp. humid., g/kg Rel. humid., %	30 3.0 83	45 3.0 43	34 2.2 44	19 1.5 48	7 1.1 60
mT	Miami	Temp., °F Sp. humid., g/kg Rel. humid., %	77 16.3 82	68 13.3 82	55 9.8 83	46 6.2 66	37 5.2 67
	Boston	Temp., °F Sp. humid., g/kg Rel. humid., %	57 8.8 88	57 6.5 59	48 6.2 70	36 4.6 75	25 2.9 65
mT	San Diego	Temp., °F Sp. humid., g/kg Rel. humid., %	68 11.9 86	59 9.8 81	50 6.8 70	43 4.0 51	34 2.1 33

Source: After Willett.

down warmer air from aloft (Fig. 5.11). If cP air continues on to the Pacific Coast in Washington and Oregon, occasionally it produces subfreezing temperatures and snow flurries. In rare cases this weather type may extend southward to coastal California. In years when cP air is more prevalent in the region west of the Rockies, the Pacific Coast may have relatively severe winters as a result of transmontane spillovers of the air mass. Air from cold northern Asia which has crossed the ice-covered Arctic Ocean, Alaska, and the Gulf of Alaska also occasionally brings very cold weather to the Pacific Northwest (Fig. 5.9). Asian air is sufficiently warmed and humidified over the Gulf of Alaska to yield

Figure 5.11 In North America the western mountains tend to obstruct and modify winter cP air masses moving westward toward the Pacific Coast. (*After Phil Church in Weatherwise, April, 1962.*)

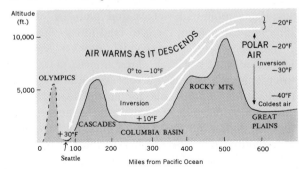

showers and squalls when it is forced to ascend the coastal highlands.

mP-Pacific air masses.   It is mP-Pacific air which largely controls the Pacific Coast weather of North America in winter (Fig. 5.8). The source region of these air masses is the northern part of the North Pacific Ocean, an area which in winter is dominated by the cyclonic circulations of the Aleutian Low and its traveling disturbances. The eastern part of the Pacific in these latitudes is a region of relatively warm surface waters. Most of the air that enters the mP-Pacific source region originates in cold continental areas to the north and west and is drawn into the source region by the strong northwesterly flow converging on the Aleutian cyclone. Warmth and humidity from the ocean surface are added to the stable $cPWs$ air, and it becomes involved in the prevailing cyclonic circulation, which acts to lift the air mass. Thus it is gradually transformed into unstable $mPKu$.

As it arrives on the Pacific Coast of North America, $mPKu$ air is relatively mild, with temperatures well above the freezing point. It has a steep lapse rate and is accompanied by low clouds with frequent showers. Convective instability extends up to about 10,000 ft. As this humid, unstable air advances inland, its shower activity is greatly increased when it is forced to ascend over the cooler land air along the coast and also over the coastal ranges. Rain in the lowlands and heavy snowfall in the mountains are characteristic of the winter season.

Modified mP-Pacific air east of the Pacific Ranges.   As the maritime air continues inland over successive mountain ranges and plateaus of the intermontane region, the cold land lowers the air's surface temperature, while condensation on the highlands causes the low levels of the air mass to become drier. This mP air becomes involved in an anticyclonic circulation over the intermontane plateau region and also to the east of the Rocky Mountains, so that its stability at upper levels increases and the u gradually changes to s. Thus the mild, moist, unstable air ($mPKu$) of the West Coast is slowly transformed into a cold, dry, stable continental air mass

($cPWs$) east of the Rockies in the central United States. But is not nearly so cold or so dry as fresh cP air from arctic Canada.

The weather associated with this greatly modified mP air over the central part of the country is some of the finest that winter has to offer—clear skies, light winds, and moderate temperatures. But along frontal zones, where it makes contact with mT air from the Gulf, or with fresh cP air from Canada, widespread bad weather conditions may result.

mP-Atlantic air masses.   This polar maritime air originates over the abnormally cold North Atlantic waters (35 to 40° in winter, and 50 to 60° in summer) off Newfoundland, Labrador, and Greenland (Fig. 5.7). It was originally cP air that moved eastward off the continent and subsequently was modified over the cold waters, which acted as a secondary source region. Owing to the prevailing west-to-east air movement in middle latitudes, the North Atlantic is not an important source region for air masses affecting North America. This is especially true in winter. Normally, mP-Atlantic air moves eastward across the ocean toward Europe. Under certain synoptic weather conditions the westerly flow is temporarily reversed, and Atlantic air may enter the continent shallowly. Normally in such cases it keeps east of the Appalachians and north of Cape Hatteras.

In winter, mP-Atlantic air ($mPKs$) is dry and stable aloft as a result of subsidence, while the surface layer is moderately unstable, moist, and chilly. Temperatures are raw rather than bitterly cold. Compared with mP-Pacific air at Seattle, the low-level mP-Atlantic air is colder, drier, and more stable, because of both the colder waters in the North Atlantic and the shorter trajectory of mP-Atlantic air over the water (Fig. 5.8).

The weather associated with an invasion of mP-Atlantic air is distinctly unpleasant. Surface temperatures near freezing or somewhat below, high relative humidity, strong northeast winds, low, thick clouds, and variable amounts of precipitation, depending on the synoptic pattern—such is a typical "northeaster" of the New England coast.

mT-**Gulf-and-Atlantic air masses.** These air masses greatly affect the weather and climate of much of Anglo-America east of the Rockies. Their source regions are the exceptionally warm ocean surfaces of the Gulf of Mexico, the Caribbean Sea, and the subtropical western Atlantic (Fig. 5.7). Consequently *mT*-Gulf air is characteristically warm and humid, with specific humidities and temperatures higher than those of any other American air mass in winter. Its properties aloft—absence of pronounced subsidence, and a neutral or unstable vertical structure (*mTK*[*u*])—reflect the source region's dominance by the weak western limb of the North Atlantic subtropical anticyclone (Fig. 5.8).

During the colder months, polar air prevails in the central eastern United States well to the south. As a result the polar front separating *mT*-Gulf and *cP* air lies close to the northern and western portions of the *mT*-Gulf source region. Such a condition does not favor easy entrance of *mT* air into eastern and central North America in winter.

In the American South, *mT* air masses are associated with mild, humid winter days that have a good deal of cloudiness of the stratus type, especially at night and in early morning. As *mT* air moves northward, the ground strata are cooled by contact with a progressively colder land, and the surface stability of the air mass is increased (*mTW*). Convective showers consequently are uncommon in winter. But if the northward-flowing *mT* air is drawn into a cyclonic circulation or encounters a relief barrier, its forced ascent may cause heavy and widespread precipitation. Much of the winter rain and snow over central and eastern North America are the result of *mT*-Gulf air being lifted along fronts in cyclonic circulations. If nothing forces it to rise, however, northward-moving *mT* air frequently develops a dense advection fog because of cooling at the surface.

mT-**Pacific air masses.** Chiefly the extreme southwestern United States and northwestern Mexico are affected by these air masses. They originate in the subtropical eastern Pacific Ocean, in almost identical latitudes to those in which *mT*-Gulf air develops

(Fig. 5.7). But although the latitudes of their source regions are similar, their other characteristics are not. The eastern subtropical Pacific westward from Mexico and California is dominated by the circulation around the *eastern* end of an oceanic subtropical high, where strong upper-level subsidence produces marked stability (*mTs*). Therefore *mTs* air which arrives along the North American Pacific Coast is considerably cooler, drier, and more stable than the *mT*-Gulf air which affects the southeastern United States.

As *mT*-Pacific air moves northward along the coast of California, occasionally reaching the latitudes of Oregon and Washington, it is cooled at the surface by the colder water and is further stabilized, acquiring *W* characteristics. Fog is often the result. When, as frequently happens, this *mT* air is drawn into a frontal or cyclonic convergence, its *s* property changes to *u*, so that moderate precipitation may be caused by lifting along fronts or topographic obstacles. Ordinarily *mT*-Pacific is not as good a rainbringer as *mT*-Gulf air, which is potentially more unstable. As an *mT*-Pacific air mass moves inland aloft over the western states, it continues to yield moderate precipitation as it ascends over colder air or over mountains. East of the Rockies, it can rarely be identified.

Summer

cP **air masses.** In summer this polar continental air mass has much the same geographical source region as in winter, but its properties are different (Fig. 5.12). In the absence of snow, the land surface is moderately warmed by solar energy during the long summer days. Air entering the continent from cooler seas is warmed at the base and given a *K* character. Evaporation from numerous lakes, as well as from vegetation and moist soil, provides a fair amount of moisture. A weak anticyclonic circulation causes summer *cP* aloft to be mildly stable (*s*), but less so than in winter. Surface temperatures are moderate. Strong solar heating by day and rapid radiational cooling at night create large diurnal temperature variations. At its source *cP* air is typically cloudless,

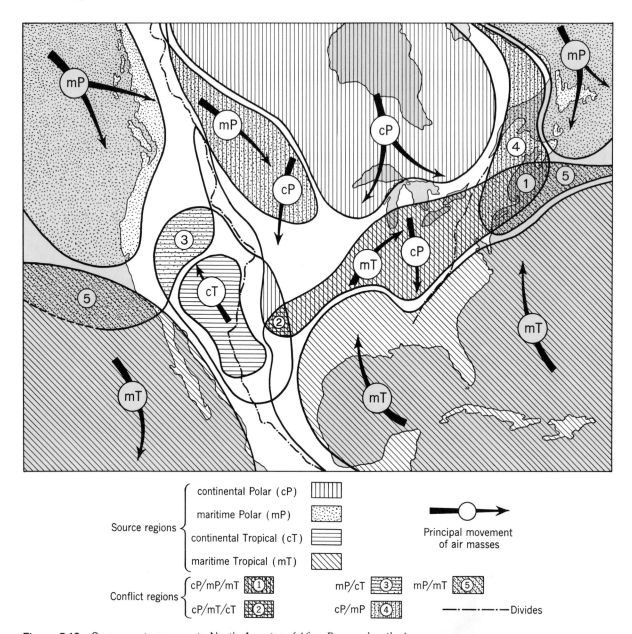

Figure 5.12 Summer air masses in North America. (*After Brunnschweiler.*)

for in spite of its daytime surface instability and the resulting convective turbulence, the condensation level is so high that a few scattered high cumulus clouds are usually the most that can develop.

In the northern half of the central and eastern United States, summer heat waves are normally broken by a southward advance of fresh *cPKs* air which, for a day or two, substitutes cool, clear weather for the sultry or desiccating heat. Southward-moving outbreaks of summer *cP* air in the United States are much less frequent than in winter, and they are also weaker and slower. As a rule they move eastward more than southward, so that the cool air rarely reaches the southern states. As *cP* air advances eastward and southward from the Canadian border, it is slowly warmed at all levels, and some moisture is added at the base. Its general upper-level stability persists, however, except when it enters a cyclonic circulation, which causes instability to develop aloft and may lead to scattered light thundershowers in the afternoon (see Figs. 3.13, 3.14, and 3.15).

mP-**Pacific air masses.**   In summer this polar maritime air has the same geographical source region as in winter, but the properties of the summer and winter *mP*-Pacific air masses are somewhat different (Fig. 5.12). During the warm season, the waters of the North Pacific are relatively cooler than the sur-

Summer characteristics of some North American air masses

Air mass	Station	Weather element	Elevation above sea level				
			Surface	1 km	2 km	3 km	4 km
cP	Ellendale, N.D.	Temp., °F	66	61	50	39	27
		Sp. humid., g/kg	6.3	5.6	3.9	3.1	2.9
		Rel. humid., %	42	45	43	44	57
	Royal Center, Ind.	Temp., °F	63	55	43	36	28
		Sp. hum., g/kg	8.3	5.8	4.5	2.6	1.4
		Rel. humid., %	68	57	64	43	27
	Pensacola, Fla.	Temp., °F	73	68	54	45	
		Sp. humid., g/kg	13.4	9.8	7.2	5.0	
		Rel. humid., %	79	65	67	57	
mP	Seattle	Temp., °F	63	48	41	34	28
		Sp. humid., g/kg	7.1	6.3	3.9	2.3	1.7
		Rel. humid., %	62	91	60	42	33
	San Diego	Temp., °F	64	72	70	57	43
		Sp. humid., g/kg	10.3	7.7	3.5	3.6	3.4
		Rel. humid., %	79	40	20	27	36
mT	Miami	Temp., °F	75	68	59	48	41
		Sp. humid., g/kg	17.3	14.9	9.3	6.3	4.3
		Rel. humid., %	93	88	74	58	48
	Royal Center, Ind.	Temp., °F	84	77	65	51	
		Sp. humid., g/kg	15.9	13.9	11.5	8.6	
		Rel. humid., %	61				
	Ellendale, N.D.	Temp., °F	84	81	72	55	
		Sp. humid., g/kg	16.5	13.3	8.7	5.7	
		Rel. humid., %	66	54	42	43	
cT	El Paso, Tex.	Temp., °F	75	81	75	64	
		Sp. humid., g/kg	11.0	9.7	9.9	7.6	
		Rel. humid., %	52	37	43	43	

Source: After Willett.

rounding lands, so that air entering the source region may be chilled at the base and stabilized (*W*). And since the summer circulation over the eastern North Pacific is less cyclonic than in winter, the air aloft is also less unstable.

During summer the strengthened Pacific anticyclone shifts poleward, so that the northeastern axis of the high along the Pacific Coast is positioned as far north as 45 to 50°N. A southward flow of cool, stable air along almost the entire United States Pacific Coast is the result. Originally, a part of this circulation is *mP*, but gradually cool, stable *mT* comes to dominate the northerly flow around the eastern end of the subtropical high.

After *mP* air has reached the interior of the continent, it cannot be distinguished from *cP*. Therefore the designation *cP* is satisfactory for both *mP* and *cP* air in summer in the North American interior.

mP-Atlantic air masses.   These polar maritime air masses occur most frequently during late spring and early summer. At that time the chilly ocean surface from Cape Cod to Newfoundland becomes a genuine source region for cool air (Fig. 5.12). As *cP* air moves eastward from the continent over the cold waters, it is chilled and stabilized (*W*) at the base, while the predominantly anticyclonic circulation produces upper-level stability (*s*). The circulation on the southerly side of this high carries chilly *mP*-Atlantic air to New England, and also occasionally to the coastal areas east of the Appalachians as far south as Cape Hatteras.

Along the North Atlantic Coast in summer, *mP*-Atlantic air brings weather with low temperatures, clear skies, and good visibility. Because of its dryness, surface fog is uncommon even over coastal waters. Thin and broken clouds are relatively frequent at the top of the turbulence layer, but precipitation never comes from these clouds in summer.

mT-Gulf-and-Atlantic air masses.   During summer these air masses largely control the weather of much of the United States east of the Rockies. Because of the prevailing sea-to-land pressure gradients over the eastern part of the country in summer, *mT* air is able to enter much deeper into the continent than in winter (Fig. 5.12). A strengthening of the Bermuda High over the western Atlantic Ocean, together with the tendency toward a thermally maintained low over the warm continent, produces a fairly persistent indraft that flows northward even into Canada. Not only do the *mT*-Gulf air masses cover much wider areas in summer than in winter, but they are present a much greater share of the time. They are responsible for the oppressive, humid summer heat that characterizes so much of the central and eastern United States. Outbreaks of polar air are comparatively weak and infrequent at this season, so that the belt of maximum frontal activity, which in winter normally lies somewhere over the Gulf States, is shifted northward to the Great Lakes or beyond.

As it leaves its source region, summer *mT*-Gulf air is relatively similar to winter *mT*, though it is somewhat warmer and more humid. Although the general circulation in which the *mT*-Gulf air is involved is anticyclonic, this is the western end of the cell, where subsidence is much less marked. Therefore upper-level instability (*mTu*) is not uncommon. And as summer *mT* air moves inland over the warm continent, its surface temperature rises (*mTKu*), with a consequent increase in surface instability. (During winter, in contrast, a cold continent has the reverse effect.) Because of the high relative humidity of this air, only a small amount of vertical lifting is required in order to start active convection and shower activity. The marked potential instability, plus the effect of daytime heating of the surface air, favors the development of cumulus clouds which produce showers and thunderstorms—features characteristic of summer *mT* air in the Gulf states. Much the greater share of this precipitation appears to be of an organized variety associated with passing synoptic disturbances.

Even in the arid southwestern United States, warm-season thunderstorms appear to be related to westward thrusts of *mT*-Gulf air aloft. These summer showers are frequently so intense that the name "cloudburst" has been applied to them. They are usually localized with respect to mountain masses. On rare occasions *mT*-Gulf air even reaches southern

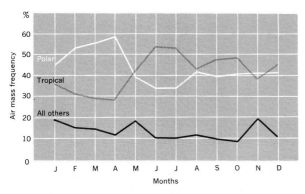

Figure 5.13 Relative frequencies of polar, tropical, and other air masses in central Pennsylvania. (*From H. Landsberg in Physical Climatology.*)

California, bringing that region its rare summer showers. Severe local thunderstorms are likewise characteristic of *mT* air as it rises over the Appalachian Mountains. Such storms may continue for 100 miles or more eastward over the coastal plain (see Figs. 5.13, 5.14, and 5.15).

mT-Pacific air masses. It is not easy to distinguish *mT* and *mP* along the Pacific Coast of the United States in summer. The circulation around the eastern end of the poleward-displaced anticyclone makes for a steady transport of cool, stable air southward along the entire American coast to southernmost California and beyond (Fig. 5.12). The result is unusually low summer temperatures along the whole Pacific littoral. Abnormally cold upwelled water along the coast of California tends to cool the northerly airflow still

further. As a consequence the maritime air at San Diego has surface temperatures similar to those at Seattle. In the north, a good part of this cool airflow probably should be classed as *mP*, but southward it gradually changes to cool *mT*. The *mT* air is stable both at the base because of the cool ocean surface, and aloft (with low inversions prevalent) because of anticyclonic subsidence. Thus lowlands throughout the entire Pacific Coast from 45 or 50°N to 20 or 25°N have a dry summer. Coastal fog is widespread. In both temperature and stability, summer *mT*-Pacific is very different from *mT*-Gulf.

cT air masses. Owing to the marked narrowing of the continent to the south and the prevalence of highlands there, North America has no extensive source region for tropical continental air. Only in northern Mexico and adjacent parts of the United States is there even a small source region (Fig. 5.12). For the most part *cT* air probably consists of *mT*-Pacific air that has stagnated over this secondary source region for several days, becoming intensely heated and desiccated in its lower strata. *cT* air is a feature of the warm season; it is absent in winter, for the source region has no distinctive characteristics then. Very high daytime temperatures, extremely low humidities, and an almost complete lack of precipitation characterize *cT* air in summer. Outside its source region *cT* air is found chiefly in the southern Great Plains, where it is associated with severe drought. It rarely moves east of the Mississippi River or north of Nebraska.

Figure 5.14 Relative frequencies of maritime and continental air masses in central Pennsylvania. (*From H. Landsberg in Physical Climatology.*)

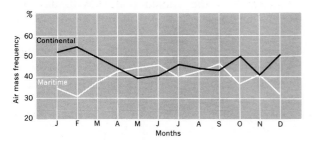

Figure 5.15 Percentage of days annually with air-mass changes in central Pennsylvania. (*From H. Landsberg in Physical Climatology.*)

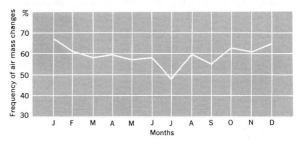

AIR MASSES OF EUROPE

In accordance with the general circulation patterns Europe, which forms the western part of the great Eurasian continent, has air masses that often resemble those of western North America in similar latitudes (Figs. 5.8 and 5.12). In many ways *mP*-Atlantic air in western Europe resembles *mP*-Pacific air along the Pacific margins of Anglo-America, while *mT*-Atlantic air in Portugal-Spain resembles *mT*-Pacific air in California. There are several significant differences, however. Mainly, the trend of highlands in Europe is approximately east-west, or parallel with the westerly circulation, while those of North America lie athwart the westerlies. In Europe, maritime air masses from the west therefore enter the continent more readily and more deeply, and retain their maritime properties much longer, than their counterparts in western Anglo-America. Because of the Pacific Coast highlands in North America, moderate *mP*- and *mT*-Pacific air is rapidly transformed into more severe and dry continental air.

It would seem as if these differences in terrain arrangement between the two continents would make it easier for *cP* air to reach the Baltic countries and Germany than to invade the Pacific Coast of Anglo-America. However, Europe thrusts far westward in its lower latitudes and withdraws eastward in its higher latitudes, a configuration which is opposite to Anglo-America's. This means that most polar-air invasions of western Europe are necessarily of maritime origin, a feature much less true of western North America east of the Pacific highlands.

It might be expected also that Europe's air masses would be strongly influenced by the large subtropical bodies of warm water along the continent's southern borders. But the high east-west mountain chains of Europe tend to confine the effects of these water bodies chiefly to the great southern peninsulas. The Gulf of Mexico, in contrast, has a marked influence on North American weather. Still, the Mediterranean Sea does play a great part in the generation and routes of cyclonic storms within its basin and hence in its weather as well.

cP **air masses.**   Polar continental air masses in *winter* chiefly affect the weather of Russia and central Europe. It is only occasionally that they reach western Europe, for except under certain synoptic conditions, the west-to-east atmospheric circulation hinders a reverse movement of air from the source regions farther east. Moreover, since Europe narrows in a poleward direction, the source region for *cP* air is limited in extent. Most *cP* air affecting central and western Europe originates in Fenno-Scandia or western Russia. It has temperatures less severe than air from Siberia or subarctic Canada, so that it shows more resemblance to the modified *cP* air found in the central United States. A European invasion of Russian *cP* air usually develops in connection with a synoptic condition involving an anticyclone over northern Russia and a deep low over Scandinavia. Cold air then enters central-western Europe as a thrust of anticyclonic air from the east and north. Clear skies lead to relatively low night temperatures, although the minima decrease rapidly in intensity toward the coast as the *cP* air is swiftly modified.

cP air in *summer,* though it is quite different from that of winter, still has its source in northern Russia. Summer *cP* is fairly warm and humid at the surface and cool aloft, so that it is much less stable than winter *cP*. Since it has probably developed from *mP* air, its moisture content is higher than that of its counterpart in the United States. With daytime heating cumulus clouds and thundershowers may develop, especially if the circulation is cyclonic. European *cP* in summer is only slightly cooler than *cT* air in western Europe, but it is somewhat warmer than *mP*. Summer air masses of central and western Europe lack important temperature contrasts. Consequently summer weather in central and western

Europe is not characterized by the amount of temperature variability that it has in central and eastern North America, where air masses show greater contrasts. In Europe the diurnal range is large, however, with cool nights and warm days. Summer *cP* is uncommon in westernmost Europe.

mP **air masses.** Polar maritime air, because of the westerly circulation, tends to dominate the weather of western and central Europe in all seasons. Since in *winter mP* is sea-modified *cP*, its lower layers have been warmed, humidified and made unstable, while instability aloft may have been induced through circulation in the North Atlantic Low. Instability showers are therefore common over the ocean and along the coasts of Europe. As *mP* progresses eastward, surface instability decreases owing to loss of heat to the underlying cold land surface.

Depending on the ocean route traveled by the air mass, *mP* in western Europe brings a variety of weather. If it comes from a northerly quarter with a relatively short trajectory over open water, it arrives in Europe as some of the earth's coldest maritime air, with a surface temperature around freezing. Winds are strong and gusty, the lapse rate steep, and humidity in the lower layers high, so that brief, heavy snow showers are common. If the *mP* air has had a longer trajectory, surface temperatures are likely to be 10 to 15° warmer, and the humidification reaches up to higher levels. In such air the lapse rate is not quite so steep, but rain and snow showers are still common. On occasion *mP* air may enter Europe from a southwesterly direction, having had a long trajectory into southerly latitudes. Its surface temperature may then be warmer than that of the winter ocean (*mPW*), so that it is stable near the surface. Stratus cloud and drizzle are usual in such air. Fronts between different *mP* air masses are common, and many cyclonic disturbances that affect western Europe have warm sectors of warm *mPW* air rather than of *mT*.

mP air in Europe in *summer* shows considerable variation in character, depending on where it originates within its extensive source region and how long it has traveled over the ocean. If it forms in the southern part of the source region and reaches Europe after a long trajectory over the water, it is generally stable. This air mass gives rise to cool fair weather and is a rain producer only when it undergoes a marked lift along fronts in well-developed cyclones. On the other hand, air that reaches Europe more directly from the northern part of the source region is mildly unstable and may show some convective activity. Heavier showers result when this air is lifted along frontal surfaces. Summer *mP* air is distinctly cooler than the land it invades, so that its general effect is to give western Europe a cool, marine summer climate.

cT **air masses.** Tropical continental air in *winter* is not of great importance in Europe, at least not at the surface. Mild and dry in character, it originates over the Sahara in North Africa and over dry southwestern Asia. Only occasionally does it invade southern and central Europe at the surface. But frequently, after being shallowly humidified over the Mediterranean Sea, it is drawn into atmospheric disturbances where it is caused to rise over frontal surfaces, with resulting moderate precipitation. No doubt a part of the cool-season cyclonic precipitation in southern and central Europe is from *cT* air modified over the Mediterranean.

cT air masses are found over Europe mainly in *summer*. Since they originate in the Sahara, southern Russia, and Asia Minor, they are extremely dry and hot. Although lapse rates are steep, the unmodified air is too arid to produce much rainfall. Under the influence of low-pressure centers poleward of 40 or 45°N, *cT* air occasionally flows northward across the Mediterranean Sea in the form of a hot sirocco wind. These winds are very desiccating in areas of southern Europe where the southerly airstream has crossed only a narrow expanse of water, but they are more humid and sultry where the trajectory has been long. Such modified *cT* air masses provide a fair share of the moisture for the modest summer rainfall of parts of southern and central Europe.

Winter air masses in Europe

	Elevation, m	Temperature, °F	Specific humidity, g/kg
	1. cP air		
	———	1	1.0
	800	7	1.0
	1,650	3	1.0
Moscow	2,600	− 9	0.56
	3,700	−26	0.39
	4,950	−42	0.20
	800	12	1.4
	1,700	1	1.0
Munich	2,650	− 6	0.60
	3,750	−15	0.38
	5,050	−33	0.16
	2. cP (arctic) air, modified over the Norwegian Sea		
	———	36	3.7
	800	28	2.9
	1,700	16	2.0
Berlin	2,700	5	1.1
	3,850	− 9	0.56
	5,150	−26	2.26
	4. mT-Atlantic air		
	———	39	4.4
	850	34	3.5
	1,750	23	2.2
Hamburg	2,750	14	1.3
	3,950	0	0.8
	5,250	−17	0.5
	3. mP-Atlantic air		
	———	48	6.2
	850	41	5.4
	1,800	36	3.7
Hamburg	2,850	25	2.2
	4,000	10	1.4
	5,400	− 2	0.8

Source: After Petterssen.

mT **air masses.** Tropical maritime air masses in Europe strongly resemble *mT*-Pacific air along the West Coast of the United States. They are cooler, drier, and more stable than *mT*-Gulf air in the southeastern United States. *mT* air that arrives in Europe comes from the northern and eastern flanks of the Atlantic subtropical high-pressure cell, where subsidence is strong. Although relatively warm and moist compared with polar air, it is markedly stable aloft. A pronounced inversion is present at relatively low levels. After leaving its source in the subtropical anticyclone, this air moves over a colder surface as it travels progressively northward, so that surface stability likewise evolves (*mTWs*). Widespread sheets of stratus cloud develop underneath the inversion and penetrate well inland. Some drizzle may fall from such clouds, but owing to the pronounced stability aloft, rainfall from this air is modest even along fronts. *mT* air reaches western Europe chiefly in the form of warm sectors of cyclonic storms. As an element of the weather of that region, it is more conspicuous in the cooler seasons and relatively unimportant in summer.

In summary, European *winter* air masses cover a much smaller range of temperature than those of North America, a feature which reflects the greater marine influence in Europe and greater continentality in America. As a consequence fronts are less sharp and less active in Europe, and weather less changeable and extreme. Also, *mT* winter air plays a much less significant role in European weather. The *mT* that reaches Europe, being from the eastern side of an oceanic subtropical anticyclone, is definitely more stable than winter *mT*-Gulf air in North America.

In *summer,* it is Europe's cooler air masses that are most unstable and bring showery convective precipitation, while warmer *mT* is stable. In North America the opposite is true, for *mT*-Gulf air is rich in heat energy and moisture and is relatively unstable. Europe has no tropical air-mass conterpart to *mT*-Gulf. In general, Europe's air masses are characterized by greater uniformity in lapse rates, the main contrasts being in temperatures. As might be expected, the North American air masses show greater differences both in vertical structure and in temperatures.

Summer air masses in Europe

	Elevation, m	Temperature, °F	Specific humidity, g/kg
		1. cP air	
Berlin	——	63	9.6
	850	57	7.5
	1,850	46	5.7
	2,900	36	3.9
	4,050	21	2.3
	5,450	7	1.3
		2. mP air	
Hamburg	——	59	8.5
	850	50	6.3
	1,800	39	4.7
	2,850	28	3.1
	4,050	16	1.8
	5,400	1	1.0
		3. mT air	
Hamburg	——	68	8.9
	900	57	7.5
	1,850	48	6.2
	2,900	37	4.6
	4,100	25	3.3
	5,500	12	2.1
		4. cT air (source region in Europe)	
Berlin	——	68	9.5
	900	64	8.5
	1,850	52	6.5
	2,925	39	4.6
	4,150	27	2.7
	5,500	7	1.6

Source: After Petterssen.

AIR MASSES OF EAST AND SOUTH ASIA

Because of the direction of the general circulation, eastern Asia's air masses are more like those of eastern North America than those of western Europe and western North America (Figs. 5.8 and 5.12). The larger continent of Eurasia tends to create greater air-mass temperature extremes than exist in North America. But because of the east-west mountain chains of Asia, polar and tropical air masses do not come into conflict there as readily as in Anglo-America, which has no zonal terrain barriers in its central and eastern parts.

cP **air masses.**   Polar continental air in *winter* originates in the cold anticyclone centered over central eastern Siberia. At its source, it is bitterly cold and very dry, even more so than its North American counterpart. As *cP* surges seaward in the form of great thrusts of cold, dry air, spaced an average of about a week apart, at least two important types of modification occur. First, the air is forced to travel over extensive highlands before descending to the plains of China. Mechanical turbulence caused by the highlands dissipates the strong surface inversion and increases the temperature of the lower air, as well as raising its humidity somewhat. Second, before reaching Japan this continental air is forced to traverse several hundred miles of open sea. Here such large amounts of heat and moisture are added at the surface that instability results. Over the sea and along the windward western side of Japan, this modified *cP* air gives rise to heavy snow showers.

cP air reaching western Korea also has been modified in different degrees by longer or shorter sea journeys. The same is true for subtropical China south of the Yangtze. In this case the flow of air is from a northeasterly direction, for it originated in more northerly latitudes on the back side of a cold anticyclone centered east of the mainland and moving eastward. The arid winters of northern China, including Manchuria, are largely caused by the dominance of dry, cold land *cP* in these parts. Likewise sea-modified *cP* is at least partly responsi-

ble for the wetter winters of Japan, Korea, and subtropical southern China.

Along the sea margins of Asia, each fresh surge of *cP* air comes into conflict either with air of genuinely maritime origin or with sea-modified *cP*, giving rise to atmospheric disturbances and fronts. It is in such disturbances that most of the winter precipitation of Japan, Korea, and southern China is generated. If the outbreak of polar air is unusually strong, it may carry with it a large amount of fine dust picked up from the interior dry lands. This is the source of the extensive loess deposits of North China. *cP* air usually does not invade southern Asia deeply, for the high mountains and plateaus tend to isolate the south from the north. Only at the eastern and western extremities of the highlands—in North Vietnam in Southeast Asia and in northwest India-Pakistan—are there significant intrusions of modified *cP*. In India-Pakistan these intrusions aid in the generation of weak winter cyclones which bring modest amounts of cool-season precipitation, chiefly to the northern and western parts of the Indian subcontinent.

cP air masses in *summer* are relatively unimportant in eastern and southern Asia, where *mT*, the summer monsoon, dominates the weather. Usually the summer *cP* is felt only in northernmost China and to some degree in northern Japan. In both regions it makes fronts with the tropical air, giving rise to precipitation. Some of the *cP* that enters northern China, and certainly the *cP* in Japan, has been more or less modified over cool waters and hence is more humid in its lower layers than most summer *cP* in North America.

mP **air masses.**   Polar maritime air masses which have had a long trajectory over oceans play a minor role in the weather of eastern Asia. In *winter,* the strong westerly circulation in eastern Asia almost precludes the possibility of genuine *mT* reaching the coast, although as mentioned earlier, sea-modified *cP* does have some influence. In *summer, mP* air from the Sea of Okhotsk takes on modest importance, for the summer monsoon north of about 40° probably is chiefly *mP* air. In Japan modified *mP*-Okhotsk air moves southward in early summer, forming a front with *mT* air. The disturbances along this zone of conflict produce overcast, rainy weather and so create the first of the two summer maxima of summer precipitation.

mT and *cT* air masses. Tropical maritime air masses in *winter* are largely excluded from East Asia by the Siberian anticyclone and its land-to-sea monsoon winds, so that they play only a modest role in the cool-season weather there. Surface winter *mT* is rarely found as far north as the Yangtze Valley; farther south it occurs somewhat more frequently at the ground. Characteristically it is to be observed aloft in cyclonic storms, where it overruns *cP* air and causes precipitation. Since *mT* air is warmer and moister than other winter air masses in East Asia, fog, low stratus cloud, and misting rain may occur when it moves northward over a cooler land surface. South Asia in *winter* is chiefly dominated by the northeast trades, which have *mT* characteristics in the insular and coastal parts but take on *cT* attributes over the broader parts of the two large peninsulas of Southeast Asia and India-Pakistan. Rainfall is slight except along the windward eastern sides of these land masses.

mT (tropical maritime, including equatorial) air masses in *summer* largely dominate the weather of eastern and southern Asia, for they represent the monsoon circulation of that season. Except in extreme northwest India-Pakistan, where the main air masses are *cT*, South Asia is under the influence of a deep southwesterly circulation of equatorial origin that is warm, humid, and convectively unstable to a remarkable degree. Naturally it has a high potential for precipitation when it is lifted over highlands or in convergent circulations of atmospheric disturbances. A lift of only a few hundred meters is sufficient to saturate the air and bring about heavy showery rainfall. As *mT* air moves inland over the heated land surface, instability is further increased.

The equatorial current of southwesterly air continues northward over humid eastern China clear into North China and Manchuria, where it meets *cP* air along the polar front. Heavy summer precipitation is the result. This same current carries its heat and moisture to Korea and Japan. Still another branch of the summer monsoon in East Asia is derived from the western limb of the North Pacific subtropical anticyclone. It may arrive in Japan and eastern China as a southeasterly, southerly, or even southwesterly current. Because of its anticyclonic origin, even though it comes from the anticyclone's moister western flanks, this Pacific air may not be quite as humid and unstable as the equatorial southwesterlies from the Indian Ocean.

SELECTED REFERENCES FOR FURTHER STUDY OF TOPICS IN CHAPTER FIVE

1. **World.** H. C. Willet, *Descriptive Meteorology,* 1944 ed., pp. 181–196; Petterssen, *Weather Analysis and Forecasting,* 2d ed., McGraw-Hill Book Company, New York, 1956, pp. 138–204; Petterssen, *Introduction to Meteorology,* pp. 189–203; John R. Borchert, "Regional Differences in the World Atmospheric Circulation," *Ann. Assoc. Amer. Geographers,* Vol. 4, pp. 14–26 1953; Dieter H. Brunnschweiler, "Die Luftmassen der Nordhemisphäre," *Geographica Helvetica,* Vol. 12, pp. 164–195, 1957; *Aviation Weather,* pp. 62–72; Byers, *General Meteorology,* 3d ed., pp. 325–342, 1959; Hare, pp. 57–69; Blair and Fite, pp. 169–177, Haurwitz and Austin, pp. 101–105.

2. **North America.** H. C. Willet, *Descriptive Meteorology,* 1944 ed., pp. 196–224; Willet, "Characteristic Properties of North American Air Masses," in *Air Mass and Isentropic Analysis,* Milton, Mass., 1940, pp. 73–108; Byers, *Synoptical and Aeronautical Meteorology,* pp. 121–136, Byers, *General Meteorology,* 1944 ed., pp. 255–277; Dieter H. Brunnschweiler, "The Geographic Distribution of Air Masses in North

America," *Vierteljahresschr. naturforsch. Ges. Zürich*, Vol. 97, pp. 42–49, 1952.

3. **Europe.** Hare, pp. 157–161; Petterssen, *Weather Analysis and Forecasting*, numerous scattered references to European air masses on pp. 138–204; Byers, *General Meteorology*, 1944 ed., pp. 278–287; J. E. Belasco, "Characteristics of Air Masses in the British Isles," *Geophys. Mem., no.* 87, Great Britain Meteorological Office, 1952. Rudolph Treidl, *European Air Masses*, Canada, Meteorological Division, circular 2298.

4. **Eastern and southern Asia.** H. Arakawa, "The Air Masses of Japan," *Bull. Amer. Meteorol. Soc.*, Vol. 18, pp. 407–410, 1937; Chang-Wang Tu, "Chinese Air Mass Properties," *Quart. J. Roy. Meteorol. Soc.*, Vol. 65, pp. 33–51, 1939; Byers, *General Meteorology*, 1944 ed., pp. 287–291. A. Liu, "The Winter Frontology of China," *Bull. Amer. Meteorol. Soc.*, Vol. 26, pp. 309–314, 1945.

5. **General references on air masses and fronts.** J. Gentilli, "Air Masses of the Southern Hemisphere," *Weather*, Vol. 4, pp. 258–261, 292–297, 1949; H. H. Lamb, "Essay on Frontogenesis and Frontolysis," *Meteorol. Magazine*, Vol. 80, pp. 35–36, 65–71, 97–106, 1951; A. Miller, "Air Mass Climatology," *Geography*, Vol. 38, pp. 55–67, 1953; J. Namias, "An Introduction to the Study of Air Mass Analysis and Isentropic Analysis," *Amer. Meteorol. Soc.*, Milton, Mass., 1940; I. J. W. Pothecary, "Recent Research on Fronts," *Weather*, Vol. 12, pp. 147–150, 1956.

CHAPTER SIX
ATMOSPHERIC DISTURBANCES AND THEIR ASSOCIATED WEATHER

If solar control of the earth's weather were complete, climate would exhibit perfect diurnal and annual rhythms. As the previous chapters have shown, however, the rhythms are there but are far from perfect, for the nonperiodic effects of another control—that of atmospheric disturbances—are superposed on the regular daily and yearly march of solar energy. Atmospheric disturbances are extensive waves, eddies, or whirls of air embedded in the earth's major wind systems. It is they that create the great diversity of weather from day to day and week to week, for they are irregular in their occurrence and have time scales of variable magnitude.

The geographer's interest in atmospheric disturbances stems from the powerful influence they have on weather, and therefore on the distribution of the main climatic elements—solar energy, cloud-precipitation, and temperature. Except where highlands cause an ascent of air, traveling disturbances, or perturbations, furnish the chief mechanisms for elevating deep and extensive masses of the earth's atmosphere. Since these mechanisms in turn generate most of the earth's precipitation, the present chapter concentrates especially on types of disturbances that influence rainfall, either positively or negatively.

Other climatic effects of atmospheric disturbances are also important, however. Through their cloud systems, these storms substantially affect the distribution of solar energy and so are among the determinants of air temperature. And their wind systems carry out the advection which leads to major latitudinal, as well as land-sea, exchanges of heat and moisture.

The atmosphere's traveling disturbances cannot be observed on average monthly, seasonal, and annual charts of pressure and winds; they are entities of shorter, although variable, duration. On the other hand, the seasonal isobaric and wind-flow patterns described in Chapter 3, and shown in Figs. 3.30 and 3.31, are not so easy to see on any particular day's weather map, such as that of the United States or that of the Northern Hemisphere. This is because of the great variety of transient local wave and vortex disturbances which are superimposed on the broader hemispheric patterns of the general circulation (Fig. 6.1). These disturbances, sometimes called the *secondary* circulation, are so numerous that they tend almost to mask the general circulation, just as

Figure 6.1 A series of three vortex disturbances and their associated fronts over the North Pacific Ocean and North America, with TIROS cloud pictures, superimposed on a conventional surface weather chart, May 20, 1960. Such traveling disturbances are especially characteristic of the middle-latitude westerly wind belts and are responsible for much of the weather of those latitudes. (*Prepared by V. J. Oliver, U.S. Weather Bureau.*)

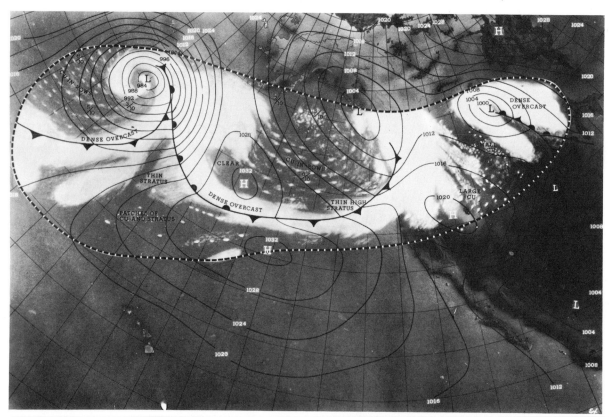

eddies, whirls, and crosscurrents of a river can nearly obscure the general downstream flow of the main current. The disturbance provides the dynamic element in weather and cannot be divorced from climate.

MIDDLE-LATITUDE TRAVELING CYCLONES AND ANTICYCLONES

Although the many disturbed pressure and wind fields shown on the daily surface weather charts have various shapes and patterns, the two most common, and most important in weather and climate, are the cyclone and the anticyclone. In the middle latitudes a succession of alternating low- and high-pressure systems moves from west to east in the stream of the prevailing westerlies (Fig. 6.1). These disturbances, with their accompanying wind, cloud, rainfall, and temperature phenomena, infest the belts of westerly winds and cause the variability and fickleness of weather characteristic of the middle latitudes. Here synoptic- or disturbance-scale systems dominate the distribution of pressure, temperature, and wind at any time; larger- or smaller-scale systems are less important. It is in the middle latitudes that weather forecasting services are most necessary and best developed.

General features. No two cyclones or anticyclones exactly resemble each other. They vary in size, shape, and intensity, as well as in their cloud and rainfall. So the following generalizations must not be expected to apply in all respects to any individual disturbance. Atmospheric disturbances also differ to some extent from one part of the world to another. Even within an area the size of the continental United States, they look and act somewhat differently from region to region.

As can be seen on a surface weather map, cyclones have centers of relatively low pressure surrounded by concentric closed isobars, while anticyclones have cores of relatively high pressure surrounded by closed isobars (Figs. 6.2 and 6.3). A middle-latitude cyclone, therefore, frequently goes by the name of low, depression, or trough if it is elongated. An anticyclone is called a high or, if

elongated, a ridge. Since its surface pressure is low, the cyclone must be a column of air with less mass than an anticyclone. While the isobars of lows and highs are roughly concentric, the shapes of individual storms vary greatly.

In a cyclone the pressure is lowest at the center and increases toward the margins of the storm. In an anticyclone the highest pressure is at the center. However, the terms low and high as applied to pressure in these storms are not precise but relative. No specific amount of pressure separates lows from highs; it is always a comparative matter. Pressure at the center of a weak or moderate low is about 1,000 mb or a little more. It may be as low as 940 to 980 mb in a strong cyclone. Normally the pressure difference between the center and margins of a low is 10 to 20 mb, or several tenths of an inch. In an unusually large and deep winter low, the pressure difference may be as much as 35 mb, or 1 in. An intense high may possibly show an equivalent pressure difference between center and circumference, although normally the difference will be half that amount. There are many more large and vigorous

Figure 6.2 Model cyclone (*A*) and anticyclone (*B*), Northern Hemisphere, showing arrangement of isobars, winds, air masses, and surface fronts.

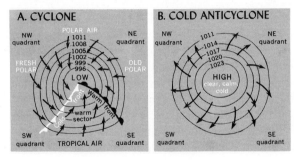

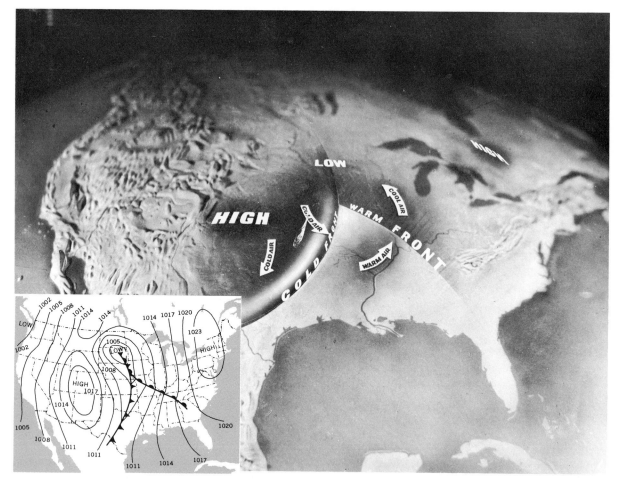

Figure 6.3   If the air masses and fronts were actually visible, the cyclonic disturbance shown on the small inset weather map might appear as represented in the three-dimensional illustration. (*U.S. Weather Bureau.*)

cyclones and anticyclones in winter than summer, so that the cooler seasons have more variable weather.

Because the cyclone is a low-pressure storm, it has a converging surface-wind system of moderate velocity. Rarely are its winds violent or destructive, however. Earth rotation causes the converging winds to approach the low center obliquely, so that the surface-wind arrows make an angle of 20 to 40° with the isobars. Because surface airflow in a low is converging, there must be upward movement and a compensating outflow aloft, commonly with cloud

and precipitation. In the Northern Hemisphere such a converging system of surface winds usually results in a warm sector to the south and east of the center, where the winds are from a southerly direction, and a more extensive cool or cold section to the north and west, where the winds are northerly. The surface winds in a high move obliquely outward from the center toward the circumference; in other words, an anticyclone is a diverging system, with inflow aloft and vertical settling or subsidence feeding the surface currents.

Note, however, that a cyclone or an anticyclone

is not composed of the same air at different times as it shifts its position. Such disturbances are simply pressure systems through which the air moves.

There are great variations in the size of these storms, but typically they spread over extensive areas. Sometimes they cover as much as one-third of the conterminous United States, or 1,000,000 square miles, although most of them are smaller. They are extensive rather than intensive, so that a normal cyclone with a vertical thickness of 6 to 7 miles probably will have a diameter one hundred times as great. Cyclones tend to be elliptical or egg-shaped, with the narrow end toward the equator. The long axis, extending in a northeast-southwest direction, is commonly nearly twice the length of the shorter one. Thus a typical well-developed winter cyclone might have long and short diameters of 1,200 and 650 miles, respectively. Anticyclones are apt to be somewhat larger, with diameters roughly 25 percent longer than those of lows.

Direction and rate of movement. As mentioned earlier, middle-latitude cyclones and anticyclones are carried along by the deep westerly circulation, so that they travel in a general west-to-east direction. This is not to say that such storms always move due east, for they follow different routes, concentrating in some regions and spreading out in others. But in spite of their vagaries in direction, and also in rate of movement, their general progress is eastward.

The direction and rate of movement of cyclones are approximately those of the winds in the free atmosphere. This is why a weather forecaster in the middle latitudes bases his prediction upon weather conditions to the west, rather than to the east, of his station. Disturbances to the east already have gone by; those to the west are approaching. Storms have a tendency to follow certain very general tracks, whose worldwide patterns will be described later in the chapter. Keep in mind that the movement of an atmospheric disturbance involves a pressure system, not a particular body of air. In this respect atmospheric disturbances resemble ocean waves.

Rates of storm movement are variable both as to season and as to individual disturbances. In the United States, cyclones move eastward across the country at velocities averaging 20 miles an hour in summer and 30 miles an hour in winter. Highs are somewhat slower than lows. Speeds are reduced in summer because the whole atmospheric circulation is slowed down, and as a consequence warm-season weather is less changeable. In the winter a well-developed low characteristically requires 3 to 6 days to cross the United States.

Just as temperature, pressure, and wind belts follow the movements of the sun's rays, shifting poleward in summer and equatorward in winter, so also do the storm tracks. This fact helps to explain why storms are fewer and weaker over the lower middle latitudes in summer than in winter.

Origin and structure of middle-latitude cyclones

Middle-latitude depressions appear to consist of a variety of disturbances, not all of which have the same origin. A few seem to develop as eddies on the lee side of highlands—for example, in the eastern foothill region of the North American Rockies. Occasionally small, short-lived depressions form within homogeneous, unstable polar maritime air. Such depressions are fairly common in the British Isles. Other weak disturbances appear to develop as a consequence of intense and prolonged solar heating. But the great majority of surface cyclonic storms of middle latitudes which appear on the daily weather map seem to begin as waves along surface fronts separating cold and warm air masses.

Doubtless the genesis of many surface cyclones and anticyclones is closely linked to conditions in the upper-troposphere waves and jet streams. On occasions the flow patterns aloft favor cyclogenesis at low levels; at other times they are neutral or oppose it. However, the same patterns do not produce the same results in all locations. Figures 6.4 and 6.5 represent a fairly common situation in the case of a developing cyclone. Since surface barometric pressure varies only modestly, mass convergence at the surface must be nearly compensated for by divergence aloft. Conversely, divergence at

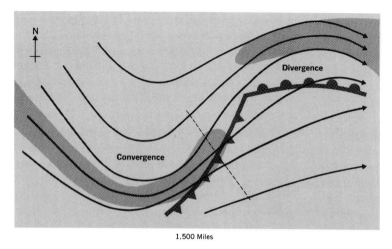

1,500 Miles

Figure 6.4 Model of flow pattern in troposphere above a developing wave cyclone. Cold and warm surface fronts are shown. Shaded bands indicate location of jet streams. (*From Herbert Riehl, Introduction to the Atmosphere.*)

the surface must be replaced by convergence aloft.

Although many times the upper flow provides the key for a cyclone's beginning, yet there is also clear evidence of instances where surface disturbances build upward from the earth's surface to create the wave aloft. Since historically it was the surface disturbances that were studied first, and since it is these which are most easily observed and about which most is known, cyclones will be analyzed here in relation to fronts at the lower levels.

Preceding cyclogenesis, there is a quasi-stationary front separating a colder and a warmer air mass. The winds in each are parallel to the surface front, and they may blow from opposite directions (Fig. 6.6A), or even from the same direction provided they have different speeds. As noted in Chapter 5, because of Coriolis force the colder air underlies the warmer in the form of a gently sloping wedge, whose inclination may be on the order of 1 to 100. At this stage neither air mass has a significant sustained component of motion toward the front; any upglide of the warm air over the cold wedge is minor. That there is some, however, is indicated by a fair amount of cloud—usually stratus—within the warm air just above the frontal surface. Since well-developed fronts rarely remain stationary or undisturbed for long, the existence of such a front portends imminent wave and cyclone development.

Stages in the life history of a cyclone. Often the most easily detected first evidence of wave development along a front is an expansion and intensification of the cloud and precipitation areas, together with a general fall of pressure, around the nascent wave. When this occurs, closer inspection usually reveals that a shallow indentation is forming along the front (Fig. 6.6B). Such an incipient wave is observable both on the above-surface discontinuity and along the surface front.

Exactly how a frontal wave gets its start is not always clear. Some may result just from the temperature contrast or the opposing air motion along a front. Others appear to develop in what may be called favorable type locations—for example, on the lee side of highlands, or in areas where steep temperature gradients exist between continents and oceans. Still others may be induced by a neighboring disturbance, or by the approach of an upper-level trough. In its initial stage, where the warm air thrusts only a shallow salient into the colder air mass, there is no great difference between the warm and cold fronts.

The incipient wave moves rapidly eastward along the front. If the length of the wave is less than about 300 miles, it is said to be stable, for it does not evolve into a full scale cyclone, although it usually intensifies the bad weather. Larger waves, on the other hand, ordinarily grow rapidly as the wedge of warm air becomes increasingly more deeply embedded in the mass of cold air. Pressure falls, weather worsens, and a young cyclone with closed isobars forms at the apex of the wave.

Anywhere from 30 to 60 hours after the first appearance of the wave, the cyclone reaches the stage of early maturity (Fig. 6.6C). The depression is roughly circular, the warm sector is broad and deep, clearly defined warm and cold fronts have evolved, and cloud and precipitation are widespread.

From this stage on through full maturity, decline, and finally old age, the more rapidly advancing cold front begins to overtake the slower-moving warm front. Commencing at the warm-sector apex, the warm air is gradually pinched out at the surface, and *occlusion* is said to occur (Fig. 6.6E). With oc-

Figure 6.5 Coupling between waves in the upper westerlies and high- and low-pressure systems near surface. *Top:* Horizontal view of upper jet-stream core in relation to surface systems. *Bottom:* Vertical cross section showing the convergent and divergent parts of the atmospheric motion in the horizontal plane, and vertical motion (white arrows). (*From Herbert Riehl, Introduction to the Atmosphere.*)

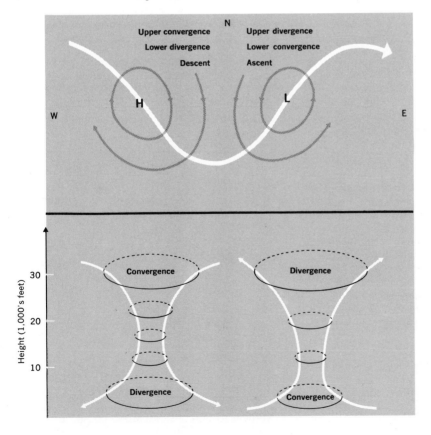

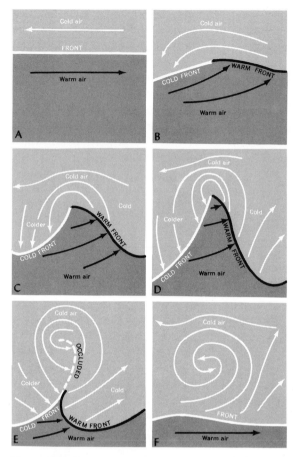

During the life cycle of a middle-latitude cyclone, the warm air which initially existed side by side with the cold air is lifted to higher and higher levels, and the cold and heavier air comes to occupy the lower levels. By this process the center of gravity of the whole cyclone system is lowered and potential energy is released. Such vertical movement provides the main source of energy for cyclone growth as represented in the kinetic energy of the cyclone's wind system. A subordinate source of energy is latent heat of condensation.

The cyclone model. A well-developed cyclone in a stage of early maturity is portrayed in Fig. 6.7. The middle drawing, (b), represents the cyclone as it appears on the surface weather map. The upper part of the figure (a) is a vertical cross section through

Figure 6.6 Six stages in the life cycle of a frontal cyclone. Drawing *B* shows the beginning of a small horizontal wave along the front. In drawing *C* the wave development has progressed to the point where there is a definite cyclonic circulation with well-developed warm and cold fronts. Because of the more rapid movement of the cold front, drawing *D* shows a narrowed warm sector as the cold front approaches the retreating warm front. In drawing *E* the occlusion process is occurring, the cyclone has reached its maximum development, and the warm sector is being rapidly pinched off. In drawing *F* the warm sector has been eliminated; the cyclone is in its dying stages and is represented only by a whirl of cold air.

Figure 6.7 Cyclone model: Ground plan (b) and vertical sections (a) and (c) of a Northern Hemisphere cyclone in a stage of early maturity, before occlusion has commenced.

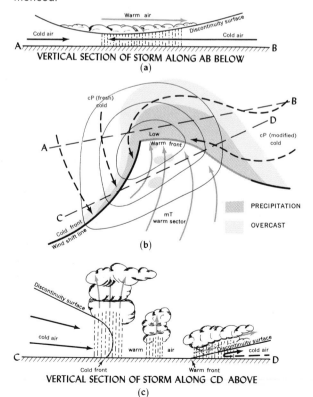

clusion the total area of the warm sector shrinks. Eventually as the warm air disappears at the surface, the cyclone at lower levels becomes an immense vortex of relatively homogeneous air (Fig. 6.6 *F*).

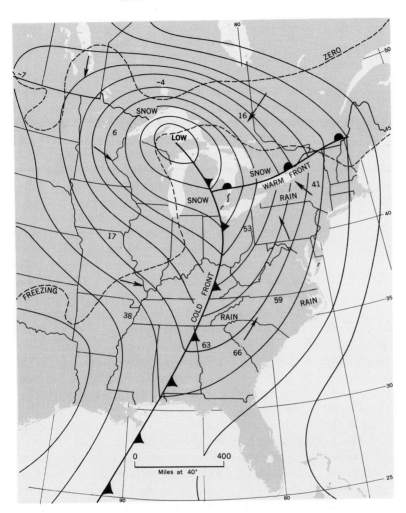

Figure 6.8   Section of a surface weather map showing a well-developed wave cyclone over central and eastern North America. This representation of a particular cyclone should be compared with the ground plan of the model cyclone in Fig. 6.7b.

the cyclone north of its center. The lower part (c) is a similar vertical cross section south of its center. In the cross section *AB* to the north of the storm center, the warm air is present aloft but does not reach the earth's surface. It is the continued lifting of the warm air aloft that produces the precipitation shown. South of the center, warm air does reach down to the earth's surface. As the vertical cross section along line *CD* shows, this warm sector is bounded by two surface fronts.

Thus a cyclone consists of two essentially different air masses separated from one another by fronts (Figs. 6.7 and 6.8). To the south and east is the warm sector—a poleward projection of warmer air, many times of tropical origin, which is enveloped on its western, northern, and northeastern sides by colder air, usually of polar origin. The nature of this polar air varies with different locations and source regions. In North America east of the Rocky Mountains, the fresh polar air to the west and

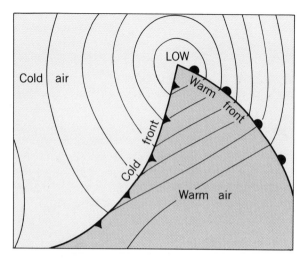

Figure 6.9 A cold front and a warm front on a surface weather map.

northwest is usually colder than the old polar air to the east and northeast, which has been considerably modified by several days' travel over the middle latitudes.

The discontinuity surface separating the polar and tropical air masses may be classified as a warm or a cold front, depending on whether the warm or the cold air is the aggressor (Fig. 6.9). Where warm air leaves the earth's surface and actively moves upward over a retreating wedge of cold air, as it does ahead of the eastward-shifting tongue of tropical air, a warm front develops. On the other hand, a cold front forms when advancing cold air aggressively undercuts warm air and brings about its forced ascent, which happens to the rear, or west, of the warm sector. Along a warm front, warm air replaces cold air at the ground; along a cold front, cold air replaces warm. Warm fronts in the central and eastern United States most commonly develop as a consequence of *mT*-Gulf air overrunning modified polar air with a southerly component. The latter is returning poleward on the rear of a retreating anticyclone (Fig. 6.6D). Note that there is an upward movement of air in at least two separate areas: (1) along the warm front, where the faster-moving warm air upglides over the eastward-retreating

wedge of cold air, and (2) along the cold front, where the more rapidly advancing cold air thrusts under the warm air ahead of it.

Warm fronts. The inclination of the surface of discontinuity in a warm front is relatively gentle, usually on the order of 1:100 to 1:200. In other words, if an aircraft were flying 5,000 ft above the ground and at right angles to the front, it would cross the boundary separating the two air masses 100 to 200 miles ahead (east) of the surface front (Figs. 6.9 and 6.10). As the warm air slowly glides up the gently inclined surface of the cold-air wedge, adiabatic cooling results and may lead to cloud condensation and precipitation. Any vertical component of the warm air along the warm-front surface of discontinuity is likely to be small, except where convection develops. Frictional drag tends to thin out and flatten the wedge of retreating cold air near the surface front. This, together with the mixing of air that occurs along the front, tends to blend the two air masses within the contact zone so that it may be difficult to locate the warm front at the surface with any precision. The change in temperature and wind direction is transitional rather than abrupt.

Because of the west-to-east movement of the cyclone and the arrangement of fronts within it, warm-front weather phenomena are the first indications of an approaching cyclonic storm. Since the discontinuity surface has such a mild inclination, signs of it in the form of certain high-level cloud types may be seen as far as 500 to 1,000 miles ahead of the surface front. The first clouds heralding the storm are the high cirrus and cirrostratus, the latter creating the familiar halos around sun and moon. If the overrunning warm air is unstable, cirrocumulus will appear, producing the well-known "mackerel sky" recognized by sailors as a harbinger of stormy weather. As the front approaches and the wedge of cold air thins, the cloud deck becomes lower and thicker. Altostratus and altocumulus deepen into stratocumulus and finally nimbus. Seen from below, the warm-front cloud deck is a formless gray overcast, known as nimbostratus. Precipitation usually begins with the altostratus and continues until the surface front has passed. Soon after the rain starts, clouds and fog commonly form within the cold air mass below the discontinuity surface. These are largely the result of evaporation from raindrops and

Figure 6.10 Warm fronts in vertical cross section: (*a*) A warm front with stable warm air. (*b*) A warm front with unstable warm air. (*c*) A wavy warm-front surface.

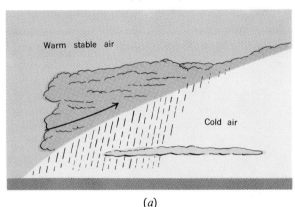

Warm stable air

Cold air

(*a*)

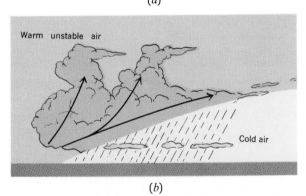

Warm unstable air

Cold air

(*b*)

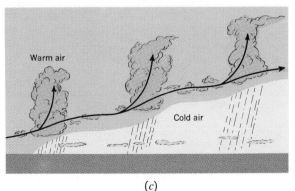

Warm air

Cold air

(*c*)

surface water. The suddenness with which these lower clouds and fog appear makes them a hazard to air navigation.

The character of the weather at the warm front depends mainly upon the nature of the overrunning warm air. If it is dry and stable, considerable ascent will be necessary to produce any condensation forms, and precipitation will be light if it occurs at all. On the other hand, if the warm air is conditionally or convectively unstable, ascent over the cold wedge may be vigorous enough to trigger showers, and even thunderstorms in the warmer months (Fig. 6.10). To the observer at the ground, the rain appears to be coming from the cold air. Most of it, however, has its origin in the overrunning warm air aloft. Because of the cold air at the surface, the weather is likely to be chilly, damp and disagreeable, with low visibility. It was such weather that a New England poet had in mind when he wrote

> The day is cold and dark and dreary;
>   It rains and the wind is never weary.
> The vine still clings to the moldering wall,
>   And with every gust the dead leaves fall,
> And the day is dark and dreary.

Because of the slight inclination but great horizontal extent of the surface of discontinuity, warm-front precipitation is inclined to be fairly steady, long-continued, and widespread. It is not unusually heavy, however; unless the ascending air is so unstable that convective showers result from the lifting along the front.

With the passage of a warm front at the surface, the following weather changes are likely: (1) marked clearing, (2) a distinct temperature rise, (3) a rapid increase in specific humidity, (4) a slight barometric trough, (5) a small shift in wind direction—usually about 45°.

Warm sector. Within the warm sector of a cyclone, which is situated south of the center and between the warm and cold fronts, the weather depends on the nature of the air mass and the season (Fig. 6.7). Here there is no large-scale upglide of air along fronts. Still, the wedge of warm air, gradually shrinking in area because of the scissors action of the two bounding fronts, is a region of convergence which has some upward air movement and cloud. In summer over the central and eastern United States, the unstable *mT* air in the warm sector may give rise to a broken cloud deck, with cumulus clouds and occasional convective showers and thunderstorms. In western Europe, warm-sector air is more stable in summer, and a stratus overcast with drizzle is characteristic. Warm-sector winter weather in the United States, especially where the surface has a snow cover, brings more stratus cloud, drizzle, and advection fog.

Cold fronts.   In this type of discontinuity the warm air is forced to rise by the aggressive action of the eastward-moving wedge of cold air (Fig. 6.11). Along such a front, cold air replaces warmer air. When cold fronts are well developed, they are easily recognized on the weather map by their marked wind discontinuities, which are known as wind-shift lines.

Under normal conditions the slope of a cold-front surface of discontinuity is considerably steeper than that of a warm front, being usually on the order of 1:50 to 1:100. This difference between cold and warm fronts is largely due to the contrasting effects of frictional forces. Along the warm front, a drag effect upon the retreating wedge of cold air tends to thin it out and reduce its slope. Along the cold front, the advancing cold air at the ground is held back by friction, which gives it a tendency to push forward aloft, thereby increasing the discontinuity slope. Characteristically the forward edge of a rapidly moving cold front is steepened and blunted, as shown in Fig. 6.7c. Here the cold air aloft may even push out ahead of the front at the ground, obviously creating a highly unstable condition and tumultuous weather. Where the front moves more slowly, the air aloft has less tendency toward overrunning, and the weather is less turbulent.

Since the surface of discontinuity slopes upward away from the direction of storm movement, the approach of the cold front is not heralded far in

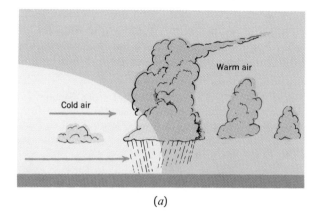

(a)

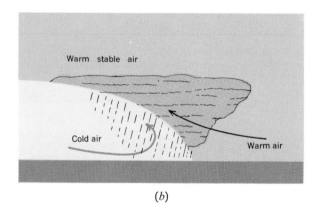

(b)

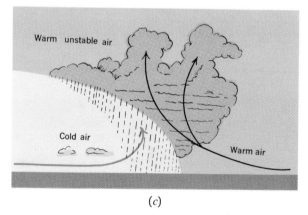

(c)

Figure 6.11   Cold fronts in vertical cross section: (a) A fast-moving cold front, with unstable warm air. (b) A slow-moving cold front, with stable warm air. (c) A slow-moving cold front, with unstable warm air.

advance by cloud forms or other weather phenomena. Moreover, the zone of bad weather associated with rising air is much narrower at the cold than at the warm front and so passes more rapidly. To some extent the cold front's comparative narrowness is due to its greater speed and steeper slope. Mainly, however, this difference exists between the two fronts because warm air moves in opposite directions with respect to them. If the cold front moves rapidly and steadily, clearing takes place quickly after it has passed. If it is retarded for any reason, the sky may remain cloudy for some time.

The nature of the weather along the cold front depends in a large degree upon the structure of the warm air that is being displaced. If it is dry and stable, the front may be accompanied only by broken clouds, with no precipitation (Fig. 6.11). On the other hand, if it is warm, humid mT-Gulf air, cumulonimbus clouds and frontal thunderstorms are likely. But on the whole, owing to the steeper slope of the cold-front surface of discontinuity, and to the blunter forward nose of the rapidly advancing wedge of cold air, the upthrust of warm air along the cold front is more vigorous than along the warm front. This results in more tumultuous weather and in pelting rains, although their duration is shorter than warm-front rains. Cloud forms along a cold front tend to be of the cumulus and cumulonimbus types, but stratus types may also appear. In some cases most of the precipitation falls in advance of the front; in others it occurs in the cold air behind the front.

If an unusually cold and vigorous air mass back of a cold front passes over a warmer water surface, the addition of heat and moisture in the lower layers often leads to development of heavy rain or snow showers, with the precipitation originating in the cold air. This phenomenon is most common in late fall and early winter, when temperature contrasts between air and water are most marked. Similar snow flurries may occur over land areas where the land is distinctly warmer than the southward-advancing cold air mass.

With the passage of a cold front, the following

weather changes are characteristic: (1) a marked clearing and improvement in the weather, usually fairly rapid, (2) an abrupt fall in temperature, (3) a well-defined barometric trough, (4) a pronounced decrease in specific and relative humidity, and (5) a pronounced wind shift of 45 to 180°.

Occluded fronts.   Since the cold front of a cyclone normally travels at about twice the speed of the warm front, it gradually approaches and eventually overtakes the warm front. Occlusion is a normal development in the life history of middle-latitude cyclones (Fig. 6.6). It begins at the apex of the warm sector near the center of the storm and gradually progresses equatorward until the warm sector has been completely obliterated at the surface. Thus the cyclone is partly occluded during the major part of its life history. Actually it usually reaches its maximum intensity 12 to 24 hr after the beginning of the occlusion process. Although the two polar air masses involved in the occlusion may have had a similar origin, their routes since leaving the source regions have usually been different enough that their temperatures, humidities, and densities are no longer the same. Consequently as the cold front overtakes the warm front, a new discontinuity—this one between the two polar air masses—is created. When the air behind the cold front is colder than that ahead of the warm front (which is usually the case in the central and eastern United States) the resulting discontinuity will resemble a new cold front to some extent, although one without sharp temperature contrasts (Fig. 6.12). But when the air ahead of the warm front is colder than that behind the cold front, the occlusion, and the weather, at the surface will be more of the warm-front type (Fig. 6.12*b*).

Precipitation along occluded fronts results from both the continued lifting of the warm air aloft and the vertical displacement of the less dense of the cold air masses. As occlusion continues, the depth of cold air along the occluded front increases, and the warm air is crowded further upward until it is high enough to spread out laterally over the cold air masses enclosing it. When it does spread lat-

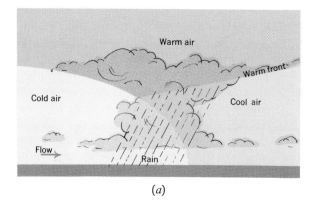

(a)

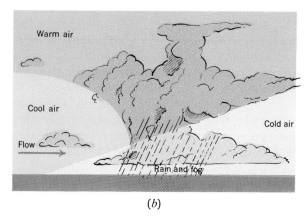

(b)

Figure 6.12 An occluded cyclone in vertical cross section: (a) Cold-front occlusion. (b) Warm-front occlusion.

erally, further lifting of the warm air ceases, and that particular air mass plays no further part in cloud and rain production. Subsequently the weather conditions are governed by the contrasts in the characteristics of the two cold air masses, one on either side of the occluded front.

In its later stages of occlusion a cyclone weakens, and precipitation is less abundant than earlier in the storm's life cycle. The temperature and density contrasts between the cold air masses comprising the cyclone are not marked, and the heat of condensation derived from lifting the cool air is not great, so that the storm's energy sources are reduced. There may be an extensive cloud cover, but usually the clouds are not thick and the precipitation is

light. Lifting of the cool air mass does not ordinarily lead to heavy rains, for the air's moisture content is relatively low and the air mass is likely to be stable. Regions with a predominance of occluded cyclones, such as western Europe, have a great deal of low cloud, usually only modest amounts of precipitation, and small daily as well as nonperiodic temperature changes.

Stationary fronts. A front between two opposing air masses which shows little or no movement, with neither air mass replacing the other, is a stationary front. The weather along such a front resembles that accompanying a warm front, but is usually less intense. A feature of stationary fronts is that their bad weather conditions may persist over a region for a number of days.

Families of cyclones. Toward the terminal part of a cyclone's occluded stage, and along its southwesterly-trailing cold front, a new wave often develops. And as this second wave matures, still a third and a fourth may develop behind it. Thus there comes to be a whole family of four or five cyclones strung out along a single frontal system, each progressively smaller than the preceding one, and each developing farther equatorward. In such a family of cyclones the easternmost unit is likely to be fully occluded, while that farthest to the southwest is still in an incipient stage. The last wave in such a series is commonly followed by a great outbreak of fresh polar air, which may surge far southward, even into the tropics.

Origins and structure of middle-latitude anticyclones

Chapter 3 on pressure and wind systems described the great seasonally permanent anticyclonic systems: both the cold anticyclones of high latitudes and the warm subtropical anticyclones of lower latitudes. This chapter will deal with moving anticyclones of the middle latitudes. These are by no means, however, completely divorced from the larger more permanent systems of Chapter 3.

Anticyclonic disturbances have received less attention from students of the atmosphere than cyclones, so that less is known concerning their origin and structure. Probably there are various types of moving anticyclones, but the usual classification recognizes two main groups: the cold and the warm. This obviously follows the division made for Chapter 3's more durable and stationary high-pressure systems. Some authorities would also specify a third type which includes the sluggish systems which seem to fill the spaces between the more vigorous individual cyclones. These somewhat inert wedges of high pressure bring clearing weather after the cyclone's cloud and rain. Their clear skies in turn promote large diurnal ranges in temperature, with marked night cooling. Although they probably have various origins, superficially they come to resemble a mild form of cold anticyclone over middle-latitude continents.

Cold anticyclones, which have abnormally cold air in the lower troposphere, are sometimes called "polar-outbreak highs." They are rapidly moving masses of cold air that emerge from the subpolar regions and are drawn toward lower latitudes on the rear of a well-developed depression, often the last in a cyclone family. Such cold polar-outbreak highs slow down as they move equatorward and eastward across the middle latitudes. In the subtropics they are gradually transformed into warm anticyclones. Occasionally, however, they break through into the inner tropics. In the Northern Hemisphere there are two general major routes, one from northern Canada southward and southeastward across the central eastern United States, and the other from intensely cold eastern Siberia across northern China and Japan. Such cold anticyclones are dome-shaped pools of cold air whose high pressure is due to the weight of this dense air.

The exact ways by which a cold anticyclone is formed are still somewhat obscure. One element seems to be the strong radiational cooling of the lower air as it rests on a snow-covered polar or subpolar surface. A strong southward surge of cold air in the surface anticyclone, however, is usually initiated by an expulsion of cold Arctic Basin air aloft, acting in conjunction with an upper-troposphere long wave. Cold anticyclones are commonly con-

fined to the lower 5,000 to 10,000 ft of atmosphere. There is usually marked subsidence within them, so that a pronounced inversion is present and the air is very stable. When they have little wind, a surface inversion likewise develops. Such anticyclones typically bring clear, dry, cold weather.

Warm anticyclones, while certainly arising from dynamic (not thermal) effects, remain something of a mystery as far as origin is concerned. They are characterized by slow rates of movement, great vertical depth, and unusual warmth throughout the troposphere (except in the lowest layers, where there may be some radiational cooling). Subsidence is marked throughout, inversions often develop, and clear, dry weather is the rule. Precipitation is uncommon, although along certain subtropical west coasts paralleled by cool ocean currents, a deck of stratus cloud associated with a strong low-level inversion may produce some drizzle.

Warm anticyclones are most common in the subtropical latitudes, especially over the oceans and adjacent parts of continents. This is the realm of the great semipermanent highs. From these extensive subtropical anticyclones, local buds or cells in the form of slow-moving warm highs frequently emerge and travel eastward and poleward into the middle latitudes. There, if their trajectory is over continents in winter, they are gradually transformed into cold anticyclones. In reality, some of the so-called permanent subtropical high-pressure cells seem to be just monthly and seasonal averages of traveling warm anticyclones, especially in the Southern Hemisphere.

Compared with cyclonic weather, weather associated with an anticyclone is much more autonomous or independent of influences outside its own system. The clear skies, weak and divergent air movement, and general subsidence of anticyclones make for weather that is strongly regional and diurnal in character. It is little affected by advection from outside sources. By contrast, cyclonic weather, in which the emphasis is on advective processes, is powerfully influenced by outside conditions, that are brought by a converging circulation into the cyclone's system. This advection, together with the cloud cover characteristic of cyclones, results in weather that is more nonperiodic than diurnal.

Wind systems

Cyclones.   Paramount features of cyclones are the surface convergence and ascent of air within them (Figs. 6.2 and 6.13). Various modifications of a simple converging spiraling system of winds result from such effects as terrain irregularities, as well as from the fact that the depression is not a stationary but a moving system traveling at speeds of 500 to 1,000 miles a day. Also, in any converging system of winds in middle latitudes, air masses of contrasting temperatures and densities are almost bound to be drawn into the vortex system on its northern and southern sectors in a manner which departs from a symmetrical in-spiral. In Fig. 6.7b, for example, although a convergent airflow is still conspicuous, there are two contrasting air masses: a warmer one to the south and a colder one enveloping it on the north, west, and northeast.

As a result of the converging circulation about a cyclonic center, surface winds on the front of the center (east, or in the direction the storm is traveling) are from a general easterly and southerly direction—southeast, east, and northeast in the northeastern quadrant, and south and southeast in

Figure 6.13   Circulations in a cyclone and anticyclone in the Southern Hemisphere. Note that the cyclonic circulation here is clockwise and that of the anticyclone is anticlockwise—just opposite to those in the Northern Hemisphere.

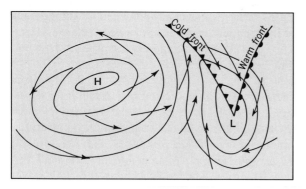

the southeastern quadrant. These easterly and southerly winds on the front of the cyclone can be either polar or tropical air, depending on the directional trend of the warm front. One cannot be certain of the primary origin of the air merely by observing wind direction, for the modified polar air on the front of a cyclone is frequently a southeasterly current. This is polar air that was brought southward in a preceding anticyclone and has had a relatively long trajectory over the middle latitudes.

Obviously all these easterly winds on the front of a cyclone are blowing opposite to the deep planetary westerlies in which they exist, and also opposite to the direction of storm movement. Thus while the storm travels from west to east, the winds on its front typically have an easterly component. This characteristic of a cyclone, which as a whole is an eddy or vortex in the westerly circulation, has a counterpart in the whirlpool in a river. The whirlpool of water is carried downstream by the major current just as the cyclonic vortex is carried eastward by the westerlies. On the whirlpool's downstream side, the water flows into the whirl in a direction opposite to that of the general current, and also opposite to the downstream movement of the whirlpool itself.

Wind shift with the passing of a cyclone.   When a cyclonic center approaches and passes by an observer, he will have general easterly winds as long as the low center is to the west of him and he is on the front of the vortex. As the center passes by, leaving him in the western, or rear, part of the low, the winds shift to the west. Easterly winds, therefore, frequently indicate the approach of a cyclone with its accompanying rain and cloud, while westerly winds more often foretell the retreat eastward of the storm center and the approach of clearing weather accompanying the following anticyclone.

In many cyclones this shift from easterly to westerly winds is gradual. But in others—especially in storms that have a marked equatorward elongation, so that the isobars are roughly in the form of the letter V—the wind shift is likely to be abrupt (Fig. 6.8). Along the wind-shift line, which is approximately a line joining the apexes of the V-shaped isobars south of the center, winds of contrasting temperature, humidity, and density meet at a sharp angle, and in the warmer months vigorous thunderstorms and turbulent weather conditions often result. This wind-shift line is the cold front described earlier.

Veering and backing winds. If the center of a cyclone passes to the north of the observer, so that he is in the southern quadrants of the storm, the succession of winds will be from southeast to west and northwest by way of south (Fig. 6.14). This is called a veering wind shift. If the storm center passes south of the observer, so that he is on the north side of the cyclone, his winds will shift from northeast to northwest by way of north. This is known as a backing wind shift.

Backing and veering winds have important climatic significance. A veering wind shift is likely to involve a succession of modified polar air, tropical air, and fresh polar air, as well as one or more fronts. With a backing wind shift, the observer is continuously in air of polar origin, and surface fronts are less likely. Therefore regions which commonly lie on the equatorward sides of passing cyclones and experience veering winds advecting some warm air are likely to have relatively higher average temper-

atures, greater variability of temperature, stronger convection, and more cumulus clouds than they would if they were located poleward of the cyclonic centers. Backing winds with their cold-air advection are associated with generally lower temperatures, less variability in temperature, a more continuous cloud cover, and greater likelihood of snow in winter.

Anticyclones. Key elements of anticyclonic circulation are subsidence and surface divergence. The wind systems of highs and lows, therefore, are opposite—in direction of gradient-induced flow, in direction of spiral rotation, and in the nature of the vertical movement.

Anticyclonic wind systems are usually less well developed than those of cyclones, so that no characteristic wind shift is forecast as they pass by. In general, however, winds on the front (east) of an eastward-advancing high are northwesterly, while those on the rear are southeasterly (Figs. 6.2*B* and 6.15). Since lows and highs often alternate with one another as they move across the country, it is evident that the westerly winds on the front of a high and the rear of a low have a similar origin and are much alike in character.

Pressure gradients are usually less steep, and wind velocities lower, in anticyclones than in cyclones. Weak pressure gradients are particularly conspicuous toward the centers of slow-moving or stagnant highs, where there is much light wind and calm. The strongest winds are likely to be found on the front margin of a rapidly advancing cold high, for there the high is merging with the preceding low. In this location between a cyclonic and an anticyclonic system, the isobars, which are closely spaced, tend to become nearly parallel straight lines trending in a general north-south direction. Winds here are vigorous northwest ones, a feature stemming from a steep surface pressure gradient and a strong westerly circulation aloft. Cold waves and blizzards over central and eastern North America are associated with these strong outpourings of cold air in the transition areas between the rears of lows and the fronts of cold highs. (See Fig. 6.15.)

Figure 6.14 Illustrating veering and backing wind shifts with the passing of a cyclonic disturbance to the north or to the south of a station. Numerals 1, 2, 3 represent a time sequence.

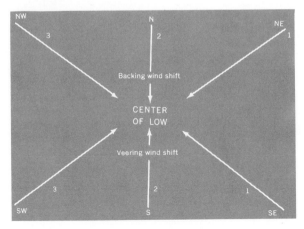

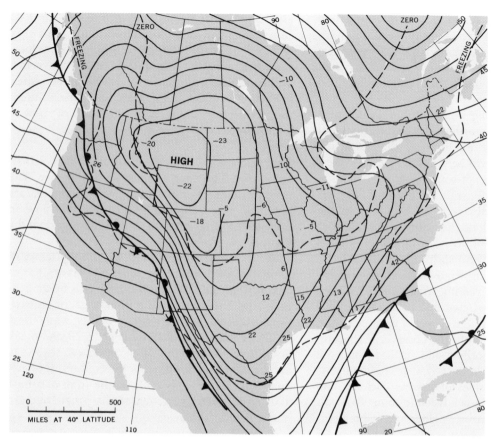

Figure 6.15 Polar-outbreak cold anticyclone advancing rapidly southward as a mass of unusually cold and stable *cP* air. On this occasion Minot, North Dakota, had a minimum temperature of 23° below zero, Denver −18°, and Jackson, Mississippi, 15°. Below-freezing night temperatures were common along the margins of the Gulf of Mexico. (*From Weatherwise, June, 1962.*)

Warm highs, which are subtropical in origin, normally have weaker pressure gradients and less well developed wind systems than cold highs, and their movement is likely to be much slower (Fig. 6.16). They are apt to remain stagnant over an area for days at a time.

Precipitation

Since the convergent circulation and upward air movement of cyclones are conducive to condensation, they are commonly accompanied by large areas of cloud, and often by precipitation as well. To be sure, not every cyclone brings rain, but many of them do. Anticyclones, in contrast, are likely to be fair-weather areas with fewer clouds and meager rainfall. This is because the subsidence and lateral spreading of the air in an anticyclone operate to create stability and to prevent a conflict of air masses and the formation of fronts.

Even though anticyclones are in general fair-weather systems, it is not correct to assume that rainfall is never associated with them. If the easterly and southerly circulation on the rear of a warm anti-

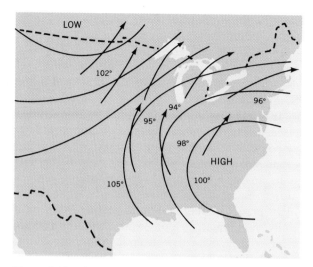

Figure 6.16 A warm anticyclone with clear skies, relatively stagnant over the southeastern United States. Such a synoptic feature produces unseasonably hot weather in the central and eastern parts of the country.

cyclone comes from a warm water surface, it may provide an environment modestly conducive to some shower activity. Similarly, the cold northwest winds on the front of a polar-outbreak anticyclone in winter may generate snow showers on the windward shores of a large lake. And occasionally the circulation aloft may be opposite to that at the surface—for example, a surface anticyclone may be capped by a cyclonic circulation at higher levels—creating circumstances which produce uncertain weather conditions.

Precipitation areas within a cyclone. In both summer and winter, cyclones are the great generators of precipitation within the middle latitudes. Even most of the convective shower activity and thunderstorms of the warmer months appear to be of an organized type, patterned in distribution and located within the generally convergent wind systems of passing extensive depressions. It should be stressed that precipitation in any disturbance would be minor and brief if new supplies of water vapor were not constantly being imported by winds to any area where rain is falling.

Neither the probability of precipitation nor its nature and origin are the same in all parts of a cyclone. In general, the front or eastern half has more cloud and rain than the rear or western half, although the rear is not completely rainless. Clouds usually extend much farther ahead of the center than to the rear, partly because of the location and arrangement of fronts within the cyclone and partly because the front or eastern half of a low is an area of more pronounced and extensive horizontal convergence than the rear. In well-developed winter lows, snow is more common in the cooler northern and northeastern parts, while rain occurs more frequently in the warmer southerly sections. Heavy snows over the central and eastern United States usually arrive when storms travel the more southerly routes, so that the central and northern states are on the poleward sides of the cyclones.

As discussed in an earlier section, two of the main areas of precipitation within a cyclone develop in conjunction with the broad-scale lifting of air that occurs along both the warm and the cold fronts (Fig. 6.7). As occlusion proceeds within the maturing or aging depression, the occluded front as well may tend to localize precipitation. In addition to frontal shower activity, non-frontal rain resulting from general convergence occurs in other parts of a cyclone. In Anglo-America and eastern Asia, showery rains unrelated to fronts are most common within the warm sector of lows. A feature of the warm sector of certain cyclones with especially well-developed cold fronts is the prefrontal squall line, which is accompanied by strong winds, heavy showers, and thunderstorms (Fig. 6.29). Such prefrontal squall lines may precede the actual cold front by 100 to 200 miles. Their origin is not well understood.

Surface temperatures

In themselves cyclones and anticyclones are neither always warm nor always cold. Their surface temperatures depend upon (1) the source and nature of the air masses involved, (2) the season of the year with their varying lengths of day and changing angle of sun's rays, and (3) the degree of humidity and cloudiness. To a large degree an analysis of surface-air temperatures in cyclones becomes a study of the air masses that comprise individual disturbances, for both advection and the heat exchange between atmosphere and ground are major determinants of temperature. In addition, temperature is almost as much a function of the cloud deck (or lack of it) as of the air mass. Winter night minima between nearby stations, one cloudy and the other clear, may differ by as much as 20 to 30°.

Anticyclones. In the winter season a vigorous, well-developed high, advancing rapidly toward the central and eastern United States from northern Canada, moves as a mass of cold, dry polar continental air with clear skies (Fig. 6.15). Such a cold anticyclone brings the cold waves and bitterest winter weather. This type of high is cold for two reasons: (1) it travels rapidly southward from subarctic regions as a mass of cold polar continental air, and (2) its dry, clear air fosters rapid and prolonged losses of the earth's heat during long winter nights. An anticyclone composed of modified polar maritime air brings much less severe winter weather to the interior of the country, although its night temperatures also are likely to be below normal. Even in summer, a well-developed polar continental high advects unseasonably low temperatures, providing several days of clear, cool delightful weather. Pleasantly warm days are followed by cool nights, creating large diurnal ranges. Thus in the middle latitudes many people associate highs with low temperatures for the season.

In summer, however, when a large, relatively stagnant warm high composed of air of subtropical or tropical origin spreads over the south central part of the country, it is likely to produce excessively high temperatures, called hot waves, over the central and eastern United States (Fig. 6.16). The same clear skies and dry air that make for rapid terrestrial radiation during the long winter nights are conducive to maximum receipts of strong solar radiation during long summer days. Moreover, as the tropical air from this anticyclone moves northward over the

country, the south winds carry heat absorbed in the lower latitudes. These same stagnant warm highs over the south central part of the country can also bring clear, mild days in the cooler seasons, such as October and November's much-cherished Indian Summer weather.

In summary, anticyclones may be composed of either polar or tropical air masses and so may be responsible for either cold or warm weather. Vigorous moving cold highs arriving from higher latitudes are likely to bring lower-than-normal temperatures, especially in winter. Weak, stagnant warm highs produce abnormally high temperatures, especially in summer. In both winter and summer the clear skies associated with anticyclones are conducive to large diurnal swings in the temperature curve.

Cyclones. A well-developed cyclone, accompanied by an extensive cover of low clouds and perhaps precipitation, is likely to bring temperatures that are higher than average in winter and somewhat lower than average in summer—just the opposite of those induced by an anticyclone. During the long winter nights, the cloud cover and humid air of a cyclone tend to prevent rapid loss of earth heat. The same conditions in summer, when days are long and the sun stronger, tend to reduce incoming solar radiation.

Temperature contrasts within different parts of a cyclone. These general rules concerning lows and seasonal temperatures cannot be accepted too literally, however. Within its several parts or quadrants a cyclone usually has marked temperature contrasts, depending upon the air masses that are represented. Thus in central and eastern North America the south and southeast part of a low, which is the warm sector of tropical air, is considerably warmer than the north and west portion, where the air movement is from cooler higher latitudes. These temperature importations cause the isotherms in cyclones to be skewed in a counterclockwise fashion, so that they assume a north-northeast by south-southwest alignment instead of the normal east-west direction. Warm-air advection by southerly

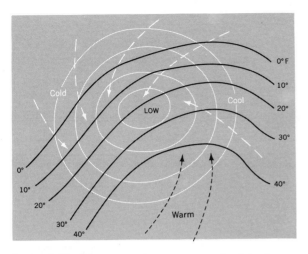

Figure 6.17 Characteristic arrangement of isotherms in a cool-season cyclone over the central and eastern United States.

winds on the front of the storm pushes the isotherms poleward, and cold-air advection by northwest winds on the rear bends them equatorward (Fig. 6.17). To the east and north of the storm center, where the air mass is of a modified polar character—and therefore colder than the tropical air but less severe than the fresh cP air to the rear—the isotherms follow the parallels more closely.

In general, the average rise of temperature above seasonal normal in front of a winter storm in the central eastern United States is not far from 10°, although it may be as high as 20 or 30°. Between the front and rear of a well-developed winter cyclone in the same part of the country, temperatures may differ by as much as 30 to 40° or even more. If the temperature of the center of a low is taken as a standard, the average departures of the four quadrants of well-developed winter cyclones in the eastern United States are as follows: northwest, −8.7°; northeast, −5.6°; southeast, +6.3°; southwest, +2.6°.[1] Stations on the southern side of a passing low therefore experience a greater change in temperature than those to the north of the center,

[1]Robert De C. Ward, *Climates of the United States,* Ginn and Company, Boston, 1925, p. 56.

even though the average temperatures are not so low to the south.

Cyclonic-anticyclonic control

The essence of the cyclonic-anticyclonic control of weather is its irregularity or nonperiodic character. Marked nondiurnal weather changes are characteristic of regions and seasons where cyclones and anticyclones are numerous and well developed—as they are, for instance, over central eastern North America. Throughout the middle latitudes temperature changes with passing storms are especially pronounced in winter, when latitudinal temperature gradients are steepest and cold and warm advection by winds is consequently most striking. In summer, with the poleward migration of the frontal zones, cyclones are fewer and weaker, temperature gradients are milder, and sun control, with its daily periodicity, is more influential.

Cyclonic control is not identical, however, in different parts of the earth. Although they all conform to the same general laws, storms differ in character with regions and seasons. Even within the United States, for example, storms act differently over the Pacific Coast or the western plateaus from the way they behave east of the Mississippi. If northwest winds on the rear of a cyclone come from the open ocean, as they usually do in northwestern Europe and on the Pacific Coast of the United States, they obviously cannot advect severe low temperatures as they do in the central and eastern United States.

Typical cyclone and anticyclone: eastern United States. This section summarizes weather changes that might be expected during the passage of a well-developed cyclone and a following anticyclone over the eastern United States (Figs. 6.18 and 6.19). As the cyclone approaches from the west and the barometer falls, skies gradually cloud up. The first evidence of ascent along the warm-front surface of discontinuity is fine veils or films of cirrus and cirrostratus, which produce circles around the moon or sun. These distant heralds of the storm appear as

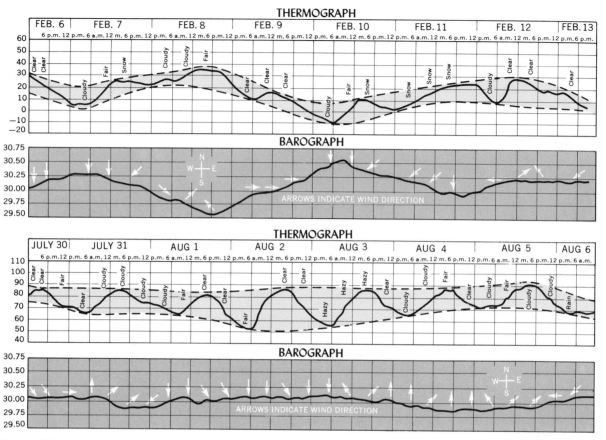

Figure 6.18 Barograph and thermograph traces for a week of winter (*top*) and summer (*bottom*) weather. Note that the barograph trace for winter shows much wider fluctuations than that of summer, indicating much stronger cyclonic-anticyclonic control in the cooler months. The two temperature traces demonstrate that diurnal sun control is stronger in the warm season, when the rise and fall in temperature is diurnal and regular. If a temperature "belt" (represented by shading) is created for each of the two temperature traces, by connecting the diurnal crests and troughs, it will be noted that the temperature belt of winter shows wide nonperiodic oscillations, while that of summer is relatively flat. The wide winter oscillations of the belt are induced by the air masses of passing cyclones and anticyclones. The flat belt of summer indicates weaker air mass and cyclonic-anticyclonic control in that season.

much as 500 to 1,000 miles ahead of the surface warm front, where the inclined wedge of cold air may be several miles thick. Together with the arrival of the cirrus and cirrostratus clouds, the wind sets in from an easterly direction, and it will continue easterly until the surface warm front passes.

As the surface warm front moves closer and the wedge of cold air becomes thinner, the clouds gradually thicken, darken, and lower. Precipitation

usually begins several hundred miles ahead (east) of the surface warm front and continues until the front has passed. Temperature increases somewhat as the surface warm front draws nearer, but since the air on the front of the storm may be modified polar in character, there is no abrupt temperature rise until the warm front at the surface has gone by. The passage of the warm front at the surface, with an associated shift from polar to tropical air,

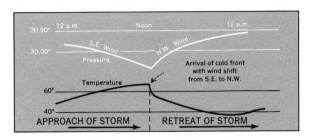

Figure 6.19 Barograph and thermograph traces registered during the approach and retreat of a middle-latitude cyclone in the central and eastern United States.

is marked by a number of weather changes (described on page 203).

Weather conditions within the warm air mass may vary considerably depending on the nature of the air and the season of the year. In summer, air from the Gulf of Mexico creates hot, sultry weather with showers and thunderstorms. Tropical air from a drier source brings heat that is less oppressive but more desiccating. In winter, a tropical air mass produces mild weather and rapid thaws, often associated with fog.

The arrival of the cold front at the surface, with an accompanying shift from the warm to the cold air mass, frequently results in strong turbulence, particularly if the cold front is well developed. In summer, severe thunderstorms with strong squall winds are common. Other weather changes associated with cold-front passage are noted on page 205. The anticyclone which follows the cyclone moves southeastward as a mass of cold polar continental air with northwest winds. It continues to reduce the temperature until its center has passed. Toward this center winds are light and calms are prevalent, and in winter surface temperatures may be extremely low. As the anticyclone retreats, the cycle is complete: winds again become easterly, and another approaching cyclone begins a new sequence.

Obviously storms can vary considerably from this generalized description. The weather phenomena noted in any individual storm depend on the nature of its air masses and on its route with respect to the observer.

Distribution of middle-latitude disturbances

All parts of the middle latitudes, including the adjacent margins of the low and high latitudes, are affected by the traveling cyclones and anticyclones of the westerlies. Not all parts are affected to the same degree, however. While there is no rigid system of clearly defined *storm tracks,* there are certain broad belts over which storm centers travel more frequently than elsewhere. There are also regions where cyclones originate more frequently and are more numerous than elsewhere. Of course, the effects of a disturbance are felt far beyond the path of its center. In a general way, the path of a disturbance follows the upper-flow pattern. In all parts of the world cyclones move chiefly toward higher latitudes, while anticyclones move toward lower latitudes.

Cyclones. In the following discussion Figs. 6.20 to 6.22 showing world distribution of cyclones should be compared with Figs. 5.3 and 5.4, on which the main frontal zones are charted. Although locations of the frontal zones are indicated by single lines, these show only mean positions of convergences that oscillate within wide limits, depending on the season and on actual air-mass distribution.

In the Southern Hemisphere, cyclonic storms are vigorous in all seasons as a result of a very stable and intense cold source over the Antarctic Continent throughout the year. These storms appear to concentrate along the subpolar low-pressure trough, and their belt of maximum frequency is continuous around the earth. The northerly margins of the cyclones, however, affect the poleward parts of all the Southern Hemisphere continents, especially in the low-sun season. The Cape Horn region of South America, extending as it does nearly to latitude 55°S, is stormy the year round. Winter cyclones are also relatively numerous over the Argentine Pampa.

In the Northern Hemisphere, the arctic and subarctic cold sources which provide the southward thrusts of cold air essential to the mechanism of cyclone formation are strong in winter but relatively weak in summer. Accordingly, while winter cyclonic

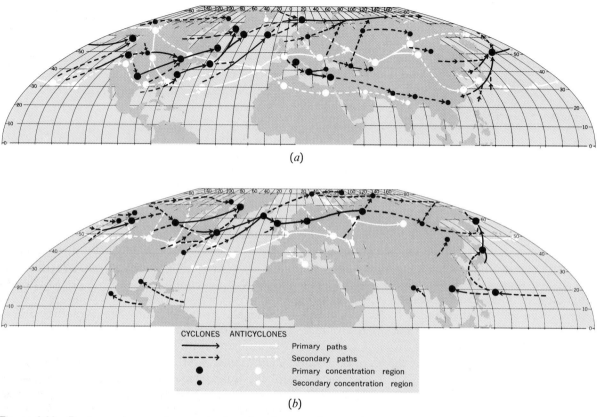

(a)

(b)

CYCLONES   ANTICYCLONES

→ ———————— →   Primary paths

- - - - →   - - - - →   Secondary paths

●   ○   Primary concentration region

●   ○   Secondary concentration region

Figure 6.20   Routes and areas of concentration of cyclones and anticyclones in the Northern Hemisphere: *a*, January; *b*, July. (*After W. Klein.*)

activity is vigorous, that of summer is comparatively mild. In addition, there is a general poleward shift of the cyclone belt in the warmer months.

Although *winter* cyclones originate in almost any and all parts of the middle latitudes, two of the most important cyclogenetic regions are the frontal zones of steep temperature gradients positioned off the east coasts of Asia and North America. Other cyclones form inland over China and Siberia, but most western Pacific storms appear to develop along the polar front over the relatively warm waters around Japan. These Pacific depressions move northeastward toward the Aleutian Low, which is a center of maximum cyclone frequency, and then along a route south of the Aleutian Islands into the Gulf of Alaska. Because of the concentration of storm

tracks, the Gulf of Alaska has one of the largest number of lows on earth. A second center of cyclone frequency is located near Vancouver Island, which receives some depressions from the Gulf of Alaska besides being the terminus of many storms that develop in the eastern Pacific (Figs. 6.20*a*, 6.21).

Unlike interior Asia, interior North America is a region both of major cyclogenesis and of frequent vigorous cyclonic storms. Most of the continent's storms either originate or redevelop in two centers just east of the Rockies—one in the Alberta region and the other in Colorado–western Nebraska. The primary Alberta storm track, reaching from southern Alberta to a center of maximum frequency in the vicinity of the Great Lakes, is probably the best defined in all North America (Fig. 2.20*a*).

In the Great Lakes region the Alberta track is joined by cyclonic tracks from other areas of the United States. The most important of these is the route followed by the Colorado lows, which move northeastward across the central part of the country. Others from Texas and the Ohio Valley also converge on the Great Lakes center, from which they move eastward through the St. Lawrence Valley to a center of maximum frequency in the vicinity of Newfoundland. This center also receives many lows from the region of cyclogenesis lying close off the Atlantic seaboard from Cape Hatteras northward, where the thermal contrasts between cold land and warm water favor cyclone development (Fig. 6.23).

Interior and eastern North America is the world's most cyclonic continental area. This unique distinction derives in part from the numerous disturbances which originate on the lee side of the Rocky Mountain barrier and whose development is subsequently promoted by the free clash of contrasting air masses over the great central lowlands which reach from the Arctic to tropical latitudes.

From the western Atlantic, Newfoundland cyclones and those from south and east of that island move northeast toward the Iceland Low, some being shunted into Davis Strait by the Greenland ice plateau. Cyclones emerging from the eastern end of the Iceland Low travel northeastward to a strong center of maximum cyclone frequency in the vicinity of the Barents Sea north of Scandinavia (Fig. 6.20a).

Figure 6.21 Percentage frequency of cyclone centers in winter. (*From Sverre Petterssen, Introduction to Meteorology.*)

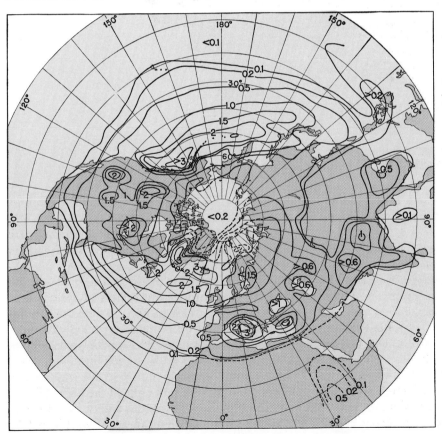

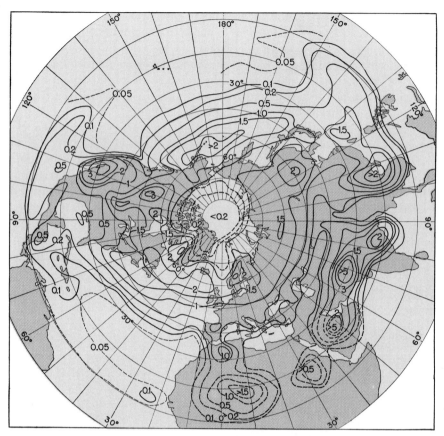

Figure 6.22 Percentage frequency of cyclone centers in summer. (*From Sverre Petterssen, Introduction to Meteorology.*)

Within Europe, cyclones move in a generally eastward direction along two primary routes located along the northern and southern margins of the continent, and a lesser intermediate track across the North and Baltic Seas. The Mediterranean Basin is one of the earth's great regions of winter cyclogenesis and cyclone frequency. From the eastern Mediterranean, secondary tracks extend eastward across Iraq and Iran into northern India-Pakistan, which also acts as something of a center of cyclogenesis. A few of these storms may even reach China. Other Mediterranean cyclones travel northeastward across the Black and Caspian Seas, and a few move north into Russia. Siberia, because of its prevailing cold anticyclone, is markedly free of deep winter cyclones—a situation which contrasts with that of interior North America.

By *midsummer* in the Northern Hemisphere there has been a considerable northward shift of most features of the general circulation, and with it a corresponding poleward displacement of the principal storm tracks and centers of cyclone concentration. As a consequence, the important storm tracks in the subtropics and lower middle latitudes have generally disappeared. Now they concentrate in the high latitudes of the Bering Strait and in the American and Russian subarctic and Arctic. The western and southeastern parts of the United States are free of major storm tracks, and the same is true of China and the Mediterranean Basin (Fig. 6.20*b*).

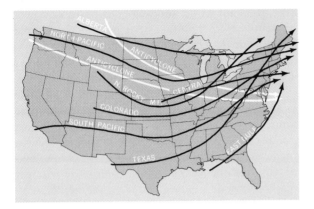

Figure 6.23 Main tracks of cyclones and anticyclones in the United States. Note how the cyclone tracks converge toward the northeastern part of the country. Cold anticyclones have a dual origin. Those which move south from northern Canada (cP air) bring severe cold in winter; those from the Pacific Northwest (modified mP air) bring only moderate cold. Many of the latter are in the nature of weak highs separating traveling cyclones. Warm anticyclones are not shown.

Anticyclones. Cold and warm anticyclones have quite different regions of origin and routes of progression. Unlike extratropical cyclones, which have a northward component of movement, cold anticyclones, since they originate in high latitudes, usually move southward. But the warm anticyclones of middle latitudes have more of a west-to-east progression—as many cold anticyclones do also, after they have reached about latitude 40°. Like cyclones, the prevailing tracks of highs and their areas of maximum genesis and occurrence are generally farthest south in late winter and farthest north in late summer.

The highest frequency of individual cold anticyclones in *January* is found in two major centers: northwestern Canada and east central Siberia (Fig. 6.20). From the North American center the cold highs push rapidly southward along a primary track into a center of maximum in the Dakotas (Figs. 6.20 and 6.23). In about the latitude of the Ohio Valley the main track gradually bends eastward, so that its highs contribute to the center of maximum frequency in the Middle Atlantic states. It is these

Canadian anticyclones that bring cold waves, blizzard conditions, and minimum temperatures to the Mississippi Valley. A few of the Canadian anticyclones, instead of taking an eastward course, push farther south into the Gulf states, where their advance is heralded by the notorious "norther." In the western Gulf states, the track of these southward-displaced highs merges with that of highs arriving from the Great Basin. Strong westerlies appear to shunt some anticyclones onto an eastward course, which carries them along a route north of the Great Lakes.

From the Siberian center, cold highs move south and east over northern China, usually crossing the seaboard between Shantung and the mouth of the Yangtze River. There a strong maximum of anticyclone occurrence is located. These highs continue eastward over Japan.

A less severe variety of cold anticyclone originates in the Great Basin area of the intermontane western United States. In this region the frequency of both anticyclones and anticyclogenesis is higher than anywhere else in the Northern Hemisphere. Most of the air in such highs is of Pacific origin, although there has been some addition of colder air from Canada west of the Rockies. Stagnation of air masses within the Great Basin gradually gives them a degree of continentality, but they never approach the severity of the Arctic anticyclones composed of fresh cP air. After crossing the Rockies, they redevelop farther east over the southern Plains states.

As for the European continent, it has some winter anticyclones which move southward from the Scandinavian centers. Most European highs, however, are in the form of warm cells emerging from the subtropical Azores High which cross the continent on a main track located at about 50°N.

In *July* the main anticyclonic tracks and centers of maximum occurrence are displaced northward. One major zonal track across the northern United States is followed by cells derived from both the Pacific and northernmost Canadian sources. This track has pronounced centers of maximum anticyclone frequency positioned over the Great Lakes and northern Great Plains (Fig. 6.20*b*). In eastern Asia, anticyclone frequency is greatly reduced in the summer monsoon, so that there are only secondary tracks across China. In Europe, one primary track located at about 50°N is fed principally by cells from the subtropical high and to a lesser degree by anticyclones from high latitudes. A second route of warm highs is through the Mediterranean Basin.

Large-scale weather situations, singularities, and the weather calendar

In addition to the local circulation patterns of migratory and transient cyclones and anticyclones, there are others of a broad-scale, quasi-stationary type which account for the longer weather episodes of a region. In response to a particular and persistent type of extensive circulation pattern, the weather of a region may remain fairly consistent for as much as several weeks, although minor changes will occur. According to some atmospheric scientists, such spells of fairly homogeneous weather tend to recur annually at about the same times in the calendar year. In the United States, examples of such large-scale weather episodes, sometimes called natural seasons, are the Indian Summer of autumn and the January Thaw of midwinter. Each of these is controlled by a particular synoptic pattern. In the case of Indian Summer, a large, stagnant warm anticyclone is positioned over the southern and southeastern part of the United States, with the circulation around its western end advecting warm air from the southwestern dry areas of the country.

If the transition from one large weather episode to another occurs within a relatively short time range, and if it is associated with recognizable broad-scale synoptic changes, it is spoken of as a *singularity* (described in Chapter 2). A chronological table of the year's natural seasons, or longer weather episodes, is designated as the *weather calendar*. Unfortunately, no one has yet developed a widely accepted classification of large-scale weather situations, singularities, and weather calendars that can be applied to the whole earth, or even to the Northern Hemisphere. By far the greatest progress in this direction has been made in the application of these concepts to European weather.

If large-scale weather patterns are genuine entities, physically conditioned, that tend to recur at particular times of the year, it might be expected that their weather calendar could be useful in long-range forecasting. One group of weather scientists does hold this point of view. Others are inclined to look upon the larger weather episodes as somewhat fortuitous circumstances, the result of chance fluctuations caused by the coincidence of many minute elements not readily observable.

TROPICAL DISTURBANCES

As discussed in Chapter 3, the increase in information about tropical weather disturbances since World War II has tended to undermine earlier ideas about the monotonous, uneventful, and generally fair weather of the low latitudes. Today there is a general awareness that a considerable variety of weather disturbances exist within the tropics. At the same time, the literature on low-latitude weather is confusing when it attempts to distinguish and classify the various types of disturbances, describe their distinctive weather features, and trace their geographic distributions.[2]

Most types of extensive tropical disturbances appear to be relatively mild phenomena as far as pressure gradients and winds are concerned. Their primary climatic significance lies in the fact that

[2] See N. E. LeSeur, "Synoptic Models in the Tropics," *Symposium on Tropical Meteorology, Rotorua, New Zealand, 1963,* New Zealand Meteorological Service, Wellington, 1964.

they generate clouds and precipitation. In the low latitudes, temperature changes and variations associated with the advective effects of disturbances are negligible. Their cloud decks, on the other hand, do perceptibly lower the average temperature as well as shrink the diurnal range.

Unfortunately for the climatologist, it is the violent and spectacular hurricane type of tropical storm which has been studied most intensively. Yet there are relatively few of these storms compared with the milder and more beneficent types, and they occur in much more restricted areas within the tropics. Genuine hurricanes cannot develop over extensive land masses or even invade them for any distance, so that in the low latitudes it is exclusively the weaker disturbances which affect the weather of any land but islands and the margins of continents.

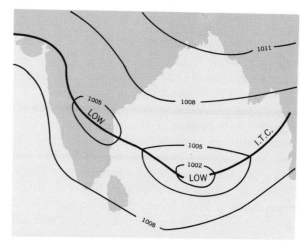

Figure 6.24 Weak tropical disturbances of the summer monsoon period over the Bay of Bengal and India. Some such monsoon lows appear to be associated with a fluctuating ITC.

Weak tropical disturbances

It is not uncommon for a spell of rainy, cloudy weather to approach and pass by a weather station in the tropics without the instruments registering any significant changes in wind and pressure that might indicate the nature and origin of the disturbed weather. On occasions it is suspected this is because the disturbance is too weak to register preceptible changes on the instruments. Moreover, many weak tropical disturbances do not exist in the lower atmosphere, but are phenomena of the mid- and upper troposphere and hence are much more difficult to detect. Then too, weather stations throughout much of the tropics are very widely spaced, and many are not well equipped with modern instruments, so that cooperative efforts in the detection and plotting of weak disturbances are rendered ineffective. No adequate classification of types of weak tropical disturbances now exists; there are probably many more varieties than this discussion indicates. As for their origins, these are uncertain also.

One type of extensive tropical disturbance which appears to be widespread throughout the humid tropics (and in summer, within parts of the humid subtropics as well) is the weak, shallow low-pressure system. It develops chiefly within the humid, unstable equatorial air that follows behind the ITC when this zone is displaced well to the north or south of the equator within the summer hemisphere. On the surface weather map such a system may be detected by its one or two widely spaced closed isobars (Fig. 6.24). Pressure gradients are weak, its convergent wind system is poorly developed, and its rate and direction of movement are sluggish and erratic. But in spite of its being weak, such a disturbance is able to induce a great deal of showery convective precipitation. When one remains fairly stationary over an area for several days, rainfall may be excessive.

While these weak tropical disturbances appear to be widespread, naturally they are best known in regions with well-developed weather services, such as India and Australia. In India, where they go by the name of "monsoon depressions," they are responsible for a large part of the summer rainfall. Originating over the Bay of Bengal, perhaps as waves along the diffuse ITC, they enter India from the east with an average frequency of about one every 6 days. Their course is northwestward, which tends to concentrate their weather effects over the northern, and especially the northeastern, parts of the subcontinent. While monsoon lows are extensive—usually several hundred miles in diameter—they are not as large as most middle-latitude cyclones. Occasionally one of these weak depressions develops into a severe hurricane or typhoon.

Another type of weak disturbance has been reported from a number of widely dispersed tropical-subtropical regions (including India, parts of Southeast Asia, subtropical China, interior Brazil south of the equator, Tropical West Africa, and the Congo Basin) and is suspected of existing elsewhere. It appears to be a surge within the equatorial westerlies, or tropical monsoon circulation, of the summer hemisphere. In India, for example, the summer southwest monsoon is not a steady current. Instead it is frequently interrupted by pulsations which move downstream with the main current, traveling in a general easterly direction. During these surges, which are only apparent aloft, wind velocities may increase to twice their normal rates. Such wind surges result in speed convergences, with the accelerated air acting to force the air ahead of it upward. The result is a spell of bad weather with cloud and rain.

A somewhat better-known weak disturbance is called an *easterly wave*. It is a feeble trough of low pressure extending in a general north-south direction, and hence lying athwart the trade-wind circulation. It moves slowly from east to west in the trade winds, mainly those of the summer hemisphere. Such weak transverse waves in the trades are easier to detect through their deformation of the wind field than of the pressure field. They are more readily observed aloft than at the surface. As the trough moves westward in the easterly circulation, there is general divergence, and subsidence takes place ahead, or west, of the trough line. There dry, fair weather prevails (Fig. 6.25). Just behind the trough line, the temperature inversion lifts and the moist surface layer of air attains great depth. This, in conjunction with widespread convergence and lifting, results in extensive convective showers and thunderstorms, with rain falling from cumulus clouds. Severe line squalls are sometimes associated with

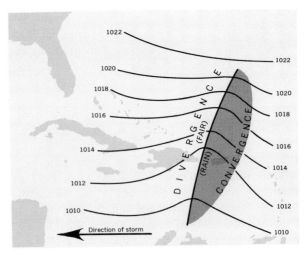

Figure 6.25   A tropical disturbance of a type known as an easterly wave. (*After Riehl.*)

easterly waves in Tropical West Africa. A few easterly waves in the more unstable western parts of the oceanic trades develop into vigorous vortex storms, some of them of the dreaded hurricane variety.

Less important than the three disturbance types just mentioned are others that result when modified polar air, preceded by a polar front, invades the tropics. The result is a trough aloft accompanied by disturbed weather. The whole system moves slowly eastward, or in the opposite direction to that of an easterly wave. On occasion what is called an "induced trough" may develop within the trades, forming in response to a young frontal wave located on the poleward flanks of a subtropical high.

Violent tropical cyclones

Vortex or revolving storms of all grades of intensity exist within the tropics, but relatively few are severe enough to warrant being officially designated a storm. And of these, very few qualify as genuine hurricanes, which must have a minimum wind speed of 75 miles per hour. The number of hurricanes is never large; even in a "good year" no more than 50 develop in the whole Northern Hemisphere. By comparison there may be 20 to 30 middle-latitude cyclones per day during the winter months. But although they are infrequent, and are restricted to a few oceanic areas and adjacent islands and continental margins, the violence and destructiveness of hurricanes cause them to be the subject of great public interest and intensive scientific investigation.

The hurricane (called typhoon in the East Asia sector) is a vertically deep and violent cyclonic whirl of air (Figs. 6.26 and 6.27). There is a spiraling inflow of air at lower levels, a rapid upward movement at intermediate levels, and a spiral outward flow aloft. The whole storm system may extend up to 35,000 or 45,000 ft. Wind speeds of over 100 miles per hour are not uncommon. Within the area of violent winds there are dense nimbostratus clouds which extend upward to more than 20,000 ft. At the very core of the cyclonic whirl of air is a region of serene calm—sultry and nearly cloud-free—where the movement of air is downward. This is called the eye of the storm.

Torrential rains, associated with large-scale rapid uplift, accompany a hurricane. Commonly 5 to 10 in. fall during a single storm, and there is an instance of 46 in. in one day. Isobars in hurricanes are nearly circular, with the diameter of the storm varying from 100 to 400 miles, or roughly one-third that of middle-latitude cyclones. Pressure gradients are excessively steep, and the pressure readings near the center of the storm may be as low as 27.0 in. (914.3 mb). Temperature distribution around the center is relatively similar in all directions, for there are no contrasting air masses or fronts. The source of energy for the maintenance of these violent storms is latent heat of condensation.

Precisely what mechanism is responsible for hurricane formation remains in doubt. Still, there is agreement on some of the requirements which must be satisfied if such a storm is to develop. These include (1) a relatively large ocean area where the sea surface temperatures are high (above about 26.5C or 80.0°F), so that the air above is warm and humid; (2) a sufficiently large value of Coriolis force to cause a vortex circulation of air—a requirement which excludes hurricanes from a belt 5 to 8° wide

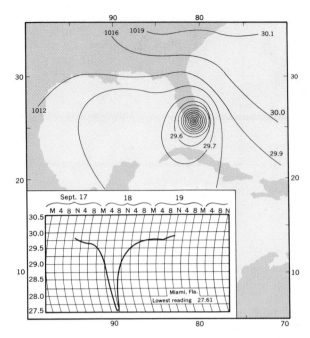

Figure 6.26 A Caribbean hurricane, together with its barograph trace as recorded at Miami, Florida.

on both sides of the equator; (3) weak vertical wind shear in the basic current, which limits hurricane formation to latitudes equatorward of the subtropical jet stream; (4) some preexisting weak tropical disturbance acting as the parent; and (5) upper-level outflow above the surface disturbance. While there is no season entirely free of hurricanes, the four months from July to October have a great preponderance of them (nearly 90 percent of the Pacific hurricanes and 75 percent of those in the Atlantic). It is probably significant that hurricanes are most prevalent in late summer and early fall. Not only is this the time of greatest oceanic warmth, but it is the period when the ITC and unstable equatorial air masses are displaced farthest from the equator, thus becoming subject to appreciable Coriolis force.

As noted above, a hurricane has its beginnings in a preexisting weak disturbance. But it is only an occasional such disturbance that develops into a violent storm, although all would appear to have that potential. A hurricane may exist in the weak-

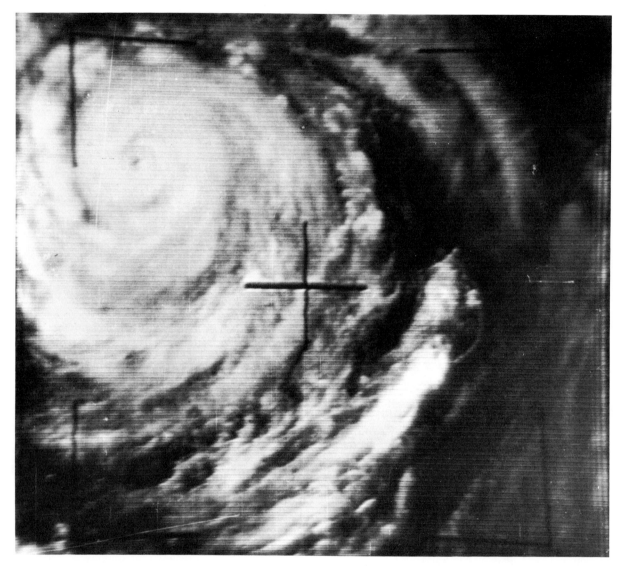

Figure 6.27 Tiros V photograph of typhoon "Ruth," at latitude 31°N, longitude 141°E, August 18, 1962. (*U.S. Weather Bureau.*)

disturbance stage for 2 to 5 days before it begins to intensify markedly, and then another 2 to 6 days may elapse before it reaches its greatest intensity. At first such disturbances move slowly westward in the trade-wind circulation, but toward the western side of the ocean they tend to recurve poleward, and subsequently eastward, as they follow the circu-lation around the western end of a subtropical anti-cyclone. As they move out of the tropics and into the lower middle latitudes, they quickly lose their intensity and become only strong polar-front cyclones. If their course takes them inland, they even more promptly lose many of their hurricane characteristics. It is mainly during the process of recurving from a westerly to an easterly course around the western end of an anticyclonic cell that they wreak their fury upon the continental margins and carry excessive rains even into the middle latitudes. The destructive force of a hurricane comes not from the violence of its winds alone, or from the flooding and washing caused by the deluges of rainfall; probably just as often it is from the sea's high water or storm surge which so frequently accompanies this type of storm as it crosses a coastline.

Regional distribution and frequency of hurricanes. Although all parts of tropical oceans in both hemispheres probably have tropical storms, there is no record of one with hurricane intensity in the South Atlantic Ocean or the eastern South Pacific. Rarely, if ever, has one been observed within 5° of the equator, where Coriolis force is absent. There are at least six general regions of hurricane origin and concentration. These are noted below, together with the special areas and seasons of occurrence and the average number of storms per year. The figure in parentheses is the number of storms reaching hurricane intensity, but for some areas these data are not known.

1. The south, and especially the southwestern, portion of the North Atlantic Ocean: 7.3 (3.5).
    a. Cape Verde Island area—August and September. Possibly these storms do not attain hurricane intensity until they reach the western part of the ocean.
    b. East and north of the West Indies, including Florida and the South Atlantic coast of the United States—June through October.
    c. Northern Caribbean Sea—late May through November.
    d. Southwestern Caribbean Sea—principally June and October.
    e. Gulf of Mexico—June through October.
2. North Pacific Ocean off the west coast of Mexico—June through November: 5.7 (2.2).
3. Southwestern North Pacific Ocean, especially the China Sea, the Philippine Islands, and southern Japan—chiefly May through December: 21.1. Here the tropical cyclones are known as typhoons.
4. North Indian Ocean
    a. Bay of Bengal—April through December: 6.0.
    b. Arabian Sea—April through June, September through December: 1.5.
5. South Indian Ocean
    a. Madagascar eastward to 90°E—November through April: 0.9.
6. South Pacific Ocean eastward from Australia to about 140°W—December through April.

The region of greatest frequency of tropical cyclones, and perhaps the one which has storms of the greatest intensity, is the typhoon area of the Philippines and the China Sea. On the other hand, the best known hurricane region is the Caribbean and western North Atlantic region. Because of numerous inhabited islands and a relatively important ocean traffic in those parts, observational data are abundant.

THUNDERSTORMS

General characteristics and structure. A thunderstorm differs from a convectional shower system only in that lightning and thunder are present. And since lightning appears to be associated with unusually vigorous updrafts, it is fair to say that a thunderstorm is simply a more violent type of instability shower. It represents atmospheric convection of unusual strength.

Fundamentally a thunderstorm is a thermodynamic machine in which the potential energy of latent heat of condensation and fusion in moist conditionally or convectively unstable air is rapidly

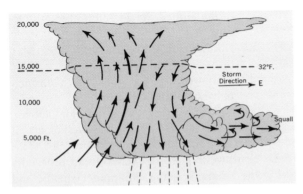

Figure 6.28 A vertical section through a thunderstorm and its cumulonimbus cloud. (*After Byers and others.*)

converted into the kinetic energy of violent vertical air currents. These produce torrential rain, hail, gusty surface squall winds, lightning, and thunder. The intensity of the storm depends upon the supply of latent energy and the rate at which the available energy is expended.

In structure, the typical mature thunderstorm is an agglomeration of convective cells. Each cell, the diameter of which may be 1 to a few miles across, is composed of chimneys of rapidly ascending warm humid air separated by compensating cooler downdrafts with less velocity. The characteristic turbulence within a thunderstorm, associated with its cellular structure, is visibly evident in the dramatic convulsions to be observed in a mass of thunderhead clouds (Fig. 6.28).

Conditions favoring thunderstorm development. Probably the most important condition for thunderstorm development is atmospheric instability, which in turn favors vertical upward motion. Moreover, instability is closely related to vertical temperature and moisture stratification in the atmosphere. The degree of instability mainly determines the intensity of the storm.

As a rule, thunderstorms are most prevalent in the warmer latitudes of the earth, in the warmer seasons of middle latitudes, and in the warmer hours of the diurnal period. This all suggests that high surface temperatures provide a favorable environment for thunderstorm development. Surface

heat is significant because it steepens the lapse rate in the lower air and thus increases its buoyancy, while at the same time it increases the capacity of the air for evaporation and for moisture.

But heat alone is not sufficient for thunderstorm development; there are many intensely hot regions, such as the tropical-subtropical deserts, where few thunderstorms occur. An ample supply of atmospheric moisture is also required in order to supply the necessary energy in the form of latent heat of condensation to maintain the storm. Normally the relative humidity of the warm air must exceed 75 percent. In addition, the lapse rate must be conditionally or convectively unstable.

Further prerequisites for thunderstorm development are some agent to trigger the convection, and a cumulonimbus cloud of great vertical development, usually over 10,000 ft. Instability in itself is not adequate; some trigger is needed to start convection even in conditionally or convectively unstable air. Such trigger action is of several kinds: (1) uplift over hills and mountains; (2) turbulence resulting from friction between the moving air and the earth's surface, or from internal forces within the air itself; (3) convergence in the airflow, with resulting uplift; and (4) upglide along fronts. Possibly intense solar heating of a land surface may sometimes trigger upward motion of the air, although there is increasing skepticism concerning the effectiveness of this method when acting alone. Nevertheless, strong surface heating does markedly raise the atmosphere's buoyancy and instability by steepening the lapse rate.

Since the lapse rate in the lower air over water bodies is normally steepest at night, it is not surprising that thunderstorm frequency over large seas and oceans should show a nocturnal maximum. More unusual is the fact that nighttime thunderstorms also predominate over certain continental regions, such as an extensive area in the middle western United States centering on Nebraska-Kansas and another smaller area in southern Arizona. Various explanations have been suggested for this phenomenon, but none seem entirely satisfactory.

Precipitation in thunderstorms. The general characteristics of convectional rainfall—including its localism, intensity, and brief duration—were discussed in Chapter 4. One speaks of *thundershowers* rather than *thunder rains*. The rainfall pattern within a thunderstorm is closely associated with the arrangement of the cells and their stages of development. Rain is heaviest under the core of a cell and decreases toward its margins. The duration of the heavy rain from a single cell varies from a few minutes in weak ones to as much as an hour in large and very active cells. In the eastern and southern United States the average duration of a thundershower at an individual station is about 25 min, although this is a mean of a strong variant. Half the total rainfall in the tropics is believed to fall in 10 percent of any time interval—from 24 hr to $\frac{1}{10}$ hr. The unusual localism of thundershower rainfall causes its distribution to be highly patchy and uneven. It is common for one part of a city to suffer a deluge while other parts remain dry.

Hail. Occasionally hail, locally the most destructive form of precipitation, falls from the cumulonimbus cloud of a thunderstorm. Fortunately it occurs in only a few storms and is confined to narrow belts within any individual storm. Hail is most frequent in spring and early summer and in the afternoon hours of the day—all times when atmospheric instability and vertical updrafts of air are strongest. Hailstones vary in diameter from a fraction of an inch to 2 or 3 in. Large stones consist of onion-like concentric shells around an ice-pellet nucleus. This indicates that they are a product of great turbulence within a vertically deep cumulonimbus cloud in which supercooled water drops, snow, and ice particles are all present. Strong vertical currents carry these precipitation products up and down through repeated cycles of melting and freezing. When hail falls to earth, its impact may be disastrous for growing crops along the narrow path of the hailstorm. Local variations in frequency of hail and amount of hail damage are striking.

The regional distribution of hail frequency is not easy to explain. It should be noted that hail frequency and thunderstorm frequency do not necessarily show the same distribution. For example, hail is rare in the wet tropics, where thunderstorms are most numerous. Within the United States, thunderstorms are most frequent in the subtropical southeastern part, especially in Florida and along the Gulf Coast, but this region has only very infrequent hail. Hail frequency is greatest over the interior of the United States, particularly over a belt about 100 miles wide east of the Rocky Mountain Continental Divide, where newly formed intense showers are relatively frequent.

Lightning and thunder. Lightning is the flash of light accompanying a discharge of atmospheric electricity. Fortunately, in terms of damage potential, lightning flashes occur more frequently within a cloud, or from one cloud to another, than from cloud to the land surface. The origin of lightning is not clearly understood. It may well be a part of the mechanism by which the standard condition of a negatively charged ground and a positively charged high atmosphere (above 50 miles) is maintained. The normal fair-weather electric current is from atmosphere to ground. A return current from ground to atmosphere is required, and it has been suggested that this occurs largely by means of the electric discharges in the cumulonimbus clouds of the earth's thunderstorms. About 3,000 such storms (averaged over a 24-hr period) are believed to be in progress over the earth at any one time.

For a return electric current to pass from ground to atmosphere, a separation of electric charges must take place within the thunderstorm cloud. Such a separation is known to exist, but how it is produced is not fully understood. However, the presence of both liquid water drops and ice particles within a cumulonimbus cloud appears to provide one favorable condition. Thunder is produced by the violent expansion of the intensely heated air along the path of the lightning flash.

The squall wind. In the beginning, or cumulus, stage of a thunderstorm the surface winds are mildly convergent. As the cell grows and the downdraft develops, the cold divergent outflow from the downdraft is strong and gusty (Fig. 6.28). The cold dome of outflowing downdraft air is asymetrically developed, extending out much farther on the downwind side, or the front, of the storm. This is the so-called thundersquall. It is associated with the squall cloud, an onrushing dark-gray boiling arch or roll of cloud which is the forward projection of the lower portion of the storm cloud.

The velocity of the squall wind at times attains hurricane violence, so that it may do serious damage to crops and buildings. The force of the squall is due in part to the cool air that has been brought down from aloft with the mass of falling rain. Being denser than the warm surface air, it spreads out in front of the storm, underrunning the warm air. In part its velocity is due also to the onrushing motion of the storm mass itself as it is carried by the upper westerlies, so that forward and outward motions are combined.

Types of thunderstorms

Observations show that a vast majority of thunderstorms occur in more or less distinct patterns; their distribution exhibits an organized arrangement. With the increase in information about thunderstorms, the less they appear to be a consequence of random thermal convection associated with solar surface heating, and the more they seem to occur in conjunction with the convergent circulations of extensive atmospheric disturbances of various kinds. In the Rift Valley of Kenya in East Africa, it was observed that only 4 percent of the annual rainfall there might possibly be attributed to random thermal convection. It is the opinion of one weather observer at Nairobi that for the tropics as a whole, the idea of scattered convectional showers, random in occurrence, is a figment of the imagination. A study of Wisconsin thunderstorms has shown nearly all to be associated with large-scale synoptic patterns. It seems probable, therefore, that so-called heat thunderstorms, local and random in their occurrence and distribution, are infrequent or possibly even nonexistent.

Air-mass thunderstorms. Close to the equator, where thunderstorm frequency is at a strong maximum, general temperature homogeneity almost precludes the existence of density fronts. Here, convective showers and thunderstorms must be largely intra-air-mass in character. Their normal occurrence is within the convergent circulations of a variety of weak tropical disturbances of an extensive character. On the surface weather maps of successive days one is able to observe the shifting patterns of thunderstorm distribution in conjunction with the movements of these widespread disturbances, of which the shower activity is an integral part. Tropical thunderstorms over lands usually show a marked diurnal periodicity, with a maximum in the afternoon and evening hours when surface heating has produced a steepened lapse rate and greater atmospheric buoyancy.

Air-mass thunderstorms in middle latitudes are moderately common when the air within the fairly homogeneous warm sectors of cyclonic storms is unstable. Here the heat and humidity are favoring factors, while the prevailing general convergence may provide the trigger action initiating uplift. Others are produced by warm-air advection at low levels or cold-air advection aloft.

Orographic thunderstorms. In both low and middle latitudes orographic thunderstorms result from the mechanical lifting of a conditionally or convectively unstable air mass by highlands. Such upward deflection furnishes the trigger effect necessary to release large reserves of latent energy of condensation in air masses which are already potentially unstable. It follows, therefore, that thunderstorms are usually more numerous in hilly and mountainous regions than they are where the terrain is flat. In the United States they are common in summer over the mountainous regions of the West and Southwest and over the Appalachians in the East. Because their formation is governed to a great extent by the local terrain, orographic thunderstorms have individual peculiarities of time, occurrence, intensity, and location which make them an easy type to forecast. A unique characteristic of many is their tendency to remain almost stationary, probably because the upward thrusts of air that feed them are distinctly localized. This feature explains their tendency to produce cloudburst rains.

Frontal thunderstorms.   These are largely phenomena of the middle latitudes, where they are triggered by a forced ascent of conditionally or convectively unstable air over a wedge of colder, denser air. Although frontal thunderstorms may be scattered within the frontal zones (cold front, warm front, occluded front) of a cyclone, they are definitely organized in their general distribution. Since they move along in conjunction with the storm's fronts and their cloud regions, such thunderstorms may occur at any time of day or night. Still, even this type benefits from daytime solar heating, and so is most numerous in afternoon and evening.

Cold-front thunderstorms, because the upthrust of warm air along the blunter nose of the advancing cold front is more rapid than that along the less steeply inclined warm front, are likely to be more vigorous. Also, much of the awesome thundercloud activity is likely to be visible to an observer at the ground. In addition, cold-front storms are normally followed by clearing weather and cooler temperatures associated with the northwesterly winds on the hind side of the front. When the cold front is also a sharp wind-shift line, as in a V-shaped cyclone, the belt of thunderstorm activity may be several hundred miles long, with individual storms strung out along the wind-shift line (Fig. 6.29). Lines of violent prefrontal squall-line thunderstorms are occasionally developed in the warm sector as much as 150 to 200 miles ahead of the cold front. In the United States, tornadoes occur most frequently in

Figure 6.29   *A.* A V-shaped summer cyclone with a well-developed cold front and associated severe thunderstorms. Regions with polar air are west of the cold front; those covered by *mT* air are between the cold and warm fronts. *B.* Traces of pressure and temperature made at the Naval Air Station, Anacostia, Washington, D.C., during the approach and passage of the cold front shown in *A.* Hours are indicated at top.

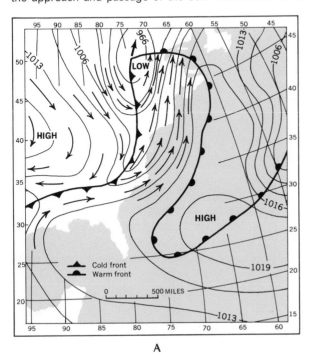

A

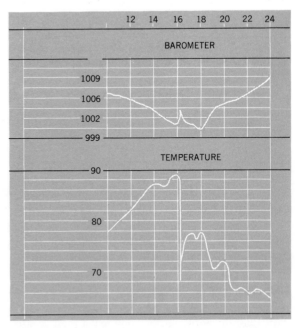

B

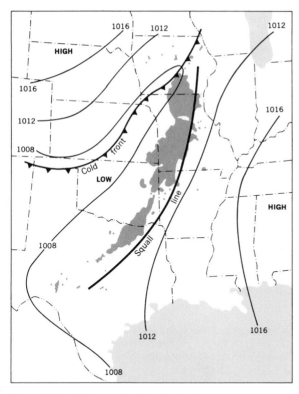

Figure 6.30 Radar echo (shaded) of precipitating clouds associated with a squall line over 1,000 miles long in the interior United States, together with a surface weather map indicating the relation of radar observations to surface fronts and isobars (*After S. G. Bigler.*)

connection with vigorous cold fronts and squall lines (Fig. 6.30).

Warm-front thunderstorms normally are less severe than those along cold fronts and squall lines. They are also less likely to be arranged in linear belts, and they are not associated with a marked wind shift followed by clear, cool weather. To the observer on the ground, their towering thunderhead clouds usually remain hidden by the heavy stratus cloud deck just above the surface of discontinuity.

Distribution of thunderstorms. It has been estimated that as many as 44,000 thunderstorms occur daily over the entire earth. They reach their greatest frequency in equatorial latitudes, where the maximum is much stronger over the warmer lands than over oceans (Figs. 6.31 and 6.32). The combination of heat, humidity, buoyancy, convergence, and the presence of numerous weak disturbances in the general vicinity of the equatorial convergence creates an ideal environment there for thunderstorm genesis. As pointed out in Chapter 3, the strong concentration of towering cumulonimbus clouds in the vicinity of the equatorial pressure trough plays an important role in the earth's latitudinal energy exchange.

From equatorial latitudes there is a general decrease in their frequency toward the poles, but with some variations (Fig. 6.31). Normally, the latitudes of the subtropical highs, more especially in the land-rich Northern Hemisphere, show up as interruptions in the orderly decrease poleward of thunderstorm frequency. At first thought one might expect to find an even greater decrease in the latitudes of the subtropical highs than actually does occur, because the tropical deserts are concentrated in these latitudes. But it must be recalled that by no means are all longitudes in the subtropics dry. Beyond latitudes 60 or 70°, thunderstorms are very few. The general latitudinal decrease of thunderstorms poleward is evidence of the importance of high surface-air temperatures in the production of strong convection. In extensive areas of the equatorial latitudes, thunderstorms occur on 100 to 180 days, and there are a few places recording more

Figure 6.31 Zonal distribution by latitude belts of days with thunderstorms. (*After C. E. P. Brooks.*)

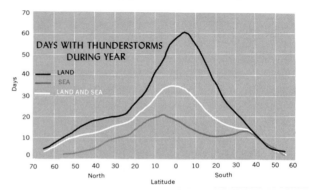

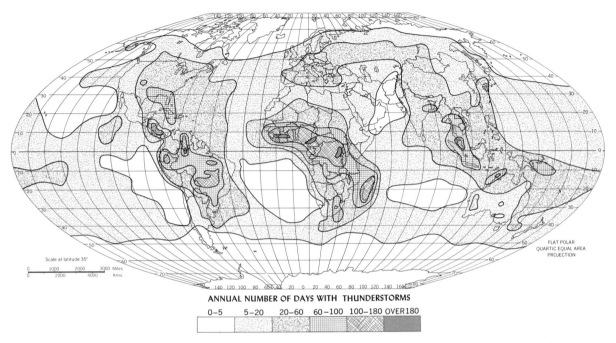

ANNUAL NUMBER OF DAYS WITH THUNDERSTORMS

0–5   5–20   20–60   60–100   100–180   OVER 180

Figure 6.32 Average number of days with thunderstorms for the year. (*After World Meteorological Organization, 1950.*)

than 180. Most parts of low-latitude deserts have only 5 to 20 days with thunderstorms, and some local areas have fewer than 5.

There is a latitudinal displacement of thunderstorm belts following a similar seasonal shift of solar radiation. Since thunderstorm genesis is intimately related to high surface temperatures, it is to be expected that they will reach a maximum in the summer hemisphere. Land areas, with their high summer temperatures, show a greater number of thunderstorms in the warm season than oceans do.

In the United States the fewest days with thunderstorms are found in the Pacific Coast lowlands, which in summer are dominated by cool coastal waters and by stable *mP* air from the eastern end of an anticyclonic circulation (Fig. 6.33). There are two regions of maxima: (1) the southern and southeastern states, especially the Gulf Coast and Florida, and (2) the Rocky Mountain area. The eastern Gulf Coast region of the United States is the most

thundery area outside the tropics, for it has 70 to 90 days a year with thunderstorms. Here heat, humidity, and atmospheric instability combine to produce an environment conducive to strong convectional activity. The number decreases to the

Figure 6.33 Average number of days with thunderstorms in the United States.

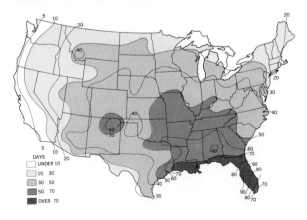

DAYS

UNDER 10
10–30
30–50
50–70
OVER 70

north and west: the central tier of states have 40 to 50 such days, and the northern tier 30±.

Tornadoes.   This most violent of the earth's storms consists of a small funnel cloud generally less than $\frac{1}{4}$ mile in diameter with revolving winds of several hundred miles an hour. The origin of tornadoes is not known, but they usually occur in conjunction with severe thunderstorms along vigorous cold fronts and squall lines. Although they are highly spectacular, tornadoes are a relatively unimportant feature of the earth's climates. In the United States they are apparently confined to areas east of the Continental Divide, where a few hundred are reported each year. The greatest frequency of occurrence is in a belt extending from Iowa through Kansas, Arkansas, and Oklahoma to Mississippi. Iowa has the most: an average of 2.8 tornadoes per year. A few tornadoes each year wreak genuine havoc, but since the average area of a tornado's surface path is about 3 square miles, only a minute part of the earth, or even the United States, feels their terror.

SELECTED REFERENCES FOR FURTHER STUDY OF TOPICS IN CHAPTER SIX

1. **Middle-latitude cyclones and anticyclones.** *Compendium of Meteorology,* pp. 577–629; Byers, *General Meteorology,* 3d ed., pp. 304–324, 302–303; Critchfield, pp. 108–121; Petterssen, *Introduction to Meteorology,* pp. 218–235; Blair and Fite, pp. 152–165, 178–183; Hare, *The Restless Atmosphere,* pp. 70–90; Willett and Sanders, pp. 244–286; Reiter, *Jet-stream Weather,* pp. 324–351; William H. Klein, "Principal Tracks and Mean Frequencies of Cyclones and Anticyclones in the Northern Hemisphere," U.S. Weather Bureau, Research Paper 40, 1957; Riehl, *Introduction to the Atmosphere,* pp. 145–169; *Aviation Weather,* pp. 73–91.
    a. Broad-scale weather situations and singularities. *Compendium of Meteorology,* pp. 814–840; Reid A. Bryson and James F. Lahey, *The March of the Seasons,* University of Wisconsin Department of Meteorology, March, 1958; Eberhard Wahl, "A Weather Singularity over the U.S. in October," *Bull. Amer. Meteorol. Soc.,* Vol. 35, pp. 351–356, 1954.

2. **Tropical disturbances.** *Compendium of Meteorology,* pp. 868–878, 887–913; Blair and Fite, pp. 165–167, 186–195; Byers, pp. 368–392; Petterssen, pp. 236–250; Hare, pp. 104–115; E. M. Watts, *Equatorial Weather,* pp. 45–49, 156–177; P. Koteswaram and C. A. George, "On the Formation of Monsoon Depressions in the Bay of Bengal," *Indian J. Meteorol. Geophys.,* Vol. 9, pp. 9–22, 1958; R. H. Eldridge, "A Synoptic Study of West African Disturbance Lines," *Quart. J. Roy. Meteorol. Soc.,* Vol. 83, pp. 312–312, 1957; Willett and Sanders, pp. 208–243. A. G. Forsdyke, *Weather Forecasting in Tropical Regions, Great Britain Meteorological Office,* Geophysical Memoirs, no. 82, pp. 35–44, 1949; Riehl, *Introduction to the Atmosphere,* pp. 171–195.

3. **Thunderstorms.** Byers, pp. 458–479; Blair and Fite, pp. 221–230; Petterssen, pp. 113–131; Riehl, *Introduction to the Atmosphere,* pp. 101–115; *Aviation Weather,* pp. 92–113. *Compendium of Meteorology,* pp. 681–693; Willett and Sanders, pp. 297–303, 308–312.

4. **General references on atmospheric disturbances.** J. S. Arnett, "Principal Tracks of Southern Hemisphere Extratropical Cyclones," *Monthly Weather Rev.,* Vol. 86, pp. 41–44, 1958; Louis J. Battan, *The Nature of Violent Storms,* Doubleday & Co., Inc., Anchor Books, Garden City, N.Y., 1961; C. J. Boyden, "Jet Streams in Relation to Fronts and Flow at Low Levels," *Meteorol. Mag.,* Vol. 92, pp. 319–328, 1963; J. L. Galloway, "The Three-front Model, the Developing Depression and the Occluding Process," *Weather,* Vol. 15, pp. 293–309, 1960; F. K. Hare, "The Westerlies," *Geog. Rev.,* Vol. 50, pp. 345–367, 1960; W. H. Klein, *Principal Tracks and Mean Frequencies of Cyclones and Anticyclones in the Northern Hemisphere,* Res. Paper No. 40, U.S. Weather Bureau, Washington, D.C., 1957; N. E. LeSeur, "Synoptic Models in the Tropics," *Symposium on Tropical Meteorology,* pp. 319–328; J. S. Malkus, "Tropical Weather Disturbances: Why So Few

Become Hurricanes, *Weather,* Vol. 13, pp. 75–89, 1958; Sverre Petterssen, *Weather Analysis and Forecasting,* 2d ed., Vol. II, *Weather and Weather Systems,* McGraw Hill Book Company, New York, 1956; Daniel F. Rex, "Blocking Action on the Middle Troposphere and Its Effect upon Regional Climate," *Tellus,* Vol. II, 1950, pp. 196–211, 275–301; Herbert Riehl, *Tropical Meteorology,* pp. 210–357; Herbert Riehl, "On the Origin and Possible Modification of Hurricanes," *Science,* Vol. 141, pp. 1001–1010, 1963; *Symposium on Monsoons of the World,* Indian Meteorological Department, New Delhi, 1960, pp. 145–174, 237–256; Ivan Ray Tannehill, *Hurricanes,* 7th ed., Princeton University Press, Princeton, N.J., 1950;

Morris Tepper, "Tornadoes," *Scientific American,* Vol. 198, no. 5, pp. 31–37, 1958; "The Thunderstorm," *Report of the Thunderstorm Project,* U.S. Weather Bureau, Washington, D.C., 1949; Glenn T. Trewartha, *The Earth's Problem Climates,* The University of Wisconsin Press, Madison, Wis., 1961, pp. 56, 76–80, 96–97, 100–102, 113–116, 126–129, 140–144, 154–157, 160–164, 172–174, 182–186, 207–211, 219–222, 229–233; J. Vederman, "The Life Cycle of Jet Streams and Extratropical Cyclones," *Bull. Amer. Meteorol. Soc.,* Vol. 35, pp. 239–244, 1954; *World Distribution of Thunderstorm Days,* Tech. Pub. 6, 1953, and Tech. Pub. 21, 1956, World Meteorological Organization, Geneva.

PART TWO

THE WORLD PATTERN OF CLIMATES

CLIMATIC TYPES AND THEIR DISTRIBUTION

CHAPTER SEVEN

CLASSIFICATION OF CLIMATES AND THE WORLD PATTERN

The composite climate of an earth region.   Part One of this book analyzed the important individual elements out of which climates are composed, and discussed the controls which affect the distribution of these elements over the earth's surface. Regional variations in the amount, intensity, and seasonal distribution of the elements, as determined by the climatic controls, create the variety of climates which will be described in Part Two.

A composite picture of a climate cannot be assembled apart from its individual climatic elements and the weather types which generate them. This might seem to suggest that the student who has mastered Part One already understands the composite climates of the earth's regions—and in one way this is true. The climate of any locality, however, is not created by a single climatic element but by the distinctive regional combination and interrelation of several elements. Thus in another way, the material of Part One requires focusing and integrating, together with further refinement and detail, before it becomes meaningful in terms of individual regions. This is the function of Part Two, which will describe the earth's climatic types and regions according to a system of classification outlined in the present chapter.

Periodic and nonperiodic climatic elements. Most descriptions of regional climates are made from instrumental data collected by national weather services and organized according to solar controls, fundamentally periodic in nature, whose two basic rhythms are diurnal and seasonal. Published weather bureau records fail to present in its essential integrity that other great control, the nonperiodic weather disturbance, whose beginning, ending, and duration are not readily related to the regular course of radiation geometry, and so to the calendar units of days, weeks, and months. There has been little or no attempt to collect and organize climatic data by this irregular synoptic unit, either ephemeral or quasi-stationary. Ward had this deficiency in mind when he wrote, "Anyone who seriously attempts to study the climatology of the United States should have a series of weather maps in one hand and a set of climatic charts in the other."

Classifying climates. Classification, a process basic to all sciences, consists of recognizing individuals with certain important characteristics in common and grouping them into a few classes or types. By reducing the many to a few, the scientist introduces simplicity and order into bewildering multiplicity and thereby establishes general truths from a myriad of individual instances.

The intent in formulating a classification of climates is scientific, educational, and philosophical. The scientific need is to process the vast amount of climatic data available for the earth so that distribution patterns become apparent. Since the climate of even a very small area is composed of a variety of climatic elements, it is nearly impossible for two places to have identical climates. Accordingly an unaltered and unsynthesized climatic map of the world would be a mosaic composed of thousands of parts. To reduce the thousands to a few (probably under 20) so that the great mass of climatic facts can be comprehended, understood, appraised, and remembered is a feat of no mean educational value. But such a condensing and ordering process, besides exemplifying scientific method, also has the still more important function of facilitating scientific analysis and explanation. Moreover, the process of classifying, generalizing, and mapping presents philosophical problems involving the merits of genetic versus empirical classification methods, the selection of criteria for the grouping of local climates, and the choosing of meaningful climatic boundaries.

A sometimes-heard criticism of all schemes of climatic classification covering the entire world is that if they are generalized enough to be memorized and remembered, they are already too generalized to be valuable. This is by no means the case. Even a simple climatic classification provides a basic framework for a comparative study of climates, and one within which subsequently acquired knowledge can be fitted.

Classification by solar illumination zones. One of the first and simplest climatic classifications, many elements of which are derived from the ancient Greeks, divides the earth into five zones (one tropical, two temperates, two polars) bounded by four astronomically significant parallels. These are the two tropics at $23\frac{1}{2}°$ N and S, and the Arctic and Antarctic Circles at $66\frac{1}{2}°$ in either hemisphere. The former define the extreme seasonal limits of the sun's vertical rays; the latter the limits of the tangent rays.

But although the five zones are astronomically determined, and are based on solar illumination, they obviously have important temperature differences. Between the two tropics, the warm winterless zone, all localities are crossed twice by the vertical rays of the noon sun during the year. Days and nights are nearly equal in length, and the sun's noon rays are never far from the vertical. As a consequence seasonal contrasts in temperature are small, the differences between day and night usually being much larger. By contrast, solar illumination within the summerless polar areas is more a seasonal and less a diurnal affair. Continuous daylight and continuous darkness prevail for long periods, which reach a maximum of 6 months each at the poles. Diurnal variations in temperature are at a minimum, while seasonal variations are strong. Between the $23\frac{1}{2}°$ and the $66\frac{1}{2}°$ parallels, in the intermediate or temperate zones, diurnal and seasonal variations in solar illumination are both strong. Temperature variations are also, with the seasonal usually the larger, so that a cold winter and a warm summer are ordinarily well defined.

Climatic regions and climatic types. The above classification of the earth's climates into tropical, middle-latitude, and polar zones chiefly emphasizes two elements: solar illumination and (indirectly) temperature. It does not take into consideration that other primary element, precipitation. Yet within both the low and the middle latitudes there are moist and dry climates, and some moist and some dry climates have both wet and dry seasons, while others have no dry season or no wet season at all. It is obvious that the geographer-climatologist requires not only a more detailed and refined classification, but also one in which the climatic subdivisions are based upon precipitation as well as directly upon solar illumination, and hence indirectly temperature, characteristics. Such a subdivision of the land areas of the earth into climatic types and climatic regions is presented on the map inside the front cover of this book.

Any portion of the earth's surface over which the important climatic elements, and therefore the broad climatic characteristics, are similar (not necessarily identical) is called a climatic region. Note that not all the subdivisions on the color map inside the front cover differ from one another climatically, for regions with similar climates are found in widely separated parts of the earth, although often in corresponding latitudinal and continental locations. The fact that this is so suggests that there is order and system in the origin and distribution of the climatic elements. It also makes possible the classifi-

cation of the numerous climatic *regions* into a relatively few great climatic *types* (11). The types in turn can be reduced to still fewer climatic *groups* (6). Thus regions are combined into types and types into groups (Figs. 7.1, 7.2).

If the earth's surface were homogeneous (mainly either land or water) and lacking in terrain irregularities, doubtless winds, temperature, and precipitation would be arranged in zonal or east-west belts resembling the zones of solar illumination. An approach to such a zonal arrangement can be ob-

Figure 7.1 Arrangement of the six great groups of climate on a hypothetical continent. Note that *B*, the dry group (shaded), cuts across four of the five others. *B* is the only group not defined in terms of temperature.

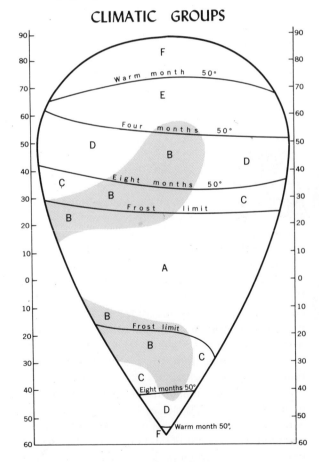

CLIMATIC GROUPS

CLIMATIC TYPES

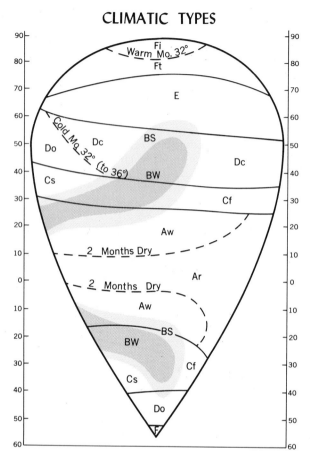

Figure 7.2 Arrangement of the principal types of climate on a hypothetical continent.

served in the more uniform Southern Hemisphere. Because the earth's surface is not uniform but composed of continents and oceans of various sizes, shapes, and latitudinal locations, with land surfaces characterized by many sorts of terrain irregularities, there is a considerable modification of the zonal belts of pressure and winds. This in turn greatly complicates temperature and precipitation distributions.

In spite of the complications imposed by a nonhomogeneous earth's surface—and by land masses with great variety in location, dimension, shape, and terrain—Part One of this book has demonstrated that there is a recognizable world pattern of dis-

tribution for each of the climatic elements. It follows that the climatic regions and types, which are composites of the various climatic elements, also have a patterned arrangement. This means that the operation of the great planetary controls is sufficiently regular and dependable that it tends to produce relatively similar climatic conditions in corresponding latitudinal and continental locations, even though the latter may be separated by great linear distances. Of course it is this repetition of approximate climatic conditions in far-flung regions that makes it possible to classify the many regional, and innumerable local, climates into a relatively few general types. Figures 7.1 and 7.2 show climatic arrangement, or the world pattern of climatic groups and types, as they might appear on a hypothetical continent of relatively low and uniform elevation.

In its climatic arrangement, each of the world's actual continents exhibits features which, in varying degrees, correspond to the general world pattern as determined by the great planetary controls, and as represented in Figs. 7.1 and 7.2. But there are numerous modifications of, and deviations from, any idealized genetic scheme of world climatic distribution. This is one indication that there are important terrestrial controls such as size, shape, and position of land and water bodies, magnitude and directional alignment of terrain features—besides others which are suspected, but whose operations are not entirely understood. One of the most fertile fields of climatic investigation involves a search for explanations of the numerous departures from what is considered to be the normal world pattern. While world pattern is emphasized in this book, the individual climatic regions comprising each of the types, as they are developed on the separate continents, are given brief attention when they depart somewhat from the standard for their type.

Climate and other world patterns. Climate is the most fundamental dynamic force affecting distribution of most natural things on the face of the earth. This is particularly true of natural (wild) vegetation and soil, and to a much smaller degree, of many

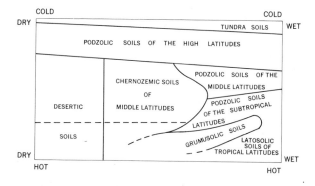

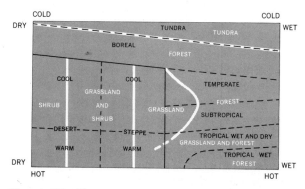

Figure 7.3 The approximate spatial correspondence on the earth between the broad categories of climate, vegetation, and soils is impressive. Note that on these diagrams, annual temperature increases from top to bottom, and annual rainfall from left to right.

gradational terrain features as well. Since all living things require moisture and warmth in varying amounts, their distributional arrangement on the earth is influenced by these climatic elements. In turn, climate and the climatically induced plant formations combine to become important determinants of soil character. Thus when the three great world patterns of climate, natural vegetation, and soil are superimposed, their boundaries roughly coincide (Fig. 7.3). Indeed, the broad coincidence between climate and vegetation is so well recognized that certain vegetation formation types, such as tropical rainforest, tundra, and steppe are employed as names for the approximately corresponding types of climate.

Genetic versus empirical classifications.[1]   There are over a score of different schemes of classification of world climates, most of them possessing genuine merit. Unfortunately a good number distinguish so many types that their value for educational purposes is reduced.

Almost all schemes of climatic classification have subdivisions and boundaries partly based upon temperature and rainfall parameters which are meaningful not in themselves, but in terms of some nonclimatic feature such as wild vegetation, individual cultivated plants, human comfort, or the like. The reason seems to be that such a limited number of statistical values for either temperature or precipitation have an objective existence. In the range of precipitation from 1 to 100 in., there is no particular value that is much more important than any other. The same is true for temperatures from 0° to 100° except one—the value of 32° (0°C)—which is unique because it marks the freezing point of water. However, other temperatures are sometimes employed as climatic boundaries: the average monthly temperature of about 42° as the growth threshold for important domesticated plants, 60 to 65° as the lower limit of human comfort, 50° for the warmest month as broadly coincident with the poleward limit of forest, and 65° (coolest month) as the limit of some tropical crops. These are significant only in terms of their supposed effects on something other than climate (and probably most classifications have been constructed to a greater or lesser degree upon the relation of climate to plant life). If one disregards the distribution of nonclimatic phenomena, it is difficult to provide meaningful temperature-rainfall limits of climatic types. The majority of classifications of climate, therefore, are of an "applied" character.

One basis for grouping the various schemes of climatic classification is to divide them into genetic and empirical types. In genetic classifications an attempt is made to group climates according to the causative factors (e.g., air masses, wind zones) that may be responsible for them. In empirical classifications, origin is discarded as an organizing principle, and observation and experience provide the essential elements for climatic differentiation. The history of classification as a process seems to indicate an increasing dependence upon observed characteristics and a declining use of origin as a basis for the ordering and systematizing of natural phenomena. Among the reasons for this trend toward empirical classification is the fact that ideas regarding origin are likely to change much more as knowledge increases than are carefully observed and described facts about vegetation, animals, soils, or climate. Many descriptive observations of climate made by the classical Greeks and Romans are as valid today as when they were recorded two millenniums or more ago. The same cannot be said for most of their proposed climatic explanations.

It is the author's belief that empirical method is basic to good climatic classification—that a purely genetic approach cannot do justice to the complex climatic patterns of this earth. If the genetic classification is not to be pushed beyond its natural capacity, a genetic map of world climates should be restricted to a relatively few climatic zones. This is not to say that origin should be completely abandoned as an organizing principle in climatic classification, but only that it should be supplemental to careful observation.

The very fact that there is an observable world pattern of climatic distribution underscores the operation of genetic factors. Obviously some of the most universally recognized and extensively developed of the earth's climatic types can be related to well-known features of the atmosphere's general circulation. But it is equally true that within a particular wind system's domain, there are numerous areas whose climates do not fit the expected regime. These should not be unnaturally constrained within the genetic pattern. If empirical and genetic methods can be combined in forming a classification of climates, so much the better. But the empirical should always be paramount, while the genetic should pro-

vide a background which illuminates and rationalizes certain broad zonal and meridional climatic patterns. One such empirical-genetic scheme is the widely used Köppen classification of climates.

Three recent attempts at genetic schemes of climatic classification, accompanied by world maps showing distribution, have been made by Kupfer, Hendl, and Allisow.[2] Flohn also has proposed what is a somewhat more rudimentary scheme involving only seven climatic zones, unaccompanied by a world map, but with the position of the seven zones represented on a hypothetical continent.[3] For each climatic zone he indicates the corresponding pressure and wind belts, as well as the prevailing winds in the extreme seasons. Flohn attempts to relate each of the seven zones to a corresponding climatic type and to suggest the typical vegetation forms. Four of the zones remain perennially within one wind belt; the others undergo alternations of wind belts with the seasons. Flohn refers to the first group as *constant* climatic zones and to the second as *alternating* climatic zones. In the genetic classification he proposes, which is outlined in the following table, precipitation plays the major role in differentiating the seven climatic zones. Flohn considers temperature to be a more general element which changes only gradually.

Köppen classification of climates. Köppen's scheme of classification (used only in greatly modified form in this book) has outstanding merits demonstrated by its widespread acceptance for more than four decades. First published in 1901 and subsequently changed and modified a number

[2] E. Kupfer, "Entwurf einer Klimakarte auf genetischer Grundlage." *Zeitschrift für der Erdkundeunterricht,* Vol. 6, pp. 5–13, 1954; M. Hendl, "Entwurf einer genetischen Klimaklassifikation auf Zirkulationsbasis," *Zeitschrift für Meteorologie,* Vol. 14, pp. 46–50, 1960; B. P. Allisow, O. A. Drosdow, and E. S. Rubenstein, *Lehrbuch der Klimatologie,* VEB Deutscher Verlag der Wissenschaft, Berlin, 1956 (in Russian: Leningrad, 1952).

[3] H. Flohn, "Neue Anschauungen über die allgemeine Zirkulation der Atmosphäre und ihre Klimatische Bedeutung," *Erdkunde,* Vol. 4, pp. 141–162, 1950; Flohn, "Zur Frage der Einteilung der Klimazonen," *Erdkunde,* Vol. 11, pp. 161–175, 1957.

Atmospheric climatic zones of the earth

Zone	Precipitation	Wind belt and pressure belt	Winds*		Typical climate, Köppen	Typical vegetation forms
			Summer	Winter		
1. Inner tropical zone	Constantly wet, mostly heavy rains	Equatorial west-wind zone† ≧8 months	T	T	Af, Am	Tropical rain-forest, monsoon forest
2. Outer tropical zone (tropical margins)	Summer rain (zenithal rain)	Equatorial west-wind zone† <8 months, alternating with trades	T	P	Aw, in part Cw	Savanna with galeria forest, dry forest
3. Subtropical dry zone‡	Prevailingly dry (infrequent downpours)	Trades or subtropical high	P	P	BS, BW	Steppe, desert-steppe, semi-desert, true desert
4. Subtropical winter-rain zone‡	Winter rain, in part equinoctial rain	Summer subtropical high, winter middle-latitude westerlies	P	W	Cs	Hardleaf woods
5. Moist temperate zone	Rain in all seasons	Middle-latitude westerlies	W	W	Cf, in part Cw	Broadleaf and mixed forest
6. Boreal zone§	Rainfall predominantly in summer, winter snow cover	Middle-latitude westerlies, in part polar esterlies	W	E	Df, Dw	Coniferous forest and birches
6. Subpolar zone	Meager rain throughout year	Polar easterlies and west winds (subpolar low)	W	E	ET	Tundra
7. High polar zone	Meager snowfall throughout year	Polar easterlies	E	E	EF	Cold desert (ice)

* T = equatorial westerlies and doldrums.
   P = tropical easterlies (trades) and subtropical high.
   W = middle-latitude westerlies.
   E = polar easterlies.
† Or doldrums.
‡ Absent on east side of continent.
§ Only on the continents; absent in Southern Hemisphere.
Source: After Flohn.

of times, the latest world map by the author himself appears in Köppen's book, *Grundriss der Klimakunde*, Berlin, 1931.[4]

The Köppen classification is based upon annual and monthly means of temperature and precipitation. It accepts native vegetation as the best expression of the totality of a climate, so that many of the climatic boundaries are selected with vegetation limits in mind. Köppen recognizes that the effectiveness of precipitation in plant development and growth depends not alone upon amount of precipitation, but also upon the intensity of evaporation and transpiration, by which processes water is lost from soil and plants. The part of the rainfall which is evaporated is of no direct value in vegetation growth. Köppen's method of indicating evaporation intensity, and hence precipitation effectiveness, is to combine precipitation and temperature in a single formula. Thus the same number of inches of rainfall falling in a hot climate, or concentrated in a hot season when evaporation is great, is less effective for plants than the same amount falling in a cooler climate or season. Although useful, this method of measuring precipitation effectiveness is not entirely satisfactory.

A unique feature of the Köppen system is its ingenious symbolic nomenclature for the climatic types. This makes the repetition of cumbersome descriptive terms unnecessary. Each principal type of climate is described by a formula consisting of a pair of letters with precise meanings. Thus the formula *Af* for "tropical wet climate" may be trans-

lated as follows: A = constantly hot, average temperature of the coldest month above 18°C (64.4°F); f = constantly wet, no month of the year having on the average less than 6 cm (2.4 in.) of precipitation.

An additional advantage of the Köppen classification is its adaptability for use at different educational levels. It is at the same time both simple and detailed. It recognizes five great groups of climate, and these, together with the eleven principal types of climate into which the groups are divided, provide the essentials for a rudimentary knowledge of the earth's climatic pattern. But through the use of additional symbols which can be joined to the pair representing the main types, this classification provides an abundance of useful detail for those who wish it.

Another benefit is that Köppen's is a quantitative system. It uses numerical values for defining the boundaries and symbols not only of the great groups and types of climate, but of the lesser subdivisions and characteristics as well. Since specific values of temperature and precipitation are given, it becomes possible for other scientists to question the validity of particular boundaries. Moreover, such boundaries are subject to checking and revision as new data become available. Köppen selected many of the numerical values he employed to establish climatic boundaries because they appear to coincide fairly well with certain significant landscape features, particularly those of native vegetation.

Although climatic boundaries quantitatively defined are a commendable feature in climatic classification, there is a danger in such quantification, for it tends to give a false impression of the degree of accuracy intended by the author. All climatic boundary definitions should be viewed as convenient approximations only. Such a boundary drawn on a map usually represents a broad zone of transition, and it is an exercise in futility to debate the correct classification of stations situated within some scores of miles of the boundary. Indeed, a climatic boundary on a map indicates only the mean position of numerous individual climatic-year boundaries, which typically depart by hundreds of

---

[4]Still more recent and detailed maps, covering only individual continents or parts of continents, are contained in Volumes II to V of the Köppen-Geiger *Handbuch der Klimatologie* (see the reference list at the end of this chapter). Volume I, Part C (W. Köppen, *Das geographischen System der Klimate*, 1936) of the above handbook contains the author's latest analysis of his own classification. See the appendix for a detailed presentation of the Köppen classification, and refer to the world map showing distribution of his climatic types. What is probably the latest Rudolph Geiger edition of a somewhat simplified Köppen map has been published in Joachim Blüthgen, *Allgemeine Klimageographie*. In wall-map form (scale 1:16 mm), under the authorship of Rudolph Geiger and Wolfgang Pohl, it has been issued by Justus Perthes, 1961.

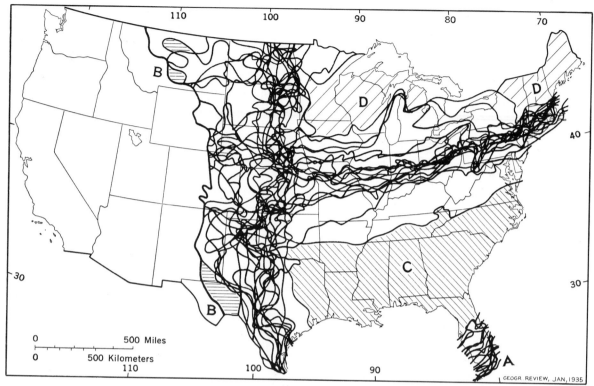

Figure 7.4 Climatic-year boundaries (Köppen system of classification) in the central and eastern United States. Each heavy line represents the climatic boundary between Köppen's dry (B) and humid climates, or between his mesothermal (C) and microthermal (D) climates, for a single year. Clearly, climatic boundaries shift position from one year to the next. Therefore the boundaries drawn on a map showing climatic types and regions (such as the map inside the front cover) are simply the means of different locations for a large number of individual climatic years.

miles from the mean (Fig. 7.4). Because of the inherent pseudoaccuracy of a mean climatic boundary, not much time should be spent in trying to draw it too precisely or in memorizing its exact location after it has been drawn.

Köppen's is an empirical classification in that its climatic types and boundaries are based upon observed features of temperature and precipitation, and have not been constrained to fit a genetic pattern emphasizing the general atmospheric circulation or other controls. Yet a considerable number of the types and subtypes have some degree of areal coincidence with certain broad-scale features of the atmospheric circulation and are partly to be

explained by them. This system therefore has the merit of being an empirical classification with a genetic underpinning. (See the appendix for a detailed presentation of the Köppen classification.)

Climatic classification in this book. The general scheme of climatic classification used here is designed for the first course in a geography of climate, which concentrates on the world pattern of climates. Such a classification should be kept simple, and consequently ought to recognize only a limited number of principal climatic types (usually under 15). Increasing the number tends to obscure the elemental features of the climatic pattern and makes it difficult to memorize the climatic types and their distributions. Where further detail is required, as many second-order and third-order subdivisions can be added within a climatic type or region as are needed.[5] It is believed there is great value in orienting climatic description with respect to the framework of some standard and recognized classification of climates.

Since the needs of geographers provide the essential focus for this book, an empirical type of classification seems to be the most appropriate. People such as geographers, biologists, or agriculturists, who need to understand and use the climatic environment for their own purposes, should have the

[5] For examples of detailed regional studies of climate which have followed the principle suggested above of creating subdivisions within the recognized world types of a standard climatic classification, see R. J. Russell, "Climates of California," *Univ. Calif. Pub. in Geog.,* Vol. 2, no. 4, pp. 73–84, 1926; "Climates of Texas," *Ann. Assoc. Amer. Geographers,* Vol. 35, pp. 37–52, June, 1945. See also John Kesseli, "The Climates of California according to the Köppen Classification," *Geog. Rev.,* Vol. 32, pp. 476–480, 1942.

facts of climate presented realistically, not forced into a preconceived genetic structure or scheme of type location. First and foremost they must be guided by the observed data.

On the other hand, description without reference to genesis or origin soon becomes dull and tiresome— features which unfortunately characterize much of the climatic literature on regions. A recognition of the importance of genesis not only increases interest and adds to the scientific quality of climatic analysis, but also gives an extra dimension of insight to the student's understanding of the description. The very fact that there is a clearly recognizable world pattern of climates suggests the operation of genetic controls. To be sure, there are numerous and important deviations from the standard world pattern, but these departures require explanation just as much. Therefore it seems best to supplement the empirical classification of climates in every way possible by genetic classification.

Earlier editions of this book employed a greatly modified form of the Köppen classification. But in

Figure 7.5 Generalized arrangement of the main climatic groups with respect to temperature and precipitation. Note that temperature increases from left to right, precipitation from bottom to top.

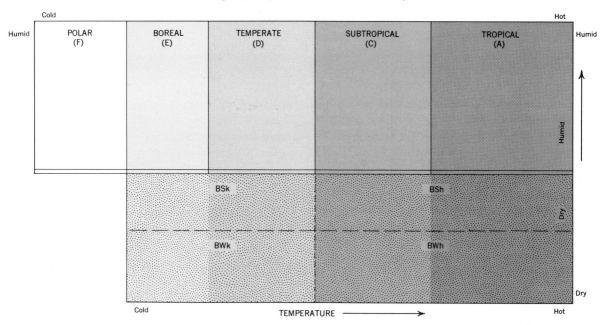

the fourth edition so many further alterations have been made that in fairness to the Köppen system its name probably should no longer appear on the classification. Still, there remain significant vestiges of that distinguished ancestor, and a continuing debt to Köppen is gladly acknowledged. (Again, those who prefer the Köppen system of climatic classification can find it in the appendix and the world map near the end of this book.)

Like most other climatic classifications, the one used here recognizes temperature and precipitation as the two elements of paramount importance. Whether they should be coequal or of different rank is debatable. In three fairly recent climatic classifications and climatic maps by European geographers, the primary groupings are thermic, while rainfall differences create the subdivisions within the great temperature zones.[6] There is no primary group of dry climates. Thornthwaite's well-known classification recognizes five grades of precipitation effectiveness, six of temperature efficiency, and four of seasonal concentration of precipitation. Of his eight main climatic groups, five give primary emphasis to precipitation and three to temperature. The Köppen classification identifies five main groups of climate, all but one—the dry group—being thermally defined. They are as follows:

A. Tropical rainy climates
B. Dry climates
C. Warm temperate rainy climates
D. Boreal climates
E. Snow climates

Unfortunately, the one which is nonthermally defined (B, dry climates) is sandwiched in with the other four, rather than being set apart in a position at the end or the beginning of the list to emphasize its unlike basis of classification.

The classification used in this book has six main climatic groups (Figs. 7.1 and 7.5). Five are based on five great thermic zones; the sixth is the dry group, which cuts across four of the thermic zones,

[6]H. von Wissman (in Blüthgen, *Allgemeine Klimalehre*), Carl Troll (with C. Paffen) and N. Creutzburg (see reference list at end of this chapter).

the polar alone excepted. Accordingly, temperature differentiates five of the main climatic subdivisions, and precipitation one. As might be expected, the five thermic groups have a strong zonal orientation. This is much less true of the dry group.

The 6 great climatic groups and their poleward boundaries[7]

Based on temperature criteria

A. Tropical: Frost limit in continental locations; in marine areas 65° (18°C) for the coolest month (after Wissmann)
C. Subtropical: 8 months 50° (10°C) or above[8]
D. Temperate: 4 months 50° or above
E. Boreal: 1 (warmest) month 50° or above
F. Polar: All months below 50°

Based on precipitation criteria

B. Dry: Outer limits, where potential evaporation equals precipitation

In the low latitudes astride the equator (Fig. 7.1), there is a winterless belt with constantly high temperatures and adequate annual rainfall (A). This is the zone of the humid tropics. It has no frost; in marine areas the temperature for the coolest month

[7]Because of the widespread use of, and familiarity with, the Köppen classification among American geographers, it was decided to continue the use of the letter B to designate dry climates even though that procedure fails to adequately set the dry group apart from all the others. To emphasize the uniqueness of the B group, it has been put at the end of the list.

[8]For more than three-quarters of a century climatologists have been employing the average monthly temperature of 50° as a significant climatic boundary in terms of plant growth and human comfort. Thus 1 month (warmest) with a temperature of 50° is thought to coincide approximately with the poleward limits of forest in continental locations. A period of 4 months with 50° or more is commonly used as the boundary separating cool from warm climates. Climates having fewer than 4 months with average temperatures of 50° are considered to be lacking in significant agricultural potential. While the temperature threshold for growth varies considerably between different plants, it is probably true that an average monthly temperature of about 50° seems to mark the threshold of active growth for a number of them. Conrad suggests 50° as the lower limit of human comfort and relates that temperature to the length of the active season at many resorts.

is 65° or above. Within this group are two main types of climate (Fig. 7.2): the tropical wet type (*Ar*)[9] with a wet season 10 to 12 months in length, and the tropical wet-and-dry type (*Aw*), which has predominantly zenithal or summer rains and a low-sun dry season of over 2 months (see table following).[10] The tropical wet type coincides fairly well with the ITC, doldrums, and equatorial westerlies, where general wind convergence is characteristic. This is also the realm of the tropical rainforest. The tropical wet-and-dry type is alternately under the influence of the ITC–equatorial westerlies during high sun, and of the dry trades and subtropical anticyclone during low sun. Native vegetation varies from semideciduous or deciduous forest to savannas, or combinations of trees and grass.

Within the humid middle latitudes are three climatic groups: subtropical (*C*), temperate (*D*), and boreal (*E*) (Fig. 7.1). The subtropical group has occasional freezing temperatures in its continental parts, but in its frostless marine areas the equatorward boundary is the isotherm of 65° for the coolest month. In this group 8 months or more are above 50° and therefore classed as warm. Two principal climatic types are included within the subtropics (Fig. 7.2): the subtropical humid (*Cf* [*w*]) and the subtropical dry-summer (*Cs*). The subtropical humid type is characteristically positioned on the eastern side of a continent. There it is influenced by the unstable or neutral air in the western end of a subtropical anticyclone in summer, and by the westerlies and their cyclonic storms in the cooler months, so that it may have no distinctly dry season (see the following table). Summer is the wettest season more often than not, and when a monsoonal circulation is well developed, as it is in parts of eastern Asia, winters may be so moisture-deficient that the summer emphasis is strong. The subtropical dry-summer type with its winter rainfall and summer drought is alternately influenced by middle-latitude westerlies and their wave disturbances in

winter, and the stable eastern end of an anticyclonic cell in summer. Unlike its more humid counterpart, this dry-summer type is typically located on the subtropical western side of a continent.

Within the temperate group (*D*), 4 to 7 months have average temperatures of 50° or more. Two divisions are recognized (Fig. 7.2): the oceanic or marine (*Do*), and the continental (*Dc*). The boundary separating the two is usually the isotherm of 32° (0°C) for the coolest month,[11] so that mild winters are characteristic of the oceanic type, and more severe winters of the continental type (refer to the table of climatic groups and types). Typically the oceanic type is located on the windward western side of a continent, or on islands. The continental type is situated either farther inland on the western side of a continent than *Do*, or else on the leeward eastern side.

The boreal climate (*E*) of the higher middle latitudes is supercontinental in its temperature features, with a short cool summer, a long cold winter, and a very short freeze-free season. It has only 1 to 3 months with an average temperature of 50° or over. Coniferous forests dominate. The boreal climate is so severe that it discourages human settlement, and population is sparse.

Finally, in the high latitudes there are the summerless polar climates (*F*), where the average temperatures of all months are below 50°. Two subdivisions are recognized: the tundra type (*Ft*), where the warmest month, while less than 50°, is above 32° (0°C); and the icecap type (*Fi*), where all months are below 32°.

The dry climates (*B*) form the only group not defined by temperature criteria. Here a deficiency of precipitation (i.e., evaporation exceeds precipitation) is the dominant climatic characteristic. In terms of temperature, dry climates may be tropical, subtropical, temperate, or boreal. They are divided into an arid or desert type (*BW*) and a semiarid or steppe type (*BS*). A further subdivision separates the *hot* tropical-subtropical deserts and steppes (*BWh*,

---

[9] Letter symbols are defined in a later section.

[10] Only rarely in the tropics is the wet-and-dry type characterized by zenithal drought and winter rains (*As*), so that this is not recognized as a significant climatic type.

[11] Or up to 36° (2°C) in some locations inland. An annual temperature range of 36° has also been suggested for the *Do/Dc* boundary.

Scheme of climatic groups and climatic types

| Groups of climate | Types of climate | Pressure system and wind belt | | Precipitation |
		Summer	Winter	
A. Tropical humid	Ar, tropical wet	ITC, doldrums, equatorial westerlies	ITC, doldrums, equatorial westerlies	Not over two dry months
	Aw, tropical wet-and-dry	ITC, doldrums, equatorial westerlies	Drier trades	High-sun wet (zenithal rains), low-sun dry
C. Subtropical	Cs, subtropical dry-summer	Subtropical high (stable east side)	Westerlies	Summer drought, winter rain
	Cf, subtropical humid	Subtropical high (unstable west side)	Westerlies	Rain in all seasons
D. Temperate	Do, oceanic	Westerlies	Westerlies	Rain in all seasons
	Dc, continental	Westerlies	Westerlies and winter anticyclone	Rain in all seasons, accent on summer; winter snow cover
E. Boreal	E, boreal	Westerlies	Winter anticyclone and polar winds	Meager precipitation throughout year
F. Polar	Ft, tundra	Polar winds	Polar winds	Meager precipitation throughout year
	Fi, icecap	Polar winds	Polar winds	Meager precipitation throughout year
B. Dry	BS, semiarid (steppe)			
	BSh (hot), tropical-subtropical	Subtropical high and dry trades	Subtropical high and dry trades	Short moist season
	BSk (cold), temperate-boreal		Continental winter anticyclone	Meager rainfall, most in summer
	BW, arid (desert)			
	BWh (hot), tropical-subtropical	Subtropical high and dry trades	Subtropical high and dry trades	Constantly dry
	BWk (cold), temperate-boreal		Continental winter anticyclone	Constantly dry

Undifferentiated highlands

BSh) from the *cold* temperate-boreal deserts and steppes (*BWk, BSk*) of middle latitudes. The *h/k* boundary separating hot from cold dry climates is the isotherm of 8 months with a temperature of 50°F (10°C) or above—the same that separates the subtropical and temperate climatic groups (Fig. 7.1). Hot tropical-subtropical dry climates more or less coincide with the more stable parts of subtropical anticyclones and trades, where subsidence and divergence are characteristic. The cold dry climates, which are a poleward extension of the hot variety, normally have type locations leeward of high mountains or in the interiors of large continents.

Definitions of climatic symbols and boundaries

$A =$ killing frost absent; in marine areas, cold month over 65°F (18.3°C)

    r (rainy) = 10 to 12 months wet; 0–2 months dry

    $w =$ winter (low-sun period) dry; more than 2 months dry

    $s =$ summer (high-sun period) dry; rare in *A* climates

$B =$ evaporation exceeds precipitation. Boundary,

$$R = \frac{1}{2}T - \frac{1}{4}PW$$

where $R =$ rainfall, in.
$T =$ temperature, °F
$PW = \%$ annual rainfall in winter half year[12]

Desert/steppe boundary is

$$R = \frac{\frac{1}{2}T - \frac{1}{4}PW}{2}$$

or half the amount of the steppe/humid boundary

W (German *Wüste*) = desert or arid
$S =$ steppe or semiarid
$h =$ hot; 8 months or more with average temperature over 50°

---

[12]This single formula represents Patton's approximation of the more elaborate Köppen formulas, three in number, for the boundary of dry climates.

    k (German *kalt*) = cold; fewer than 8 months average temperature above 50°
    $s =$ summer dry
    $w =$ winter dry; $n =$ frequent fog

$C =$ 8 to 12 months over 50°; coolest month below 65°F (18.3°C)

    $a =$ hot summer; warmest months over 72°F (22.2°C)

    $b =$ cool summer; warmest month below 72°

    $f =$ no dry season; difference between driest and wettest month less than required for s and w; driest month of summer more than 1.2 in. (3 cm)

    $s =$ summer dry; at least three times as much rain in winter half year as in summer half year; driest summer month less than 1.2 in. (3 cm); annual total under 35 in. (88.9 cm)

    $w =$ winter dry; at least ten times as much rain in summer half year as in winter half year

$D =$ 4 to 7 months inclusive over 50°F (10°C)

    $o =$ oceanic or marine; cold month over 32°F (0°C) [to 36° (2°C) in some locations inland]

    $c =$ continental; cold month under 32° (to 36°)

    $a =$ same as in *C*
    $b =$ same as in *C*
    $f =$ same as in *C*
    $s =$ same as in *C*
    $w =$ same as in *C*

$E =$ 1 to 3 months inclusive over 50°F (10°C)

$F =$ all months below 50°F (10°C)

    $t =$ tundra; warmest month between 32°F (0°C) and 50°F (10°C)

    $i =$ icecap; all months below 32°

A/C boundary = equatorial limits of freeze; in marine locations the isotherm of 65° (18°C), for the coolest month

C/D boundary = 8 months 50° (10°C)

D/E boundary = 4 months 50°

E/F boundary = 50° for warmest month

t/i boundary in F climates = 32° (0°C) for warmest month

B/A, B/C, B/D, B/E boundary = evaporation equals precipitation

BS/BW boundary = one-half the B/A, B/C, B/D, B/E boundary

h/k boundary in dry climates = same as C/D

Do/Dc boundary = 32° (0°C) [to 36°F (2°C)] for coolest month

Owing to the scarcity of climatic data for many highland areas and also to the great complexity of climates within highlands, no attempt has been made to differentiate climatic types within the highland areas on the climate map inside the front cover.

Distribution of climates on a hypothetical continent. In the following chapters on climate types, keep referring to the color map at the front of the book, which illustrates distribution of the types over the earth's land areas, and Figs. 7.1 and 7.2, which diagram characteristic arrangements of climatic groups and types on a hypothetical continent. This continent's shape roughly corresponds to that of a composite of the world's actual land masses, so that it illustrates the positions of the climatic types as they probably would be if there were no modifications and complications resulting from varying shapes, sizes, positions, and elevations of land masses. The strong resemblances between Fig. 7.2 and the map of actual climates inside the front cover are obvious.

GENERAL REFERENCES FOR PART TWO

Ackerman, Edward A., "The Köppen Classification of Climates in North America," *Geog. Rev.,* Vol. 31, pp. 105–111, 1941.

Alissow, B. P., et al., *Lehrbuch der Klimatologie,* VEB Deutscher Verlag der Wissenschaft, Berlin, 1956.

Atlas of American Agriculture, Part 2, Climate, 3 sections: "Frost and the Growing Season"; "Temperature, Sunshine and Wind"; "Precipitation and Humidity"; U.S. Government Printing Office, Washington, D.C. Contains excellent and detailed maps of the climatic elements.

Atlas of Climatic Types in the United States, 1900–1939, Misc. Publ. 421, U.S. Department of Agriculture, 1941.

Blair, Thomas A., *Climatology: General and Regional,* Prentice-Hall, Inc., Englewood Cliffs, N.J., 1942.

Blüthgen, Joachim, *Allgemeine Klimageographie,* Walter de Gruyter and Co., Berlin, 1964, pp. 453–488.

Brooks, Charles F., A. J. Connor, et al., *Climatic Maps of North America,* Harvard University Press, Cambridge, Mass., 1936.

Chang, Jen-Hu, "Comparative Climatology of the Tropical Western Margins of the Northern Oceans," *Ann. Assoc. Amer. Geographers,* Vol. 52, pp. 221–227, 1962.

Climate and Man, Yearbook of Agriculture, 1941, U.S. Department of Agriculture, Washington, D.C.

Critchfield, Howard J., *General Climatology,* 2d ed., Prentice-Hall, Inc., Englewood Cliffs, N.J., 1966.

Creutzburg, N., "Klima, Klimatypen und Klimakarten," *Petermanns Geograph. Mitt.,* Vol. 94, 57–69, 1950.

Flohn, H., "Neue Anschauungen über die allgemeine Zirkulation der Atmosphäre und ihre Klimatische Bedeutung," *Erdkunde,* Vol. 4, pp. 141–162, 1950.

———, "Zur Frage der Einteilung der Klimazonen," *Erdkunde,* Vol. 11, pp. 161–175, 1957.

Garbell, Maurice A., *Tropical and Equatorial Meteorology,* Pitman Publishing Corporation, New York, 1947.

Hann, Julius, *Handbook of Climatology,* Part I, English translation by Robert De C. Ward, The Macmillan Company, New York, 1903. 4th rev. German ed. by Karl Knoch, J. Engelhorn's Nachfolger, Stuttgart, 1932. Parts II and III (untranslated) deal with regional climates.

Hare, F. Kenneth, "Climatic Classification," Chap. VII in L. Dudley Stamp and S. W. Woolridge (eds.). *London Essays in Geography,* Harvard University Press, Cambridge, Mass. 1951.

————, *The Restless Atmosphere,* Harper & Row, Publishers, Incorporated, New York, 1963, pp. 116–182.

Haurwitz, Bernard, and James M. Austin, *Climatology,* McGraw-Hill Book Company, New York, 1944.

Hendl, Manfred, "Einführung in die physikalische Klimatologie," Band II, *Systematische Klimatologie,* VEB Deutscher Verlag der Wissenschaften, Berlin, 1963.

Heyer, Ernst, *Witterung und Klima,* B. G. Teubner Verlagsgesellschaft, Leipzig, 1963.

Kendrew, W. G., *Climates of the Continents,* 4th ed. Oxford University Press, Fair Lawn, N.J.,

————, *Climatology* (3d ed. of *Climate*), Oxford University Press, Fair Lawn, N.J., 1949.

Knoch, K., and A. Schulze, "Methoden der Klimaklassifikation," Erganzungsheft N. 249, *Petermanns Geog. Mitt.,* 1952.

Köppen, W., *Grundriss der Klimakunde,* Walter de Gruyter and Co., Berlin, 1931. Contains a relatively complete analysis of the Köppen scheme of climatic classification.

———— and R. Geiger, *Handbuch der Klimatologie,* Gebrüder Borntraeger, Berlin, 1930 and later, 5 vols, not completed. Vol. 1 covers the field of general climatology; the other four are on regions. Those parts dealing with the United States, Mexico, West Indies, Central America, Australia, New Zealand, and parts of eastern Africa are in English; the other parts are in German.

 Knoch, K., "Klimakunde von Südamerika," Vol. 2, part G, 1930.
 Sapper, K., "Klimakunde von Mittelamerika," 1932.
 Ward, Robert De C., and Charles F. Brooks, "Climatology of the West Indies," Vol. 2, part I, 1934.
 Birkeland, B. J., and N. J. Föyn, "Klima von Nordwesteuropa und den Inseln von Island bis Franz-Josef-Land," Vol. 3, part L, 1932.
 Alt, E., "Klimakunde von Mittel- und Südeuropa," Vol. 3, part M, 1932.

Braak, C., "Klimakunde von Hinterindien und Insulinde," Vol. 4, part R, 1931.
Taylor, G., "Climatology of Australia," and Kidson, E., "Climatology of New Zealand," Vol. 4, part S, 1932.
Robertson, C. L., and N. P. Sellick, "The Climate of Rhodesia, Nyasaland, and Mozambique Colony," Vol. 5, part X, 1933.
Ward, Robert De C., and Charles F. Brooks, "The Climates of North America: The United States, Mexico, Alaska," Vol. 2, part J, 1936.
Köppen, W., "Das geographische System der Klimate." Vol. I, part C, 1936.
Sverdrup, H. U., Helge Petersen and Fritz Loewe, "Klima des kanadischen Archipels and Grönlands," Vol. 2, part K, 1935.
Connor, A. J., "The Climates of North America: Canada," Vol. 2, part J, 1938.
Schott, G., "Klimakunde der Südsee-Inseln," Vol. 4, part T, 1938.
Meinardus, W., "Klimakunde der Antarktis," Vol. 4, part U, 1938.
Köppen, W., "Klimakunde von Russland," Vol. 3, part N, 1939.

Kupfer, E., "Entwurf einer Klimakarte auf genetischer Grundlage," *Zeitschrift für den Erdkundeunterricht,* Vol. 6, pp. 5–13, 1954.

Lauer, W., "Humide und aride Jahreszeiten in Afrika und Südamerika und ihre Beziehung zu den Vegetationsgürteln," *Bonner Geog. Abh.,* Vol. 9, pp. 15–98, 1952.

de Martonne, Emmanuel, *Traité de géographie physique,* 7th ed., Librairie Armand Colin, Paris, 1948.

Miller, A. Austin, "Air Mass Climatology," *Geography,* Vol. 38, pp. 55–67, 1953.

————, *Climatology,* 3d ed. E. P. Dutton & Co., Inc., New York, 1953.

Riehl, Herbert, *Introduction to the Atmosphere,* McGraw-Hill Book Company, New York, 1965, pp. 215–244.

————, *Tropical Meteorology,* McGraw-Hill Book Company, New York, 1954.

Schulze, A., "Weg und Ziel der Klimaklassifikation," *Geographischen Taschenbuch,* pp. 429–433, 1956–1957.

Shear, James A, "The Polar Marine Climate," *Ann. Assoc. Amer. Geographers,* Vol. 54, pp. 310–317, 1964.

Thornthwaite, C. Warren, "The Climates of North America According to a New Classification," *Geog. Rev.,* Vol. 21, pp. 633–655, 1931.

———, "The Climates of the Earth," *Geog. Rev.,* Vol. 23, pp. 433–440, 1933.

———, "Problems in the Classification of Climates," *Geog. Rev.,* Vol. 33, pp. 232–255, 1943.

———, "An Approach toward a Rational Classification of Climate," *Geog. Rev.,* Vol. 38, pp. 55–94, 1948.

Trewartha, Glenn T., *The Earth's Problem Climates,* University of Wisconsin Press, Madison, Wis., 1961.

Troll, C., "Climatic Seasons and Climatic Classification," *Oriental Geographer,* Vol. 2, pp. 141–165, 1958.

———, "Karte der Jahreszeiten-Klimate der Erde," *Erdkunde,* Vol. 18, pp. 5–28, 1964 (colored map).

Visher, S. S., *Climatic Atlas of the United States,* Harvard University Press, Cambridge, Mass., 1954.

Ward, Robert De C., *Climates of the United States,* Ginn and Company, Boston, 1925.

Watts, I. E. M., *Equatorial Weather,* University of London Press, Ltd., London, 1955.

Sources of World Climatic Data:

Tables of Temperature, Relative Humidity, and Precipitation for the World, Parts I, II, III, IV, V, and VI, 1958, Great Britain Meteorological Office.

World Weather Records. Issued 1921–1930, 1931–1940 as Smithsonian Institution Miscellaneous Collections; 1941–1950 by the U.S. Weather Bureau, 1959.

CHAPTER EIGHT

TROPICAL HUMID CLIMATES (A)

Type location and boundaries. The humid tropics form a somewhat interrupted and irregular belt 20 to 40° wide around the earth astride the equator (see Fig. 7.1 and climate map inside the front cover). This belt is distinguished from all other humid regions of the earth by the fact that it is constantly warm; in other words, it lacks a winter. Throughout the tropical humid climates the temperature difference between day and night, while modest, exceeds by several times the difference between the warmest and coolest months of the year (Fig. 8.1).

Heat is so constant and so all-pervading in the humid tropics that their poleward limits are set by low temperatures (except where dry climates establish the poleward boundaries). As noted in Chapter 7, the temperature limits are either the equatorial limits of freeze, or in marine locations that are without freezing temperatures, the isotherm of 65° for the coolest month. These temperatures were selected because they generally coincide with the poleward limit of certain plants which grow only in the warmest regions and cannot tolerate marked seasonal changes in temperature. The chief interruptions of the belt of humid tropical climates over the continents are caused by highlands, where altitude reduces temperatures below the permissible limits. In the vicinity of the

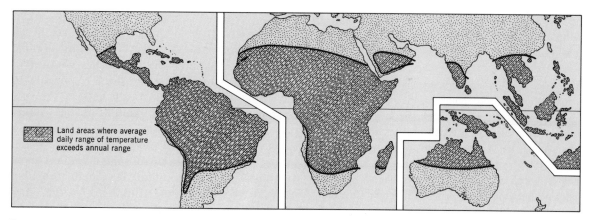

Land areas where average daily range of temperature exceeds annual range

Figure 8.1 A distinctive feature of most tropical climates is that average daily range of temperature exceeds average annual range. (*After Troll.*)

equator, *A* climates usually prevail up to elevations of 3,000 to 4,000 ft.

A climates are by far the most widespread of any of the great climatic groups. According to Hermann Wagner, they occupy about 36 percent of the entire earth's surface—nearly 20 percent of the land surface, and approximately 43 percent of the ocean surface.

Normally the tropical humid group has its greatest latitudinal spread toward the eastern or windward side of a continent (Fig. 7.1). It is typically more restricted toward the center and west. On the eastern side, *A* climates are usually bounded on their poleward margins by subtropical humid regions (*Cf*), one of the milder middle-latitude climates (Fig. 7.2). Since both *A* and *C* climates are humid, the *A/C* boundary must be one of reduced temperature, as explained above. Toward the center and western side, on the other hand, the *A* group is terminated poleward by dry climates, *B* (Fig. 7.1). Instead of low temperatures in winter, the limiting factor in these sectors is increasing aridity. This arid boundary usually shows a maximum equatorward thrust along the western oceanic margins.

The somewhat asymmetrical development of the *A* group, and the contrasting climates and boundaries which limit it in its eastern and western parts, are largely attributable to certain features of the atmospheric circulation. The western margins of the oceanic subtropical anticyclones, which affect the eastern sides of tropical continents, are characterized by neutral or unstable maritime air masses. Here subsidence is weak or nonexistent and the trade-wind inversion is either absent altogether or positioned at a high altitude, so that deep convectional overturning is possible. This unstable air favors the development of various kinds of rain-bringing atmospheric disturbances. In addition, the eastern side is predominantly the windward side of the continent, so that much of the time there is an onshore movement of humid air coming off a warm ocean and warm ocean currents. Any orographic lifting of this air is likely to produce heavy precipitation.

Western sides of tropical continents, except for those close to the equator, are more likely than the eastern sides to be affected by the stable eastern margins of the oceanic subtropical anticyclones, where subsidence is strong and the inversion layer low. In some continents, especially western South America and Africa south of the equator, the drying effects of the anticyclones cause the *B* climates to thrust within about 5° of the equator (see climate map). Anticyclonic subsidence, with perhaps some aid from the prevailing cool ocean currents, produces a stable atmosphere which is opposed to the development of convective overturning and rainmaking disturbances.

The intensity of sunlight, both direct and reflected, is another noteworthy feature of *A* climates. Maud D. Haviland writes:

Except in the very deepest jungles, some sunlight filters to the forest floor through chinks in the foliage canopy overhead. These shafts of light strike as bright and hot as the rays from a burning glass; and as they move over the leaves, small invertebrate life creeps out of their way. I once watched such a sunbeam searchlight overtake a party of ants who were devouring the decomposing body of a caterpillar. Within half a minute they fled helterskelter and the remains of their meal shrivelled up as if before a furnace.[1]

Precipitation.   Rainfall in the humid tropics is relatively abundant—rarely lower than 30 to 35 in., and usually well over that amount. Its origin is multiple. Most of it falls as heavy intermittent convective showers accompanied by thunder and lightning. However, this shower activity is mainly of an organized type, occurring, as mentioned above, in conjunction with the convergent circulations of weak atmospheric disturbances.

To be sure, much remains unknown about the dynamics of tropical convection. It is observed, however, that tropical cumuli are organized into extensive systems, which appear to be controlled by feeble but large-scale disturbance circulations. And in turn the development, growth, and dissipation of tropical cumuli alter the delicate balance of heat and humidity sufficiently to react upon the wind systems. Cloud systems are such a dominant feature in tropical weather—a fact recently made evident by satellite photographs—to suggest that descriptions of the cloud systems may provide the best means of characterizing this weather.

Unlike the uniform temperature conditions, rainfall in *A* climates is more variable in amount and in both seasonal and areal distribution. Accordingly the two principal climatic types within the humid tropics are distinguished from each other mainly on

---

[1]Maud D. Haviland, *Forest, Steppe, and Tundra,* Harvard University Press, Cambridge, Mass., 1926, pp. 37–38.

the basis of their seasonal distribution of precipitation. Throughout both types, however, much of the rainfall is associated with the ITC and its unstable air masses, so that precipitation reaches a maximum at the time of high sun when the ITC prevails. In the tropics, rainfall emphatically follows the sun.

Diurnal variations of rainfall in the tropics present a complex situation, difficult to describe in simple terms and even more difficult to explain. Many, but by no means all, inland stations show a primary afternoon rainfall maximum, probably induced by solar heating (Fig. 8.2). On the other hand, over tropical oceans, including small islands, and many coasts, it has been fairly well established that a night rainfall maximum exists. But complicated diurnal rainfall curves are numerous in both continental and marine locations.

Based upon seasonal rainfall contrasts, two subdivisions of tropical humid climates are recognized—tropical wet (*Ar*), and tropical wet-and-dry (*Aw*) (Fig. 7.2). In tropical wet, 10 or more months of the year are classed as wet; if there is any dry season at all, it must be brief (Fig. 8.3). In tropical wet-

Figure 8.2   Diurnal march of rainfall at Kuala Lumpur on the west side of Malaya. Here there is a striking rainfall peak in the warmer afternoon hours. Such a daily pattern is fairly common over tropical lands, including large islands; but there are many complications. A night rainfall maximum is more frequent over tropical oceans. (*After Ooi Jin-bee in Journal of Tropical Geography, Vol. 12, March, 1959.*)

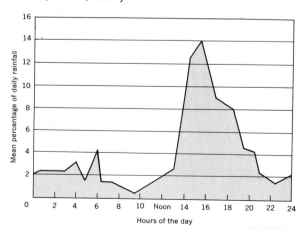

and-dry, the dry season is longer than 2 months, and ordinarily the drought is more severe as well. Total annual rainfall is usually less in *Aw* than in *Ar*. A dense broadleaf evergreen forest is characteristic of *Ar* climate; lighter deciduous forest, thorn forest, and tall grasses are found in *Aw*.

TROPICAL WET CLIMATE (*Ar*)[2]
(Tropical rainforest)

Type location.   Uniformly high temperatures and heavy annual precipitation distributed throughout the year, so that there is either no dry season or at most 2 dry months, are the two distinguishing characteristics of tropical wet climate. Typically this climate is found astride the equator and extending out 5 or 10° on either side. (Fig. 7.2). The latitudinal spread may be increased to 15 or even 20° along the eastern or windward margins of a continent, where the subtropical anticyclone is relatively weak and its air neutral or unstable. *Ar* is associated with the equatorial trough of low pressure and with the ITC and equatorial westerlies, which prevail in that general low-pressure zone (Fig. 8.3). Tropical wet regions may be encroached upon by the dry trade winds at the time of the trades' maximum equatorial migration, but never for long enough to produce more than a brief slowing up of the rains. Along

[2]In the symbol *Ar, r* = rainy for 10 to 12 months, or only 0 to 2 months dry. Definition of a dry month is derived from Clyde Patton's simplification of Köppen's three formulas for the dry-humid boundary (see page 250). A dry month will, therefore, be $\frac{1}{12}$ of the annual value derived from the Patton formula. In equatorial lowlands, where the average annual temperature is close to 80°, a dry month will usually have about 2.3 in. of average rainfall.

Figure 8.3   Hypothetical arrangement of tropical wet (*Ar*), tropical wet-and-dry (*Aw*), and dry (*B*) climates with respect to latitude, ITC, and wind and pressure belts at the time of the times of the extreme seasons.

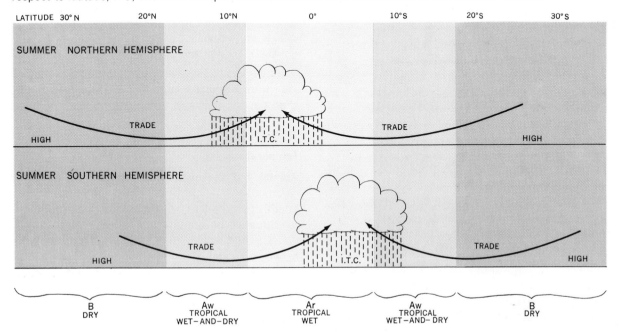

most of its poleward margins *Ar* climate gradually passes over into *Aw*, the boundary between them being the isoline of 2 dry months. Along the wetter eastern margins of a continent, however, *Ar* climates may extend far enough poleward that they adjoin subtropical humid climates (*Cf*) of middle latitudes (Fig. 7.2 and climate map). This boundary, as mentioned earlier, is set by low winter temperature instead of by length of the dry season.

Geographical location. The Amazon Basin of South America; the Congo Basin of Africa and oceanic margins of parts of Tropical West Africa; and the insular-peninsular area of Southeast Asia comprise the most extensive regions with tropical wet climate. Eastern Central America and parts of the Caribbean islands, western Colombia, the Guianas, the Atlantic margins of Brazil, eastern

Figure 8.4 Average monthly temperatures and precipitation for a representative station with tropical wet climate. Monthly temperatures are much more uniform than monthly amounts of precipitation. Note that Colombo has no dry month.

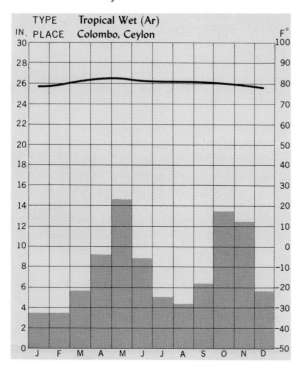

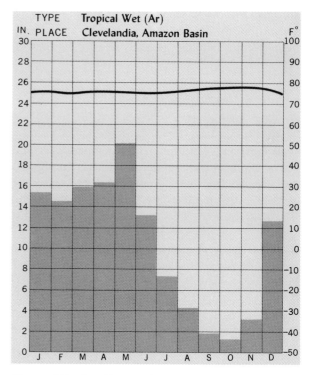

Figure 8.5 At Clevelandia in the Amazon Valley, monthly temperatures are very similar to those at Colombo. But here there are 2 months that may be classed as dry. Extensive areas of *Ar* climate have 1, or at most 2, dry months.

Madagascar, and southern Ceylon are other smaller and more dispersed parts (see climate map inside front cover).

Temperature

Annual and seasonal temperatures. Lying, as it commonly does, athwart the equator and consequently in the belt of near-maximum solar radiation, *Ar* climate has monthly and annual temperatures that are uniformly high. Yearly averages usually lie between 77 and 80°+. Since the sun's noon rays are never far from a vertical position, and days and nights vary little in length from one part of the year to another, not only are annual averages high, but temperature hardly changes from month to month (Figs. 8.4, 8.5, and 8.6). On continents, the annual

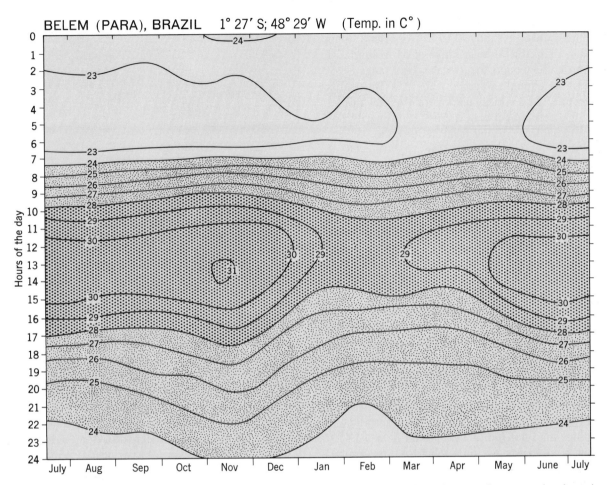

BELEM (PARA), BRAZIL   1° 27′ S; 48° 29′ W   (Temp. in C°)

Figure 8.6 Thermoisopleths for Belém, an *Ar* station in the Amazon Valley. Note how much greater the diurnal range is than the annual range. (*After Troll.*)

temperature range, or difference between the warmest and coolest months, is usually less than 5°. Ranges over the oceans in these low latitudes are even smaller: Jaluit in the Marshall Islands in mid-Pacific records only 0.8° difference between the extreme months.

It is not excessively high monthly averages but rather the uniformity and monotony of this constant succession of hot months, with no relief, that characterize the tropical rainforest climate. Actually, the average July temperatures of many subtropical American cities—such as Charleston with 82°, Galveston with 83°, and Montgomery with 82°—

may equal, or even exceed by a few degrees, those of the hottest months at stations near the equator. In the tropical rainforest the abundance of cloud and heavy forest cover act to prevent excessively high temperatures such as occur in tropical deserts. The hottest month at Belém (Amazon Basin) is only 80°, and at most stations in the Congo Basin it is slightly under 80°. The minor temperature contrasts between the warmest and coolest months are determined not so much by the position of the sun as by the amount of cloudiness, for the highest temperature usually occurs during the seasons of least rain and clearest skies.

Daily temperatures. The daily, or diurnal, range of temperature is usually 10 to 25°, or several times greater than the annual range. For example, at Bolobo in the Congo, the average daily range is 16° while the annual range is only 2°. This range differential is a typical feature of the wet tropics. During afternoons the thermometer ordinarily rises to temperatures varying from about 85 to 93° and at night sinks to 68 to 75° (Figs. 8.7 and 8.8). It is often said that night is the winter of the tropics. Even the daily extremes of temperature are never very great, however; the average of the daily maxima at Belém is only 91°, that of the daily minima, 68°. The highest temperature ever recorded at Santarém (Amazon Basin) is 96°, while the lowest is only 65°. This absolute maximum of 96° may be compared with 105° for Chicago and 112° for St. Louis, located in the middle latitudes.

Although daytime temperatures may not be excessively high in *Ar* climate, the heat, together with slight air movement, intense light, and high relative and absolute humidity, produces an atmospheric condition with low cooling power. It is oppressive and sultry, so that one's vitality and energy are sapped. Sensible temperatures are therefore excessively high, even though the thermometer readings may not indicate abnormal heat.

Even the nights give little relief from the oppressive warmth. Yet to the poorly clad natives, who are sensitive to even the slightest drop in temperature, the humid night air may appear chilly. Fires are often lighted at night if the temperature drops

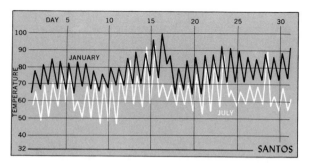

Figure 8.8 Daily maximum and minimum temperatures for the extreme months in one year at a station with tropical wet climate located on the east coast of Brazil at 20°S. Note the somewhat greater nonperiodic temperature changes caused by advection associated with atmospheric disturbances from the middle latitudes. Because of the station's considerable distance from the equator, low-sun seasonal temperatures are somewhat lower than normal for *Ar*.

below 70°. Some Negro groups in central Africa use heated sleeping quarters during the coolest season, when the average temperature may drop into the upper 60s. Rapid nocturnal cooling is not to be expected in regions of such excessive humidity and abundant cloudiness. The nighttime temperature drop is often sufficient, nevertheless, to cause surface condensation in the near-saturated air, so that lowland radiation fog and heavy dew are common. The periods of least rainfall and clearest skies have the lowest night temperatures, which on occasions fall below 60°.

Daily march of temperature. Figures 8.7 and 8.8 show the daily march of temperature for the extreme months at representative stations within the tropical wet (*Ar*) climate. These graphs illustrate a temperature regime in which sun is almost completely in control. There is a striking diurnal regularity about the changes: Temperatures rise to about the same height each day and fall to about the same level each night, so that one 24-hr period almost duplicates every other. Irregular invasions of warm and cold air masses, of the type so common in the middle latitudes, are practically unknown. This absence of nonperiodic and erratic temperature variations results from (1) the great width of the

Figure 8.7 Daily maximum and minimum temperatures for the extreme months in one year at a representative station with tropical wet climate (*Ar*). Diurnal solar control is almost complete, as shown by the regular daily rise and fall of temperature.

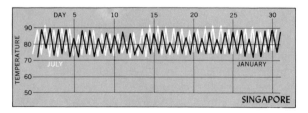

tropical zone, which makes invasions of cold air relatively impossible, and (2) the general lack of vigorous, moving cold anticyclones, which are the instigators of many of the great nonperiodic temperature changes of middle latitudes. What small temperature variations do exist from day to day are largely a result of variations in cloudiness.

Precipitation

Amount. Annual rainfall in the wet tropics is heavy—commonly 70 to over 100 in., with less than average over the continents and more over the oceans (Figs. 8.4 and 8.5; also see data on page 262). Taken as a whole, *Ar* climate coincides with the earth's belt of heaviest precipitation. Because of the abundant precipitation, surface ocean waters in the doldrums are less salty than in the trades. The largest measured amount of rainfall in *Ar* climates, and perhaps the greatest for any place on the earth, is on the windward side of a low mountain on the island of Kauai in the Hawaiian group, where the average annual amount is over 450 in. Near the foot of Cameroon Mountain in equatorial Africa, the annual rainfall averages about 400 in. Cherrapunji, in the Khasi Hills of northeastern India, receives an average of 426 in. In all these stations, however, the excessive annual precipitation is associated with orographic effects. Such amounts of rain are unknown over extensive lowlands.

Conditions close to the equator are ideal for rain formation. A main reason is the directional convergence of tropical air masses, with associated lifting of the air. Supplementing this convergence are the high temperature and abundant humidity, which produce a nearly saturated condition throughout a deep atmospheric layer. The reservoir of atmospheric moisture for precipitation is therefore unusually great. In this warm, humid, and highly unstable air, only a slight amount of original lifting is required to trigger strong convective overturning with associated heavy showers. Weak atmospheric disturbances are numerous.

Cloudiness, much of it cumulus in character, is fairly abundant in *Ar* climates, averaging about 60 percent. At Manaus, in the Amazon Valley, cloudiness varies between $\frac{6}{10}$ and $\frac{7}{10}$ for each month. At Belém it is $\frac{4}{10}$ in the driest month and $\frac{8}{10}$ in the rainiest. Completely clear days are almost unknown. Considering the fact that *Ar* climate is the rainiest of the earth, it may seem strange that the percentage of cloudiness is not as great near the equator as it is in the higher middle latitudes, where rainfall is much less. This is related to the fact that a larger proportion of the cloud in equatorial latitudes is of the cumulus type, which is capable of producing a maximum of rainfall with a minimal duration of cloudiness. A dull gray solid overcast is atypical. Cloudiness in continental *Ar* climates has a distinct diurnal periodicity, with the maximum usually in the warmer hours of afternoon or evening when convectional overturning is at a peak. Nights and early morning hours are usually clearer.

Diurnal march of cloudiness at Belém (In tenths of sky covered)

6 A.M.	3.6	2 P.M.	5.7
8 A.M.	3.8	4 P.M.	6.0
10 A.M.	5.5	10 P.M.	5.2

Sky conditions are lively and animated as the upward-surging air currents produce clouds full of motion and variety in form and shadings. The predominantly convectional rain, reflecting the unstable character of the atmosphere, falls in hard showers from towering cumulonimbus clouds. Maximum precipitation over lands usually occurs during the warmer hours of the day, when convectional ascent is at a maximum. Early mornings may be relatively clear, but as the sun climbs toward the zenith and temperature increases, cumulus clouds begin to appear. These grow in number, diameter, and height with the heat of the day, until by afternoon they become giant ominous thunderheads if the circulation is convergent, as it is in the presence of a weak disturbance. Several thunderstorms, accompanied by thunder and lightning, in a single afternoon are not unusual. The rain may continue on into the evening, although there is a tendency for skies to become clearer as the heat wanes. The cloud cover and downpour of rain temporarily cool the air, but with the passing of the storm and the sun's appearance again, the usual oppressive conditions return. As described in Chapter 3, the few thousand cumulus "hot towers" active at one time in the equatorial pressure trough play a key role in maintaining the tropical circulation. Vast amounts of heat of condensation are released in them.

Within the equatorial-trough region, thunderstorms reach their maximum development for any latitude of the earth; on the average there are 75 to 150 days with such storms during the course of the year. Tropical thunderstorms, although localized, are extremely intense. The great thickness of the heated and humidified air in equatorial latitudes provides an abundance of storm energy. These paroxysms of nature, with their fierce lightning, crashing thunder, and deluges of rainfall, are awesome spectacles. One traveler writes:

The force of the downpour is another factor in the oecology of the forest. In the wet season thunderstorms of great violence are frequent, and the rain descends with a suddenness and volume unknown outside the tropics. The sun is shining, the forest glitters with a million lights, birds are on the move, and insects hum and dance from leaf to leaf. All at once a shadow is drawn over the sun, and all activity of bird and beast ceases as the sound of rushing rain rapidly approaches. An avalanche of water then crashes down, blotting out surrounding objects and, as it seems, sweeping the very breath from the nostrils, bewildering and benumbing the senses. Every twig and leaf is bent and battered, and in a few seconds streams pour down the paths and the world seems changed into a thundering cataract. Then, as suddenly as it came, the storm passes, and the sun blazes out again before the roar of the storm sweeping over the treetops has died away in the distance. Even before the leaves have ceased to drip, or the land-crabs, tempted forth by the teeming water, have scuttled to cover again, the life of the forest is resumed. It is almost incredible how some fragile forms escape destruction under such terrific bombardments. . . .[3]

While solar heating unquestionably produces a strong diurnal periodicity in thunderstorm, cloud,

[3] Haviland, *op. cit.*, p. 39.

Climatic data for representative stations with tropical wet climate (*Ar*)

	J	F	M	A	M	J	J	A	S	O	N	D	Yr	Range
Belém, Amazon Valley, 1°18′S														
Temp., °F	77.4	77.0	77.2	77.9	78.4	78.4	78.4	78.6	78.4	79.0	79.3	78.6	78.3	2.3
Precip., in.	13.4	16.0	17.2	13.5	11.3	6.9	5.7	5.0	4.7	3.6	3.4	6.9	108.0	
Stanleyville, Congo Basin, 32′N														
Temp., °F	77.2	77.0	77.4	77.5	76.6	75.7	74.3	74.3	75.2	75.6	75.7	75.7	76.0	3.1
Precip., in.	3.3	4.1	6.9	5.6	6.1	3.5	4.4	8.9	7.5	9.8	6.7	2.8	69.4	
Singapore, 1°18′N, 103°52′E														
Temp., °F	79.5	80.5	81.5	81.5	82.0	81.5	81.5	81.0	81.0	80.5	80.5	80.5	80.5	2.5
Precip., in.	9.9	6.8	7.6	7.4	6.8	6.8	6.7	7.7	7.0	8.2	10.0	10.1	95.0	
Belize, British Honduras, 17°31′N														
Temp., °F	74.8	76.8	79.2	79.2	81.9	82.4	82.6	82.6	82.0	79.3	76.1	73.6	79.3	9
Precip., in.	5.1	2.6	1.6	1.5	4.1	9.1	9.6	8.5	9.4	11.0	10.2	6.3	79.0	
Manaus, Amazon Valley, 3°1′S														
Temp., °F	79.2	79.2	79.5	79.2	79.3	79.9	80.2	81.5	82.2	82.0	81.7	80.2	80.4	3
Precip., in.	10.5	9.7	10.6	10.5	7.6	4.0	2.5	1.5	2.3	4.9	6.0	8.5	78.6	

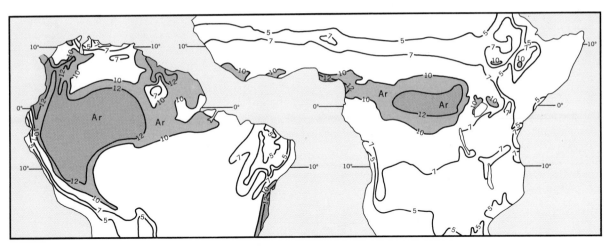

Figure 8.9 Differentiating those parts of tropical South America and Africa where 12 months are classed as wet (none dry), 10 or 11 months are wet (1 or 2 dry); and 9 or fewer months are wet (over 2 dry). (*After W. Lauer.*)

and shower occurrence at many land stations, there are significant departures from this regular pattern. Usually the course of the weather over a period of several weeks combines features of periodic solar control with some of nonperiodic control. The non-periodic weather element originates in the frequent weak but extensive atmospheric disturbances whose passage brings spells of bad weather involving increases in cloud, shower activity, and the number of thunderstorms. In the irregular intervals between such disturbances skies are clearer and there is less, or even no, rainfall. But even during a cloudy, rainy spell accompanying a weak disturbance, the diurnal pattern ordinarily is not obliterated, for daytime solar heating adds its effects to the instability associated with general convergence within the disturbance. The violent hurricane type of storm does not occur in those *Ar* climates situated close to the equator where Coriolis force is absent. Only littoral and insular locations poleward of about 10° may be afflicted with hurricanes.

Seasonal distribution, or annual march. It is untrue that in *Ar* climate as a type, abundant rainfall is so well distributed throughout the year that no months are dry (Figs. 8.4 and 8.5). There are extensive regions, to be sure, where such perfection in

wet equatorial climate exists: for example, the western Amazon Basin and a core region in the innermost Congo Basin. But more extensively developed in equatorial latitudes is a slightly different rainfall regime which, while annual rainfall may total equally as much, is characterized by a brief dry season of 1, or at most 2, months (Fig. 8.9). In both types a rainforest vegetation prevails. Almost certainly more than half the total area with tropical wet climate seems to have this short dry season; it represents more the standard for *Ar*, therefore, than the constantly wet regime.

Heavy equatorial rainfall with a brief dry season not only is typical of *Ar* climate in parts of the Asiatic sector, where a monsoon system of winds prevails. It probably also predominates in equatorial Africa, and it is extensively developed in the middle and lower Amazon Basin. According to Lauer, the single largest area of *Ar* with no dry season is the upper three-fifths of the Amazon Basin.

It would seem logical if the constantly wet phase of *Ar* everywhere went through a gradual change to tropical wet-and-dry climate, or *Aw,* by way of a transitional zone of *Ar* with a brief dry season. But actually, in many equatorial parts the brief dry season appears to be typical of core areas, so that it cannot be considered only as a transition phase.

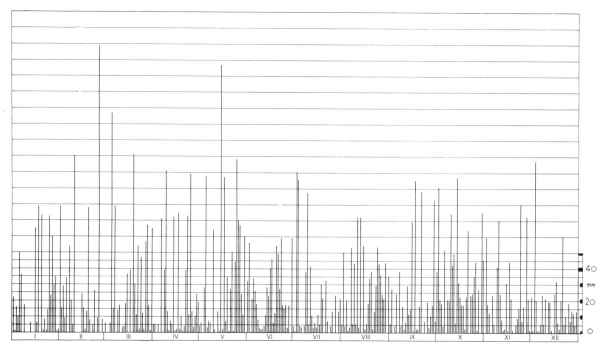

Figure 8.10 Daily rainfall amounts for one year (1928) at Andagoya, an *Ar* station in western Colombia inland from the Pacific coast. Here the average annual rainfall is exceedingly heavy (7,089 mm, 282 in.), and no month is dry. In 1928 there were only 48 days on which no rain fell. (*After M. Hendl, Einführung in die physikalische Klimatologie, Band II.*)

Even in places where all 12 months are wet, however, it should not be inferred that the year's rainfall is evenly distributed. In comparison with the rainiest months, there are others that are much less wet, although scarcely dry.

Theoretically it might be supposed that stations in equatorial latitudes would have two periods of maximum and two periods of minimum rainfall during the course of a year. The two maxima logically would coincide with, or closely follow, the zenithal positions of the sun, and hence the ITC. The two periods of less heavy rain should coincide with or follow the solstices, when the drier trades advance closest to the equator. Actually this ideal equatorial regime with two symmetrical maxima and two minima, although it is found in some areas, certainly is not a widespread feature. The seasonal rainfall mechanism is not that perfectly geared to the astronomical controls.

Rain-days. Not only is rainfall abundant in the wet tropics, but the number of days with rain is large (Fig. 8.10). Belém in the Amazon Valley has 94 in. of rain and 243 rainy days. During the rainier season or seasons, precipitation falls on a large majority of the days, although there are always some without any. During the drier periods, not only are rain-days fewer, but the amount per day is also less. Thus at Belém, March, which is the wettest month, has 6 to 7 times as much rain as November, which is the driest (see the table on page 265); but even in November there are 10+ rainy days with a total of more than 2 in. of precipitation. On the other hand, March has nearly 14 in. of rain, falling on 28+ days. Thus 91 percent of the days in the wettest month are rainy, and only 34 percent of those in the driest month. The fact that not all days have rain in spite of constant heat and humidity is another indication that thermal convec-

Average precipitation and rain-days at Belém, Amazon Valley

Month	Rainfall, in.	Rain-days
January	12.68	26.8
February	13.90	26.1
March	13.94	28.2
April	13.07	26.4
May	9.45	22.6
June	5.87	20.5
July	5.24	18.5
August	4.72	16.2
September	3.70	15.4
October	3.35	12.6
November	2.13	10.3
December	5.98	19.5
Year	94.03	243.1

tion due to solar heating cannot entirely explain the temporal distribution of rainfall.

It is clear that in tropical wet climate there are rainy spells in the drier seasons and short dry spells even in the rainy seasons. This comes about partly as a result of fluctuations in the positions of the intertropical convergence—fluctuations which not only are regular and seasonal, but also occur irregularly within short periods of time. The more frequent shower activity of the wet season indicates the proximity of the ITC and equatorial westerlies, while rainy spells even in the drier months probably are signs of a temporary reestablishment of these controls. The less rainy seasons and the drier spells denote a greater prevalence of dry trade-wind air masses. A second feature controlling the frequency of spells of showery weather is the passage of traveling weak disturbances, whose occurrence is nonperiodic.

Rainfall variability. In spite of the heavy rainfall characteristic of this climate, there may be considerable variations from year to year in total amount, although usually they are not large enough to have serious consequences. Certainly annual fluctuations of rainfall are much greater than those of temperature. Variability in precipitation is a definite feature of subhumid and dry climates, but strange as it may seem, droughts sometimes also occur in the humid climates near the equator. Occasionally they may

Figure 8.11 Daily cloudiness (in tenths of sky covered) and precipitation amounts (in millimeters) for one year (1914) at Batavia (now Djakarta), Java. Note the single dry season, June–October, which is also the period of least cloud. In this particular year Batavia was *Aw*, not *Ar*. (*After J. Blüthgen.*)

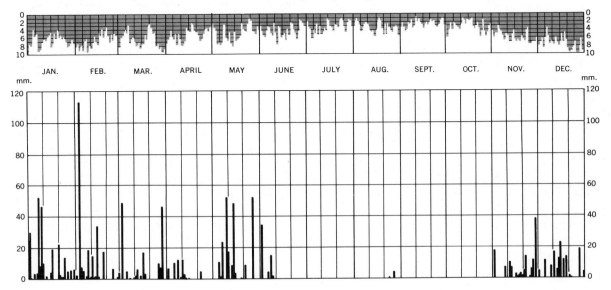

even jeopardize crops, though not necessarily because the rainfall is meager in an absolute sense, but because it is relatively so. In these low latitudes where temperatures are constantly high, evaporation is excessive. Moreover, the crops grown are of a kind that require abundant precipitation. Consequently a total that might be judged more than adequate in the middle latitudes could represent a deficiency and be injurious in the wet tropics.

Rainfall variability at two tropical stations (Inches)

Station	Driest year	Wettest year	Average
Colombo, Ceylon	51.6	139.7	83.8
Singapore	32.7	158.7	92

Winds

The feeble temperature gradients create weak pressure gradients, so that air movement is commonly slight, and also fickle. The whole region is poorly ventilated, and this, in conjunction with high temperatures and excessive humidity, causes physical discomfort. Temporary relief may be brought by the strong but brief squall winds associated with thunderstorms. Occasionally, especially in the drier periods, the trades advance far enough equatorward to bring brief spells of desiccating weather. Such a wind, known as the harmattan along the Atlantic coast of Tropical West Africa, is usually described as cool, particularly at night. This is probably owing to its great evaporation.

Along coasts in the low latitudes, sea breezes are important climatic phenomena. The importation of cooler air from the sea during the heat of the day is a great advantage to residents along the littoral, causing tropical coasts to be much more livable than the interiors. Ordinarily the effects of the sea breeze reach inland only 30 to 60 miles.

Weather in *Ar* climate

Preceding sections have emphasized the diurnal regularity found in individual elements of *Ar* climates. This is especially true of temperature, for deviation from a sun-controlled regime is very slight.

Rarely does advection significantly modify the diurnal monotony. Cloud may be somewhat more effective, since the seasons or periods of greatest cloudiness usually show appreciably lower daytime temperatures, as well as smaller diurnal ranges.

Cloud and precipitation do not have the same high degree of diurnal regularity as the temperature element. This reflects the extensive traveling disturbances, nonperiodic in occurrence, which stimulate convective shower activity of an organized character. However, solar daytime heating also acts to intensify the shower activity during the warmest hours.

Regional features[4]

Although this book is concerned mainly with the world pattern of climates as exemplified by the climatic types and their distribution, that does not necessarily exclude giving some attention to separate climatic regions on the various continents, providing that such a region has individuality within the type.

Latin America. The Amazon Basin in South America is distinguished both by the extensiveness of *Ar* development and by the great overall quantity of its annual precipitation. No other large region equals it in this combination of features. Not only is the basin freely open to equatorial air from the Atlantic, but as Fig. 8.12 shows, during the Southern Hemisphere summer it is flooded by a humid, unstable northwesterly current, probably a segment of the equatorial westerlies (see Chapter 3). Still, the Amazon lowland is by no means a region of rainfall uniformity, either in annual amounts or in annual march. The belt of heavy precipitation (2,000–3,000 mm; 80–120 in.) lies in the deepest interior of the middle and upper Amazon Basin. This very wet interior is partly the result of its invasion by humid unstable northwesterly air in the Southern Hemisphere summer. The westerly flow appears to provide a bountiful advected moisture supply. But in

[4] Much of this section is taken from the author's book, *The Earth's Problem Climates,* University of Wisconsin Press, Madison, Wis., 1961.

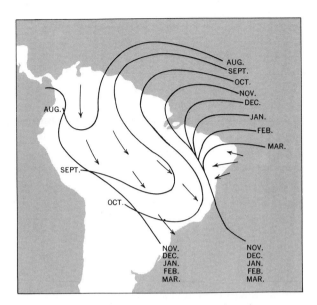

Figure 8.12 Stages in the advance south and east over Brazil in spring and summer (Southern Hemisphere) of the humid, unstable equatorial westerlies and the ITC. Note that the rate of southeastward advance of this northwesterly air is much more retarded along the north coast than it is in the interior, and that it normally does not succeed in overrunning extreme eastern Brazil. (*After Coyle. From Trewartha, The Earth's Problem Climates.*)

the downstream part of the basin between the interior and coastal regions of heavy rainfall, precipitation drops as low as 70 in. (1,750 mm), for reasons which are obscure.

The heavy annual rainfall over most of the Amazon Basin also shows a distinct periodicity. All 12 months are wet only in the middle and upper parts upriver from Manaus; most of the remainder has 1 or 2 dry months. But in that less wet part of the lower basin where rainfall drops as low as 70 in., there appear to be spots, or even a northwest-southeast corridor, of *Aw* climate with more than 2 dry months. Over nearly the whole basin, however, including the wet upper part, winter and spring of the Southern Hemisphere have lower rainfalls than the other seasons (Fig. 8.13). This is because of the deep westward penetration of the South Atlantic subtropical anticyclone and its more stable easterly flow during the low-sun period.

Little is known about rainbringing disturbances in the Amazon country, though one in particular has often been described. This is a wind surge representing a speed convergence in the humid unstable flow from the northwest which invades the basin from August to March. Such surges travel southeastward in the northwesterly flow. They appear to resemble the speed convergences described for the Indian summer monsoon, and like them they generate spells of bad weather with cloud and instability showers.

Much smaller regions of *Ar* climate in Latin America occur in (1) the Guianas, which is a northwestward continuation of the Amazonian *Ar*, (2) the coastal strip and slopes in Brazil bordering the South Atlantic, (3) the Pacific lowland and slopes of Colombia, and (4) the Caribbean lowlands of Central America, together with certain more elevated islands and parts of islands in the West Indies.

Ar along the Atlantic margins of Brazil south of Cape St. Roque is distinguished by the fact that the northern part from the Cape to about 13°S receives some 70 to 80 percent of the year's rainfall in low-sun autumn-winter. Spring-summer is relatively dry (Fig. 8.14). Such a seasonal distribution, which is unusual in the tropics, appears to be a consequence of a strong buildup in spring-summer of

Figure 8.13 Annual march of rainfall at three stations in the Amazon Basin. Uaupés is located in the extreme western part, where annual rainfall is both heavy and well distributed throughout the year, with no dry months. Belém, on the oceanic eastern margins, likewise has heavy annual rainfall, but there is greater seasonal variation. Obidos, situated between the other two stations, has much less total annual rainfall, and even a short dry season. The Southern Hemisphere spring is normally the driest season.

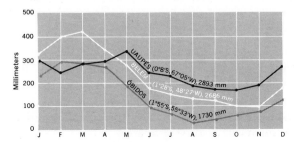

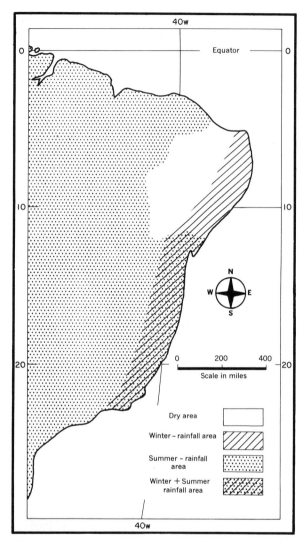

Figure 8.14 The dry area in eastern Brazil occupies an intermediate position between the winter-rainfall region to the east, and the strong summer-rainfall region to the interior and west. It normally escapes the full effects of the disturbances which produce these contrasting seasonal rainfalls. (*From Trewartha, The Earth's Problem Climates.*)

the subtropical anticyclone over the "hump" of easternmost Brazil. This high holds at bay the northwesterly flow of equatorial air which is such a potent rainbringer to the Amazon. It also blocks the normal migration of the ITC south of the equator along the coast (Fig. 8.12).

Ar along the Pacific lowlands and slopes of Colombia is notable for its excessively large annual amounts of precipitation, usually between 150 and 400 in. Such abnormal rainfall reflects the prevalence of westerly-southwesterly flow of unstable equatorial air which is blocked by high mountains not far inland. Supplementing these orographic effects is the influence of an ITC positioned almost constantly a few degrees north of the equator. Another unusual feature is the fact that the coastal strip has a strong predominance of night rains, usually concentrated between midnight and 4 A.M.

A widespread feature of *Ar* in the Caribbean lowlands and slopes of Central America, and many islands in the West Indies as well, is the two summer maxima (May-June and September-October-November), with a secondary minimum in mid- and late-summer (July-August) called the *veranillo*. The summer "dent" in the top of the annual rainfall curve occurs at the time of a slight increase in atmospheric pressure associated with an extended subtropical anticyclone in the westernmost Atlantic. Hurricane rainfall is an important part of the second, or autumn, maximum.

Africa.   In the Congo Basin of Africa, annual rainfall is distinctly less than in the Amazon lowland. Although it is generally over 60 in., it exceeds 80 in. only in restricted areas. In part this reduced Congo rainfall reflects the influence of dry Saharan air coming from the north. No such deeply humidified mass of unstable *mT* air invades the Congo as that which floods the Amazon from the northwest for much of the year. Entrance of Indian Ocean air is made difficult by the East Africa highlands. Also, much of the *mT*–South Atlantic air which enters from the west originates in the northern and eastern limb of a subtropical cell and has traveled over a cool current, so that its vertical structure is fairly stable. Why the interior and lowest part of the Congo Basin, the Cuvette Central, should have the most extensive area of greatest rainfall remains unclear.

At least two types of rainbringing disturbance in the Congo have been described: surges in the southwesterly flow, and line squalls that commonly move

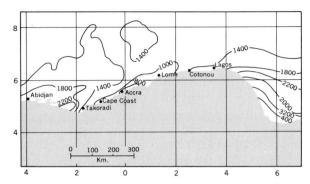

Figure 8.15 Annual rainfall amounts along the West African coast from the Ivory Coast to Nigeria. The 1,000 mm (40 in.) isohyet (line of equal rainfall) approximately defines the Accra dry belt. (*From Climatological Atlas of Africa, 1961.*)

from east to west being carried by the easterly flow aloft. Many of these squalls seem to develop along the convergence zone between easterlies and equatorial westerlies.

Along the Atlantic coast, in Liberia and the Ivory Coast in Tropical West Africa, is a somewhat smaller region of *Ar* climate. Here a well-developed south-

west summer monsoon, or equatorial westerlies, results in a large rainfall total strongly concentrated in the high-sun period. "Winter," when the dry easterlies reach nearly to the coast, is distinctly drier, so that ordinarily 2 months are classed as dry. Separating the Congo and West Africa *Ar* regions is a distinctly drier (30 to 40 in.) *Aw-BS* area in Ghana-Togo-Dahomey (Fig. 8.15). Its origin is obscure, although since the driest part (under 30 in.) is along the coast, it seems likely that the drought is partly associated with winds whose direction is parallel to the coastline or slightly offshore.[5] Madagascar shows a rainy east (windward) side in trades, so that the location of *Ar* climate there resembles the situations in eastern Brazil and in eastern Central America.

Southeast Asia and others. Southeast Asia, a much-fragmented insular and peninsular region with highly diverse directional alignments of coasts and terrain features, naturally exhibits numerous

[5] See Trewartha, *The Earth's Problem Climates*, pp. 106–110.

Figure 8.16 A mercator projection satellite photograph showing the equatorial region centered on the central and eastern Pacific Ocean. A striking feature is a pair of cloud bands, coincident with heavy rainfall, which parallel the equator, each band situated a few degrees north and south of 0°. Between the two cloud bands is a narrow belt with little cloud (shown as a dark band bisected by the equator) which extends westward from South America to beyond 160°E. This is the equatorial Pacific dry belt. The photograph is not a single exposure, but rather is a multiple-exposure "average" from ESSA III and V computer-produced mosaics, March 16–31, 1967. (*Courtesy of J. Kornfield and A. F. Hasler.*)

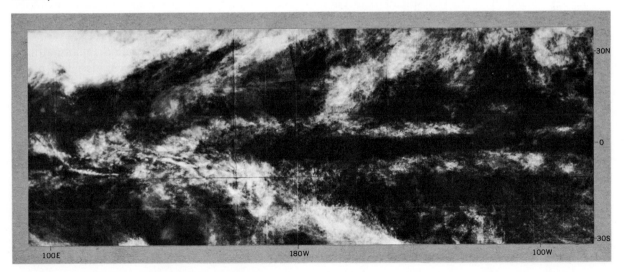

regional and local modifications of *Ar* climate. During the course of a year much of the region is influenced both by the southwest monsoon, or equatorial westerlies, and by the tropical easterlies, or trades. Since the monsoon is usually the heavier rainbringer, a high-sun precipitation maximum is the rule over the greater part of the area, and west sides of islands and peninsuals have the heaviest annual rainfalls. But at least three fairly extensive areas, all located along eastern littorals backed by highlands, exhibit a trade-wind low-sun winter maximum: the northeastern Philippines, the east side of the Indochina Peninsula, and the eastern margins of the Malay Peninsula. Stations with 1 or 2 dry months are very common.

One of the earth's most striking climatic anomalies is the rainfall deficiency in the equatorial eastern Pacific ocean (Fig. 8.16). In the form of a long thin wedge tapering toward the west, its apex in the vicinity of 160° to 170°E, a narrow zone of greatly diminished rainfall follows the equator for a distance of 7,000 miles or more westward from the Ecuador-Peru coast. Rainfall increases westward—from 5 to 10 in. in the extreme east to 30+ in the far western part. Belts of heavy rainfall flank this zone to the north and south. The dry belt is remarkably persistent in location; its latitudinal shift during the year is slight. What the origin of this longitudinally extensive equatorial drought may be remains obscure. Some would attribute it to the narrow band of equatorial cool water that thrusts westward from the South American coast. Others attach importance to the lack of equatorial westerlies, and the prevalence of an easterly flow, probably associated with divergence and subsidence. Additional published solutions are known to be imminent.[6]

TROPICAL WET-AND-DRY CLIMATE (*Aw*)

Aw climate differs in two principal respects from *Ar*: It usually has a smaller total precipitation, and the annual rainfall is less well distributed throughout the year. The wet season is shorter and the dry season longer, with the drought more severe. As a result the dense *Ar* rainforest gives way in *Aw* regions to lighter, more deciduous forest and tree-studded grasslands. It is this widespread occurrence of tall, coarse grass (called *savanna*) which has led to *Aw* being often referred to as savanna climate. This name may not be so appropriate, however, for many students of climate doubt whether tropical grasslands are climatically induced. Moreover, pure savannas, without trees, seem to be the exception rather than the rule.

Type location.   Typically *Aw* is bounded by *Ar* on its equatorward side and by dry climates (*B*) or subtropical humid climate (*Cf*) on its poleward side (see Fig. 7.2 and map of climate types inside front cover). These boundaries were precisely defined earlier in the chapter in the general discussion of the *A* group of climates. The reason why *Aw* usually grades into a dry climate on the western side of a continent and into a humid climate on the eastern side lies in the contrasting nature of the oceanic subtropical anticyclones in its eastern and western parts. This too has been discussed earlier.

The typical latitudinal location of *Aw* is from about 5 or 10° out to 15 or even 20° (Figs. 7.2 and 8.3). On the generalized latitudinal profile of sea-level pressure, *Aw* is therefore located between the equatorial low-pressure trough and the subtropical highs. Thus on a mean wind chart it will be found somewhat toward the more humid equatorial margins of the tropical easterlies, or trades. This places *Aw* in an intermediate, or transitional, position between the humid unstable air masses associated with the ITC and equatorial westerlies on one side, and the stable subsiding air masses of the subtropical anticyclones on the other (Fig. 8.3).

During the course of a year, with the north-south

[6] *Ibid.,* pp. 86–88. Heinz H. Lettau, *Physical Coupling between the Dry Belt of the Lower Atmosphere and the Cromwell Current of the Upper Ocean, along the Pacific Equator,* ATS—1 Volume, University of Wisconsin Press, Madison, Wis., 1968. J. Kornfield and K. J. Hanson, *Seasonal Displacement of the ITC,* ATS—1 Volume, University of Wisconsin Press, Madison, Wis., 1968.

shifting of the solar radiation belts and the consequent pressure and wind migrations, *Aw* latitudes are alternately encroached upon by the wet ITC and equatorial westerlies (convergent) at the time of high sun, and by the drier parts of the trades and subtropical anticyclones (divergent) in the low-sun period. In some *Aw* regions this seasonal wind reversal is called a monsoon. The result is a rainy "summer" and a dry "winter." In a genetic sense, *Aw* may be classed as one of the "alternating" climates mentioned in Chapter 7, since its most distinctive characteristic of a wet and dry season is closely associated with its dominance by contrasting elements of the general circulation in the opposite seasons.

Because *Aw* lies between dry climates on its poleward side and wet climates on its equatorward side, it is to be expected that within an *Aw* region there will be a gradual change in climatic character from the wetter equatorial margins toward the drier poleward margins. Naturally the dry season becomes increasingly longer and more severe toward the poleward side. These latitudinal contrasts are less marked toward the eastern side of a continent.

Geographical location.   Study of the climate map inside the front cover shows that many, if not most, large *Aw* areas do have the type locations described above and shown graphically in Figs. 7.2 and 8.3. This is true of the two extensive *Aw* areas in South America, one to the north of the Amazonian *Ar*, in Venezuela, Colombia, and the Guianas, and the other to the south of the *Ar*, in south central Brazil and adjacent parts of Bolivia and Paraguay. It is equally true in Africa, where the extensive Sudan *Aw* lies north of the equator and the large veld *Aw* to the south. The *Aw* in equatorial eastern Africa is less typically located, however, and a large part of the *Aw* in both eastern and southern Africa is somewhat atypical because of the many plateaus whose altitude often reduces the temperature below that which is normal for *Aw*. Highlands have the same effect on *Aw* climate in parts of southeastern Brazil. The *Aw* of northern Australia and that of southern and southeastern Asia are relatively typical in location.

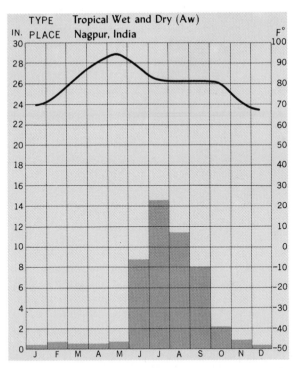

Figure 8.17 Average monthly temperatures and precipitation amounts for a representative station with tropical wet-and-dry climate (*Aw*) in India. Note that the highest temperatures are in May preceding the rains.

Temperature

Temperature characteristics of *Aw* and *Ar* climates are fairly similar. Constantly high temperatures prevail in both, for the noon sun is never far from a vertical position, and days and nights change little in length from one part of the year to another. As a rule the annual range of temperature in *Aw*, while small, is somewhat greater than in *Ar*—over 5° but seldom exceeding 15° (Figs. 8.17 and 8.18). The modest diurnal range during the rainy season in *Aw* resembles that in *Ar*, but in the dry season *Aw*'s range is likely to be greater. Like *Ar* climates, diurnal range in *Aw* is usually consistently larger than annual range.

Many times the hottest month or months do not coincide with the time of highest sun but somewhat precede it (Figs. 8.17 and 8.18). This is because the greatest heat occurs before the height of the rainy

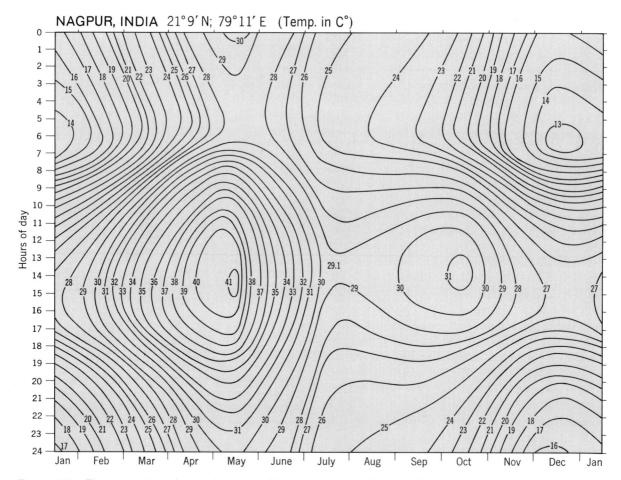

Figure 8.18 Thermoisopleths for an *Aw* station. Note that the annual range of temperature is considerably greater than in the *Ar* climate (Fig. 8.6), for it equals or exceeds the diurnal range in some months. The hottest period is in late April and May, preceding the time of highest sun. There is a secondary peak in October following the rainy season. (*After Troll.*)

period, at which time the more persistent cloud cover and heavier precipitation tend to lower the temperature. Thus in the Northern Hemisphere March, April, and possibly May are likely to be hotter than June or July, which are the rainiest periods for *Aw*. In some *Aw* regions the inhabitants recognize three temperature periods: the *cool dry season* at the time of low sun, the *hot dry season* just preceding the rains, and the *hot wet season* during the rains. Temperatures may rise again very slightly just after the rainy period as a result of the clearer skies and drier atmosphere (see the table on

page 273 for data for representative stations).

During the so-called cool dry season (period of lowest sun), day temperatures are still high, with afternoon maxima between 80 and 90° and occasionally above 90°. The humidity is low, however, so that the heat is not oppressive (Figs. 8.19 and 8.20). Nights at this season are inclined to be pleasantly mild—usually below 70° and often below 60°—for the dry air and clear skies are conducive to rapid terrestrial radiation.

During the hot dry season, which usually begins about the time of the spring equinox, increased

Climatic data for representative stations with tropical wet-and-dry climate (Aw)

	J	F	M	A	M	J	J	A	S	O	N	D	Yr	Range
Navrongo, Ghana, 10°53′N														
Temp., °F	81	85	89	90	87	82	80	79	79	82	82	80	83	10
Precip., in.	0.0	0.2	0.6	1.9	4.4	5.7	7.9	10.4	9.0	2.7	0.2	0.1	43.1	
Timbo, Guinea, 10°40′N														
Temp., °F	72	76	81	80	77	73	72	72	72	73	72	71	74	9.7
Precip., in.	0.0	0.0	1.0	2.4	6.4	9.0	12.4	14.7	10.2	6.7	1.3	0.0	64.1	
Calcutta, India														
Temp., °F	65	70	79	85	86	85	83	82	83	80	72	65	78	21
Precip., in.	0.4	1.1	1.4	2.0	5.0	11.2	12.1	11.5	9.0	4.3	0.5	0.2	58.8	
Cuiabá, Brazil, 15°30′S														
Temp., °F	81	81	81	80	78	75	76	78	82	82	82	81	80	6.6
Precip., in.	9.8	8.3	8.3	4.0	2.1	0.3	0.2	1.1	2.0	4.5	5.9	8.1	54.6	
Normanton, Australia, 17°39′S														
Temp., °F	86	85	85	82	78	73	72	75	80	85	88	87	81	15
Precip., in.	10.9	10.0	6.1	1.5	0.3	0.4	0.2	0.1	0.1	0.4	1.8	5.6	37.5	

intensity and duration of solar radiation cause the daily maxima to rise well above 90° and often over 100° (Figs. 8.19 and 8.20). With the beginning of the rains, however, temperature conditions very much resemble those of the tropical wet climate. The diurnal range becomes somewhat smaller, and while the heat is not so intense as in the hot dry season, the higher humidity causes the sensible temperature to be much more oppressive and sultry.

Figure 8.19 Daily maximum and minimum temperatures for the extreme months in one year at a station with tropical wet-and-dry climate (Aw) in Brazil. Note the dominance of periodic or solar control and the relatively large diurnal range of temperature at this interior station.

Precipitation

Annual amount. Since temperatures are not very different within the tropics, rainfall becomes the critical element in setting apart the several climatic types of the low latitudes. Characteristically, the total annual amount of rainfall of Aw (40 to 60 in.)

Figure 8.20 Daily maximum and minimum temperatures for the extreme months at Havana, Cuba, at about 23°N. Its coastal location causes the daily range to be smaller than at Porto Nacional (Fig. 8.19). Located on the margins of the tropics, Havana also has a somewhat larger temperature difference between the warmest and coolest months than Porto Nacional. In addition, there is evidence of a very weak nonperiodic air-mass control in January.

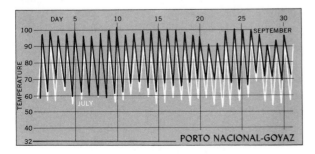

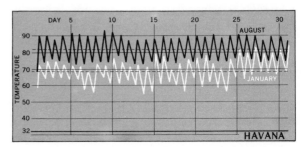

is less than that of *Ar* climate (see data). The smaller annual rainfall in *Aw* reflects the transitional nature of this type, located as it usually is between very wet ITC climates equatorward, and dry climates of the subtropical anticyclones poleward. As mentioned earlier, rainfall within *Aw* declines with increasing latitude.

Rainfall regime.   It is seasonal distribution rather than amount of precipitation, however, which chiefly distinguishes the two climates of the humid tropics. The *Aw* type has a marked dry season of more than 2 months' duration, which characteristically comes at the time of low sun. In that season desert-type weather prevails, for usually the drought is intense. This contrast between the two tropical types is mainly due to their latitudinal locations—*Ar* occurs fairly consistently in the equatorial convergence zone, while *Aw* is intermediate between the ITC and dry trades (Fig. 8.3). In the wet season *Aw* is like *Ar*; in the dry season it resembles the desert.

The Sudan *Aw* of northern Africa is a good example of this rainfall regime. As the sun's vertical ray moves northward from the equator after the spring equinox, pressure and wind belts shift in the same direction, although lagging a month or two behind the sun. The convergent ITC belt of heavy rains gradually creeps northward, and thunderstorms begin to appear in March or April over the Sudan. Rainfall continues to increase until July or even August, when the ITC reaches its maximum northward migration. With the southward retreat of the ITC following the sun, the rains decline. By October or November the dry, subsiding trades again prevail over the Sudan, and drought grips the land. The length of the wet and the dry seasons is variable, depending upon distance from the equator.

There is no abrupt boundary between tropical wet *Ar* and tropical wet-and-dry *Aw* climates—only a very gradual transition from one to the other. On the equatorward margins of the *Aw*, the rainy season persists for 8 to 10 months. In such locations there may be even a slight depression at the crest of the annual precipitation curve occurring in the short interval between the northward and southward shifts of the ITC (Fig. 4.31, Zungeru). Usually the farther poleward one travels in the *Aw*, the shorter the period of ITC control and the longer that of the subsiding trade-wind air masses, so that the dry season increases in length while the wet period shrinks. Emphatically, rainfall follows the sun. This rule holds for either hemisphere, although of course it should be kept in mind that when a Northern Hemisphere *Aw* is having its rainy season, a similar region south of the equator is experiencing drought, and vice versa.

Rainfall reliability.   Not only is *Aw* rainfall lower in total amount and more seasonal in distribution throughout the year than *Ar*, but it is likewise less reliable, with wider fluctuations in quantity from year to year (Fig. 8.21). One year may bring such an abundance of rain as to flood the fields, rot the crops, and increase the depredations of injurious insects and plant diseases; in the following year there may be even more severe losses from drought. In northern Australia the average rainfall variation from the normal is as much as 25 percent.

Seasonal weather

During its rainy season, the weather of *Aw* climate closely resembles that of *Ar* at its worst. This period usually is ushered in and out by violent thunderstorms and severe squall winds. In these transition periods the weather is very trying, with violent short deluges of rain and intensely hot sunshine alternating. As the rainy season advances, sunny days become rarer, showers more frequent.

During the height of the rains, violent thunderstorms appear to be less prevalent than they are in the transition periods, while convective showers, organized in distribution, reach maximum frequency. These showers, like those of *Ar* climates, probably originate in extensive atmospheric disturbances of the wave and weak-cyclone types. According to the Australian Weather Bureau, most of the mid-rainy-season showers of northern Australia

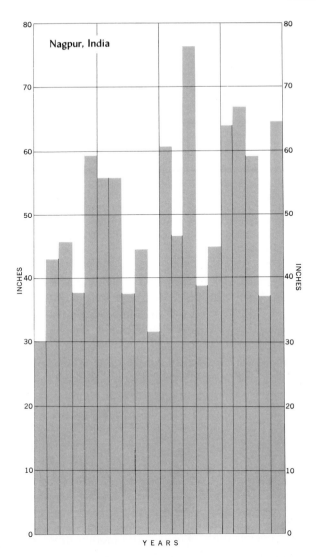

Figure 8.21 Variations in amounts of annual rainfall over a 20-year period at Nagpur, India, a station with tropical wet-and-dry climate. Large annual variations in precipitation are characteristic of this type of climate.

accompany weak tropical lows. Similarly, much of the *Aw* rain of India occurring during the height of the monsoon is received from weak depressions which form over the head of the Bay of Bengal and move slowly in a northwesterly direction across India. Other disturbances in the nature of speed

convergences are also numerous in *Aw* climates.

In the low-sun, or dry, season the weather is like that of the deserts. In spite of the aridity, the dry season is welcomed after the humid, oppressive heat of the rainy periods. Occasional showers may occur during the months of drought; the number depends upon which margin of the *Aw* is being considered. On the dry margin the period of absolute drought may be of several months' duration, while on the rainy margin, where *Aw* makes contact with *Ar* climate, there may be no month absolutely without rain. Remember that none of these climatic boundaries is sharp; there are very gradual transitions from one type to another. During the dry season the savanna landscape is parched and brown. The trees lose their leaves, the rivers become low, the soil cracks, and all nature appears dormant. Dust and smoke from grass fires fill the air, so that visibility is usually low.

Following is a description of the seasonal weather and related landscape changes in an *Aw* region *south* of the equator in Africa.

The winter months, or dry season, extend, with a slight variation, from April to November. They are, as I have said, pleasant and healthy in the extreme. Now the traveller and hunter of big game make their appearance; the deciduous trees are leafless; the grasses dry, yellow, and ready for the chance spark or deliberate act which, with the aid of a steady breeze, will turn vast expanses of golden grasslands into so many hideous, bare deserts of heat-tremulous black. All nature seems to be at a standstill, hibernating. The rivers are low. Where, but a few short months since, wide, watery expanses rushed headlong toward the sea . . . there now remain but tranquil, placid channels, flowing smilingly at the bottom of steep, cliff-like banks. . . .

With October the heat becomes very great. Vast belts of electrically charged, yellowish clouds, with cumulus, rounded extremities, begin to gather and at the close of day are seen to be flickering in their murky centres with a menacing tremor of constant lightning. This may go on for a week or more, and then Nature arises like a strong man in anger and looses the long pent-up voice of the thunder and the irresistible torrents of the early rains. The first manifestation may come at evening and is a soul-moving display of natural force. . . .

After such a disturbance as the one I have just described, rain is fairly continuous for some time, and the effect of this copious irrigation makes itself felt in every branch of animal and vegetable life. Within a few days the change is startling; the paths and roadways choke themselves with a rich clothing of newly sprung grasses, whilst the trees, the extremities of whose twigs and branches have been visibly swelling, now leap into leaf and blossom. The mosses, which for months past have looked like dry, bedraggled, colourless rags, regain once more their vivid, tender green. Now the forest throws off its puritanical greyness and, with an activity and rapidity beyond belief, decks itself in flowers of a thousand gorgeous shades of colour, from chrome-yellow and purple to grateful mauve.

The birds now put on their finest feathers, the animals appear in their brightest hues. Colour and warmth run riot in the brilliantly clear air now washed clean from the mist and smoke which for so many months have obscured it. The clear verdant green of rapid-springing grasses and opening fronds clothes the landscape, and the distant peaks of the mountains lose their pale, bluey-grey haziness and stand boldly out in the light of the sun. The months succeed each other, bringing with them new and strange beauties, for summer is now at its height, and trees and flowers at their most perfect period. . . . April comes, and suddenly Nature holds her hand. The swollen rivers and inundated plains shake themselves free from the redundant waters. The grasses have now reached a formidable height. The rains now cease, and the land begins to dry up. Rich greens turn to copper, and brown, and yellow, and little by little, with the advent of May, the winter returns with its sober greyness.[7]

Upland *Aw*

In tropical latitudes on several continents, particularly in Africa and South America, there are extensive uplands a few thousand feet in elevation which

[7]R. C. F. Maugham, *Zambezia,* John Murray, London, 1910, pp. 383–388.

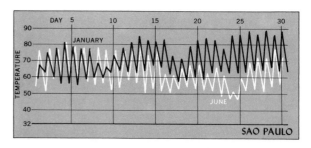

Figure 8.22 Daily maximum and minimum temperatures for a station with tropical wet-and-dry climate on the Brazilian upland at nearly 24°S. Note the lower temperatures imposed both by altitude and by the latitude. While solar control is dominant, nonperiodic air-mass control is also evident here on the margins of the humid tropics.

have most of the normal *Aw* characteristics but differ chiefly in lower temperatures (Fig. 8.22). Depending on their height, some of these upland stations are likely to show cool-month temperatures that are below the minimum for the tropics, and so represent *C* climates. Others qualify as *A*. But in most instances, whether they are tropical (*A*) or subtropical (*C*) in temperature, their seasonal distribution of rainfall remains that of the *Aw* type. Consequently a tropical upland often shows an intermingling of local *Aw* and *C* climates. On the climate map in the front of the book these slightly atypical tropical upland climates continue to be represented as *Aw*, even though some parts certainly are subtropical (*C*) rather than tropical. Their very general distribution is indicated on the climate map by a light overshading. (For climatic modifications imposed by altitude, see Chapter 11.)

Regional features

Latin America. Interior Brazil south of the equator, called the Campos, represents one of the earth's most extensive regions of *Aw* climate. Since it is also relatively uncomplicated in its main climatic lineaments, it constitutes almost a textbook example of *Aw* characteristics. The annual rainfall of 40 to 60+ in. is strongly concentrated in the high-sun period, when the Campos is dominated by a northwesterly

Climatic data for an upland *Aw-Cw* **station: Zomba, Northern Rhodesia** (Lat. 15°22′S, long 38°18′E, elevation 3,042 ft)

	J	F	M	A	M	J	J	A	S	O	N	D	Yr
Temp., °F	72	72	72	70	67	64	63	65	70	74	75	73	69.7
Precip., in.	13.9	8.9	8.9	36	0.5	0.6	0.3	0.4	0.2	1.0	4.5	10.4	53.3

flow of moist, unstable equatorial air from the Amazon forests. In the eastern parts, which have uplands a few thousand feet high, areas of *Aw* climate are intermingled with those that show *C* temperature characteristics.

The smaller Venezuela-Colombia *Aw*, or Llanos, is the Northern Hemisphere counterpart of the Brazilian Campos. Along its Caribbean littoral, there is an anomalous situation where a dry climate—mostly steppe, but possibly with restricted areas of desert—prevails in a location which seemingly should be wet. Parts of the coast have an annual rainfall of less than 500 mm (20 in.); in a few restricted areas it may be as low as 300 to 400 mm (12 to 16 in.). In part the precipitation deficiency is related to a downwind acceleration of the resultant winds, with vertical subsidence aloft. In part also, it is caused by coastal divergence in a surface airflow which nearly parallels the east-west stretches of coast. Significantly, along short stretches of north-south coast where the tendency of onshore winds to pile up is accentuated, rainfall is much heavier. In addition to its dryness, a further peculiarity of

this littoral is that its modest precipitation is concentrated at the time of low sun (Fig. 8.23).[8]

Other *Aw* areas in Latin America include a small one in Pacific Ecuador close to the equator, which typically would be located some 10° farther south. Its northward displacement results from the unusual intensity of the desert-making mechanisms farther south along the coast of Peru. *Aw* is also characteristic of the leeward Pacific side of Central America and southern Mexico. In addition, it prevails on the low-elevation islands of the West Indies and the lowland Yucatán Peninsula.

Africa. In Africa north of the equator, the huge east-west Sudan *Aw* is typically located between the Congo *Ar* and the Sahara *B* climates. It is relatively narrow in a north-south direction, owing to the far southward thrust of Saharan aridity. During midsummer the superheated Sahara has the effect of displacing the surface ITC unusually far poleward (20–21°N). South of this convergence are the equatorial southwesterlies, while above them is dry Saharan air from the northeast. Thus little rain falls along the ITC, and even for several hundred miles south of it, because the surface westerly flow is so shallow, and the rising arid air aloft has too little moisture to permit much precipitation. Still farther south, over the Sudan belt where the southwesterly air is deeper, summer rainfall is much more abundant.

Two weather types which are important rain generators for the Sudan *Aw* are the disturbance line and the surge or speed convergence in the monsoon-like southwesterly flow. The disturbance line superficially resembles a cold front, being accompanied by thunderstorms and turbulent squall winds. In reality, however, these storms develop not

Figure 8.23 Composite annual rainfall profile of 17 stations in the Netherlands West Indies. Average annual rainfall is only 569 mm, or 22.4 in. (*After Lahey. From Trewartha, The Earth's Problem Climates.*)

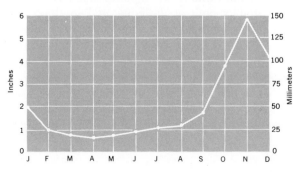

[8]Trewartha, *The Earth's Problem Climates*, pp. 57–64.

along a front, but within the deep easterlies of the Sudan, underlain by the humid equatorial southwesterlies. They move in a westerly direction, carried by the easterly flow aloft; but the accompanying cloud and rain come from the moisture contained in the underlying southwesterlies. The second Sudan weather type, the surge, is a feature of the surface equatorial southwesterly current during the high-sun period. As the surge moves onshore from the Atlantic Ocean and the Gulf of Guinea, it produces cloudy, rainy weather, but without the accompanying turbulence, wind shifts, and squall winds associated with the more vigorous disturbance line. It brings what West African meteorologists call the "monsoon rains."[9]

A special weather type characteristic of the dry season in the Sudan (also found in the Sahara) is a strong southward push of fresh, dry, northeasterly trade-wind air. This is known as the *harmattan*. It is very dry, hot by day and cool by night, and laden with dust picked up during its trajectory over the Sahara wastelands. A dense and widespread dust haze is characteristic.

A great deal of the *Aw* in equatorial East Africa and in southern Africa is of the cooler upland variety, with many areas showing *C* instead of *A* temperatures. Equatorial East Africa with its moderately high plateaus is scarcely typical of *Aw* in either temperature or seasonal rainfall distribution. There two wet and two dry seasons are common, reflecting the dual passage of the ITC. As the maps inside the front and back covers show, equatorial East Africa is drier than normal for the eastern side of a continent close to the equator. There *A(C)w* and *B* climates prevail instead of *Ar* (compare Africa with South America and Asia).

Asia.   Like most *Aw* areas, the Indian subcontinent has a marked seasonal wind shift, the so-called Indian monsoon, between low sun and high sun. But in the usual, or genetic, sense, India's seasonal wind reversal is no more a monsoon than those of most other *Aw* regions, but rather a latitudinal migration of planetary wind belts following the annual course of the sun. During the dry season of winter, the weak northeasterly flow that prevails over most of the subcontinent is essentially a trade wind. Owing to a bifurcation of the upper westerlies by the Tibetan highlands, one branch of the westerlies and its southerly jet stream move southward around the highland mass and are positioned over the northernmost part of the subcontinent. Weak cyclonic storms steered by the jet provide modest cool-season precipitation in northerly and northwesterly parts. As a result, the annual rainfall curve there, in addition to a strong primary summer maximum, has a small secondary winter one as well.[10]

The excessively hot and dry premonsoon period (March–May), with its anticyclonic control, is terminated by the "burst of the monsoon," as the southwesterly flow of unstable equatorial air surges northward over the subcontinent accompanied by turbulent weather. The southwesterly current consists of two branches. A westerly current from the Arabian Sea meets the elevated west coast of India at almost right angles, resulting in heavy orographic rainfall. In modified form it continues northeastward across the broad peninsula. The second, or Bay of Bengal, branch has an exclusively oceanic trajectory. Toward the head of the bay the two branches merge, and a portion of this current appears to recurve westward around the eastern end of a pressure trough positioned over northern India. It flows westward up the Ganges Valley on the northern side of the pressure trough.

India's summer rainfall, which is modest in amount and variable over much of the subcontinent, is a product both of the equatorial southwesterly circulation and of the several types of extensive atmospheric disturbances embedded in it. It is these disturbances that bring the spells of weather with organized cloud and shower areas. One such disturbance has been given the name "monsoon depression." Most monsoon depressions are relatively weak cyclonic circulations, but a few mushroom

[9] *Ibid.*, pp. 97–102.

[10] *Ibid.*, pp. 153–157.

into violent hurricanes. Many seem to originate over the Bay of Bengal, from which they take a course toward the northwest. This concentrates their rainfall effects mainly over the northern, and especially the northeastern, sector of India.

Other spells of India's disturbed rainy weather in summer are generated by pulsations or surges in the southwesterly current, and they move downstream in that monsoonal flow. These surges appear to resemble similar speed convergences mentioned earlier as bringing rain to the Amazon Basin and the Campos in Brazil, and to the Congo Basin and the Sudan in Africa. Significantly, a steady flow, even in a humid unstable circulation, is conducive to fair weather. It is when the steady flow is disturbed that cloud and rain result.

Aw in Southeast Asia is chiefly confined to the more inland sections of the Indochina Peninsula. The seaward margins are mainly *Ar*. The *Aw* region of northern Australia, like those of eastern India and the Caribbean, is occasionally subject to hurricanes.

SELECTED REFERENCES FOR FURTHER STUDY OF TOPICS IN CHAPTER EIGHT

Beckinsale, R. P., "The Nature of Tropical Rainfall," *Tropical Agriculture*, Vol. 34, pp. 76–98, 1957.

Chang, Jen-Hu., "Comparative Climatology of the Tropical Western Margins of the Northern Oceans," *Ann. Assoc. Amer. Geographers*, Vol. 52, pp. 221–227, 1962.

Fosberg, F. R., B. J. Garnier, and A. W. Küchler, "Delimitation of the Humid Tropics," *Geog. Rev.*, Vol. 51, pp. 333–347, 1961.

Garbell, Maurice A., *Tropical and Equatorial Meteorology*, Pitman Publishing Corporation, New York, 1947.

Lauer, Wilhelm, "Humide und aride Jahreszeiten in Afrika und Südamerika und ihre Beziehung zu den Vegetationsgürteln," in Lauer et al., *Studien zur Klima- und Vegetationskunde der Tropen, Bonner Geog. Abhand.*, Geog. Inst. der Univ. Bonn, 1952.

Lockwood, J. G., "The Indian Monsoon: A Review," *Weather*, Vol. 20, pp. 2–8, 1965.

Palmer, C. E. "Tropical Meteorology," in Thomas F. Malone (ed.), *Compendium of Meteorology*, American Meteorological Society, Boston, pp. 859–880, 1951.

Portig, W. H., "Central American Rainfall," *Geog. Rev.*, Vol. 55, pp. 68–90, 1965.

Ramage, C. S., "Diurnal Variation of Summer Rainfall in Malaya," *J. Tropical Geog.*, Vol. 19, pp. 62–68, 1964.

Riehl, Herbert, *Tropical Meteorology*, McGraw-Hill Book Company, New York, 1954.

Symposium on Monsoons of the World, Indian Meteorological Department, New Delhi, 1960.

Symposium on Tropical Meteorology, J. W. Hutchings (ed.), New Zealand Meteorological Service, Wellington, 1964.

Thompson, B. W., "An Essay on the General Circulation of the Atmosphere over Southeast Asia and the West Pacific," *Quart. J. Roy. Meteorol. Soc.*, Vol. LXXVII, pp. 569–597, 1951.

Thornthwaite, C. W., "The Water Balance in Tropical Climates," *Bull. Amer. Meteorol. Soc.*, Vol. 32, pp. 166–173, 1951.

Trewartha, Glenn T., "Climate as Related to the Jet Stream in the Orient," *Erdkunde*, Vol. XII, pp. 205–214, 1958.

Trewartha, Glenn T., *The Earth's Problem Climates*, The University of Wisconsin Press, Madison, Wis., 1961.

Watts, I. E. M., *Equatorial Weather*, University of London Press, Ltd., London, 1955.

Yin, M. T., "A Synoptic-Aerologic Study of the Onset of the Summer Monsoon over India and Burma," *J. Meteorol.*, Vol. 6, pp. 393–400, 1949.

CHAPTER NINE

SUBTROPICAL CLIMATES (C)

Although the subtropics are transitional in climatic character between tropics and middle latitudes, the classification system used here places the humid-subhumid parts of subtropical climates in the middle latitudes. Lacking the constant heat of the tropics and the constant cold of the polar icecaps, middle-latitude climates are characterized by a strong seasonal rhythm in temperatures. The largest annual temperature ranges on earth are found in the Northern Hemisphere middle latitudes with their vast continents. Thus temperature becomes coequal with rainfall in determining the various climatic types of middle latitudes. In the tropics seasons are distinguished as wet and dry, since seasonal temperature contrasts are small; in the middle latitudes they are called winter and summer, and the dormant season for plant growth usually is one of low temperatures rather than drought.

In the middle latitudes the changeableness of the weather is proverbial, for they are the realm of conflict between air masses expelled from polar and tropical source regions. Within the humid parts of these latitudes, three large groups of climates are recognized: subtropical, temperate, and boreal.

Type location. The subtropical group, the warmest and mildest of the three, occupies the equatorward margins of middle latitudes (Fig. 9.1). On its poleward frontier it joins the temperate group; on its low-latitude side it borders the tropics. Many areas of the subtropics have occasional snow, but it does not remain on the ground to form a durable snow cover. Most of this group also is subject to some freezes, although in marine locations they may be rare or even absent. The tropical boundary chosen for subtropical climates is the equatorward limits of freeze, or in marine locations, the 65° isotherm for the coolest month. The poleward boundary consists of 8 months with an average temperature of at least 50°.

Within the subtropical belt two types of humid climates are distinguished: subtropical dry-summer, usually situated on the western side of a continent, and subtropical humid on the eastern side (Fig. 9.1).

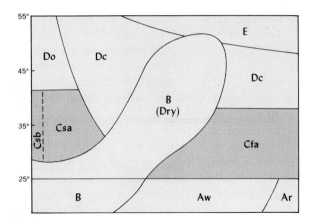

Figure 9.1 Type location of the two subtropical climates (*Cs* and *Cfa*) with respect to latitude, position on continents, and bordering types of climates.

SUBTROPICAL DRY-SUMMER CLIMATE (*Cs*)[1]
(Mediterranean)

In its simplest form this climate has three main features: (1) a concentration of the year's modest amount of precipitation in the winter season, while summers are nearly or completely dry; (2) warm-to-hot summers and unusually mild winters; and (3) abundant sunshine and meager cloudiness, especially in summer. Quite deservedly this climate, with its bright sunny weather, blue skies, few rainy days, and mild winters—and its usually plentiful fruit, flowers, and winter vegetables—has acquired a glamorous reputation.

The *Cs* type has marked climatic characteristics which are duplicated with notable similarity in the five regions where it occurs: the borderlands of the Mediterranean Sea, central and coastal southern California, central Chile, the southern tip of South Africa, and parts of southernmost Australia. According to Köppen, *Cs* occupies only 1.7 percent of the earth's land area; yet in spite of its limited extent it is one of the most distinctive and best-known types. It is the only extensive humid climate that has drought in summer and a strong rainfall maximum in winter.

Type location. Typically, subtropical dry-summer climate is located on the tropical margins of the middle latitudes (30 to 40°) along the western sides of continents (Figs. 7.2 and 9.1). It is the western sides that are affected by the stable eastern end of an oceanic subtropical high. Lying thus on the poleward slope of a subtropical high-pressure cell's

[1]*s* = Dry season in summer of the respective hemisphere. At least three times as much rain in the winter half year as in the summer half year. Driest summer month receives less than 3 cm or 1.2 in. Total annual precipitation usually less than 89 cm or 35 in.

stable side, *Cs* is between the dry subsiding air masses of the horse latitudes on the one hand and the rainbringing fronts and cyclones of the westerlies on the other. As a result of the north-south shifting of wind belts, the Mediterranean latitudes are encroached upon by each of these systems during the course of a year. At one season they are joined climatically to the dry tropics and at the opposite season to the humid middle latitudes. Tropical constancy therefore characterizes them in summer, middle-latitude changeability in winter. *Cs* is definitely a transition type between tropical dry climates equatorward and temperate climates, usually temperate oceanic (*Do*), poleward (see Fig. 7.2 and the climate map inside the front cover).

In both central Chile and California, mountains terminate the dry-summer type abruptly on the land side, and dry climates prevail on the other side of the mountains. In South Africa and southwestern Australia, the farthest poleward extent of these continents carries them barely into Mediterranean latitudes, so that subtropical dry-summer climate occupies southern and southwestern extremities rather than distinctly west-coast locations. Only in the region of the Mediterranean Basin, which is an important cool-season convergence zone and a route of winter cyclones, is this type of climate found far inland, and there it extends for 2,500 miles or more. It is the relative warmth of the Mediterranean Sea in winter, and the resulting low-pressure trough coincident with it, that makes the Mediterranean Basin a region of air-mass convergence in the cool months, with a resulting development of fronts and cyclones.

Continental interiors and eastern margins of continents, with their tendencies toward monsoon wind systems and summer maxima of rainfall, are governed by conditions opposed to the development of *Cs* climate, especially its characteristic rainfall regime. And while the eastern sides of subtropical continents come under the influence of a subtropical anticyclone in summer, they are affected by the unstable air of the western parts of the cell and so are likely to have abundant summer rainfall.

Temperature

Because of its subtropical latitude and its west-side position on the continents, *Cs* climate has very little cold weather. Average temperatures of the winter months are usually between 40 and 50° and of the summer months between 70 and 80°, so that mean annual ranges of 20 to 30°+ are common. These are relatively small for the middle latitudes but are larger than those of the tropics, except possibly for some tropical dry climates.

Subtropical dry-summer climates may be classified in two subdivisions based mainly on the degree of summer heat. This in turn is largely a function of location. First and far more extensive is a warm-summer subtype (*Csa*), situated either inland from the coast or on a coast bordered by warm water. The second, a cool-summer subtype (*Csb*),[2] occupies limited areas mainly where coasts are washed by cool currents fed by upwelling, such as the California and Chile littorals. Some elevated sites may also be *Csb*. Since *Csa* is so much more widespread that it represents the standard condition for *Cs*, the cool-water subtype is treated as only a minor variant.

Summer.   Except along cool-water coasts and on uplands, *Cs* summer temperatures are hot, resembling those of tropical-subtropical dry climates (Fig. 9.2). In July and August the dry-summer subtropics blaze under a pitiless sky. Red Bluff, California, located inland in the Sacramento Valley behind the coastal ranges, has an average July temperature of about 82°. Such temperatures are about 16° higher than the July average at Santa Monica, California, located farther south but on a cool-water coast. Of course, the summer climate of the interior valleys of California represents a somewhat extreme variety of dry-summer subtropical. Lowland stations along the borderlands of the Mediterranean Sea usually

---

[2] In the symbols *Csa* and *Csb* the letter *a* indicates a hot summer in which the average temperature of the warmest month is 22°C (71.6°F) or above. The letter *b* indicates a cool summer in which the average temperature of the warmest month is below 22°C.

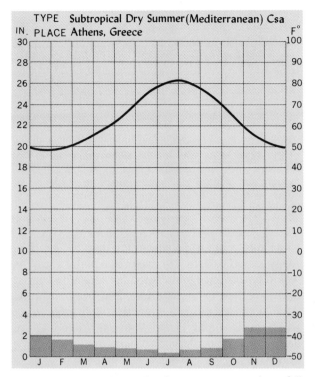

TYPE Subtropical Dry Summer(Mediterranean) Csa
PLACE Athens, Greece

Figure 9.2 Annual march of temperature and rainfall for a subtropical dry-summer station with a hot summer (*Csa*).

rapid nocturnal cooling. Consequently there is a marked contrast between day and night, especially in the drier Mediterranean climates. At Sacramento in the Great Valley, hot, clear, summer days with afternoon temperatures of 85 to 100° are followed by nights when the thermometer sinks between 55 and 60°. The daily range for this city in a recent July was 36.6°—a figure characteristic of deserts. Following the hot, glaring days, the relatively cool nights, in which a light topcoat may be comfortable, are much appreciated by the inhabitants of inland Mediterranean climates. One 24-hr period is much like another in summer, for sun is in control (Fig. 9.3).

Cool-summer coastal subtype (*Csb*).   Compared with areas inland, any coastal station is likely to have somewhat moderated summer heat. Perth, Australia has a hot-month temperature of 74°, Lisbon 72°, Casablanca (Morocco) 74°, and Istanbul 74° —all of which are 5 to 8° lower than those of interior California. Still, these are not cool by the standards of cool-water coasts (see Fig. 9.4 and the data for Santa Monica, page 286). The warm-month temperature of Santa Monica on the California coast is only 66°, San Francisco 59°, and Valparaiso in coastal Chile 66°. In summer such locations fre-

have July averages between 75° and 80° +. *Cs* stations in the Southern Hemisphere are not so warm; Perth and Adelaide in Australia record January temperatures of 74°. But while summer days are hot in most regions with this climate, it is not sultry heat, except along a coast. Dry heat like that of the desert is typical of inland California.

Averages of the daily maxima in the Sacramento Valley usually are close to 90° (Fig. 9.3). In a year selected at random, Sacramento had 27 days in July and 16 in August with maximum temperatures of 90° or above. Similar figures for Red Bluff were 30 and 30. Sacramento has recorded a temperature as high as 114°. Clear skies, dry air, and a nearly vertical sun provide ideal conditions for strong daytime heating in *Csa* climates.

These same conditions are also conducive to

Figure 9.3 Daily maximum and minimum temperatures for the extreme months in one year at a subtropical dry-summer station inland in California (*Csa*). Note the hot summer and the large diurnal range of temperature. Solar control is dominant in summer, but irregular, nonperiodic air-mass control is conspicuous in winter.

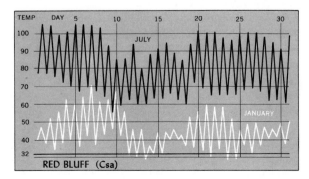

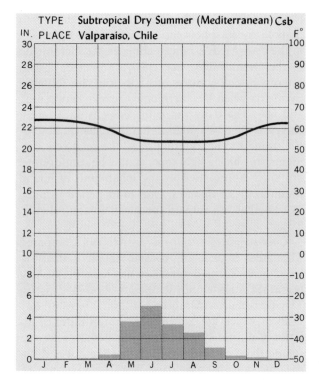

Figure 9.4 Annual march of temperature and rainfall for a Southern Hemisphere subtropical dry-summer station, located along a cool-water coast in Chile (*Csb*). Note the cool summer.

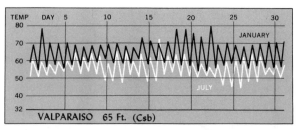

Figure 9.5 Daily maximum and minimum temperatures of the extreme months for the same station as in Fig. 9.4. Note the small diurnal range of temperature. Although sun control dominates, there is evidence of some weak nonperiodic control associated with disturbances and their advective effects.

quently have marine fog and low stratus fog, which are related to the cool water and the above-surface inversion of temperature. In many of its features— low temperature, small temperature range, fog, and aridity—the summer climate of coastal subtropical

Chile and California resembles that of the cool, foggy desert coasts (*Bn*) farther equatorward. As would be expected winters too are milder in coastal locations than in the interiors, and frosts are rare. Annual ranges are consequently small (only 9° at San Francisco and 11° at Valparaiso), and so are daily ranges (Fig. 9.5).

Winter. It is for their mild, bright winters, characterized by congenial days and crisp nights, that subtropical dry-summer climates are justly famed. People from the higher latitudes seek them out as winter playgrounds and health resorts. In northern latitudes the word winter has a congealing sound, but winter in the Mediterranean borderlands transforms the barren hills with a glow of color. Even inland locations have average cold-month temperatures 10 to 15° above freezing. Thus inland Sacra-

Maximum and minimum temperatures for some *Cs* stations

Station	Average annual minimum	Absolute minimum	Average annual maximum	Absolute maximum
Valencia	31	20	96	107
Naples	33	24	94	101
Athens	29	20	100	109
Fresno	26	17	109	115
San Diego	36	25	91	110
Perth	38	34	105	112
Cape Town	32	28	97	103

mento's average January temperature is 46°. But along coasts middle winter is even milder—55° at Perth, 53° at Santa Monica, and 48° at Naples. In southern California in January, midday temperatures rise to between 50 and 60° and at night drop to 40° ± (e.g., 39° in Sacramento at night, 45.5° in Los Angeles).

Freeze and the growing season. The growing season in *Cs* climates is not quite the whole year, for there are occasional freezes during the 3 winter months. But to say that the growing season is 9 ± months does not adequately describe the situation, for while freezing temperatures do occur during midwinter months, they come on only a few nights and are rarely severe. During a period of 41 years at Los Angeles, there were 28 in which no freeze occurred and the growing season was 12 months long. In southern California, freezes may be expected at intervals of about 10 to 15 years. During a recent year at Red Bluff there were 10 nights when the temperature dropped below 32°; at Sacramento there were 7. The lowest temperature ever recorded at Los Angeles is 28°, at Naples 24°, and at Sacramento 17°. Even on the occasional nights when temperatures do slip a few degrees below freezing, they rise well above 32° again the following day. Never does the thermometer stay below the freezing point for an entire day.

What freezes do occur are usually the result of radiation cooling following an importation of cold polar air. The subfreezing temperatures are confined to a shallow layer of surface atmosphere, particularly to depressions in which the cool, dense air has collected. For this reason such sensitive crops as citrus are commonly planted on slopes. Occasionally fires must be lighted among the citrus trees in order to prevent serious damage from freezing. At first it may seem odd that in Mediterranean climates, where freezes are neither frequent nor severe, unusual losses should result occasionally from low temperatures. But it is this infrequency and lack of severity that make frost so treacherous, since the mild winters tempt farmers to grow types of crops which are particularly sensitive to cold, such as out-of-season vegetables and citrus.

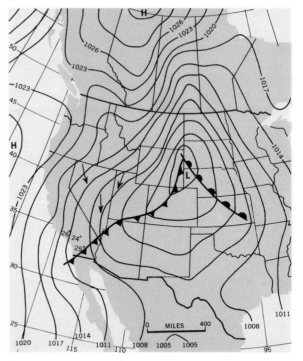

Figure 9.6 Surface weather map (January 2, 1949, 4:30 A.M.), showing a synoptic condition which brought freezing temperatures to southern California. (*After Durrenberger.*)

Weather controls associated with freeze. Typical weather controls that produce occasional killing frosts in California are illustrated by the weather map in Fig. 9.6, which shows atmospheric conditions in the American Southwest for a frost night in January. A well-developed low traveling on a southerly track, with steep gradients on its poleward side, was followed by an invasion of cold polar continental air associated with a large anticyclone which spread southward over the whole Southwest. The clear skies and dry air of the anticyclone permitted strong nocturnal cooling in the already chilly air. It was advection processes bringing fresh polar Canadian air from northerly latitudes that set the stage for the subsequent freeze. Radiation processes were effective in dropping the surface temperatures of the advected polar air below freezing during the relative calm on the night of January 2.

Climatic data for representative subtropical dry-summer stations (*Cs*)

	J	F	M	A	M	J	J	A	S	O	N	D	Yr	Range
Red Bluff, California (*Csa*, interior)														
Temp., °F	45	50	54	59	67	75	82	80	73	64	54	46	62.3	36.3
Precip., in.	4.6	3.9	3.2	1.7	1.1	0.5	0.0	0.1	0.8	1.3	2.9	4.3	24.3	
Santa Monica, California (*Csb*, cool-water coast)														
Temp., °F	53	53	55	58	60	63	66	66	65	62	58	55	59.5	13.6
Precip., in.	3.5	3.0	2.9	0.5	0.5	0.0	0.0	0.0	0.1	0.6	1.4	2.3	14.8	
Perth, Australia (*Csa*, coast)														
Temp., °F	74	74	71	67	61	57	55	56	58	61	66	71	64	19
Precip., in.	0.3	0.5	0.7	1.6	4.9	6.9	6.5	5.7	3.3	2.1	0.8	0.6	33.9	
Naples, Italy (*Csa*, coast)														
Temp., °F	48	49	53	59	65	72	77	77	72	64	56	51	62	29
Precip., in.	4.8	3.5	1.7	1.8	2.2	0.7	0.6	1.3	4.3	4.6	4.1	4.7	34.3	
Haifa, Israel (*Csa*, coast)														
Temp., °F	57	58	62	67	74	78	82	83	81	76	69	60	71	26
Precip., in.	7.1	5.7	0.9	0.7	0.1	0.0	0.0	0.0	0.0	0.5	2.7	6.7	24.4	

Precipitation

Annual amount. As a general rule dry-summer regions have too little annual rainfall rather than too much. The climate is not only subtropical but also subhumid, 15 to 25 or 30 in. being a fair annual average. If this modest amount were concentrated in the hot Mediterranean summer when evaporation is great, conditions would be semiarid rather than subhumid (Fig. 9.7). The name *subtropical dry-summer* is useful, therefore, in distinguishing this climate from its wetter counterpart, *subtropical humid* climate, situated on the eastern sides of continents in similar latitudes.

Lying as it typically does between dry climates (*B*) equatorward and moist temperate oceanic climates (*Do*) poleward, *Cs* climate usually shows a gradual increase in rainfall from its equatorward to its poleward margins. This is well illustrated by three California cities: San Diego, the farthest south, has only 10 in. of rain; Los Angeles has 16 in.; and San Francisco to the north has 23 in. Precipitation also tends to increase from the interiors toward the coasts, except where terrain features modify the pattern.

Seasonal distribution. More distinctive than the annual amount of rain, however, is its distribution over the 12-month period. Characteristically *Cs* climate has a pronounced rainfall concentration in the cooler months, while summer is relatively, and in some places absolutely, dry (Figs. 9.2 and 9.4). Since most rain comes in the cool season, less moisture is lost through evaporation, and more is available for plant and human use. Mild winter temperatures that permit plant growth also give maximum effectiveness to the modest amount of precipitation.

At Los Angeles 78 percent of the precipitation falls from December through March, and less than 2 percent from June through September. Rainfall in the European rimlands of the Mediterranean Basin does not show quite such strong seasonal contrasts: comparable amounts for Seville, Spain, are 50 and 7 percent; for Genoa, Italy, 40 and 18. The less dry summers of Mediterranean Europe are partly a result of higher latitude, which leads to development of some cyclonic rainfall even in the warm season.

Typically the rainfall regime of *Cs* regions is alternately that of the dry climates in summer and the

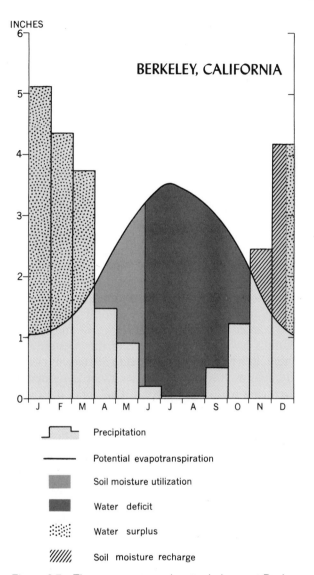

Figure 9.7 The average annual water balance at Berkeley, California, based on mean monthly values. Note that in this dry-summer climate, evapotranspiration exceeds precipitation for 7 of the warm months of the year, and there is an actual water deficit for nearly 5 months. (*Data from Thornthwaite and Mather.*)

INCHES

BERKELEY, CALIFORNIA

Precipitation

Potential evapotranspiration

Soil moisture utilization

Water deficit

Water surplus

Soil moisture recharge

As pointed out earlier, they move poleward in summer, bringing Mediterranean latitudes under the influence of the stable eastern margins of a subtropical anticyclone. As they move equatorward in winter, the same latitudes fall within the zone of middle-latitude fronts and cyclones. Thus rainfall in the dry-summer subtropics is predominantly of frontal or cyclonic origin. In Pacific North America in summer, stable anticyclonic air prevails along the coast, extending beyond southernmost California (Fig. 9.8). In addition, its basal layers have been chilled over the waters of the North Pacific and over

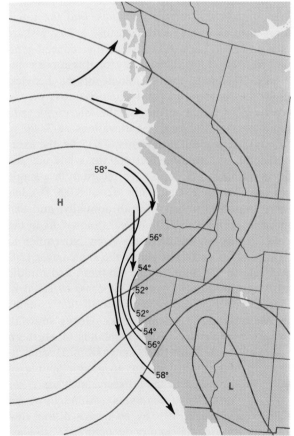

Figure 9.8 Pressure, winds, and ocean temperatures along the Pacific Coast of the United States in midsummer. Coastal climates with cool, dry summers are a consequence of these controls. (*After Patton.*)

cyclonic westerlies in winter, when rain is relatively abundant. This seasonal alternation of summer drought and winter rain results from a latitudinal shifting of wind and rain belts following the sun.

the cool coastal currents, so that inversions, both at the surface and aloft, are common and the whole air-mass structure is opposed to summer precipitation. In winter, Mediterranean California's rains are associated with an overrunning of colder air masses by *mT* air, or with *mT* or *mP* air being forced up over highland barriers.

Snowfall. At low elevations *Cs* climate has no durable snow cover, and even snowfall is rare. Over central and southern California (excluding the mountains), annual snowfall averages less than 1 in., and there is none at all along the coast from San Luis Obispo southward. In all Mediterranean lowland regions, snow is so rare that it attracts much attention and comment when it does fall.

But where highlands are present in Mediterranean latitudes, as they commonly are, they usually have an abundance of snow. Their total precipitation is greater than that of the lowlands, and the lower temperatures due to altitude cause a larger share of it to fall as snow. Because of the reduced temperatures these highlands are probably more commonly *D* climate than *C*. Some of the heaviest snowfall anywhere in the United States is on the windward western slopes of the Sierra Nevada mountains of California at elevations of 7,000 to 8,000 ft. At Summit, California (7,017 ft), the average annual snowfall is over 400 in., while 679 in., or more than 60 ft, have been recorded in a single season. Tamarack, California (about 8,000 ft.), has more than 500 in. of snowfall annually, and 884 in. have been recorded in a year. Snow falls in the Atlas region of North Africa from November to April, and in protected places the snow cover lasts well into the summer. In the southern and middle parts of Greece at elevations of 2,000 to 2,500 ft, there is relatively abundant snowfall that remains on the ground for several weeks. Heavy snowfall is also characteristic of the highlands of northern Iran and Afghanistan. This snowfall of Mediterranean highlands provides an invaluable source of water for irrigation in the adjacent lowlands.

Winter rainfall and cloudiness. Although winter is the rainy season, it is by no means dismal and gloomy, as are the temperate oceanic west-coast regions farther poleward. Since Mediterranean latitudes usually lie on the equatorward sides of the main storm tracks and centers, and are far removed from most of them, they have a less persistent cloud cover and more abundant sunshine. To be sure, winters are considerably cloudier than summers, but they are still relatively bright and sunny.

Perhaps fewer than one-tenth of the storms that cross the northern Pacific Coast region of the United States have any effect upon the weather of San Diego in extreme southern California. Occasionally a cyclone enters the country from the southwest, or one of the northern storms moves southward so that its center approaches close to Mediterranean latitudes. Under these conditions general rains may occur throughout the region. Since main cyclonic tracks coincides with the Mediterranean Basin in winter (Fig. 9.13), cool-season cloudiness is greater in southern Europe than in California.

In interior subtropical California, midsummer months have over 90 percent of the possible sunshine. In winter this is reduced to 50 percent or less, although well south (in the vicinity of Los Angeles) it reaches 60 to 70± percent. Dull, gray days with persistent rain do occur, but showery conditions with a broken sky are more common. After the rain the sun seems to shine more brilliantly than ever in the washed and dust-free atmosphere. These winter showers often are fairly heavy—more so than in regions farther poleward which lie nearer the storm centers. On the average, rain falls on only 7 days in the San Bernardino–Los Angeles region in January, the rainiest month. At Red Bluff farther north and inland, there are 11 rainy days in December, 12 in January, and 10 in both February and March. Bellingham, Washington, and Los Angeles, California, have almost identical amounts of January precipitation (3.4 and 3.3 in., respectively); yet it falls on 17 days at Bellingham and on only 7 at Los Angeles. In other words, precipitation falls harder but less frequently, and with a less persistent cloud cover, in the Mediterranean latitudes (Fig. 9.9). Even the rainiest months have few days when people are kept indoors by precipitation. At the same time the relatively abundant sunshine and

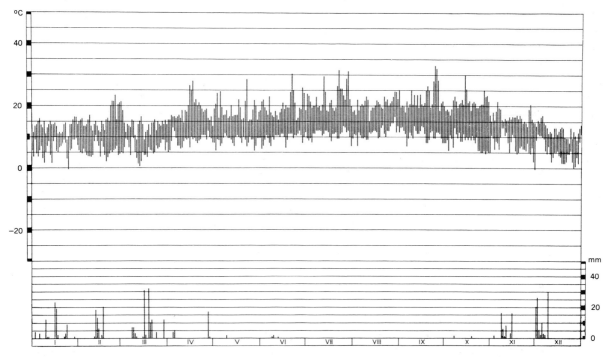

Figure 9.9 Temperature (in °C) and rainfall (in mm) at San Francisco for each day of one year (1954). The cool-season rainfall is concentrated in a number of episodes associated with the passage of cyclonic storms and their fronts. But rainless days are numerous even in the wetter months. The march of temperature shows a modest nonperiodic control. There were only two nights when the minimum temperatures dipped below freezing. The occasional hot days in summer occur when the usual flow of air from the cool ocean temporarily slackens. (*From M. Hendl, Einführung in die physikalische Klimatologie, Band II.*)

mild temperatures, make these regions ideal winter resorts.

Summer drought and sunshine. Summers in most of the dry-summer subtropics are periods of brilliant sunshine, extremely meager precipitation, nearly cloudless skies, and desertlike humidity, except along the coast. Sacramento usually has no rain at all in July and August, and in those months 95 and 96 percent, respectively, of the possible sunshine is received. Afternoon relative humidity is only about 30 to 40 percent. On the average, Los Angeles has only 1 rainy day during the 3 summer months; San Bernardino has 2, and Red Bluff 3. Mediterranean Europe's summers have more cloud and rainfall. The low rainfall, dry heat, abundant sunshine, and excessive evaporation characteristic of interior Mediterranean summers are well suited

for out-of-doors drying of fruits on a large scale.

In spite of the summer heat, thunderstorms are rare, except possibly in the mountains or hills. In southern California 2 to 4 a year are the usual number. The dry, subsiding summer air of these regions, in which inversions are common, is opposed to the formation of deep cumulus clouds.

Coastal regions that have strong anticyclonic subsidence, and are paralleled by cool ocean currents fed by upwelled water, are characterized by high relative humidity and much fog and low stratus cloud in summer. It rarely remains foggy over the coastlands for the entire day, since the mists are usually burned off by the sun after 9 to 10 A.M. Nights, however, may be damp and unpleasant. The California coast is one of the foggiest areas in the United States: parts of it have 40 days per year with dense fog. Coastal Chile has even more. The coastal redwood forests of central and northern California derive a portion of their summer moisture from fogs, while summer crops of beans and certain other vegetables on the coastal terraces of southern California also partly depend on moisture from this source. Another area with frequent summer fogs is the Atlantic coast of Morocco, where Cape Spartel has an average of 28 summer days with fog. All these regions are characterized by temperature inversions, usually close to and well above the surface.

Dependability of precipitation.   Like most subhumid climates, subtropical dry-summer regions have unreliable rainfall, although it fluctuates less than a summer-maximum regime with the same yearly amount (Fig. 4.35). At San Bernardino, California, where the annual rainfall averages 16 in., it has been as low as 5.5 and as high as 37 in. during a 48-year period. In 5 of the 48 years, it dropped below 10 in. At Santiago, Chile, rainfall is below normal in 7 out of 10 years, with a few excessively wet years making up the deficiency. The somewhat precarious, as well as subhumid, character of the precipitation compels farmers to depend upon irrigation to a relatively large degree.

Seasonal weather

Daily weather is less fickle in the subtropical climates than it is farther poleward, where it is increasingly dominated by the conflict of air masses and the development of fronts and cyclones. Because the subtropical climates border the low latitudes, where sun control prevails, they possess many of the tropics' weather characteristics. This is particularly true at the time of high sun, or *summer*, when they are essentially a part of the low latitudes. Thus a typical summer day in the California *Csa* type is almost a duplicate of one in a low-latitude desert. Moreover, one day is much like another. Drought, brilliant sunshine, low relative humidity, high daytime temperatures, and marked nocturnal cooling are repeated day after day with only minor varia-

tions. Diurnal regularity is the keynote of weather at that season. (Here again, more northerly Mediterranean Europe is something of an exception.) Regions with cool-summer *Csb* climates are famous for their well-developed sea breezes, since the cool water offshore and the excessive heating of the dry land under intense solar radiation provide ideal conditions for strong daytime indrafts of air. As a consequence the desert heat is greatly meliorated.

In *autumn*, winds become less regular and uniform. As the cyclone belt creeps equatorward following the sun's rays, an occasional low appears, with associated cloud cover and rain. The dry and dusty land begins to assume new life under the increasing precipitation. Temperatures are still relatively high, and these, together with the increased humidity, create some oppressive and sultry days. As sun control loses the almost total dominance it had in summer, diurnal regularity becomes less prevalent and "spells" of weather more frequent. Importations from the lower latitudes arriving on the front of an advancing cyclone may temporarily reestablish summer heat, as well as bring clouds and showers. This warm importation is followed by advection of cooler air from higher latitudes as the storm center retreats.

In *winter* the frequency and strength of cyclones increases, and it is then that irregular, nonperiodic weather changes are most marked. Rainy days, brought by lows whose centers are often well poleward of subtropical latitudes, are sandwiched between delightfully sunny ones in which temperatures are comfortably mild, even though the nights may be chilly with occasional frosts. The relatively abundant rainfall of this period, together with the mild temperatures, produces a green winter landscape which is uncommon throughout most of the middle latitudes, where winter is a dormant season.

Spring is a delightful season of the Mediterranean year—fresh and yet warm. On the whole, it is cooler than autumn. This is the harvest period for many grains. Passing cyclones gradually become fewer as summer approaches, although nonperiodic weather changes are still significant. The cyclonic centers are preceded by advection of hot, parching air (called *sirocco* in the Mediterranean Basin) from the already superheated low-latitude deserts. These sirocco winds, with temperatures of 100°± and relative humidities of 10 to 20 percent, blow for a day or two without halting and may do serious damage to crops. Fine, choking dust accompanies the temperature importation and at times almost obscures the sun. Following the storm center, the hot sirocco winds are replaced by chilly importations from higher latitudes. These northerly winds have the name *mistral* in southern France and *bora* in the eastern Adriatic. Such cyclonic winds are especially prominent in lands bordering the Mediterranean Sea, since traveling lows are relatively numerous there, and since an extraordinarily large and hot desert lies to the south while cold lands are located behind the bordering highlands to the north. Cool-season temperature gradients along the northern margins of the Mediterranean Basin are extraordinarily steep.

Regional features of subtropical dry-summer climates

The California subdivision of *Cs* is almost a textbook model of subtropical dry-summer climate. Its interior valleys have very hot desertlike summers, while the coast is strikingly cool, with summer fog and stratus. Total annual rainfall is modest, and there is a single winter maximum and a practically rainless summer (Fig. 9.10).

By contrast, the Mediterranean Basin, representing by far the most extensive development of *Cs* climate, and the one that has given the type its regional name, shows much more variation (Fig. 9.11). Chiefly it is the Asiatic and North African sectors of the basin's rimlands that exhibit *Cs* climate in its purest development. The three great peninsulas of southern Europe, on the other hand, display forms of *Cs* climate which are less true to type and more transitional in nature. This is scarcely surprising, since much of Mediterranean Europe lies poleward of 40° and so extends beyond subtropical latitudes and their usual weather controls. As described in the previous section, other modifications

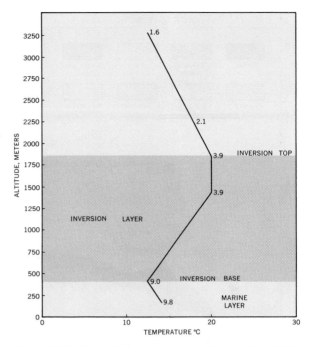

Figure 9.10 Typical lapse rate along the southern California coast in summer. The striking feature is the well-developed inversion of temperature some 1,450 m thick. Below the inversion is a shallow marine layer, where there is a normal decrease in temperature with height, and where humidity is high. The numerals to the right of the lapse rate show mixing ratios in parts per thousand. Relative humidity decreases sharply from the bottom to the top of the inversion layer. The tops of the clouds formed in the moist marine layer practically coincide with the inversion base. (*After Nieberger, Johnson, and Chien.*)

result from the fact that the European sector lies between a cold winter continent to the north, and an unusually extensive and warm inland sea and the Sahara to the south. Consequently advection plays an exceptionally important role in weather processes. Specially named local hot and cold winds, such as sirocco, bora, and mistral, have already been mentioned.

The deep inland penetration of *Cs* in the region of the Mediterranean Basin is found nowhere else. Such an extensive development of the type there appears to be a result of the greater warmth of the

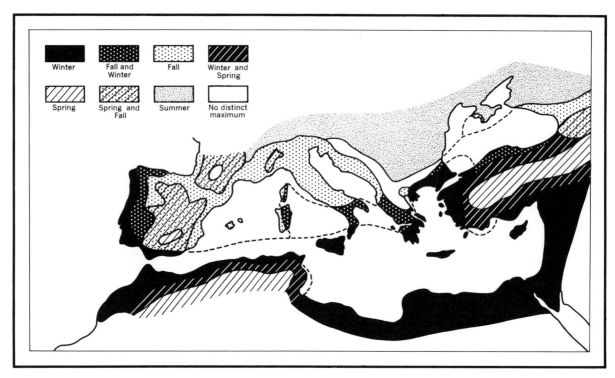

Figure 9.11 Seasons of maximum rainfall in the Mediterranean Basin borderlands. Much of the northern basin does not have a simple single winter maximum typical of the subtropical dry-summer climate. (*After Huttary. From Trewartha, The Earth's Problem Climates.*)

Mediterranean Sea in winter compared with that of the surrounding lands, especially Eurasia to the north. In the cooler months the effect of the warm sea surface is to make the cool air masses invading from higher latitudes unstable and showery. It also provides an environment distinctly favorable to cyclogenesis, so that the Mediterranean Basin is one of the earth's main tracks of winter cyclones and of air-mass convergence (Figs. 9.12 to 9.14). These winter storms move eastward along the basin for

Figure 9.12 Atmospheric streamlines in the Mediterranean Basin in January and in July. Note that in winter the Mediterranean is a region of atmospheric convergence, a condition favoring cyclogenesis. In summer, divergence and drought are more prevalent. (*After Conrad.*)

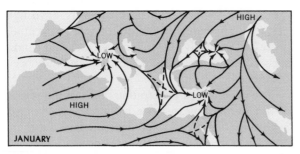
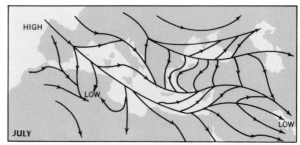

Figure 9.13 Main routes followed by cool-season cyclones in the Mediterranean Basin. Cyclones are relatively infrequent here in summer. Note how far inland the disturbances travel; it is this feature which causes the subtropical dry-summer climate to penetrate so deeply. (*After Weickmann and van Bebber.*)

several thousand miles, carrying with them a potential for creating a cool-season maximum of cloud and precipitation. It can be observed that many Mediterranean cyclonic storms develop in conjunction with an invasion of the subtropical sea by cold northerly air on the rear of an eastward-moving upper trough situated over western and central Europe. The most concentrated region of cyclogenesis is over the Ligurian-Tyrrhenian Sea just west of Italy, where surges of cold air are channeled into the Mediterranean Basin from the north through the Rhone and Carcassonne gaps in southern France.[3]

Throughout Iberia, southern France, and much of Italy, the seasonal march of rainfall becomes more complicated than the simple *Cs* winter maximum–summer minimum regime. A rainfall profile with two maxima and two minima is common, often with one of the minima in summer and the other in winter. Doubtless these rainfall complications arise because the southern European peninsulas lie on the poleward margins of the subtropics or even beyond, so that their rainfall regimes reflect continental as well as subtropical Mediterranean controls.

Subtropical Chile in South America resembles

[3] Glenn T. Trewartha, *The Earth's Problem Climates,* The University of Wisconsin Press, Madison, Wis., 1961, pp. 224–231.

California in that it has a cool coastal *Cs,* with abundant summer fog and stratus, where the warmest-month temperature is only about 64°. It is like California too in that it has a great interior north-south lowland. But unlike the Sacramento lowland, that of Chile is not a region of intense summer heat (*Csa*), for it has a moderate elevation. Santiago at 1,700 ft in the Vale of Chile has an average warm-month temperature of only 69°, which is barely 5° warmer than Valparaiso at sea level on a cool-water coast (Fig. 9.15). Winters are also more extreme in the Vale, however, with the result that interior Santiago has an annual range of 23° and coastal Valparaiso a highly marine 11°.

Cs development in southern Africa is very limited,

Figure 9.14 Seasonal frequency (percent) of cyclones on tracks 1 and 2 as shown in Fig. 9.13. (*After Conrad.*)

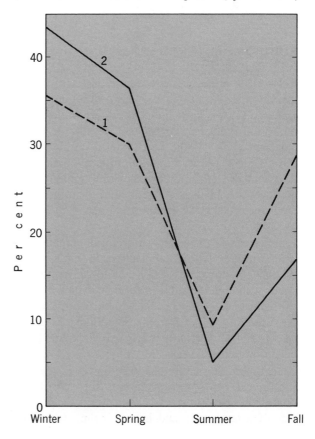

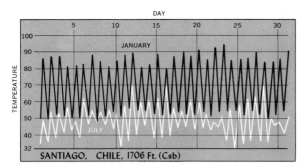

Figure 9.15 Daily maximum and minimum temperatures for the extreme months of one year at Santiago, Chile. This station, although located inland, has a cool summer (*Csb*) because of its altitude of about 1,700 ft. Compare with Fig. 9.5.

being confined to the southwesternmost extremity around Cape Town. Although the region is strongly

marine in its temperature characteristics (warm month only 71°), it lacks the chilling effects of a well-developed cold current and upwelling. While summer is much drier than winter, it is not rainless, as in southern California; the 3 summer months have a total rainfall of about 2 in.

Australia's *Cs* is in two far-separated locations. While both are marine in character, with warm-month temperatures below 75°, neither of them is a genuinely cool-water coastal type. Perth in the southwest, with about 35 in. of annual rainfall, is wet by *Cs* standards. Adelaide on the west side of southeastern Australia, with only 21 in., is closer to the type's normal, although Adelaide's 3 summer months are far from rainless, receiving about 2.5 in. The annual range of rainfall is much greater at Perth than at Adelaide.

SUBTROPICAL HUMID CLIMATE (*Cf*)

Subtropical humid climate usually differs from the dry-summer variety in at least three important respects: (1) it is located on the eastern, rather than the western, side of a continent, (2) it has more precipitation, and (3) the precipitation is distributed throughout the year, although ordinarily with some degree of concentration in the warm months. Summer drought, a hallmark of Mediterranean climates, does not occur in *Cf* regions.

Type location. The two subtropical climates are similar in their latitudinal positions in that both are on the equatorward margins of the intermediate zones, although the subtropical humid type may be shifted a few degrees farther equatorward. Characteristically its spread is from about 25° to 35 or 40° (see Figs. 7.2, 9.1, and the map of climate types inside the front cover).

In their continental locations, however, the two subtropical types are dissimilar, for subtropical humid climate ordinarily is situated on the eastern side of a land mass and hence to the east of the

dry interior. In summer this east-side location is dominated by the unstable or neutral *mT* air masses within the western parts of an oceanic subtropical anticyclone, where subsidence is weak. It is the stable structure of the eastern limb of an anticyclone which mainly accounts for the summer drought in California; the unstable western limb of such a cell favors abundant summer rainfall in the southeastern United States. A supplementary cause of the east-side location of *Cf* is the tendency for monsoon circulations to develop there, at least on the large continents of Asia and North America. Such a wind system favors wet summers and drier winters—the very antithesis of the rainfall regime in *Cs* climate. In addition, the warm ocean currents which parallel subtropical east coasts may act directly or indirectly to increase total rainfall, and make the summer season wetter.

The two subtropical climates, situated in similar latitudinal but unlike continental locations, are usually flanked by contrasting types on their equatorward and poleward frontiers (Fig. 9.1). While *Cs*

Rainfall regimes for four pairs of subtropical stations, *Cs* on the west side of a continent, *Cf* on the east (Inches)

Station	Latitude	Winter half-year	Summer half-year	Annual
San Luis Obispo (*Cs*)	35° N	18.7	2.7	21.4
Hatteras (*Cf*)	35° N	26.3	28.7	55.0
Mogador (*Cs*)	32° N	10.6	2.6	13.2
Chungking (*Cf*)	30° N	10.4	31.5	41.9
Perth (*Cs*)	32° S	28.9	5.0	33.9
Port Macquarie (*Cf*)	31° S	28.3	33.1	61.4
Valparaiso (*Cs*)	33° S	18.3	1.4	19.7
Rosario (*Cf*)	33° S	10.5	24.4	34.9

commonly adjoins hot dry climates on its low-latitude side, *Cf* borders tropical humid climates there. This difference has a great effect upon the nature of thermal and humidity advection in the two climates: parching dry heat with dust is imported into *Cs*, humid sultry heat into *Cf*. On their poleward sides these types are likewise bordered by contrasting climates. Subtropical dry-summer type generally merges into a mild marine climate, while subtropical humid is bounded by a severe continental climate. This contrast is especially strong in the large continents of Eurasia and North America, whose *Cf*

climates are more susceptible to advection of severe cold than their dry-summer subtropics are. Dry climates ordinarily flank *Cs* on its eastern side, but they adjoin *Cf* on its western margin.

Temperature

In temperature features the two subtropical types are relatively similar, although subtropical humid usually shows less contrast between coastal and interior locations (Figs. 9.16 and 9.17). This general similarity in temperature between *Cs* and *Cf* is not

Climatic data for representative subtropical humid stations (*Cf*)

	J	F	M	A	M	J	J	A	S	O	N	D	Yr	Range
Charleston, South Carolina														
Temp., °F	50	52	58	65	73	79	82	81	77	68	58	51	66.1	31.4
Precip., in.	3.0	3.1	3.3	2.4	3.3	5.1	6.2	6.5	5.2	3.7	2.5	3.2	47.3	
Chungking, China														
Temp., °F	48	50	58	68	74	80	83	86	77	68	59	50	67	38
Precip., in.	0.7	0.9	1.3	4.0	5.3	6.7	5.3	4.4	5.8	4.6	2.0	0.9	41.9	
Memphis, Tennessee														
Temp., °F	41	44	53	62	70	78	81	80	74	63	52	43	62	30
Precip., in.	4.9	4.3	5.4	5.1	4.2	3.2	3.4	3.4	2.8	2.9	4.2	4.3	48.3	
Port Macquarie, Australia														
Temp., °F	71	72	69	65	60	56	54	56	59	63	67	70	63	18
Precip., in.	5.9	7.5	6.5	5.9	5.6	4.6	4.5	3.8	3.9	3.2	4.1	5.9	61.5	
Dallas, Texas														
Temp., °F	45	47	56	65	73	81	84	83	77	66	55	47	65	35
Precip., in.	2.2	2.0	2.7	3.9	4.4	3.1	2.5	2.1	2.9	2.8	2.5	2.4	33.6	

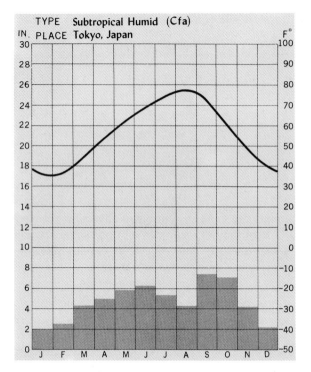

Figure 9.16 Compare with Figs. 9.2 and 9.4. The annual march of rainfall is quite different in the two subtropical climates.

surprising, since the two correspond fairly well in latitude. But because *Cf* is not subject to the influence of cool ocean currents, it has no distinctly cool-summer coastal subtype with cool, foggy stations like San Francisco. With very few exceptions, its summer is sufficiently warm to warrant adding the letter *a* to the *Cf* symbol, so that it becomes predominantly *Cfa*.

Summer. Summers are distinctly hot; average hot-month temperatures are usually around 75 to 80° (81° at Charleston, South Carolina; 80° at Shanghai, China; 77° at Brisbane, Australia, and Durban, South Africa; and 74° at Buenos Aires). Along the immediate coasts of the smaller Southern Hemisphere land masses, warm-month temperatures are as often slightly below 75° as they are above (Figs. 9.16 to 9.19).

Not only is the air temperature high, but absolute and relative humidity are too. In the American South Atlantic and Gulf states, where *mT* air almost completely dominates in summer, the average July relative humidity (8 P.M. reading) is 70 to 80 percent. High humidity in conjunction with high temperature produces sultry, oppressive weather with low cooling power. Summer heat in most *Csa* climates is drier, so that sensible temperatures are commonly higher in the humid subtropics than in *Cs* regions even when the thermometer registers the same. Summer heat in the American Gulf states closely resembles that of tropical wet climates. At New Orleans during June, July, and August, the average temperatures are 2 to 3° higher than they are at Belém in the Amazon Valley, while the amount of rainfall is nearly the same. The average

Figure 9.17 Annual march of temperature and rainfall at Memphis on the poleward margins of the humid subtropics in the United States. Note the cool-season maximum of precipitation.

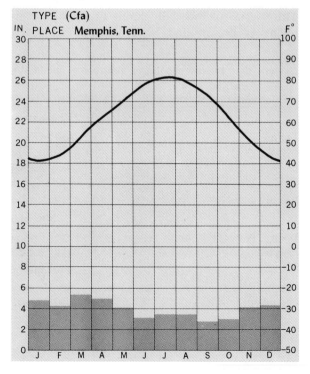

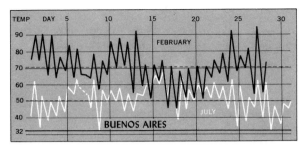

Figure 9.18   Daily maximum and minimum temperatures for the extreme months of one year at a subtropical humid station in the Southern Hemisphere. Nonperiodic air-mass control is conspicuous in both winter and summer. Winters are mild.

of the daily maxima in July throughout most of the American Cotton Belt is between 90 and 100°, while the highest temperatures ever recorded are usually between 100 and 110° (Fig. 9.19). Thus Montgomery, Alabama, has had a temperature of 106° in July and 107° in August and Savannah, Georgia, 105° in July.

Night temperatures.   Not only are the days hot and sultry, but nights are oppressive as well, resembling those in the humid tropics. The humid atmosphere, with more cloud than in *Csa* climates, pre-

Figure 9.19   Daily maximum and minimum temperatures for the extreme months of one year at a subtropical humid station in the United States. Note the strong periodic, or solar, control in summer. By contrast, winter shows strong nonperiodic, or air-mass, control. Both winter and summer temperatures are more extreme at Montgomery than at Buenos Aires (Fig. 9.18), owing to the effects of the broad North American continent.

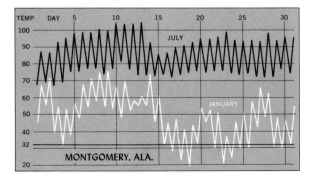

vents the same rapid loss of heat that takes place in their drier air and clearer skies. The slower night cooling results in relatively small diurnal ranges, usually only one-half to two-thirds as large as those in the inland dry-summer subtropics (Figs. 9.2, 9.3, and 9.19). For example, the averages of the July maxima for Sacramento and Montgomery are 89 and 91°, respectively, and their average July minima are 58 and 72°. This gives a diurnal range of 31° for Sacramento and 19° for Montgomery, the difference being due chiefly to Sacramento's cooler nights. Since the sun is very much in control of the daily weather, one day in summer is relatively like another in the humid subtropics. However, there are some nonperiodic variations (Fig. 9.19), which are often the result of variations in the amount of cloud.

Winter.   Winters are, of course, relatively mild in subtropical latitudes, with cool-month temperatures that usually average between 40 and 55° (Figs. 9.16 and 9.17). Montgomery, Alabama, has an average cool-month temperature of 49°; Shanghai, China, 38°; Buenos Aires, Argentina, 50°; and Sydney, Australia, 52°. Even in winter, the southeastern United States receives much warm, humid, tropical air from the Gulf of Mexico and the tropical Atlantic, but the normal seaward pressure gradient of that season makes the progress of *mT* air inland more sporadic than in summer. Usually the winter indrafts of tropical air are associated with passing cyclones. In eastern Asia, the strong monsoonal outpouring of cold *cP* air in winter from the large continent to the north and west results in the lowest *average* winter temperatures in those latitudes for any comparable part of the world (Fig. 9.20). Mobile, Alabama and Shanghai, which are approximately in the same latitude, have average January temperatures of 52 and 38°, respectively.

After subtropical China, the southeastern United States has the lowest average winter temperatures of any of the subtropical humid regions. Here, as in eastern Asia, there is a well-developed, although less strong, winter-monsoon tendency. The prevailing winter winds come from the north and north-

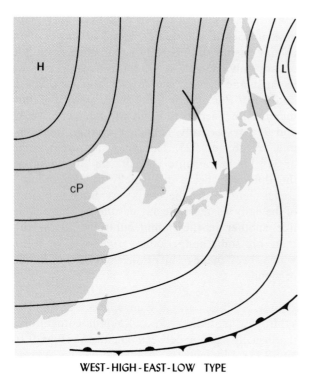

WEST-HIGH-EAST-LOW TYPE

Figure 9.20 A polar-outbreak high in eastern Asia flooding the subtropics of that region with cold air and carrying freezing temperatures far into southern China and over all of Japan. (*From Trewartha, Japan: A Geography, University of Wisconsin Press.*)

west and consequently from the cold interior and higher latitudes. In the eastern United States as compared with eastern Asia, the more numerous and better-developed moving cyclones tend to disrupt the monsoonal winds. The humid subtropical regions of the Southern Hemisphere, which have no severe continental climates on their poleward margins because of the size or the latitudinal positions of their respecitve land masses, receive no such advections of severe *cP* air and are consequently milder.

Midday temperatures in winter are likely to be pleasantly warm in the humid subtropics, with the thermometer usually rising to 55 or 60° (Figs. 9.18 and 9.19). On winter nights temperatures fall to about 35 to 45°. These certainly are not low, but combined with *Cf*'s high humidity they are likely to produce a sensible temperature which is distinctly chilly and uncomfortable. Summer is emphatically the dominant season, so that little effort is made to provide efficient heating systems in many regions with *Cfa* climate. Consequently people often feel more uncomfortable indoors than they do in colder lands farther poleward where winter heating is adequate.

Annual range of temperature. In *Cf* climates the annual range is usually modest, although there is considerable variation depending upon the size of the continent and the latitude of the particular station (Figs. 9.16 and 9.17). At Buenos Aires the annual range is only 23° and at Sydney only 19°, but at Montgomery it is 33°, and at Shanghai 43°. Apparently, the larger the land mass and the better the development of a continental system of monsoon winds, the colder the winters and the larger the annual range.

Minimum temperatures and frost. As would be expected, the growing season, or period between killing frosts, is long in subtropical humid climates— usually at least 7 months, and at most nearly, if not quite, the entire year. Even though freezing temperatures may be *expected* during a period of several months, they actually occur on only a relatively few nights of the winter season. In *Cf*, like *Cs*, climates, the long growing season and infrequent freezes create good conditions for sensitive crops and for those requiring a long maturing period.

There is scarcely any part of the continental humid subtropics which has not had freezing temperatures, except for some areas on the tropical oceanic margins of the subtropics. In sections of the Southern Hemisphere *Cf*, frost does not occur every winter, and usually it is light when it does come. Thus the average lowest winter temperature at Brisbane, Australia, is 37°, and at Sydney 39°. The lowest temperature ever recorded at Buenos Aires is 23°; at Montevideo, Uruguay, 20°; and at Brisbane, Australia, 32°.

In the humid subtropics of both the United States and China, winter minima are considerably lower than those of the Southern Hemisphere continents. Shanghai has recorded a temperature as low as 10°, and Montgomery, Alabama, −5°. New Orleans, with a normal January temperature of 55°, has the extremely low absolute minimum of 7°. Even daily maximum temperatures below freezing are not uncommon in poleward parts of the North American and Asiatic sectors.

One of the distinguishing features of the South Atlantic and Gulf states of the United States, a region where the average winter temperatures are relatively high, is the unusually low winter minima—even lower than those of China. Thus while southeastern China has lower *average* winter temperatures, the American humid subtropics have severer *cold spells* and consequently lower minima. Severe

freezes are annual in occurrence, and temperatures as low as 10° have been recorded along the ocean margins of all the Gulf states. No other part of the world near sea level in these latitudes has such low winter minima. Serious damage to sensitive vegetation results from these cold spells.

The occasional severe invasions of *cP* air which characterize the winter weather of the seaboard states of the American Gulf and South Atlantic can be attributed to the openness of the North American continent east of the Rocky Mountains. The lack of terrain barriers permits the surges of cold *cP* air to move rapidly southward into subtropical latitudes with only moderate modifications (Fig. 9.21). In subtropical California, on the other hand,

Figure 9.21 A synoptic type resulting in a severe freeze in the North American humid subtropics. Numerals on the map represent night minimum temperatures.

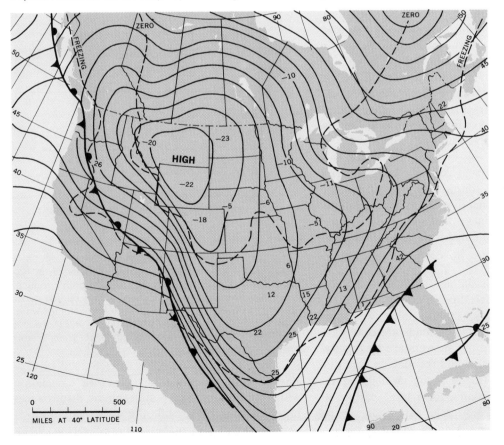

mountains tend to retard such severe invasions of cold air, so that there the absolute minima are much higher. Thus while commercial citrus production extends north to about 38° in California, it is confined to regions south of latitude 30 or 31° in the southeastern United States. In China, the more hilly and mountainous surface configuration prevents such unrestricted advection of cold *cP* air.

Precipitation

Annual amount and seasonal distribution.   Rainfall is relatively abundant within the humid subtropics, 30 to 65 in. representing the normal spread. Still, there are considerable differences between the several continental regions. On the landward frontiers of this type, where it adjoins steppe climate, rainfall is the lowest.

In contrast to the dry-summer subtropics, there is no season of drought over much the greater part of the earth's humid subtropics. Usually summer has more precipitation than winter, although winter is far from dry (Figs. 9.16 and 9.17). Summer is never a dry season. Thus as a rule, the annual march of rainfall is opposite in the two subtropical types. In the humid subtropics it is mainly where a strong monsoon circulation prevails that winter is dry, as it is in parts of interior southern China (which is therefore classed as *Cw* instead of *Cf*; see the definitions given on page 250). In the Southern Hemisphere, seasonal contrasts in rainfall are not marked. It is a fair generalization about the humid subtropics on all continents that such seasonal contrasts tend to be accentuated toward the drier interior parts (Fig. 9.22).

Summer.   Most of the summer rainfall on lowlands is in the form of convectional showers which originate in *mT* air made increasingly unstable by passage over a warmed land surface. Clouds are chiefly of the cumulus type, and the showers are frequently accompanied by lightning and thunder. In fact, the American humid subtropics is the most thundery region of the United States, for a large part of it has over 60 electrical storms a year, while a part of Florida has over 90. A great majority of the

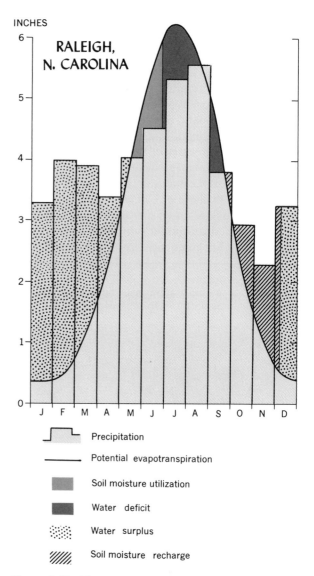

Figure 9.22   The average annual water balance at Raleigh, North Carolina, based on mean monthly values. Note that even this humid station, with a rainfall maximum in the warm months, has a period in summer when evapotranspiration exceeds precipitation, and there is a short period of actual water deficit. (*Data from Thornthwaite, Mather, and Carter.*)

showers and thunderstorms occur in association with extensive but weak atmospheric disturbances in which convergence lifts the warm humid air of tropical origin and makes it unstable (Fig. 9.25).

Consequently the showers are organized, not random, in their distribution.

Hurricane rainfall is largely confined to the American and Asiatic humid subtropics, where it contributes to the late-summer and fall rainfall maximum characteristic of parts of these regions. Not only do the heavy late-summer and early-autumn hurricane rains greatly damage ripening crops and cause serious floods, but their violent winds may play havoc with coastal shipping and port cities. In one typhoon affecting the China coast, 40,000 people are estimated to have perished, chiefly by drowning.

In spite of the plentiful summer rainfall of the humid subtropics, sunshine is relatively abundant, even though it is much less so than in *Csa* summer climates. Montgomery, Alabama, receives 73 percent of the possible sunshine in June and 62 percent in July.

Winter.   In winter the land surface in the humid subtropics is likely to be colder than maritime air arriving from tropical source regions. As a result the poleward movement of such an air mass over the cooler land chills its base layers and thereby increases stability. Consequently, convectional overturning promoted by surface heating, so prevalent in summer, is uncommon in winter. Only when the stabilized tropical maritime air masses are forced to rise over relief barriers, or when they become involved in convergences along fronts and in cyclonic systems, does precipitation usually occur. Winter rainfall over lowlands, therefore, is chiefly frontal or cyclonic in origin.

As a consequence, winter rain is usually accompanied by a general and persistent cloud cover extending over wide areas, from which precipitation may fall steadily for hours on end. Typically it is less intense but more prolonged than the showery rain in summer thunderstorms. Because there are more cyclones in winter, skies are cloudier than in summer. At Shanghai in an average January, only 2 in. of rain falls, but there are 12 rain-days; yet in August, the 6 in. of precipitation falls on only 11 days. Each rainy day in August, therefore, produces three times as much precipitation as a rainy

day in January. Montgomery, which has 73 percent of the possible sunshine in June, receives only 49 percent in January and 44 percent in December. Gray, overcast days with rain may be unpleasantly chilly.

Snow falls occasionally when a vigorous winter cyclone swings well equatorward, but it rarely stays on the ground for more than a few days. In the southernmost parts of the United States' humid subtropics snow does not even fall on an average of one day a year, and the snow cover likewise does not last for a day. On the northern margins, however, 5 to 15 days have snow, and the ground may be snow-covered for an equally long period.

Seasonal weather

A majority of the cyclonic storms in the eastern United States follow a track which approximately coincides with the Great Lakes and the St. Lawrence Valley, so that they do not strongly influence the Gulf states. It is when cyclones and anticyclones move on a southern circuit that the Cotton Belt is most affected by them.

In *summer,* when the cyclone belt is farthest poleward and the sun is largely in control, irregular weather changes are at a minimum (Fig. 9.19). Weak cyclones resembling those of the wet tropics may bring spells of showery, cloudy weather, but no marked temperature changes. Humid, sultry days, each much like the others, are the rule. The thermometer rises to about the same height each day and sinks to similar minima each night.

Late summer and fall is the season of the dreaded hurricanes, whose severity more than makes up for their infrequency. Otherwise, sunny autumn days provide delightful weather, although the equatorward-advancing cyclone belt gradually produces more gray, cloudy days and unseasonable temperature importations as winter closes in.

In *winter,* including early spring, the storm belt is farthest equatorward, so that irregular weather changes are most frequent and extreme then (Fig. 9.19). Advection of tropical air on the front of an advancing cyclone may push daytime temperatures well above 60 or even 70°, while the following *cP* air masses may reduce the temperature as much as 30° within 24 hr, occasionally bringing severe freezes. Bright, sunny winter days are pleasant and exhilarating outdoors. In *spring* the cyclonic belt retreats and regular diurnal sun control is gradually reestablished (Fig. 9.19).

Regional features of subtropical humid climates

In a number of ways the humid subtropical southeastern United States is climatically exceptional. Perhaps the outstanding anomaly is that over an extensive part of this region, characterized by leeward location on a great continent and situated mainly inland, winter rainfall exceeds that of summer (see Figs. 9.17, 9.23, and the data for Memphis). Summer is also wet, of course, but it is less so. Both to the north and west and to the east and south of the winter-rain region, the usual summer maximum prevails. More specifically, the oval-shaped region of cool-season maximum reaches from eastern Texas on the southwest to eastern Kentucky and westernmost North Carolina on the northeast. Its long and short dimensions are about 1,000 by 350 miles. Although within this large region winter's rainfall exceeds summer's, winter is not everywhere the season of maximum, for spring equals or even exceeds it in parts. There is a core, nevertheless, where winter is the wettest season (Fig. 9.23). Much of the core region has the heaviest winter precipitation anywhere in the United States east of the Rocky Mountains.

The heavy rainfall in winter and early spring is associated with a high frequency of cyclonic storms, which appear first in the Texas region and subsequently follow a northeasterly course toward the Atlantic Seaboard south of Cape Hatteras. This concentration of winter depressions and their heavy rains generally coincides with the southernmost position of the upper-troposphere jet streams during the period December through March. In summer-fall, which has the least rain, though it is still far from dry, jets, fronts, and storm tracks retreat northward. In addition, during this drier period the North Atlantic subtropical anticyclone extends westward over the southeastern United States.[4]

But while a large part of this country's subtropical interior shows a cool-month maximum, the reverse is true of the Gulf and Atlantic margins, where a strong summer maximum prevails. Here the weather in summer is conditioned by a deep current of humid tropical air aloft which is associated with an upper trough positioned over the area. An additional factor may be the directional or speed convergence associated with the sea breeze.

A second distinctive feature of the American humid subtropics is its abnormally low winter minimum temperatures. This characteristic was described in the earlier section on temperature.

Two distinguishing properties of the Asiatic humid subtropics—unusually low average winter temperatures, and the strikingly dry winters of China well inland—were also discussed earlier. An additional feature is the bimodal summer rainfall maximum which occurs in large areas of southern China and southwestern Japan (Fig. 9.24). The first of these maxima is in May-June, while the second

Figure 9.23 In an extensive region of the subtropical southeastern United States, winter precipitation exceeds that of summer. Winter and spring are the wettest seasons, and winter is wetter than spring in the central part of the region. (*From Trewartha, The Earth's Problem Climates.*)

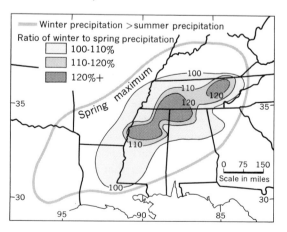

[4] Trewartha, *The Earth's Problem Climates*, pp. 293–299.

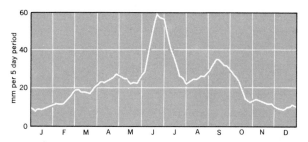

Figure 9.24 Composite annual profile of 5-day means of rainfall (overlapping method) for five stations in subtropical Japan. The primary maximum, known as *Baiu*, is in June–July. In September there is a second and less conspicuous maximum, known as *Shurin*, which originates mainly from typhoon rainfall. (*From Trewartha, The Earth's Problem Climates.*)

comes in late summer and early fall. Separating the two is a midsummer secondary minimum.

The June maximum has been linked with the summer circulation pattern over eastern Asia. During winter, the southern branch of the zonal westerlies and of the jet stream follow a course to the south of Tibet and across northern India-Pakistan, northern Southeast Asia, and southern China. In early summer, the jet stream and zonal westerlies abruptly shift to a position north of the highlands. The equatorial westerlies, or Indian monsoon, then surge northward and invade not only tropical southern Asia but also China and Japan, bringing those regions an air-mass environment in which weak disturbances can induce abundant rainfall (Fig. 9.25). The midsummer secondary minimum has been attributed to the intensification and northward and westward displacement of the North Pacific subtropical anticyclone as it follows the sun, with an associated decline in vapor pressure at the midtroposphere level. The second rainfall peak coincides with a withdrawal of the anticyclone and a restrengthening of the southerly monsoon circulation. Significantly, atmospheric pressure is lowest in August. An important part of the August-September rains is generated by tropical storms, including typhoons, which are most numerous and intense in late summer and fall.[5]

[5]*Ibid.*, pp. 191–199.

Another special variation of *Cf* climate in Asia is the heavy cool-season precipitation along the northwest side of Japan. The cold, dry winds from Asia are warmed, humidified, and made unstable over the Sea of Japan, so that they yield abundant precipitation when forced upward over western Japan's highlands. Many stations even show a winter maximum. Much of the winter precipitation falls as snow showers, resulting in a deep snow cover.

All three Southern Hemisphere humid subtropics are distinguished by unusually mild winters and small annual ranges of temperature, for none of them have a broad land source immediately poleward to provide cold advection. In both South Africa

Figure 9.25 A weak low of the early summer period in subtropical eastern Asia. Such a synoptic pattern is known in Japan as the *Baiu* type. It is disturbances of this type which produce the earlier of the two summer maxima of rainfall characteristic of much of the Asiatic humid subtropics. (*From Trewartha, Japan: A Geography, University of Wisconsin Press.*)

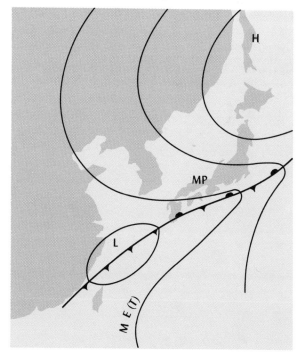

BAIU   TYPE

and Australia, subtropical humid climates are confined to fairly narrow coastal strips, so that Durban has a cold-month temperature of 63° and a range of only 13°, while the comparable figures for Brisbane are 59° and 18°, and for Sydney, 53° and 19°. In the South American sector—where the humid subtropics extend somewhat farther inland, and a land area, even though narrow, flanks it to the south—winters are a trifle more severe and ranges are slightly greater (Buenos Aires has a cold-month average of 49°, with a range of 25°).

SELECTED REFERENCES FOR FURTHER STUDY OF TOPICS IN CHAPTER NINE

Byers, H. R., "Summer Sea Fogs of the Central California Coast," *Univ. Calif. Publ. Geog.,* no. 3, pp. 291–338, 1930.

Huttary, Josef, "Die Verteilung der Niederschläge auf die Jahreszeiten im Mittelmeergebiet," *Meteorol. Rundschau,* Vol. 3, pp. 111–119, 1950.

Institute of Geophysics and Meteorology, Academia Sinica, Peking, staff members of the Section of Synoptic and Dynamic Meteorology, "On the General Circulation over Eastern Asia," *Tellus,* Vol. 9, pp. 432–446, 1957.

Lu, A., "The Winter Frontology of China," *Bull. Amer. Meteorol. Soc.,* Vol. 26, pp. 309–314, 1945.

Miller, James E., and T. Mantis Homer, "Extratropical Cyclogenesis in the Pacific Coastal Regions of Asia," *J. Meteorology,* Vol. 4, pp. 29–34, 1947.

Patton, Clyde P., "Climatology of Summer Fogs in the San Francisco Bay Area," *Univ. Calif. Publ. Geog.,* Vol. 10, no. 3, 121–125, 1956.

Ramage, C. S., "Variation of Rainfall over South China through the Wet Season," *Bull. Amer. Meteorol. Soc.,* Vol. 33, pp. 308–311, 1952.

Reichel, Eberhard, "Die Niederschlagshäufigkeit im Mittelmeergebiet," *Meteorol. Rundschau,* Vol. 2, pp. 129–142, 1949.

Trewartha, Glenn T., *The Earth's Problem Climates,* The University of Wisconsin Press, Madison, Wis., 1961, pp. 180–199, 223–247, 293–304.

Yao, C. S., "On the Origin of the Depressions of Southern China," *Bull. Amer. Meteorol. Soc.,* Vol. 21, pp. 351–355, 1940.

CHAPTER TEN

TEMPERATE CLIMATES (D)

This group of humid climates occupies a medial position within the middle latitudes—usually between subtropical climates equatorward and boreal climates poleward. Its equatorward and poleward boundaries are 8 months and 4 months, respectively, with average temperatures of 50° or above. Actually the name "temperate" is not wholly suited to all climates within this group, for the more severe continental type is scarcely moderate in its seasonal temperatures. But for want of a better title, temperate is used here to designate the climates which are intermediate in temperature between boreal cold and subtropical heat.

Two types comprise the temperate group: a milder climate called oceanic or marine (*Do*), and a more severe one that is continental (*Dc*). The boundary adopted for separating the two types is the 32°F (0°C) [to 36° (2°C) in some locations] isotherm for the coldest month. In the oceanic type, all months have average temperatures of 32°F or above.

TEMPERATE OCEANIC CLIMATE (*Do*)

Type location. As this climate's name suggests, its weather is like that of the adjacent ocean. Typically it occupies a position on the western or windward side of middle-latitude continents, poleward of about 40°. There the onshore westerly winds bring marine climate conditions to the land (refer to Fig. 7.2 and the climate map).

Temperate oceanic climate may not be completely limited to the western side in cases where land areas are relatively narrow, as they are in islands, such as Tasmania, New Zealand, and Great Britain, or where the continent extends for only a short distance into the belt of westerlies, as Australia and Africa do. But an extensive development of this type along east coasts of large middle-latitude continents is unlikely (in spite of the proximity of oceans), because there severe seasonal temperatures result from leeward location and the monsoon wind systems.

On its equatorward margins, *Do* climate characteristically borders the subtropical dry-summer type. Because of its higher latitude, ordinarily it is not strongly influenced by the stable air in the eastern parts of an oceanic subtropical anticyclone, so that *Do*, unlike *Cs*, usually does not have a pronounced dry summer. On its poleward side the temperate oceanic climate extends far into the higher middle latitudes, where it is eventually terminated by either the boreal or the tundra type. The far poleward extension of this mild climate is the result of oceanic control offsetting normal latitudinal influence. Warm ocean currents, which parallel the west coasts of continents in middle latitudes poleward from the subtropics, tend to accentuate the normal tempering effects of the ocean itself.

The depth to which oceanic climate extends into the interior of a continent is determined largely by terrain. Where mountains closely parallel the west coast, as in North and South America and Scandinavia, marine conditions are restricted to relatively narrow belts of littoral seaward from the highlands. But where extensive lowlands reach to the coast,

Climatic data for representative temperate oceanic stations in climate (*Do*)

	J	F	M	A	M	J	J	A	S	O	N	D	Yr	Range
Valentia, Ireland														
Temp., °F	44	44	45	48	52	57	59	59	57	52	48	45	50.8	15
Precip., in.	5.5	5.2	4.5	3.7	3.2′	3.2	3.8	4.8	4.1	5.6	5.5	6.6	55.6	
Seattle, Washington														
Temp., °F	40	42	45	50	55	60	64	64	59	52	46	42	51.4	24
Precip., in.	4.9	3.8	3.1	2.4	1.8	1.3	0.6	0.7	1.7	2.8	4.8	5.5	33.4	
Paris, France														
Temp., °F	37	39	43	51	56	62	66	64	59	51	43	37	50.5	27
Precip., in.	1.5	1.2	1.6	1.7	2.1	2.3	2.2	2.2	2.0	2.3	1.8	1.7	22.6	
Hokitika, New Zealand														
Temp., °F	60	61	59	55	49	47	45	46	49	53	55	58	53.0	16
Precip., in.	9.8	7.3	9.7	9.2	9.8	9.7	9.0	9.4	9.2	11.8	10.6	10.6	116.1	
Portland, Oregon														
Temp., °F	39	42	46	51	57	61	67	66	61	54	46	41	53.0	28
Precip., in.	6.7	5.5	4.8	3.1	2.3	1.6	0.6	0.6	1.9	3.3	6.5	6.9	43.8	

as in most of western Europe, the effects of the sea are carried well inland, and *Do* climate prevails over a greater east-west area. On its land side, temperate oceanic climate is characteristically bordered by severe continental types, either dry or humid. In North America, where highlands closely parallel the west coast, *Do* climate is replaced by dry climate to the east of the mountains. In Europe, on the other hand, the westerlies blowing off the ocean have freer entrance, and *Do* climate gradually passes over to temperate continental climate (Fig. 10.13 and the climate map at the front of the book).

Temperature

Summer. Although the word "temperate" is a poor one to apply to thermal conditions in middle-

Figure 10.1 Average monthly temperature and rainfall for a temperate oceanic station in lowland western Europe. Note the small annual range of temperature and the modest amount of precipitation well distributed throughout the year.

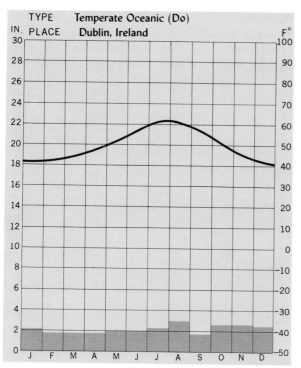

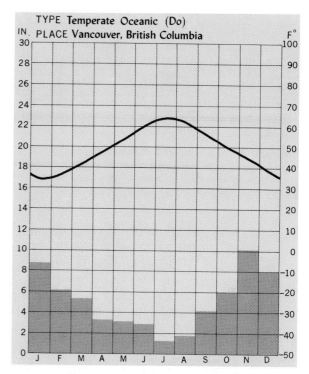

Figure 10.2 Monthly temperatures and rainfall for a temperate oceanic station on the southern Pacific coast of Canada, which is backed by highlands. Here the annual precipitation (60 in.) is greater than that for most lowland stations, and there is a pronounced maximum in winter. A strong winter maximum normally is characteristic of those parts of *Do* climate which are located closest to the subtropical dry-summer type (*Cs*).

latitude continental climates, it is relatively appropriate for the *Do* type (Figs. 10.1, 10.2, and 10.5). Summers are moderate: several degrees below the average temperature for the latitude. While they are more or less ideal for human efficiency and comfort, they are somewhat too cool for the best growth and the maturing of a number of cereal crops. Seattle, Washington, has a mean July temperature of only 63°; Dublin, Ireland, 60°; and Paris, France, 66°. Night cooling is not rapid in these humid, cloudy, marine climates, as it is in Mediterranean regions in the summer. The average of the daily minima in July is only 55° at Seattle and 51° at Bellingham, Washington, while the daily

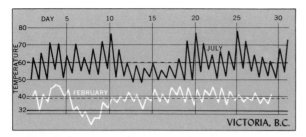

Figure 10.3 Maximum and minimum temperatures for the extreme months of one year at a station with a marine location in Pacific Canada. Note the small diurnal range, especially in winter, when cloudy skies prevail.

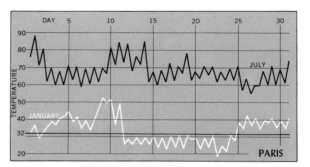

Figure 10.4 A station in western Europe inland from the coast. Here the temperature range between the warmest and coldest months is much greater than at Victoria (Fig. 10.3). Nonperiodic air-mass control of temperature is fairly conspicuous.

maxima are 73 and 72°, so that the normal diurnal range is only around 20° (Figs. 10.3 to 10.5). The average *annual* maximum temperature at Cambridge, England, is only 87°.

Occasional hot days may occur when a passing disturbance temporarily halts the invasion of cool sea air and substitutes air of land or tropical origin. Under such conditions both Seattle and Bellingham have had a temperature as high as 96°, and Paris, 100°. But severe and prolonged hot waves are rare in the temperate oceanic climate (see temperature data, page 306). A great majority of the cyclonic disturbances which affect these west coasts are strongly occluded and therefore lack extensive

warm sectors that would tend to produce frequent spells of warm weather and raise average summer temperatures.

Winter. *Do* winters are much milder for the latitude than the summers are cool. This is particularly true in western Europe, where a great mass of relatively warm water, the North Atlantic Drift, lies offshore. Thus the coastal parts of western Europe are 20 to 40° too warm for their latitudes in January, while western North America, with its less extensive and less warm ocean current, is 10°+ too mild. The

Features related to freezing temperatures

	J	F	M	A	M	J	J	A	S	O	N	D	Yr
Ice days (maximum temperature below freezing)													
Seattle	1.4	0.4									0.1	0.8	2.7
Birmingham, England	0.9	1.5	0.2								0.1	0.9	3.6
Bergen, Norway	4.3	3.6	1.2								1.1	3.6	13.8
Days with freeze (minimum temperature 32° or below)													
Birmingham, England	8.6	9.5	7.4	3.2	0.1					0.7	6.8	6.7	42.6
Falmouth, England	3.2	2.9	3.2	0.6						0.1	1.9	2.8	14.8
Paris	15.8	13.3	10.7	2.5	0.2					3.0	6.5	13.5	65.5
Seattle	7.6	5.5	1.7	0.1						0.1	0.9	5.6	21.3

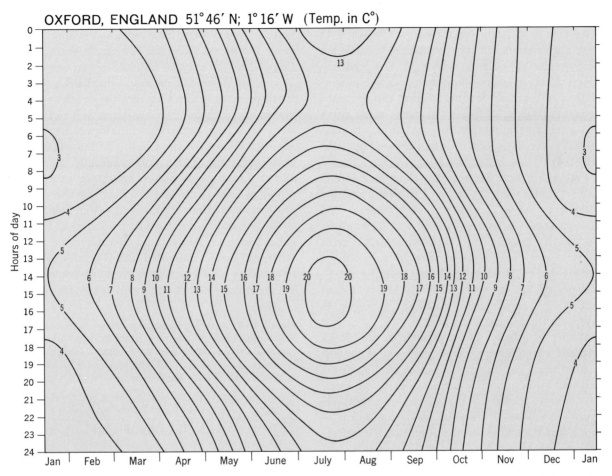

OXFORD, ENGLAND 51° 46′ N; 1° 16′ W (Temp. in C°)

Figure 10.5 Thermoisopleths for a *Do* station in western Europe. Diurnal range, small at all seasons, is somewhat greater in summer than in winter. Annual range is also small. (*After Troll.*)

dominance of oceanic control is indicated by the fact that isotherms tend to parallel these coasts in winter rather than to follow the lines of latitude. Consequently the decrease in temperature is much more rapid from the coast toward the interior than it is in a north-south direction. Paris is 7° colder in January than Brest, which is 310 miles nearer the ocean. In Norway the heads of some of the longest fiords are 10° colder than the open coasts. And Hammerfest on the coast of Norway at 71°N is an ice-free port, while icebreakers are required to keep open the river harbor of Hamburg 17° farther south. January averages of 35 to 50° in west-

ern Europe contrast with averages of 0 to −40° in the continental climates of interior Asia in similar latitudes.

Winter minima and frosts. The average cold-month temperature at London is 39°; Seattle, 40°; Valentia, Ireland, 45°; and Valdivia, Chile, 46°. Annual ranges are small: 23° at London, 24° at Seattle, 15° at Valentia, and 13.5° at Valdivia. For Seattle the average of the January daily minima is 35°, so that on a majority of nights freeze is absent. At Paris freezing temperatures occur on nearly half the nights in the 3 winter months. In London the thermometer remains above freezing on more January nights than it goes below. It is unusual for London to have a temperature below 15°, while 4° is the lowest minimum ever recorded. At Seattle the thermometer has fallen as low as 3°. The predominantly cloudy skies and humid atmosphere in winter tend to decrease daytime heating and to retard nighttime cooling, so that a flat temperature curve with small diurnal temperature variation is characteristic. Clear days show greater ranges (Figs. 10.3 and 10.4).

Freezes are more frequent, as well as more severe, than in subtropical dry-summer climates, and the freeze-free season is shorter. Nevertheless, the growing season is unusually long for the latitude: 180 to 210 days in the American North Pacific Coast region, for example. Seattle has only 4 months when temperatures below freezing are to be expected, and an average of only 21 days a year with freeze. Birmingham, England, averages 43 days with freeze, and Paris 65.

Winter is usually severe enough to produce a dormant season for most plant life, which is not true in subtropical dry-summer climates. Killing frosts occasionally occur in *Cs* regions, but freeze is almost entirely confined to night hours; temperatures rarely remain below freezing during the entire 24 hours. In *Do* climates, on the other hand, temperatures during abnormally cold spells may stay constantly below freezing for a period of several days. On the average Seattle has 2 to 3 ice days each year (i.e., days when the maximum temperature is below freezing). The comparable figure for Birmingham, England, is 3 to 4 days, and for Bergen, Norway, 13 to 14 (see the table on page 308). Midday temperatures of normal winter days are relatively high, however; the average of the daily maxima for January at Seattle is 45°, and the daily range is less than 10°. On the whole, day-to-day temperature changes are much less diurnal and regular in winter than in summer, for winter is more completely controlled by the succession of cyclones and anticyclones.

Cold spells. Severe cold spells in these marine climates are usually caused by advection of frigid polar continental air whose source is a cold anticyclone located interior and poleward. A well-de-

veloped winter high stationed over the Columbia Plateau region may force an approaching low to move southward along the American North Pacific Coast. The low may be followed by an outpouring of cold air from the interior, which descends the western slopes of the Cascades into western Washington and Oregon. Northeasterly, and not northwesterly, winds bring the coldest weather to the American North Pacific Coast. The same is true for western Europe, where both unusually cold spells and abnormally cold winters are caused by a substitution of cold northeasterly *cP* air for the normal southwesterly winds from the sea (Fig. 10.6).

During one unusual winter cold spell in Europe, the influence of the continental anticyclone and its polar air masses persisted for several weeks. As reported by Kendrew, temperatures in eastern Kent, England, remained continuously below freezing for

Figure 10.6 A synoptic pattern favoring unseasonably low winter temperatures in western Europe. A cold anticyclone to the north and east, and a trough of low pressure over the eastern Atlantic, result in advection of cold *cP* air. (*After Kendrew.*)

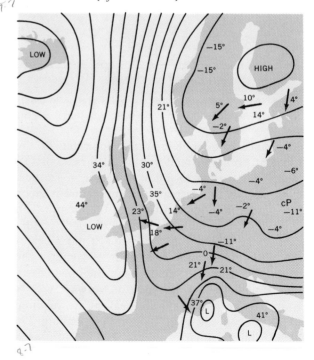

226 hr, the Thames was frozen over in many parts, and practically the whole of the British Isles was frost-bound for 5 weeks. On the continent at this time, German coastal cities had temperatures below zero, while the Rhine was frozen throughout almost its entire course. But such invasions of *cP* air are infrequent in temperate oceanic climates, for, coming as they do from the northeast, they are opposed to the general westerly air movement of the middle latitudes. The American North Pacific Coast is further protected against *cP* invasions by mountain barriers.

Annual march of temperature. In the most marine parts of these west-coast climates the march of the seasons is commonly retarded, so that autumn is relatively warmer than spring. This is particularly true in western Europe, which is more subject to invasions of cold air from the continent in spring than in autumn. At Valentia, Ireland, April has a mean temperature of 48°, while October registers 51°; at Bordeaux, France, the means for these months are 53° and 55°. The seasons of maximum and minimum temperatures are also somewhat retarded, so that at Valentia February is a trifle colder than January, and August is warmer than July.

Precipitation

Annual amount. This is a humid climate with adequate rainfall at all seasons (Fig. 10.1). Precipitation has a high degree of reliability, and droughts are uncommon. The total amount of rainfall, however, varies greatly from region to region, depending in large measure upon the character of the relief. Where lowlands predominate, as they do in parts of western Europe, rainfall is moderate—usually 20 to 35 in. But where west coasts are elevated and bordered by mountain ranges, as in Norway, Chile, and Pacific North America, precipitation may be excessive—even reaching 100 in. or more on windward mountain slopes (see the climatic data).

Moreover, where lowlands exist, moderate rainfall prevails well into the interior of the continent, but where coastal mountains intercept the rain-bearing winds, precipitation is strongly concentrated close to the littoral. East of the mountains drought conditions are likely to prevail. Of course, an extensive distribution of moderate rains is economically more desirable than the concentration of large and unusable quantities along a mountainous coast. Unfortunately, of the three continents extending well into the westerlies only Europe is freely open to the entrance of rain-bearing winds.

Seasonal distribution. Temperate oceanic climates are characterized by *adequate rainfall at all seasons,* rather than by a particular season of excess or deficiency (see Fig. 10.1 and the climatic data). This does not necessarily mean that all months have much the same amount, but only that in most parts of *Do* there is no marked seasonal emphasis, such as exists in subtropical dry-summer and tropical wet-and-dry climates, or in regions with strong monsoons. In other words, it is not a seasonal rainfall deficiency which causes the dormant period for plant growth.

In very marine and mountainous locations it is not uncommon to find that the cooler months have most precipitation, with the summers somewhat drier. At Brest, 59 percent of the year's rain falls in the winter half-year, and 41 percent in the summer half. Valentia has approximately the same seasonal distribution. But this winter maximum occurs mainly on exposed seaboard locations and ceases to be characteristic a short distance inland (Fig. 10.7). Thus while Brest shows a slight cool-season maximum, Paris, 310 miles farther inland but still within the oceanic climate, has 55 percent of the year's total in the summer half-year. It has been suggested that this coastal winter maximum may be partly the result of lifting caused by the frictional effects of the coast upon onshore highly saturated maritime air masses. Throughout much of Europe's *Do* climate, fall is slightly the wettest season and spring the driest.

As a general rule, *Do* regions that lie nearest to *Cs*—which usually means the equatorward parts of *Do*—have a somewhat drier summer than is true

Regions with more rain in winter half year than in summer half year

Figure 10.7 The stippled areas have more rain in the winter half-year than in the summer half-year. In western Europe it is mainly the more maritime sections that fall in this category. (*After Kendrew.*)

for the type as a whole. This is not surprising, for the same strengthened and poleward-displaced subtropical anticyclone which produces the summer drought in *Cs* is likely to cause reduced summer rainfall in adjacent equatorward parts of *Do*. Thus *Do* climate on the North American Pacific Coast south of 50° has a striking summer minimum of precipitation (Fig. 10.2).

Snowfall. Although winter is characteristically a wet season, snowfall is not abundant on temperate oceanic lowlands, for temperatures are too high. Snow is infrequent enough in most of northwest Europe to be a prime topic of conversation when it remains on the ground more than a few days. Paris has an average of 15 snow-days during the year. In the Puget Sound lowland there are some

10 to 15 snow-days, and the snow cover lasts for approximately the same length of time. In the northeastern part of the British Isles the lowlands have about 25 days with snow, but the southwest coast has only 4. The snow that falls is wet and heavy because of the relatively high temperatures. Upon the ground it quickly turns to slush and creates unpleasant conditions underfoot.

Where mountains border these west coasts, however, the lower temperatures and more abundant winter precipitation cause snowfall to be extremely heavy. On the western slopes of the Cascade Range, an average of 300 to 400 in. of snow falls each year. Snowfall is also heavy on the western slopes of the British Columbia Coast Ranges, the Scandinavian highlands, the mountains of southern New Zealand, and the southern Andes. In each of these regions the mountain snowfields have in the past created numerous valley glaciers, which in turn have carved the characteristically irregular, fiorded coasts.

Origin and nature of precipitation. Over lowlands precipitation is chiefly frontal or cyclonic, and a significant part of it falls as steady, long-continued light rain from a gray, leaden sky. Since it is in fall-winter that these storms reach their maximum development, it is then that cloudy, rainy days are most numerous. Cyclones are weaker and less numerous in the warm seasons; yet even so, the absolute humidity is higher at those periods, and the entrance of lows into the continents is facilitated by lower pressures. Consequently summer rain may nearly, if not quite, equal winter totals, although it falls in heavier showers on fewer days. At London, July has 13 rainy days with 2.4 in. of rain, while in January the respective figures are 15 and 1.9. Summers, therefore, are usually brighter and sunnier than winters.

The relatively cool summers and the prevalence of stable maritime air masses at that season are not conducive to the development of thunderstorms and their convective systems. Coastal stations of the American North Pacific states record only two to four a year, although thunderstorms are more numerous at higher elevations and farther inland, where turbulence and overturning are induced by the rugged land surface. At Oxford, England, only 28 percent of the rain in June, and 32 percent in July, falls on days in which thunder is heard. Still, showery, intermittent convective rain is not unusual. Oddly enough, however, this type is associated with the coldest maritime air. In Europe it is cool *mP* air from the north or northwest, which has been humidified and made unstable over the ocean, that is most likely to develop cumulus clouds and showery weather. By contrast, warmer *mP* air from the west and southwest is more stable and more likely to produce a gray overcast and light rain.

A distinguishing feature of the precipitation in *Do* climates is the relatively small amount of rain that actually falls, considering the large number of cloudy, rainy days. Although Paris has only 22.6 in. of precipitation, this is spread over 160 rain-days (an average of 0.14 in. for each rain-day). Seattle, with 33.4 in. of precipitation, has 151 rain-days; London has 24.5 in. and 164 rain-days; Sumburgh Head on the Shetland Islands has 36.7 in. spread out over 260 rain-days. London has had 72 rain-days in succession. The prevalence of strongly occluded cyclones is an important factor causing the many days in lowlands that have dull, lowering skies with low-hanging clouds and light rain or none (Fig. 10.8).

Where coasts are precipitous, abundant rains of orographic origin supplement those from cyclones and from the few convectional storms. Not only is the total precipitation greater there, but the rate of fall is heavier as well. Connor[1] has pointed out that the winter precipitation of the North American *Do* climate is frontal as well as orographic. During winter, the prevailing winds in the interior valleys and even along the coast are easterly. Hence some sort of persistent discontinuity, or front, exists between the locally generated cool easterlies of the mainland and coast, and the warmer Pacific air masses moving in from the west. No doubt a considerable

[1] A. J. Connor, "The Climates of North America: Canada," in W. Köppen and R. Geiger, *Handbuch der Klimatologie,* Vol. 2, part J, 1938, p. 345.

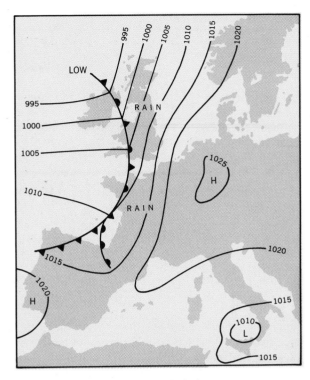

Figure 10.8 A strongly occluded storm in western Europe, producing light but steady and widespread rainfall, a low cloud ceiling, and low visibility. Most of the cyclones which affect western Europe are in an advanced stage of occlusion. Such storms are inclined to produce much cloud, but only a modest amount of precipitation on lowlands.

part of the so-called orographic rainfall is produced by the trigger effect of highlands upon conditionally or convectively unstable maritime air.

Cloudiness and sunshine. Temperate oceanic climate is one of the cloudiest of the whole earth. Relative humidity is almost always high, particularly in winter. On the American North Pacific Coast the mean annual cloudiness is 60 to 70 percent, making it the region with the most cloudiness and least sunshine of any part of the United States (Fig. 10.9). Over wide areas of western Europe cloudiness is greater than 70 percent, and the sun is sometimes hidden for several weeks in succession. Winter and fall, the seasons with most cyclones, are

Precipitation occurrence

	J	F	M	A	M	J	J	A	S	O	N	D	Yr
					Days with precipitation								
Paris	14	14	14	13	14	12	12	12	11	15	15	15	160
Oxford, England	15	15	14	13	13	12	14	14	11	16	15	17	168
Bergen, Norway	20	20	18	16	16	15	16	20	19	19	20	21	219
Vancouver, Canada	21	16	17	14	12	10	6	7	11	17	21	22	173
					Days with snowfall								
Oxford	4.0	3.9	4.1	0.9	0.1				0.1	1.2	2.6		16.8
Valentia	1.1	1.4	1.3	0.3	0.1				0.1	0.7	1.7		10.8
Bergen	9.0	9.5	8.3	4.2	0.6				0.7	4.5	5.8		42.3
Paris	3.9	3.4	3.3	0.9					0.9	2.3			14.8
Vancouver	4.9	2.2	1.4	0.1					0.6	2.7			11.9
Seattle	3.5	2.6	1.6	0.5					0.5	1.6			10.2

much darker and gloomier than spring and summer. Seattle, which has only 22 percent of the possible sunshine in November and 21 percent in December, receives 65 percent in July and 60 percent in August, so that summers there are relatively bright and pleasant. Valentia, Ireland, has only 17 percent of the possible sunshine in December, but 43 percent in May. Even though summers are sunnier than

Sunshine and cloud

	J	F	M	A	M	J	J	A	S	O	N	D	Yr
					Duration of sunshine (percent)								
Paris	21	31	36	39	49	47	50	50	42	33	23	20	37
					Number of overcast days								
Kew, England	17.4	14.8	13.0	10.2	8.6	9.5	11.9	10.0	7.8	10.5	12.6	15.0	141.3
Bergen	16.8	17.5	14.9	13.5	14.3	13.3	14.9	16.6	15.8	15.7	16.4	17.4	187.1
				Number of clear days (cloudiness 0 to 20 percent)									
Victoria, Canada	1.8	4.2	8.0	6.2	6.0	7.2	13.6	12.6	6.8	4.4	0.8	1.6	73.2
Kew	1.7	2.2	1.3	2.9	3.8	2.8	1.6	2.1	3.7	2.6	2.1	1.1	27.7
Bergen	4.2	2.5	3.1	3.6	3.1	3.8	2.1	1.5	2.3	3.0	2.8	3.0	35.1
				Cloudiness (in tenths of sky covered)									
Dublin	6.4	6.4	5.9	5.8	6.0	6.2	6.8	6.3	5.8	6.0	6.2	6.3	6.2
Bergen	7.1	6.9	6.8	6.1	6.2	5.9	6.8	7.1	7.0	6.9	7.1	7.2	6.8
Paris	7.0	6.5	5.8	5.7	5.7	5.5	5.2	4.9	5.1	5.9	6.9	7.2	6.0
Vancouver	7.6	6.9	6.3	6.0	6.1	5.6	4.1	4.3	5.2	6.8	7.7	7.7	6.2

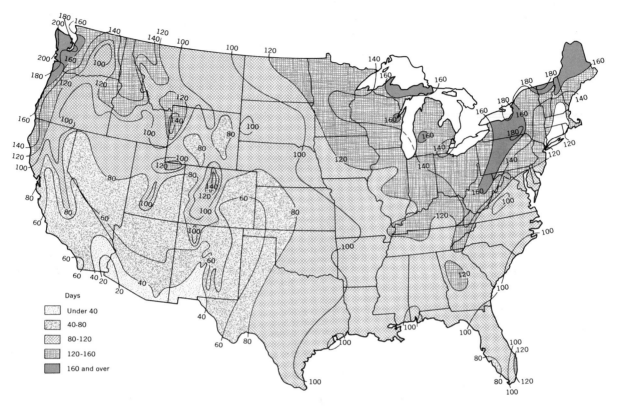

Figure 10.9 Average number of cloudy days in the United States. Note that the Northwest and the Northeast, both regions of cyclone concentration, have the most cloudiness. (*U.S. Department of Agriculture.*)

winters, they are still much cloudier than those of Mediterranean climates. Fog and mist are characteristic weather elements of the marine climate. The American North Pacific Coast has over 40 days with dense fog during the year; Bergen, Norway, has 37.7; and Fanö, Denmark, 53.6.

Seasonal weather

The nonperiodic or cyclonic element. Because *Do* regions have so many cyclonic storms, the weather is dominated by these disturbances and their accompanying nonperiodic temperature and precipitation changes. The diurnal element, or sun control, is correspondingly weak.

But in spite of cyclonic control of weather, temperature changes associated with the approach and passage of disturbances are not nearly so striking

as they are in continental climates—the North American Middle West, for example. Temperature changes are moderate because the air masses involved in the cyclonic circulations affecting *Do* climates are usually maritime, so that temperature contrasts along fronts are not great. In addition, since most *Do* cyclones are strongly occluded, the majority do not have an extensive warm sector of *mT* air; they are essentially converging systems of relatively cool maritime air (Fig. 10.8). Air temperatures in these storms show nothing comparable to the contrasts between winter *cP* and *mT*-Gulf present in interior North America. As previously noted, isotherms tend to parallel the coast, especially in the cooler seasons, so that advected temperatures from either north or south are not severe. It is only from the eastern continental interior that severe cold can be derived, and such air movement is opposed to the general west-to-east circulation in the middle latitudes.

Traveling disturbances in temperate oceanic climates also produce great nonperiodic variability in the precipitation element. As explained in the previous section, overcast days with light precipitation of frontal origin are numerous. When the cyclonic disturbances slow up or stagnate, as they commonly do, a succession of gray, dripping days results.

Winter, in spite of its mild temperatures, is a stormy period. The westerlies themselves are strongest at that season, and at frequent intervals the pressure gradients are made steeper by passing cyclones. In coastal locations, gales are numerous as one storm follows another in rapid succession. The high seas generated by winter winds are strong enough to make navigation difficult, and unusually severe storms may do serious damage to shipping. The fog and mist create poor visibility and add to the difficulties of navigation.

Winter precipitation, most of it rain rather than snow, is relatively abundant and very frequent. Long periods of dark, gloomy, dripping weather make winters depressing and hard to endure. Not only is frontal cloud abundant, but it also persists in the strong flow of *mP* air following the cold front. If this air has had a northerly or northwesterly trajectory it is unstable, producing cumulonimbus clouds and showery precipitation over the sea and along the coast. Inland there is some clearing at night, but showers predominate by day. If the airflow is westerly and southwesterly, it is likely to be less chilly but more stable, often resulting in gray skies with stratocumulus cloud and light rain.

Between the frequent cyclones there are occasional sunny winter days with crisper weather, but these are the exception rather than the rule. Night freezes are not unusual, especially when skies are clear, but ordinarily they are not severe. Now and then *cP* air masses push westward and create a succession of clear days in which temperatures may remain continuously below freezing.

As the days lengthen with the advance of *spring*, cyclones become less frequent and sunshine more abundant. The air is still cool but the sun is warm,

and in western Europe spring is acclaimed the most delightful season.

Summer temperatures are pleasant and conducive to physical well-being. Where sunny days are numerous, as they are in the United States Pacific Northwest, a more charming summer climate would be hard to find (Fig. 9.8). In the higher middle latitudes, or in very exposed marine locations, there are still many chilly, gray, overcast days even in summer. Rain is also relatively abundant, but it falls on fewer days than in winter.

In *autumn* the equatorward swing of the storm belt brings an increase in cloudiness, and perhaps in precipitation. On the whole, autumn is cloudier than spring. The season remains mild, however; September and October (in the Northern Hemisphere) are usually 2 or 3° warmer than May and April.

Regional characteristics

North America. There are two unusual features of this climatic region, both of them in the southern part. The first is the modest total annual rainfall along the margins of northern Puget Sound and the straits of Georgia and Juan de Fuca. Here, over a considerable area which includes southeastern Vancouver Island and parts of the state of Washington, annual rainfall is below 30 in., and there is a core area where it is only 15 to 20 in. (Fig. 10.10). Coupeville, Washington, has only 17 in., Sequim 16 in., and Port Townsend 18 in. Authorities usually attribute these abnormally low totals to the rain-shadow effects of the Olympic Mountains and Vancouver Island. However, it seems likely also that local airstreams moving through restricted oceanic channels, together with peculiarities of coastal alignment with respect to these local air currents, may be an auxiliary factor in reducing rainfall along littorals.

The second abnormal feature of the United State's *Do* is the dry summers. A number of stations show July and August rainfalls of only $\frac{1}{2}$ to 1 in. (Fig. 10.11). Victoria has 3 summer months each with less than 1 in., Seattle 2, and Portland 1. Such summer highest pressure in summer appears to be as far north as 50°. A temperature inversion exists about 20 percent of the time at Tatoosh Island, 48°N. The northward-displaced anticyclone is not only effective in stabilizing the air, but also acts to block most summer cyclones from penetrating to the coast.[2]

Europe. The European sector, the only extensive lowland region with temperate oceanic climate, is also by far the largest sector with abnormally high winter temperatures. That winters are exceptionally mild for the latitude over larger areas in Europe than elsewhere is related both to the openness of the continent to Atlantic air and to the unusual

[2] Glenn T. Trewartha, *The Earth's Problem Climates,* The University of Wisconsin Press, Madison, Wis., 1961, pp. 270–272.

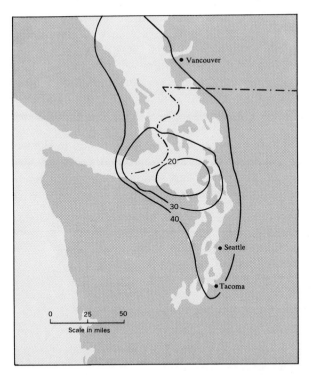

Figure 10.10 Generalized isohyets showing location of areas of modest annual precipitation (in inches) in the northern Puget Sound region of the United States and Canada. (*From Trewartha, The Earth's Problem Climates.*)

drought is more typical of subtropical dry-summer climates than of *Do.* To be sure the total annual rainfall in most parts is large for *Cs.* Still, this is not the case in the drier sections mentioned in the paragraph above. These are saved from being classified as *Cs* only because they have too many months in which the average temperature is below 50°.

This abnormally low summer precipitation in a west-coast position so far poleward is caused by the unusual northward displacement along the coast of an arm of the North Pacific high (Fig. 9.8). The cool coastal waters generated by the cell's circulation may be an auxiliary factor. While the center of the anticyclone over the ocean is positioned at about 38°N, the isobars on its land side bulge in a northeasterly direction, so that along the coast the

Figure 10.11 Annual march of rainfall at a station in the Puget Sound region of modest rainfall. The small annual total, together with the relatively dry summer, makes this station resemble subtropical dry-summer climate, except that its temperatures are not subtropical.

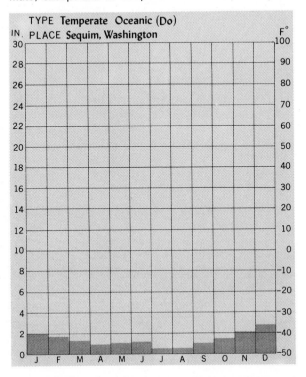

warmth of the eastern North Atlantic Ocean. A January air temperature 50° too warm for the latitude (termed a positive or plus anomaly of 50°) is characteristic of the ocean space 200 miles off the coast of Norway at about 65 to 70°N. The 20° January isanomal follows the coast of France and West Germany and crosses southernmost Sweden.

Another temperature peculiarity of the maritime sections of northwestern Europe is the rapid decrease with altitude in the length of the growing season. The unusual coolness of uplands in Britain creates a low tree line; landscapes in the Pennines at eleva-

tions as low as 1,700 ft resemble tundra. The rapid shortening of the growing season with elevation is chiefly a consequence of the steep lapse rate in the predominately cool maritime air masses.

Noteworthy features of annual rainfall on lowlands in western and central Europe are its modest amount (commonly 20 to 35 in.) and its slow decline inland. A few areas have less than 20 in. Some of the lowest annual totals are to be found in the lee of higher land, or along flat coasts and on low islands where winds are strong. The generally modest rainfall of these lowlands, freely open to Atlantic

Figure 10.12 Annual frequency of cyclones with central pressure less than 1,013 mb. High frequency is characteristic of the Mediterranean–Black Sea borderlands in the south, and likewise of the higher middle latitudes in the vicinity of ±60°N. Low frequency is typical of western and central Europe in the general proximity of ±50°N. (*After Schedler. From Trewartha, The Earth's Problem Climates.*)

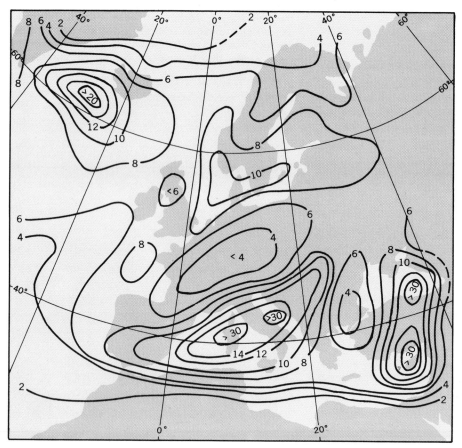

air, is related to the relative infrequency of rain-bringing disturbances in latitudes 45 to 55°N, the approximate position of Europe's lowlands (Fig. 10.12). Cyclones are more frequent to both the north and the south. This minimal frequency of cyclones in a zone astride the 50°N parallel results at least partly from the frequent blocking of Atlantic storms by stagnant warm highs centered in the easternmost Atlantic at about latitudes 45 to 60°N. During such periods of anticyclonic blocking, not only are depressions prevented from passing directly inland, but subsidence in the highs themselves also promotes stability.[3]

Other sectors. The Chilean *Do* is a mountainous, cloudy, rain-drenched region swept by strong winds. Valdivia, situated close to the region's subtropical margins, has an annual precipitation of 3,700 mm (150 in.). Of this 70 percent is concentrated in the winter half-year, which suggests that some anticyclonic influence is present in summer. Southward the anticyclonic effects diminish rapidly, and so also does any seasonal accent of rainfall.

Restricted areas of temperate oceanic climate are found in southernmost eastern Australia, Tasmania, and South Island, New Zealand. In South Island, precipitation distribution resembles that in South America poleward of 40°. Abnormal amounts of rain for *Do* climate (150 to 200 in.) fall on the windward mountain slopes of Westland, New Zealand, while the subhumid Canterbury Plain east of the highlands receives only 20 to 30 in. Any seasonal concentration is slight.

TEMPERATE CONTINENTAL CLIMATE (*Dc*)

Type location. Although it is scarcely "temperate," at least in its winter weather, this fairly severe climate is found in some of the earth's most populous and economically well-developed countries in all three continental sectors—Anglo-America, Europe, and Asia. In this respect it is unlike that still more severe group of continental climates, the boreal type located farther poleward, in which population is indeed very sparse.

In temperate continental climate a genuine winter, with a durable snow mantle, is combined with an authentic summer season to produce the annual climatic cycle. Fall and spring, the transition seasons, not only are brief, but are also chiefly composites of winter and summer weather types. Colder and snowier winters, shorter frost-free seasons, and larger annual ranges of temperature differentiate the more severe continental climate from the temperate oceanic type.

This greater severity is caused primarily by locational differences, for continental climate occupies interior and leeward areas on the great land masses rather than the west coasts dominated by the oceanic

type. Emphatically, continental climate is land-controlled (Figs. 7.2 and 10.13). And because it is associated with large continents in middle latitudes, this type is confined to the Northern Hemisphere. Only Eurasia and North America are able to generate it. Of the Southern Hemisphere continents, South America alone extends sufficiently far poleward to have rigorous climates, but its narrowness south of latitude 35° obviates genuinely severe conditions in spite of the latitude. Temperate continental climate, which does not occur on western, or windward, coasts because of their dominance by maritime air masses, occupies the interiors of land masses and commonly extends down to tidewater on their leeward, or eastern, sides. On east coasts, in spite of their proximity to the sea, modified continental conditions usually prevail.

The latitudinal spread of temperate continental climate is mostly about 10 to 20°, but the particular latitude belts occupied are not identical in all three continental sectors. Where, as in North America and Asia, the continental type is on the lee side of the land mass, it extends from about 35 or 40° to 50°±. In Europe, on the other hand, since the continental type is located windward of the Eurasian

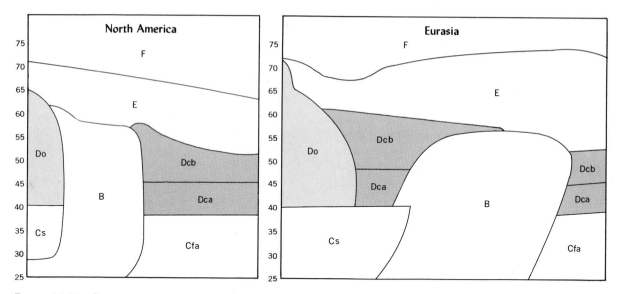

Figure 10.13 Contrasting arrangement of temperate continental climates (*Dc*) in North America and Eurasia. In Eurasia they are found both to the east and to the west of the dry interior; in North America they are located almost exclusively to the east of the dry climates.

land-mass center, temperatures are less severe and the latitudinal spread is from 40° + to 60° or more. Thus the European sector is positioned farther poleward.

The previous section on temperate oceanic climate described the contrasting depths of penetration of marine influence in North America and Eurasia. There are also contrasting arrangements of temperate continental climate on the two continents (compare Fig. 7.2 with the climate map inside the front cover). In North America, because marine conditions close to the west coast are terminated abruptly by mountain ranges, extensive dry climates intervene between temperate oceanic and temperate continental types (Fig. 10.13). Leeward from the west-coast mountains, temperatures suddenly change character from marine to continental, and simultaneously precipitation drops to low levels. Thus a humid oceanic climate passes abruptly to a dry continental one with no humid continental condition between. In Eurasia, on the other hand, where lowlands stretching inland from the west coast permit deep entry of oceanic air into the con-

tinent from the west, temperate continental climate lies not only to the east of the dry interior but also to the west. Consequently this type is to be found both in central and eastern Europe and in eastern Asia. As can be seen on the climate map, the North American and Asiatic temperate continental regions are similar in location; the European is different.

Typically, temperate continental climate is bounded by boreal climate on its poleward side. There the accepted limits are set by the isoline of 4 months with an average temperature of 50° or above. On the south, where its limit is 8 months with a temperature of 50° or over, the *Dc* type adjoins subtropical humid climate in North America and Asia. But in Europe its southern border is mainly set by dry climates or the subtropical dry-summer type.

It may seem unusual that this relatively severe land-controlled climate should extend eastward to the ocean margins. But since the eastern side is the leeward side, the west-to-east general circulation acts to hinder deep entrance of maritime easterly air from the adjacent ocean. In addition, the tendency toward monsoon circulation on the eastern or lee sides of middle-latitude continents accentuates the seasonal temperature extremes, making for cold winters and warm summers.

Temperature

A feature of the annual temperature curve in continental climates is its approximate symmetry, for corresponding spring and fall months have about the same temperatures. In marine climates, by contrast, seasonal lags in temperature distort this symmetry.

Because they have a wide latitudinal spread, *Dc* climates show marked temperature contrasts between their poleward and equatorward parts. An indication of these contrasts is the great difference in values of the isolines marking *Dc*'s northern and southern limits—4 months and 8 months with an average temperature of 50° or above. Still, for any particular latitude this climate is sure to have relatively severe winters and summers, so that annual ranges are large (Fig. 10.14). Of the two extreme

Figure 10.14 Thermoisopleths of a station with only a moderately severe temperate continental climate. (*After Troll.*)

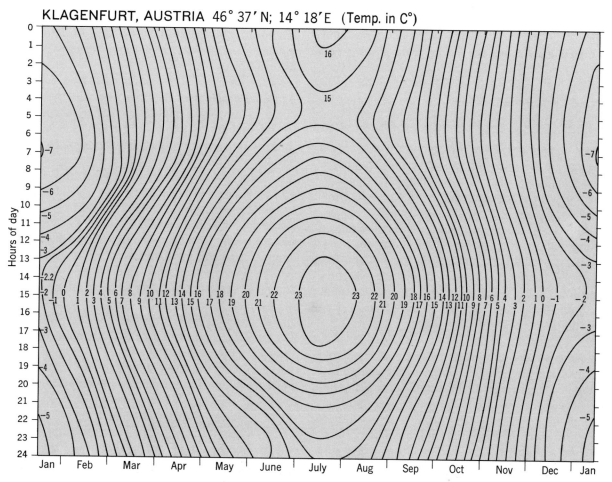

KLAGENFURT, AUSTRIA 46° 37′ N; 14° 18′ E (Temp. in C°)

seasons, it is the winter cold, rather than the summer heat, which is most pronounced. Nevertheless, summers are warm for the latitude.

Not only are the seasons extreme, but temperatures are variable from one year to another. In marine climates one winter is usually much like another, but wide departures from the normal seasonal temperature are characteristic of continental climates—in extreme instances, as much as 30°.

Effects of a snow cover upon air temperature. Only in continental, boreal, polar, and some highland climates does the snow cover last long enough to have a marked effect upon cool-season air temperatures. Once a region is overlain by a snow mantle, the soil surface itself ceases to influence air temperature. As Chapter 1 explained, light falling upon snow is largely reflected, so that little of it is effective in heating the ground or the atmosphere. Moreover, while a snow surface loses energy very rapidly by earth radiation, the low conductivity of snow acts to retard the upward flow of heat from the ground to replace that which is being lost. Observations made at Leningrad after a fall of 20 in. of loose, dry snow showed a temperature of −39° at the top of the snow surface, while the soil surface underneath was only 27°—a difference of 66°. cP air masses moving southward over this cold snow surface are only very slowly modified.

Obviously, the effect of a snow cover is to reduce winter temperatures markedly. As spring advances, it also retards the warming of the air, for much of the solar energy is expended in melting the snow and ice. On the other hand, the snow cover tends to keep the ground warmer and so prevents deep freezing.

Seasons severe. Warm to hot summers and cold winters are characteristic of temperate continental climate. Any monsoon-like winds, advecting temperatures from lower latitudes in summer and from higher latitudes in winter, function to accentuate the normal seasonal severity. In general, the climate becomes more rigorous from south to north and from the coast toward the interior.

Although westerly winds and winter monsoons tend to carry continental air masses down to the eastern littorals, there is some onshore wind of cyclonic origin which meliorates conditions slightly, with the result that east coasts have *modified* continental climates. For example, at New York City and Omaha, Nebraska, which are in similar latitudes although New York is on the Atlantic seaboard and Omaha lies deep in the interior, July temperatures are 74° and 77° respectively, while January temperatures are 31° and 22°. Consequently the annual range is 43.0° at New York and 55.0° at Omaha. However, the higher atmospheric humidity of the air along the seaboard makes summer heat more oppressive and sultry, and winter cold more raw and penetrating, than the drier extremes of the interior. The degree of marine modification is greatest where coasts are deeply indented—as they are in extreme eastern Canada, for example.

Seasonal gradients. Summer and winter in temperate continental climate present marked contrasts in latitudinal temperature gradients. (Compare these with seasonal solar radiation gradients as described in Chapter 1.) In the warm season the few isotherms that cross the central and eastern United States are spaced far apart, so that temperature changes very gradually from north to south: about 1° for every degree of latitude, or approximately every 70 miles (Fig. 10.15). Similar weak summer gradients are found in eastern Asia. In winter, however, temperature changes abruptly from north to south: in the eastern United States, about 2.5° for each degree of latitude, or two to three times more rapidly than in summer. Between Harbin (Haerhpin) and Wuhan in China, there is only 13° difference in July, but 42° in January. Between St. Louis and Winnipeg, the January contrast amounts to 34°, the July contrast to only 13°. Obviously, there is much more reason for northerners to go south to escape winter cold than for southerners to go north to escape summer heat.

The steeper temperature gradients of winter lead to much sharper advected temperature variations

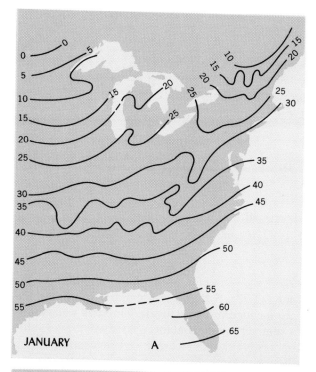

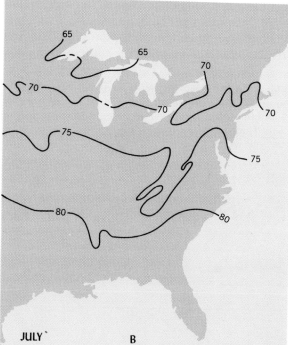

accompanying changes in wind direction. The growing season varies greatly in length from north to south in the continental climates, approaching 200 days on the low-latitude margins and decreasing to 100± days on the subarctic side.

Subtypes. Based largely on temperature contrasts, two subtypes of temperate continental climate will be recognized here: one with a warm summer (*Dca*) and the other with a cool one (*Dcb*). The boundary between them is the July isotherm of 72° (22°C).

Warm-summer subtype. Because this is the warmer and less severe phase of temperate continental climate, it typically occupies the more southerly parts of the general type. As the climate map shows, in the United States it is found in a tier of states extending from central Kansas and Nebraska on the west to the Atlantic seaboard and including Iowa, northern and central Missouri, Illinois, Indiana, Ohio, Pennsylvania, and parts of adjacent states both to the north and to the south. The Corn Belt lies within its borders. In Europe the *Dca* type is found chiefly in the lower Danube Valley—and it is on the plains of the Danube that much of Europe's maize crop is grown. The third principal *Dca* region lies in eastern Asia and includes much of North China, most of Korea, and northern Honshu in Japan.

Summer in this less severe subtype is characteristically long, warm, and humid, owing to the general prevalence of conditionally unstable *mT* air masses (Fig. 10.16). The North American and Asiatic *Dca* regions have summer temperatures that are almost subtropical in character—July at Des Moines averages 77°; New York, 74°; Tientsin, 81°; Mukden (Shenyang), Manchuria, 77°. On the whole, the European *Dca* has less intense summer heat, with July averages more often under than over 75° (e.g., Bucharest is 73°). Typical American Corn Belt cities have average July temperatures in the neighbor-

Figure 10.15 Surface-temperature gradients in the temperate continental climates of the central and eastern United States are much steeper in winter than in summer.

Climatic data for representative *Dca* stations

	J	F	M	A	M	J	J	A	S	O	N	D	Yr	Range
Peoria, Illinois														
Temp., °F	24	28	40	51	62	71	75	73	65	53	39	28	50.8	51.6
Precip., in.	1.8	2.0	2.7	3.3	3.9	3.8	3.8	3.2	3.8	2.4	2.4	2.0	34.9	
New York City														
Temp., °F	31	31	38	49	59	69	74	72	66	56	44	34	52	43.0
Precip., in.	3.3	3.3	3.4	3.3	3.4	3.4	4.1	4.3	3.4	3.4	3.4	3.3	42.0	
Bucharest, Rumania														
Temp., °F	26	29	40	52	61	68	73	71	64	54	41	30	50.7	47.5
Precip., in.	1.2	1.1	1.7	2.0	2.5	3.3	2.8	1.9	1.5	1.5	1.9	1.7	23.0	
Peking, China (marginal)														
Temp., °F	24	29	41	57	68	76	79	77	68	55	39	27	53	55
Precip., in.	0.1	0.2	0.2	0.6	1.4	3.0	9.4	6.3	2.6	0.6	0.3	0.1	24.9	

Figure 10.16 A station representing the warm-summer subtype of temperate continental climate. Large annual range of temperature, and precipitation concentrated to a moderate degree in the warm season, are characteristic.

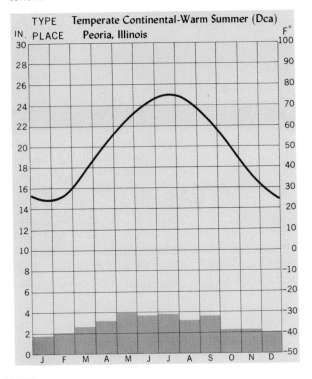

hood of 77°. Not only are summers warm, but they are inclined to be relatively humid as well, so that a summer month contains a large number of sultry, oppressive days which are very uncomfortable for the inhabitants. At Urbana, Illinois, in the heart of the Corn Belt, where the average July temperature is 75°, the mean of the daily maxima is 86°, and the highest temperature ever recorded is 105° (Fig. 10.17). Not only are the days hot, but because of

Figure 10.17 Daily maximum and minimum temperatures for the extreme months of one year at a station with temperate continental climate, warm-summer subtype. Nonperiodic air-mass control is conspicuous, especially in winter.

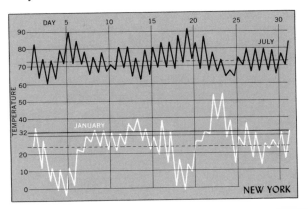

Features related to freezing temperatures

	J	F	M	A	M	J	J	A	S	O	N	D	Yr
Days with freeze (minimum temperature 32° or below)													
Berlin	19.3	17.4	11.3	2.6	0.1					1.2	8.7	16.4	77
Warsaw	23.8	22.6	20.1	5.2	0.3				0.2	3.0	14.8	22.5	112.5
Bucharest	28.3	20.8	13.4	2.0					0.1	1.2	12.4	22.0	100.4
Dubuque, Iowa	29.1	28.0	20.8	6.5	0.3				0.1	3.6	17.5	27.2	132.5
Duluth, Minnesota	31	28	24	16	3					7	25	30	164
Ice days (maximum temperature below freezing)													
Boston	9.4	9.9	2.6								0.8	6.7	29.0
Dubuque	17.4	16.1	5.2	0.2						0.2	3.6	14.1	56.2
Duluth	26.2	25.6	15.3	2.1						1.2	10.5	24.1	104.3

the high absolute humidity, nocturnal cooling is slow, so that nights too are often uncomfortably warm. Urbana has a July mean daily minimum temperature of 64°.

Summer weather, with its prevalence of tropical air masses, is much less variable than that of winter. Occasional summertime invasions of polar air following cold fronts and their associated thunderstorms interrupt the standard succession of hot days (Fig. 10.17). In addition to being hot, summers are relatively long: the period between killing frosts is in the neighborhood of 150 to 200 days. As a result, this is a highly productive climate agriculturally.

Winters are likely to be relatively cold. Spells of overcast, raw, sometimes foggy, and generally disagreeable weather associated with tropical air masses are sandwiched between periods of crisp cold. The average January temperature at Urbana is 26°, and the average of the daily minima is only 18°, although 25° below zero has been known to occur (Figs. 10.16 and 10.17). Peoria, Illinois, has an average January temperature of 24°; Bucharest, Rumania, 26°; and Peking, China, 24°. Monthly averages, however, are not really appropriate for describing winter temperatures, since these are composed of wide variants. Because *Dca* climate has such different temperature conditions on its northern and southern frontiers, either subpolar or

subtropical temperatures can be advected there in the space of a few hours.

Cool-summer subtype.   This more severe of the two subtypes occupies the northerly parts of the temperate continental realm. It is sometimes called the "spring wheat" climate, since that important commercial crop reaches its most specialized development in the subhumid parts of *Dcb*. In North America the subtype is found in general east of the 100th meridian and includes the northern tier of states in the United States and portions of southern Canada (see the climate map). In Eurasia it includes most of Poland, eastern Germany, southern Sweden, and a large part of the central Russian plain between latitudes 50 and 60° +. Beyond the Urals it extends on into Siberia as a narrowing belt in the vicinity of latitude 55°. In much of the U.S.S.R. it is terminated on the south by steppe climate. The third large representative area is in northeastern Asia—especially central and northern Manchuria, southeastern Siberia, and northern Japan.

Because of its characteristic location in higher latitudes, temperatures are generally lower than in the *Dca* subtype farther south (Figs. 10.18 and 10.19). The differential is much larger in winter than in summer, for while the hot months are only 5 to 10° cooler than those in *Dca,* average winter temperatures are 10 to 30° lower. It is the severer

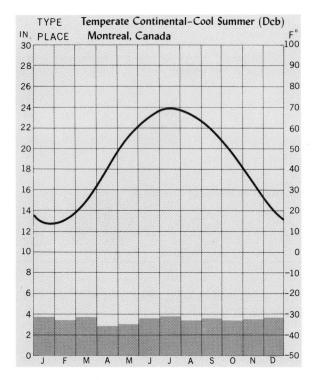

Figure 10.18 Temperature and rainfall conditions at a station with temperate continental climate, cool-summer subtype. Note the large annual range of temperature. At this station there is no seasonal concentration of precipitation—a feature characteristic of the northeastern United States and adjacent parts of Canada, where winter cyclones are numerous.

At the time of the Northern Hemisphere summer solstice, Winnipeg has a daily period of solar energy which is more than 1 hr longer than that of St. Louis.

Summer midday temperatures in July are likely to be warm to hot, especially when the sun is shining. Overcast days, on the other hand, are apt to be cool. Days with temperatures of 90° and above are not unusual (Fig. 10.19). In a recent summer, Bismarck, North Dakota, had 20 days when the thermometer reached 90° or above and 4 when it touched or exceeded 100°. The next year there were 14 days with 90° or above, but none that reached 100°. *Dcb*'s hot waves, which are similar in origin to those in regions farther south, are usually not quite so severe or so prolonged. On the other hand, there are more spells of cool weather associated with polar air masses than in the *Dca* type, for (in North America, at least) *Dcb* is closer to the tracks of summer cyclones. It is the more frequent invasions of cool polar air that pull down the general summer temperature average.

Winter is characteristically the dominant season. At Barnaul, Siberia, the January average is −2°;

Figure 10.19 Temperate continental climate, cool-summer subtype. Note the very large and irregular temperature changes indicating strong air-mass control associated with cyclones and anticyclones.

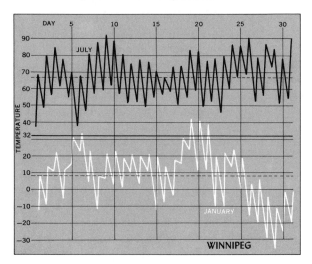

winters, then, that chiefly account for the larger annual ranges.

Summers are usually moderately warm for a few months: average July temperatures are about 65 to 70° (Grand Forks, North Dakota, 69°; Montreal, 69°; Moscow, 66°; Barnaul, Siberia, 67°; Sapporo, Japan, 69°). But the climate is handicapped by the short duration of summer. Thus while Indianapolis (*Dca*) has 7 months with average temperatures of 50° or over, Fargo and Winnipeg (*Dcb*) have only 5. Freeze comes early and remains late, so that the growing season is only 3+ to 5 months long—too brief for a number of crops. Somewhat offsetting the disadvantages of shorter and cooler summers are the longer summer days in the higher latitudes.

Climatic data for representative *Dcb* stations

	J	F	M	A	M	J	J	A	S	O	N	D	Yr	Range
Montreal, Canada														
Temp., °F	13	15	25	41	55	65	69	67	59	47	33	19	42	56
Precip., in.	3.7	3.2	3.7	2.4	3.1	3.5	3.8	3.4	3.5	3.3	3.4	3.7	40.7	
Moscow, U.S.S.R.														
Temp., °F	12	15	23	38	53	62	66	63	52	40	28	17	39	54
Precip., in.	1.1	1.0	1.2	1.5	1.9	2.0	2.8	2.9	2.2	1.4	1.6	1.5	21.1	
Duluth, Minnesota														
Temp., °F	9	13	24	38	48	58	65	64	56	45	29	16	39	56
Precip., in.	1.0	0.9	1.5	1.9	2.9	3.7	3.6	3.0	3.3	2.2	1.5	1.0	26.5	
Harbin (Haerhpin), China														
Temp., °F	−2	5	24	42	56	66	71	69	58	40	21	3	38	74
Precip., in.	0.1	0.2	0.4	0.9	1.7	3.8	4.5	4.1	1.8	1.3	0.3	0.2	19.3	

Bismarck, North Dakota, 8°; Sapporo, Japan, 21°; Uppsala, Sweden, 24°. But these averages are composed of very unlike temperature elements, since the succession of fronts and air masses brings much subzero weather as well as some that is considerably above freezing (Fig. 10.18). At Bismarck, although the average January temperature is 8°, the average of the daily minima is −2.8°. Even the highest temperatures on most January days are well below freezing, for the mean of the daily maxima for that month is only 18.0. At Winnipeg the mean of the daily maxima for January is 6.2°, and that of the daily minima −14.7° (Fig. 10.19). The comparable figures for milder Quebec are 17.7° and 1.6°. In a recent January, Bismarck had 5 days in which the temperature did not rise to zero and 13 in which it was constantly above zero. There were 14 days in which the minimum temperatures went below −10°. The lowest temperature for that particular year was about −37°, although −45° has been recorded. But winters differ greatly from year to year in the continental climates; the following January, Bismarck had only 1 day with a temperature below −10°, as compared with 14 the previous year. As in the *Dca* type, large nonperiodic air-mass-controlled temperature fluctuations within a short period of time are also characteristic. Changes of 40° within 24 hr are relatively common at Bismarck.

On one March day, a rise from −15° to nearly 50° was recorded.

In the western portions of Europe's *Dcb* (Germany, Poland, southern Sweden), although summers are cool so that the region must be classified as *b,* the winters are not correspondingly severe. The mean January temperatures of Vienna (29°) and Warsaw (26°), for example, are higher than those of many *Dca* regions in eastern Asia and the eastern United States.

Precipitation

Annual amount. Although temperate continental is classed as a humid climate, more of its total area has too little annual precipitation than too much. Since probably more than half the area with *Dc* climate receives an average of 30 in. or less, large parts must be judged subhumid. Apparently this is to be expected in land-controlled climates.

Rainfall decreases from the seaward margins toward the interiors, and usually from the lower toward the higher latitudes as well (see the climatic data). Thus along its interior margins temperate continental climate borders dry climate, and it is these interior parts which are especially subhumid. The prairies, in interior parts of both North America and Eurasia, represent this drier subtype.

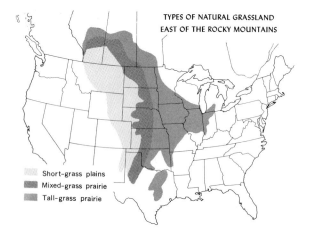

Figure 10.20 Extensive areas in the western parts of the North American temperate continental region are included within what is known as the "prairie wedge." Here the original vegetation was tall-grass prairie, which thrust eastward like a wedge into the humid and forested east central United States. (*After J. Richard Carpenter.*)

In North America the prairie of the temperate continental climates extended eastward in the form of a wedge into humid Illinois and Indiana (Fig. 10.20). This eastward projection of the grasslands into the forest has been interpreted various ways. Some authorities maintain that the humid prairie region was climatically capable of supporting forest, but was prevented from doing so by fires (set both by lightning and by man) which killed the woody plants but not the grass, and by the injurious effects of grazing animals. Others believe that the moist prairie had a climatic origin.[4]

The regional distinctiveness of the "prairie wedge" lies basically in its precipitation characteristics: (1) Low snowfall and low rainfall are typical of winter. (2) In the prairie there is a greater risk of a large rainfall deficit in summer than exists in the forest regions to the north and south. (3) The prairie has fewer days with precipitation, less cloud, and lower relative humidity in July and August

[4] John Borchert, "The Climate of the Central North American Grassland," *Ann. Assoc. Amer. Geographers,* Vol. 40, pp. 1–39, 1950.

than the forested region to the north. (4) Dry summers in the prairie wedge are characterized by large positive departures from average temperatures and by frequent hot winds. These climatic characteristics of the prairie wedge are related to its position in the general circulation pattern over North America, for this region approximately coincides with the greatest mean transport of dry westerly continental air from the eastern base of the Rocky Mountains (Fig. 10.21).

Seasonal distribution.   Although winters are by no means dry, summer is predominantly the season of maximum rainfall (Fig. 10.16). This seasonal distribution is related to the following conditions:

Figure 10.21   Average number of months per year with a mean transport of dry continental air eastward from the eastern base of the Rocky Mountains. One of several explanations offered for the prairie wedge is this greater frequency of dry continental air, resulting in a unique combination of climatic characteristics. (*After Borchert.*)

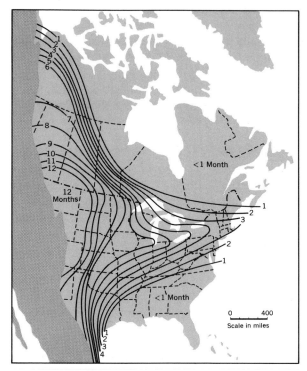

(1) The specific humidity, or reservoir of water vapor in the atmosphere, is much lower over the continents in the winter cold than in the summer heat.

(2) During winter the subsiding air in the continental seasonal anticyclone is likewise conducive to low specific humidity. This subsidence tends to develop a strong temperature inversion and thus to increase the stability of the air mass—a condition which is opposed to precipitation.

(3) Continental anticyclones, which develop over the colder parts of land masses in winter, tend to repel or divert cyclonic storms. The diverging surface winds of these high-pressure cells are opposed to the formation of fronts. Cyclones in summer, although they may be weaker and less frequent, can nevertheless penetrate deeper into the continents.

(4) Convection is at a maximum during the summer months, for the warm land surface has a tendency to make the air masses flowing over it unstable. In winter, on the other hand, the cold snow surface increases low-level stability.

(5) Owing to the seasonal extremes of temperatures, and hence of pressure, seasonal monsoon circulations tend to develop over the large continents. These lead to an inflow of warm, humid tropical maritime air with high rainfall potentialities in summer, and to an outflow of dry, cold polar continental air in winter.

Because of its effect on agricultural productivity, the characteristic summer maximum of rainfall in continental climates is one of the most important facts about the whole climate type. This is especially true where the total amount of precipitation is relatively modest, as it is over extensive areas within *Dc*. In tropical climates, where the *temperature* growing season is 12 months in length, it does not matter much when the maximum precipitation comes, for at any time of year the rainfall will be effective for plant growth. Even in the subtropical parts of middle latitudes—California and Florida, for example—the winters, although they have some frosts, still are so mild that a completely dormant

season for plants is not imposed. Consequently winter rainfall has direct value for crops.

In continental climates, on the other hand, relatively long and severe winters create a completely dormant season for vegetation. There it is essential that the periods of sufficient heat and adequate rainfall coincide, for winter precipitation, much of it in the form of snow, is of no immediate benefit in supplying moisture to plants. A rainfall regime with a winter maximum and summer drought probably is the most efficient one for subhumid subtropical California, but for the upper Mississippi Valley it would be disastrous. A general principle of climatology is that in the middle latitudes, the *distribution of rainfall throughout the year,* or its *regime,* is just as important as the annual *quantity* of rain that falls.

It is especially the deep continental interiors and the regions of marked monsoonal tendencies whose summers are emphatically rainier than winters. At Peking in North China, a station typical of regions with well-developed monsoons, December and January each have only 0.1 in. of precipitation, while July and August have 9 and 6 in., respectively. Throughout North China winters are exceedingly dry (see the climatic data). Omaha, Nebraska, which is typical of an interior regime in North America, has 0.7 in. in January and 4.7 in June. Over much of the United States *east* of the Mississippi, however, the discrepancy between winter and summer precipitation is not so marked (Fig. 10.18). The same is true in most of continental Europe. New York City, which receives 3.3 in. in each of the three winter months, has only slightly more, 4.1 and 4.3 in., in July and August. Its total for the year, however, is 42.5 in. Leningrad, U.S.S.R., has 2.5 and 2.8 in. in July and August but 1.0 and 0.9 in. in January and February.

In spite of a prevailing summer maximum, however, midsummer in extensive areas with continental climate is a period of water deficiency (Fig. 10.22). This is a result of the large evaporation at the time of greatest heat. During July and August pastures and lawns often become sere, and crops suffer from the water deficiency.

Early-summer maximum.   In the more subhumid

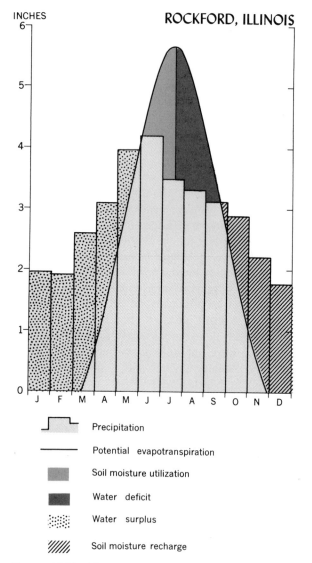

Figure 10.22 The average water balance, based on mean monthly values, at Rockford, Illinois, a temperate continental station with warm summers. Note that for about 4 months in summer, water losses through evapotranspiration exceed the water gained through precipitation. An actual water deficit prevails in late summer. As a consequence crops, pastures, and lawns may suffer. (*Data from Thornthwaite, Mather, and Carter.*)

interior locations the period of maximum rainfall, more often than not, is in early summer or even late spring rather than at the time of greatest heat

(Fig. 10.23). This is the case in the Danube Basin and in the western part of the prairie region of the United States. At Belgrade, Yugoslavia, June is the wettest month, and May has more precipitation than July. At Omaha the maximum amount is also received in June. The fact that rainfall in these areas drops off in July, even though heat and moisture are at a maximum then, appears to be related to the decrease in disturbed weather conditions later in the summer compared with June. In frequency of fronts and cyclonic storms, June resembles spring more than summer. Between June and July the circulation features, including the main storm tracks, shift northward considerably.

Agricultural production benefits from having the year's rainfall relatively concentrated in the early part of the growing season. It is in their tillering period, which is spring and early summer, that cereal crops are developing stems and basal leaves and therefore require the greatest amounts of moisture. The maturing and harvesting season for small grains preferably should be warm, bright, and dry.

Winter precipitation. Winter precipitation is largely frontal and cyclonic in origin. In North America, *mT* air masses moving poleward up the Mississippi Valley are continuously being chilled at their base, so that stability is increased and convectional overturning is unlikely. But usually this air does not advance very far northward before coming into conflict with denser polar air masses, over which it is forced to ascend. Sometimes the front develops even before *mT* reaches the northern

Figure 10.23 An early summer maximum (June) of rainfall characterizes extensive subhumid interior parts of the temperate continental regions.

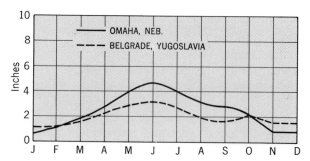

Gulf Coast, and only occasionally does the tropical air advance at the surface farther north than the Great Lakes region.

Even in winter, *mT* air is sufficiently humid that when it is forced up over the colder air it yields moderate amounts of precipitation, which usually falls from a dull, gray overcast that blankets the sky from horizon to horizon. The lively skies of summer with their tumultuous cumulus clouds are largely lacking in winter. In northeastern Asia, with its stronger winter monsoon, the *cP* surges are so frequent that surface *mT* air is practically absent in northern China in the cool months. Winter precipitation in these regions is very meager.

Snow.   Cool-season precipitation in continental climates is partly in the form of snow, and a permanent snow cover, varying from a few weeks to several months in duration, is typical. Because it takes 5 to 15 in. of snow to equal an inch of rain, and because snow tends to remain on the ground while rain does not, the smaller total precipitation of winter may be more impressive than summer's greater amount. Also, the cyclonic winter precipitation is continuous over longer periods of time than the briefer convectional showers of summer.

In those parts of the northeastern United States and Canada where winter cyclones are particularly numerous and well developed (Great Lakes region, St. Lawrence Valley, New England, and the Canadian Maritime Provinces), snow becomes exceedingly deep. Northern New England and New York have more than 7 ft of snowfall during an average winter, and the snow cover remains on the ground for more than 4 months (Fig. 10.24). In parts of the Adirondack Mountains 150 in. or more of snow falls annually. Over the American Great Plains, on the other hand, the total is only 20 to 30 in.

Summer precipitation.   A large proportion of the total summer rain in temperate continental climates is in the form of convectional showers falling from cumulonimbus clouds. These summer showers are less extensive than the rains and snows of winter, are shorter in duration, and are likely to be more intense. Daytime solar heating of the land surface unquestionably encourages convective overturning and hence shower activity. But the majority of the

Figure 10.24   Except in highlands, the snow cover lasts longest in the north central and northeastern parts of the United States. It is almost nonexistent along the Gulf and in the extreme southwest.

summer showers are not haphazardly distributed, and of course they are not a feature of all warm afternoons. Rather, they are organized in their pattern and occur in conjunction with passing atmospheric disturbances of an extensive character.

Unfortunately, these summer showers have certain characteristics that make the warm-season rainfall less effective than its total amount might indicate. Many of them come as pelting rain, so that too much of the water runs off rather than soaking in. Furthermore, they are local and spotty; crops in some localities may be suffering from a water deficiency, while in others they are being injured by an excess. Feast or famine, too much or too little, is a feature all too common. If the 4± in. of rainfall typical of the individual midsummer months in the upper Mississippi Valley could be depended upon, and if this amount were spaced so that about ½ in. fell twice a week as widespread soaking rains, the actual amounts would be adequate for field crops and lawns. But that is not the way nature provides it.

In spite of the fact that the warm season has more total precipitation than winter, it has a smaller proportion of cloud. Thunder and lightning frequently accompany the summer showers. In Hungary, 61 percent of the rain in June comes on days with thunderstorms. Steady cyclonic rains falling from gray, overcast skies are not absent but this type of weather is less common in summer than in the cooler seasons when the polar front is farther equatorward. On the whole, cyclonic weather is most typical of *Dc*'s poleward margins.

Seasonal weather

Strong nonperiodic weather element. No other type of climate has such rapid and marked nonperiodic weather changes in winter as the temperate continental, for it is there that the conflict between polar and tropical air masses reaches its maximum. Actually, spells of weather associated with the passage of cyclonic and anticyclonic storms are equally, if not more, numerous in temperate oceanic climates, but in those locations the accompanying temperature changes are not nearly so severe. In the central and eastern United States, which is freely open to air masses from both north and south, storm control is especially powerful. The weather element is less pronounced in eastern Asia, where an unusually strong winter anticyclone and its monsoon wind system hinders cyclonic development. Greater surface relief in eastern Asia likewise obstructs the free latitudinal movement of air masses. The net result is that the principal tracks of winter cyclones are located over the ocean to the east of Asia, and there is less storm activity over the mainland itself than in North America.

It is in the cold season, when the sun, and with it the storm belt, has retreated farthest south that nonperiodic control of weather is strongest in the continental climates. At that season the diurnal sun control is usually subordinate; weather is dominated by moving cyclones and anticyclones associated with rapidly shifting polar and tropical air masses and the fronts that develop along their boundaries. Many times the daily rise and fall of temperatures with the course of the sun are obscured by larger nonperiodic oscillations resulting from temperature advections by polar and tropical air masses (Figs. 10.17 and 10.19). These sharp temperature changes are made possible by the steep thermal gradients of winter, because of which a north wind brings frigid cold, while a south wind advects unseasonable warmth.

Both cyclones and anticyclones tend to move faster—and to be larger, more frequent, and more severe—in winter than in the warmer seasons. As a consequence, changes in temperature, wind, and weather in general are more severe and more frequent in winter. Since there is a distinct concentration of winter storm tracks over the northeastern United States and adjacent parts of Canada, it is this region which has the most weather changes. With increasing distance from the northeastern region of concentration, both to the south and to the west, storm control weakens and weather changes diminish.

Winter weather types. The usual cycle of weather changes that occur with the passage of a winter cyclone, followed by an anticyclone, has been described in Chapter 6. But there can be an almost infinite number of weather variations in these cycles, depending on the season, the intensity and extensiveness of the storm, the types and characteristics of the air masses and fronts involved, the tracks taken by the storm, and the patterns of high-level atmospheric circulation. As a consequence, so far it has been impossible to work out a satisfactory classification of weather types. However, even the layman is conscious of certain weather types: among the examples mentioned in Chapter 6 were cold waves, warm waves, January thaw, and Indian Summer. But there are many more recognizable although less distinctive ones without names. A number of the commoner weather types are illustrated by the sketches of synoptic conditions in Figs. 10.25 to 10.34. These are worth careful study, for continental climates cannot be understood apart from the weather types which dominate them.

Among the weather types of winter is the *blizzard,* which is so spectacular that it has gained a reputation out of proportion to its climatic importance and frequency. The genuine blizzard is more than just a blinding snowstorm, for it involves a gale wind, below-zero cold, and drifting powdery snow. Actually there may be no precipitation falling at the time; yet the air is filled to a height of several hundred feet with swirling masses of dry, finely pulverized snow whipped up from the freshly fallen snow cover. Sometimes the sun can be dimly seen shining wanly through the shroud of flakes. It is the combination of wind, cold, and blinding snow that makes these storms dangerous to both men and animals caught out in them.

In one notorious blizzard over the northern American Great Plains winds of 50 miles an hour were recorded, accompanied by a temperature of 20° below zero. In this storm between two and three hundred persons are reported to have lost their lives, and thousands of cattle perished. The genuine blizzard is extremely rare in the eastern states. It occurs occasionally in the Middle West but is most truly representative of the western Prairie and Plains states. The blizzard is also found in the prairie lands of Russia and Siberia, where it has the name of *buran.*

On the synoptic chart this weather type is associated with unusually steep pressure gradients in the rapidly advancing forward part of a polar-outbreak high, and hence behind a cold front. The frontal precipitation in the cyclone lays down the necessary new cover of loose, soft snow. The violent northwest winds and rapidly falling temperatures on the rear of the cold front provide the remaining prerequisites.

More frequent and more widespread than the genuine blizzard is the *cold wave,* a typical feature of continental winters, particularly in the North American sector. Not every sharp drop in temperature is a cold wave; the thermometer must fall a certain number of degrees within 24 hr, and it must drop below a certain fixed minimum. In the northernmost United States, the temperature in an authentic winter cold wave must fall at least 20° within 24 hr and must reach zero or below.

This weather type is associated with a rapidly southward-moving polar-outbreak high (Fig. 6.15). It is usually preceded by mild weather with rain or snow—features of the front side of a cyclone. The sharp drop in temperature, which *is* the cold wave, occurs when the wind shifts from a southerly

to a northerly direction, or in other words, when the cold front separating tropical and *cP* air passes. However, the lowest temperatures may not be reached during the period when the strong northwest wind is blowing, but a day or so later, in the calm air near the center of the anticyclone where radiation produces the maximum surface cooling. Anticyclones which take the form of intercyclonic entities and are composed of modified *mP* air may bring fine, clear, crisp weather, but without subzero temperatures (Fig. 10.25).

A deep cyclonic storm, especially if it originates in the general Texas region and takes a course northeastward across the country, will probably bring widespread, and perhaps heavy, snowfall to the temperate continental regions of the Mississippi Valley and eastward (Fig. 10.26). If the cyclone travels a more northerly route, temperatures are likely to be milder and the rain (instead of snow) areas more extensive (Fig. 10.27). A weak low that follows a route north of the Great Lakes may bring

Figure 10.25 Fine, clear winter weather over the central United States associated with a high-pressure system composed mainly of modified *mP* air from the Pacific. Temperatures are for 1:30 A.M.

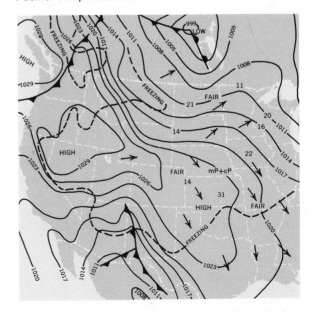

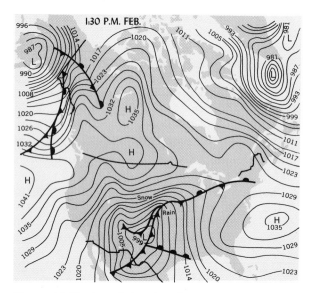

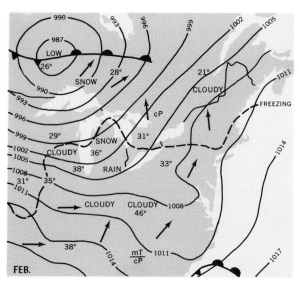

Figure 10.26   A well-developed winter storm originating in the Texas area and moving northeastward across the United States. Such storms are likely to bring heavy precipitation, much of it in the form of snow on the northern side of the storm.

Figure 10.27   A deep and extensive winter storm centered over the upper Great Lakes region. It was accompanied by widespread precipitation, snow to the north and west, and rain to the east and south in the warm sector. Temperatures are for 1:30 A.M.

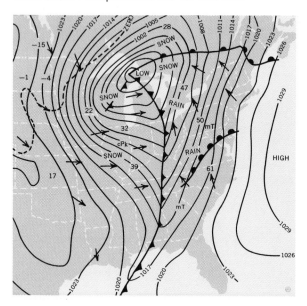

Figure 10.28   A common winter weather type. Here a February cyclone traveling on a northern track is producing cloudy, mild weather and light precipitation over extensive areas of the north central United States. Temperatures shown are for 1:30 A.M.

much gray, overcast, moderate weather, but only modest amounts of rain or snow (Fig. 10.28).

Summer weather types.   Compared with the stronger nonperiodic storm control of winter, summer has greater diurnal regularity of weather (Figs. 10.16 and 10.18). Since the polar-front storm belt swings northward with the sun, the humid continental regions lie on its southern margins. As a result weather becomes more stable and temperatures are likely to be fairly similar over wide areas. Not only are cyclones and anticyclones fewer and weaker, but the normal seasonal temperature gradients are also weak, so that advections from north or south cannot bring such striking changes. Several days in succession with south winds, however, may force maximum temperatures to 90°+ and occasionally even to 100° and over. Diurnal variations in wind velocity and temperature are characteristic. Clouds of the cumulus type and showery rainfall tend to replace winter's sullen gray skies and long-continued spells of precipitation. Summer has some of the aspects of tropical weather.

Cyclones and anticyclones, while both less frequent and weaker in summer, nevertheless serve to break the regularity of sun-controlled weather. Hot waves, frontal thunderstorms, summer cool waves, and drought spells are a few of the more common weather types of the hot season. *Hot waves* or spells of unusually hot weather, with maximum temperatures of over 90° on several successive days, as a rule are caused by long-continued advection of tropical air masses by southerly winds. The arrangement of storm areas on the weather map for such an invasion of tropical air is nearly opposite to that for cold waves. Hot waves occur with northward-sloping barometric gradients, when a relatively stagnant warm high is over the south and southwest, and a weak, slowly moving low, with little cloud, lies to the north (Fig. 10.29).

Cold-front thunderstorms are associated with elongated V-shaped lows in which there is a distinct wind-shift line (Fig. 6.30)). Preceded by days with south winds and high temperatures, the heat wave is broken when the eastward-advancing cold front,

Figure 10.29 A summer weather type in the form of a July heat wave over the central and eastern parts of the country. Temperatures shown are the maxima for the 12 hr preceding. Tropical air from the western end of a warm anticyclone centered over the Gulf of Mexico and the western Caribbean controls the weather.

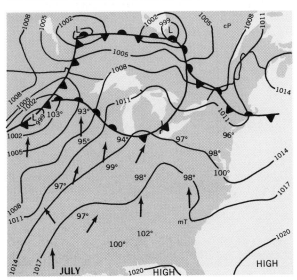

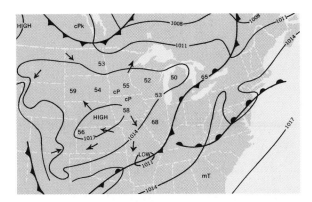

Figure 10.30 A spell of fine cool summer weather (August) produced by a high-pressure system composed of Canadian air. Temperatures are for 1:30 A.M.

with its general turbulence and thunderstorms, is reached, and the wind shifts to northwest. The delightfully cool polar air on the rear of such a storm brings the *summer cool waves* (Fig. 10.30). Many of the summer *drought spells* in the humid continental regions of the United States appear to be associated with the development of a warm anticyclone over the Gulf states. Such a high blocks the normal northward progress of *mT* air and substitutes its own dry subsiding air.

Spring and fall weather. Spring and fall, the transition seasons, exhibit a more even struggle between storm and sun control. At times the one and then the other is in the ascendance, so that there is something of an oscillation between summer and winter conditions. Mild, warm days in April and early May, with regular diurnal rises and falls of the thermometer resembling summer, may be followed by a reestablishment of winter conditions as a passing cyclone lays down a snow cover, and the succeeding polar air mass drops temperatures to an unseasonable freeze. Continental climates are famous for the capriciousness of their spring weather (Figs. 10.31 and 10.32).

Autumn brings some of the loveliest days of the entire year but likewise some of the rawest and gloomiest. Bright, clear weather with warm midday temperatures and crisp, frosty nights comes with polar air-mass control. A reestablishment of hot-

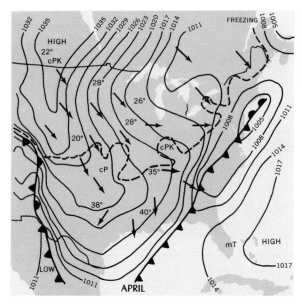

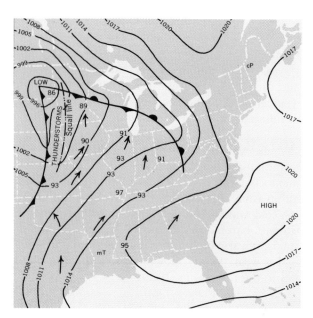

Figure 10.31 A spring weather type. Here a cold anticyclone advancing southward as a mass of cold cP air with northwest winds carries low temperatures deep into the subtropics, causing a severe spring (April) freeze in the north central states. Temperatures shown are for 1:30 A.M.

Figure 10.32 A spring heat wave over the central United States resulting from a northward flow of air from the western flanks of the Bermuda High. This air was drawn into a cyclone centered over the eastern Dakotas. Note the squall line, with thunderstorms, in advance of the cold front. Temperatures are daytime maxima for the preceding 12 hours.

Figure 10.33 Fine, clear, crisp weather in October associated with a cold anticyclone from Canada, composed of cP air. Temperatures are for 1:30 A.M. Isotherm of 32° shown by dashed lines.

Figure 10.34 A deep and extensive autumn cyclone, with steep pressure gradients, accompanied by strong winds and extensive precipitation in the form of rain and snow. Temperatures are for 1:30 A.M. Isotherm of 32° is shown by dashed line.

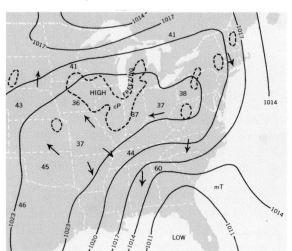

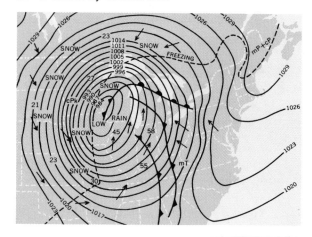

wave gradients in October and November after severe frost, and perhaps even snow, causes a temporary return of summer conditions. This is the warm weather with hazy, smoky atmosphere known as Indian Summer. But well-developed cyclonic storms may also bring raw gray days with chilly rain, and occasionally a temporary snowy winter landscape may be produced as early as October (Figs. 10.33, 10.34).

Regional characteristics

The relative severity of a climate is sometimes expressed by the index of continentality, which denotes the annual amplitude of temperature and is mainly a function of the size of a land mass. It is slightly different also for each latitude, increasing poleward as the amplitude of annual variation of solar radiation increases. The following formula is one of several that have been proposed for computing the index of continentality (C).

$$C = \frac{1.6A}{\sin \phi} - 14$$

where

A = annual temperature amplitude in °C
ϕ = latitude

From the table below it may be noted that Europe has the lowest index of continentality at all three latitudes, and Asia the highest. The continental differentials vary at different latitudes.

Some indexes of continentality

Continent	Latitude		
	68°	50°	40°
Europe	40	38	40
North America	59	53	51
Asia	72	71	60

North America.   Within an extensive area in the upper Mississippi Valley–Great Lakes region, the typical Dc annual march of rainfall is significantly modified. Instead of a single summer maximum, the crest of the annual profile is caved in, so that there is a mid- or late-summer secondary minimum. This results in a twinned summer maximum, with one peak usually in June and the other in September. July and August are drier. The core of the region with a twinned summer maximum is in southern Wisconsin, northern Illinois, and eastern Iowa. In modified form it extends out for several hundred miles around the core.

What requires explanation is not so much the two peaks of rainfall as the secondary minimum in July-August, which produces the two peaks. At least a partial answer is found in the summer circulation aloft. An anticyclonic ridge and its dry northerly tongue of air are positioned over the region in summer, and they reach their maximum development in July-August. The total effect is to depress the rain-making processes in their vicinity. It is the dry current aloft which appears to cause a falling off in the showery precipitation in mid- and late-summer.

If a rainfall profile based on 7-day means is constructed for the period May to October, the simple twinned maximum based on monthly means becomes much more complicated, with numerous ridges and hollows. In this profile there appears to be a moderately good positive correlation between summer wet periods and the combined frequency of warm, stationary, and occluded fronts, and warm sectors. There is also a general inverse correlation between the frequency of highs and the peaks in the 7-day rainfall profile.[5]

Local climatic effects of the Great Lakes, although not so striking as might be expected considering the size of the water surfaces, can be seen in the locally heavy snowfalls along the windward shores. The northern coast of upper Michigan facing Lake Superior, the western shore of lower Michigan fronting on Lake Michigan, peninsular Ontario, and those parts of New York State and Pennsylvania adjacent to Lakes Erie and Ontario, all show an excess of snowfall over that received by surrounding

[5] Trewartha, *The Earth's Problem Climates*, pp. 284–289.

areas farther removed from the lakes. This excess snow along downwind coasts comes in the form of heavy snow showers during periods of rapidly falling temperature and strong northwest winds. At these times a polar-outbreak high is advancing rapidly to the south and east. The cold dry air, warmed and humidified over the open water, is lifted by orographic effects and frictional turbulence when it comes onshore, so that it produces bursts of snow. Normally the lake snow is confined to a narrow strip not more than 20 miles wide inland from a lake.

Annual rainfall profiles within the American temperate continental region change shape from west to east. In the deep interior, rainfall is modest in amount and strongly concentrated in the warmer months, winter being relatively dry. Thus at Omaha, Nebraska, with 29 in. of precipitation, rainfall in the 3 summer months is nearly five times that of the 3 winter months. Of Winnipeg's 20.2 in., the ratio is 3.4 to 1. Eastward there is a gradual increase in the total precipitation and simultaneously winters become relatively wetter, so that the ratio of summer to winter precipitation decreases (Fig. 10.18). Thus the annual rainfall profile gradually flattens toward the east, until along the Atlantic seaboard in New England and Canada some stations actually show a slight winter maximum. There is not much change in total warm-season rainfall; it is the cool-season precipitation that increases eastward, both relatively and absolutely. This rise in winter precipitation toward the Atlantic is related to the increasing humidity caused by proximity to the ocean and also to the fact that winter storm tracks tend to converge in the Lower Great Lakes–New England area.

Europe. The European sector of temperate continental climate is the exception in location, for it is found to the west, or windward, of the dry interior. On the west it borders the temperate oceanic type, while the Asiatic and North American sectors on that side are terminated by severe dry climates. As noted earlier, Europe's Dc is also located 5 to 10°

farther poleward than those of the other two continents.

Because of its location windward from the continent's core, the European sector has temperature features somewhat unlike those in Asia and North America. In fact, it is difficult to find stations in Europe whose summer and winter temperatures both match those of stations in the other two continents. If they are similar in either the cold season or the warm season, they are different in the other, for the amplitude of the annual temperature curve is smaller in Europe. For example, Berlin and Duluth, Minnesota, have similar July temperatures (64° and 65°), but their January means (Berlin 31° and Duluth 9°) are far apart.

Temperate continental Europe also has a relatively modest amount of annual precipitation: nearly all of it under 25 in., and considerable areas under 20. This feature was discussed in an earlier section on temperate oceanic climate in western Europe. In addition to the reasons given there, it may be noted that much of the Dc in Soviet Russia is bordered on its south side by dry climate, so that drought-making controls are always close at hand.

Asia. Asia's leeward location on the largest continent and its remarkably well-developed monsoon circulation provide the necessary controls to produce unusually severe seasonal temperatures, large annual ranges, and a modest precipitation strongly concentrated in summer. Winters are very dry. Insular Japan and peninsular Korea do not fit this description so well, although their temperatures are still continental. For any selected latitude, Japan's seasonal temperatures closely match those of the eastern United States, yet they are less extreme than those in mainland Asia. Also, rainfall is much heavier in Japan and is less summer-concentrated. Most of mainland China's temperate continental climate on lowlands is so deficient in annual rainfall that a large part of the region is marginal between humid and dry climates. Dry climate may actually reach down to tidewater on the great Huang Plain.

SELECTED REFERENCES FOR FURTHER STUDY OF TOPICS IN CHAPTER TEN

Bailey, Harry P., "Toward a Unified Concept of the Temperate Climate," *Geog. Rev.*, Vol. 54, pp. 516–545, 1964.

Barry, R. G., "Aspects of the Synoptic Climatology of Central South England," *Meteorol. Mag.*, Vol. 92, pp. 300–308, 1963.

Borchert, John, "The Climate of the Central North American Grassland," *Ann. Assoc. Amer. Geographers*, Vol. 40, pp. 1–39, 1950.

Brooks, C. E. P., *The English Climate*, English Universities Press, London, 1954.

Brunnschweiler, Dieter H., "The Geographic Distribution of Air Masses in North America," *Vierteljahrschr. Naturforch. Ges.*, Zürich, Vol. 97, pp. 42–49, 1952.

Bryson, Reid A., and James F. Lahey, *The March of the Seasons*, Department of Meteorology, The University of Wisconsin, Madison, Wis., 1958.

Gregory, Stanley, "Climatic Classification and Climatic Change," *Erdkunde*, Vol. 8, pp. 246–252, 1954.

Horn, Lyle H., Reid A. Bryson, and William P. Lowry, *An Objective Precipitation Climatology of the United States*, Sci. Repts. 6, The University of Wisconsin, Department of Meteorology, Madison, Wis., 1957.

Kendall, Henry M., "Notes on Climatic Boundaries in the Eastern United States," *Geog. Rev.*, Vol. 25, no. 1, pp. 117–124, 1935.

Kimble, George H. T., *Our American Weather*, McGraw-Hill Book Company, New York, 1955.

Lamb, H. H., "British Weather around the Year," *Weather*, Vol. 8, pp. 131–136, 176–182, 1953.

Manley, Gordon, "The Effective Rate of Altitudinal Temperature Change in Temperate Atlantic Climates," *Geog. Rev.*, Vol. 34, pp. 408–417, 1945.

———, *Climate and the British Scene*, Collins, London, 1952.

Rex, Daniel F., "The Effect of Atlantic Blocking Action upon European Climate," *Tellus*, Vol. 3, pp. 100–111, 1951.

Schroeder, Mark J., "Maritime Air Invasion of the Pacific Coast: A Problem Analysis," *Bull. Amer. Meteorol. Soc.*, Vol. 48, pp. 802–808, 1967.

Trewartha, Glenn T., *The Earth's Problem Climates*, The University of Wisconsin Press, Madison, Wis., 1961, pp. 203–222, 267–306.

Villmow, Jack Richard, "Daily Weather Maps as Illustrations of Weather Types," *Ohio J. Sci.*, Vol. 58, no. 6, pp. 335–342, 1958.

Wahl, Eberhard W., "The January Thaw in New England: An Example of a Weather Singularity," *Bull. Amer. Meteorol. Soc.*, Vol. 33, no. 9, pp. 380–386, 1952.

Wallén, C. C., "Climate," in Axel Somme (ed.), *The Geography of Norden*, J.W. Cappelens Forlag, Oslo, 1960, pp. 41–53.

CHAPTER ELEVEN

BOREAL (E), POLAR (F), AND HIGHLAND CLIMATES (H)

This chapter treats three different climates whose common feature is the prevalence of cold. In all three, cold is the main obstacle to large-scale settlement and agricultural development. In them all, especially in boreal and polar climates but in many high-altitude regions as well, human population is exceedingly sparse or even completely absent in large areas.

BOREAL CLIMATE (*E*)
(Subarctic)

Type location.   Boreal climate has many features in common with temperate continental, except that it is characterized by greater severity because of its location farther poleward. Still, the differences are of degree rather than kind, for both are continental in character. Boreal represents the archetype of continentality, for no other climate has such large annual ranges of temperature. Indeed, climatic rigor is so great that cereal crops cannot be grown except in a few favored locations.

Boreal, or subarctic, climate is found only in the higher middle latitudes (50 or 55° to 65 or 70°) on the two great Northern Hemisphere continents. On its poleward side it ordinarily grades into tundra, one of the polar climates (compare Fig. 7.2 with the climate map inside the front cover). This northern boundary is approximately the isotherm of 50° for the warmest month (usually July), which coincides fairly well with the poleward limit of tree growth. In the tundra beyond the July isotherm of 50°, lowly vegetation forms, such as mosses, lichens, and bushes, predominate.

On its southern margins boreal climate usually adjoins the cool-summer phase of temperate continental climate, where the boundary is the isoline of 4 months with an average temperature of 50° or above. In some parts, middle-latitude dry climate lies adjacent to boreal on the south. The Russians have given the name *taiga* to the subarctic lands of Eurasia with their extensive coniferous forests, and this term has come to be applied not only to the comparable region in North America, but also to the type of climate that both of them possess. Thus boreal and taiga are to a large degree regionally synonymous.

The Eurasian subarctic area extends from Sweden and Finland in Europe across the whole of the continent to the coast of Siberia. It widens toward the Pacific, or leeward, side as continentality increases. In North America the boreal region stretches from Alaska on the Pacific across Canada to Labrador and Newfoundland on the Atlantic. The boreal regions of both North America and Eurasia are portions of the general high-latitude source regions for polar air masses which so greatly influence weather conditions farther south.

Temperature

Summer. Long, bitterly cold winters, very short and cool summers, and brief springs and autumns are characteristic (Figs. 11.1 and 11.2). Since the isotherm of 50° for the warmest month has been accepted as the poleward boundary of this type of climate, at least 1 month must have an average temperature of 50° or above. Yakutsk, Siberia, which

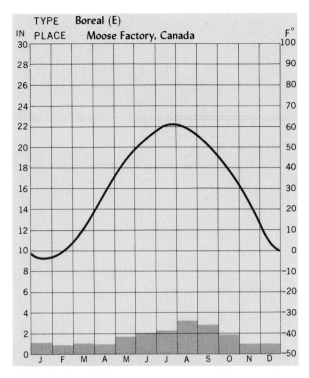

Figure 11.1 Cool summers, severe winters, large annual ranges of temperature, and modest precipitation, usually concentrated in summer, are characteristic of boreal (subarctic) climate. A marginal station.

at nearly 62°N represents the extreme in subarctic climates, has an average temperature in July, the warmest month, as high as 66°. This is 2 or 3° higher than the same month at London or Berlin and 9° higher than July at San Francisco, a subtropical station. Midsummer daily maxima of 80° are common at Yakutsk, and the thermometer occasionally reaches 90°. The absolute maximum is 102°. But at the same station, June and August have mean temperatures of only 59°, so summer is distinctly on the cool side.

Summer's briefness is even more striking than its coolness, however. At Yakutsk, there are only 3 months in which the mean temperatures exceed 50°, for both May and September have averages in the low forties. Another representative boreal station, Fort Vermilion, at 58°27′N in Canada, has a cooler July than Yakutsk's, with an average tem-

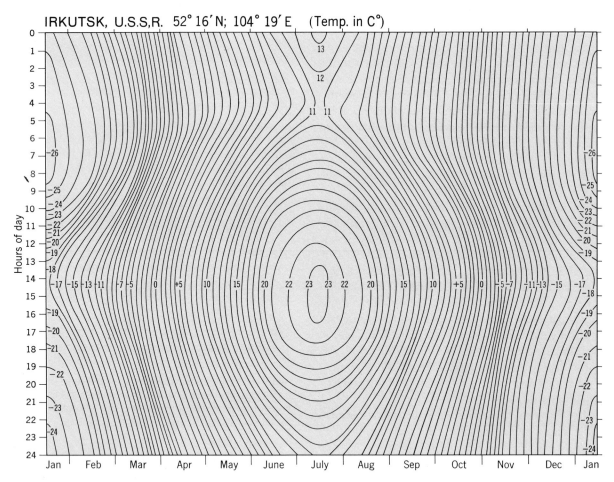

Figure 11.2 Thermoisopleths for a boreal station deep in the interior of subarctic Eurasia. The annual range of temperature is remarkably large; the diurnal range is much smaller. The pattern is that of a strongly continental climate. (*After Troll.*)

perature of only 60°. June and August average 55 and 59°, respectively. The mean of the daily maxima in July is 74°, and of the minima, 46°. Temperatures over 90° have been recorded at Fort Vermilion in both June and July. If they are sunny, subarctic summer days may be pleasantly warm and occasionally even hot (Fig. 11.3).

Another striking temperature feature of boreal climate is the small daily range in summer (and winter as well) compared with the annual range. This just reverses the situation in the humid tropics.

At Irkutsk in the U.S.S.R., where the annual range is 70°, the daily range in midsummer is only 21° (average July maximum is 73°, minimum is 52°). Such a small range is not surprising, since the hours of darkness are so few (Fig. 11.2).

Long summer days. Thus the unusually long summer days in these higher latitudes compensate somewhat for the brief and cool summers. Although the intensity of sunlight is not so great, the large number of hours during which the sun shines is an offsetting factor. Moreover, the short nights do not

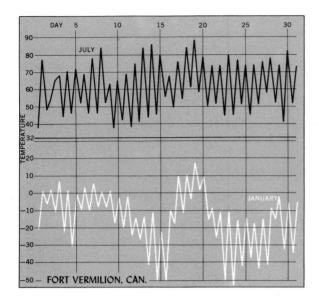

Figure 11.3 A boreal station in Canada. Note the unusually strong nonperiodic air-mass control of temperature changes in winter. Summer shows somewhat greater diurnal regularity.

permit a long period of cooling. At latitude 55°N, June days average 17.3 hr of possible sunshine; at latitude 60°N, 18.8 hr; and at latitude 65°N, 22.1 hr. Moreover, since there is still twilight when the sun is as much as 18° below the horizon, it is evident that in summer the hours of genuine darkness are few indeed. At the time of the summer solstice in the more northerly portions of the subarctic lands, one can read a paper outdoors even at midnight. Because of the long daylight period at this solstice, average daily possible receipts of solar radiation at latitude 60°N are almost equal to those at the equator.

Growing season. Unfortunately, the boreal lands have very short periods that are entirely without freeze. The growing season in the Mackenzie Valley of Canada varies from about 50 to 75 days, and many stations must expect freezing temperatures in July and August in at least half the years. A shift of wind to the north at any time brings with it the chill of the ice-laden Arctic. Thus although it is the occasional midwinter freeze which is dan-

gerous in subtropical climates, it is the midsummer freeze which damages crops in this boreal type. The coolness, shortness, and precariousness of the growing season in subarctic lands are the most serious handicaps to their agricultural development. Indeed, these are the chief disadvantages that have retarded permanent settlement. At present much of the subarctic either is totally unoccupied, or has a meager sprinkling of frontier farmers and people engaged in exploiting mineral, forest, and wild-animal resources.

Winter.   Winter follows summer with only a fleeting autumn season. Frosts may arrive in late August; ice begins to form on pools in September. By the middle of October, navigation of small craft has become difficult on the subarctic lakes of Canada. At Verkhoyansk, Siberia, the mean temperature drops 39° from October to November. Subarctic Siberia holds the world records for minimum temperatures at low elevations, for they are even lower than those of polar climates. Oimekon in the northeastern part has an average January temperature of −60°, and −90° has been recorded. This same station has an average January minimum of −85° and an average maximum of −26°. In July, the warmest month, the average minimum is only 24°, which indicates that there are some freezing temperatures; the average maximum is 90.5°. This, of course, represents an extreme case. At Yakutsk, however, where July has an average temperature of 66°, the January mean drops to approximately −46°, producing an annual range of 112°. For 7 months at Yakutsk the average temperatures are below freezing, and during 5 months they are below zero. No other type of climate can show such contrasts between summer and winter temperatures. Still, notice that it is the excessively cold winters, rather than any temperature peculiarity of the summers, which cause these much greater mean annual ranges of temperature in the taiga, as compared with those in temperate continental climates. If annual temperature curves for stations in continental and boreal climates are superimposed, the July portions are not markedly different; it is the bottoms,

Climatic data for representative boreal stations (*E*)

	J	F	M	A	M	J	J	A	S	O	N	D	Yr	Range
Fort Vermilion, Alberta, Canada (58° 27′N)														
Temp., °F	−14	−6	8	30	47	55	60	57	46	32	10	−4	26.7	74.3
Precip., in.	0.6	0.3	0.5	0.7	1.0	1.9	2.1	2.1	1.4	0.7	0.5	0.4	12.3	
Moose Factory, Ontario, Canada (51° 16′N) Marginal														
Temp., °F	−4	−2	10	28	42	54	61	59	51	39	22	5	30.4	65.6
Precip., in.	1.3	0.9	1.1	1.0	1.8	2.2	2.4	3.3	2.9	1.8	1.1	1.2	21.0	
Yakutsk, Siberia, U.S.S.R. (62° 13′N)														
Temp., °F	−46	−35	−10	16	41	59	66	60	42	16	−21	−41	12	112
Precip., in.	0.9	0.2	0.4	0.6	1.1	2.1	1.7	2.6	1.2	1.4	0.6	0.9	13.7	
Archangel, U.S.S.R. (54° 25′N)														
Temp., °F	8	9	18	30	41	53	60	56	46	34	22	12	33	52
Precip., in.	0.9	0.7	0.8	0.7	1.2	1.8	2.4	2.4	2.2	1.6	1.2	0.9	16.8	

or winter parts, of the curves that are much farther apart because of the colder boreal winters. Nevertheless, the smaller differences in summer temperatures between temperate continental and boreal climates are much more significant as far as agricultural land use is concerned. A July average of 60° as compared with 75° has far greater economic consequences than January averages that differ two or three times as much—provided, of course, the January averages are below freezing anyway.

Concerning the boreal Siberian winter, the early German climatologist Julius Hann wrote:

It is not possible to describe the terrible cold one has to endure; one has to experience it to appreciate it. The quicksilver freezes solid and can be cut and hammered like lead; iron becomes brittle, and the hatchet breaks like glass; wood, depending upon the degree of moisture in it, becomes harder than iron and withstands the ax so that only completely dry wood can be split. Every step in the dry snow can be heard for long distances; the bursting of the ice cover and the frozen ground sound like the cannonading of distant batteries.

The winter temperatures of northeastern Siberia, though bitter, are not impossible to bear, for air movement is usually slight, skies are clear, and, since absolute humidity is very low, the air is physiologically dry. For example, when −20° air with a

relative humidity of 80 percent comes in contact with the human body and is heated to 60°, the relative humidity falls to nearly 2 percent.

Boreal winters in North America are not quite so severe as those in Siberia. This is partly because Asia is a broader land mass. In addition, however, the mountains of eastern Siberia tend to dam up the outflow of cold winter air toward the Pacific. This contributes to the excessive accumulation of *cP* air over Asia, an accumulation which in turn produces the great continental anticyclone. No such blocking effect is possible in less mountainous eastern Canada, so that such representative stations as Moose Factory, Dawson, and Fort Good Hope show average January temperatures of −4, −22, and −32°, respectively. Annual ranges at these stations are 66, 82, and 93°. At Dawson in the Yukon at 64°3′N, the thermometer on an average January night falls to approximately −29° and rises to nearly −16° during the warmest hours of the day (Fig. 11.3). During the 3 winter months at this station, the average of the daily maxima does not reach zero. The lowest temperature ever recorded is −64°.

The extreme and long-continued cold of boreal winters causes large parts of these regions to be permanently frozen down to great depths (Fig. 11.4). Over extensive areas of the subarctic lands only the upper few feet thaw out during the short summers.

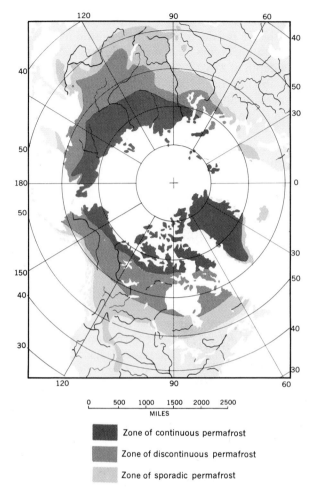

0   500 1000 1500 2000 2500
MILES

■ Zone of continuous permafrost

▨ Zone of discontinuous permafrost

░ Zone of sporadic permafrost

Figure 11.4 Distribution of permafrost in the Northern Hemisphere. Continuous permafrost characterizes large parts of the Eurasian subarctic; it is discontinuous in the North American sector. (*After Robert Black.*)

Just as long days are characteristic of boreal summers, so long nights are a feature of the winters. For example, on December 21 all places on the 60°N parallel can receive a maximum of only 5.7 hr of sunshine, while at latitude 65°N the maximum is only 3.3 hr. These long daily periods of darkness are not only dismal and wearisome, but they are in considerable measure responsible for the low winter temperatures.

As in midsummer, so in midwinter, the daily range of temperature is small. At Irkutsk, where the

annual range is 70°, the January diurnal range is only 15°. This reflects the long daily period of darkness and very short day, with a weak sun positioned not far above the horizon.

Spring, like autumn, is a short and inconspicuous season. At Yakutsk there is a difference of 25° between the mean temperatures of April and May, and 18° between May and June. The average April temperature at Yakutsk is like that of Madison, Wisconsin, in January, while May is only 4 to 5° lower than April at Madison.

Precipitation

Annual amount. Annual precipitation in boreal climates is usually meager (see Fig. 11.1 and the rainfall map inside the back cover). Over much of the Siberian taiga it is no more than 15 in., while most of subarctic Canada receives less than 20, and parts of it less than 15, in. In both Eurasia and North America the oceanic margins are the principal areas where rainfall exceeds 20 in. In most middle-latitude climates these small amounts would cause the region to be classed as semiarid, but where such low temperatures and therefore low evaporation rates prevail, and where the ground is frozen so much of the year, the precipitation is sufficient for forest growth. The relatively modest annual precipitation is related to the prevailing low temperatures and correspondingly low specific humidity, a strong continental winter anticyclone with settling air and diverging winds, and the great breadth of the land masses in these subarctic latitudes.

Seasonal distribution. Precipitation is concentrated in the warmer months, a feature typical of strong continentality (Fig. 11.1). Thus although the total amounts are small, they are adequate in most years for whatever meager cropping is carried out. At Yakutsk, where the total annual rainfall is 13.7 in., August is the wettest month with 2.6 in., and February the driest with 0.2 in. At Dawson in the Yukon the total is 12.5 in., with 1.5 in July and 0.8 in January (0.7 in. in February and 0.5 in March). Winter—with low temperatures, low specific humidity, strong anticyclone with settling air, and seaward-moving winds—presents a situation that is antagonistic to precipitation. Over east central Siberia winters are especially dry; the 3 winter months have only 10 percent of the annual precipitation, while the 3 summer months have 58 percent. This is the region of most intense cold and strongest anticyclonic control.

Because of the prevalence of anticyclones, winters over the more interior and continental portions of boreal lands are likely to have much bright, clear weather. East central Siberia is especially cloudless. Summers there are more cloudy than winters, the average being less than $3/10$ in winter but almost $7/10$ in August. In its prevailing clear skies northeastern Siberia resembles Italy; in winter it has almost as little cloud as some deserts. Hann writes, "The air in these high latitudes is remarkably clear, the color of the sky is a blue-violet, like the dress of the Sistine Madonna; sounds can be heard for long distances, so that one can hear the bark of a dog 20 km away." The meager cloud cover during long winter nights is an additional factor contributing to low temperatures.

Over eastern interior Canada in subarctic latitudes, cloudiness is not far from $5/10$ in both winter and summer. Winter days often are cloudy even when there is no precipitation, for considerable low stratus cloud and ground fog occur during that season.

Winter precipitation. Over lowlands the winter precipitation, practically all of it in the form of snow, is frontal in origin. The prevalence of the strong continental anticyclone tends to suppress cyclogenesis and to repel moving cyclones from outside, so that snow-bearing storms are usually forced to follow the southern margins of boreal regions rather than traveling directly across their centers. Over the center of North America, for example, the principal winter storm tracks loop well southward.

The fact that principal winter cyclonic tracks tend to avoid the centers of boreal regions helps to explain the meager winter precipitation. But the few fronts that do cross these areas commonly yield enough relatively dry, hard snow to form a perma-

nent snow cover lasting 5 to 7 months. Because of the shelter provided by the forest, little melting or evaporation occurs, so that winter snows accumulate to a depth of 2 to 3 ft in the taiga. The forest protection also retards melting of the snow cover in spring. In parts of Siberia, however, winter precipitation is so meager that sleighing is sometimes difficult. Strong winter winds blowing the snow and thus producing blizzard-like weather are not so characteristic of the forested taiga as they are of the open prairies to the south and the treeless tundra to the north.

Summer precipitation. Summer, the season of maximum surface heating, steepest vertical temperature gradients, and highest specific humidity, provides conditions that are relatively more favorable for rainfall than those of winter. Summer rain, like winter snow, is largely frontal in origin. Thunderstorms are not common; the total number in the Mackenzie Valley of Canada, for example, is only about 5 to 10 a year. Fort Vermilion in the Mackenzie Valley has an average of 5.3 rain-days in June, 9.1 in July, and 7.5 in August. Comparable data for Dawson in the Yukon are 11.7, 10.3, and 10.9.

Seasonal weather

The nonperiodic weather element is generally less marked in boreal lands than in the temperate continental climates farther south, where the alternation of well-developed cyclones and anticyclones is more frequent. Still, weather in the taiga varies greatly between different parts. As a rule, it is in regions closest to the sea that cyclonic control is strongest.

Winter in the taiga has much anticyclonic weather with settling air and light-to-moderate winds. The greater the continentality and the stronger the winter anticyclone, the clearer, drier, and colder the weather. Occasional cyclones bring gray skies with hard, dry, blowing snow. Cyclones are often more numerous in the short transition seasons than in the dead of winter, for in winter the subarctic lands are included within the source regions of those great masses of cold anticyclonic air which periodically surge equatorward, affecting even the lower middle latitudes. *Summer* weather is also rather settled, although cyclones make themselves felt in occasional rains and in the advection of warm and cold air masses. A strong invasion of *cP* air from higher latitudes can cause freezing temperatures even in midsummer. Hot waves are rare but not unknown.

Regional characteristics

North America. As far as weather is concerned, the American boreal region may be divided into a somewhat quieter and drier west and an appreciably more stormy east. Of the two main routes of cyclones, one from the Pacific and the other from the interior of the continent farther south, only the first group affects the region west of the 100th or 105th meridian. Moreover, the cyclones from the Pacific which have crossed the western mountains are weak and relatively inefficient as rain producers.

The somewhat stormier and wetter east is subject to both the regenerated Pacific cyclones and those from the interior. Moreover, these disturbances are operating in air that has a higher humidity content. As a result, winter weather in eastern subarctic Canada is more disturbed, with gales, heavier snowfall, and high wind chill. All the eastern half has over 10 in. of annual precipitation, and the part east of Hudson Bay has 20 to 40 in.

A common feature of boreal localities situated along the windward side of open water is a fall maximum of precipitation in the cold months. This is the case along the western or windward side of the Labrador Peninsula facing Hudson Bay. There subzero arctic air from the northwest, accompanying polar-outbreak anticyclones, is warmed and humidified over the open water of the bay in fall and early winter. Instability snow showers from dense cumulus clouds drop heavy snows on the windward shores. These effects disappear later in the winter, when the areas of open water shrink greatly or even disappear.

Eurasia. The Eurasian boreal climate somewhat reverses the weather and rainfall patterns of the North American sector. It is the western parts of Eurasia that are more humid and less severe in temperature, for since there are no high mountains the influence of Atlantic air masses is significant. It is the center and east that are most severe as well as drier, particularly in winter. The Pacific coast, however, is distinguished by its cloudy, cool summer, with much fog and drizzle. Winters there are less cold than west of the mountains. A noteworthy feature of the Eurasian boreal sector, as can be seen on the climate map inside the front cover, is its increasing latitudinal spread toward the east, a spread which parallels a similar increase in continentality.

POLAR CLIMATES (*F*)

Just as the tropics are characterized by the absence of a cool season, so the polar regions lack a period of warmth. Monotonous heat prevails in the low latitudes; enduring cold typifies the high. The polar areas cannot be made to appear warm by noting that there have been occasional days with temperatures over 80° beyond the Arctic Circle. The rare warm day does not determine the general climatic character of a region.

Phenomena of light and darkness. For 6 months at the poles, the sun is out of sight entirely. For another 6 it is constantly above the horizon, although it is never very high, so that solar radiation is weak. At the Arctic and Antarctic Circles, which lie near the equatorward margins of polar climates, the daily period of sunlight varies from 24 hr at the time of the summer solstice to zero hr at the winter solstice. At points between the poles and the 66½° parallels, the lengths of the periods of sunlight, and absence of sunlight, are intermediate between the two extremes.

These peculiarities of daylight and darkness introduce new conceptions of certain climatic phenomena. Diurnal range is bound to be small in a region that may have continuous day or continuous night, so that this measure loses some of its significance. The annual march of temperature also has a different meaning in the altered context. At the North Pole, for instance, there is no incoming direct solar radiation for a period of 6 months. Loss of heat by terrestrial radiation goes on continuously, however, so that a minimum temperature is usually reached a month or so before the spring equinox.

Type locations and boundaries.   Polar climates are mostly confined to the high latitudes of the earth. Somewhat similar conditions can be found at high altitudes in a great variety of latitudes, but usually these regions are very isolated and fragmentary, and in this book they are included within the group designated as highland climates (see Fig. 7.2 and the climate map).

In the classification of climates used here, the boundary of polar climates is the same as the one chosen by Köppen: the mean temperature of 50° for the warmest month. Thus in polar climates the average temperature of all months is below 50°. The 50° warmest-month isotherm is considered to correspond fairly well with the poleward limit of tree growth in all but a few highly marine locations. Scientists have not yet determined whether this temperature value is the active climatic control limiting tree growth, or simply a coincidence. It is significant that while a cool-month isotherm is often used to bound the tropics, a warm-month isotherm serves the same purpose for polar climates. This suggests that while a period of coolness is of great importance in influencing the type of plant life in the low latitudes, a period of warmth is likely to be the crucial element in high latitudes.

In the Northern Hemisphere, the July isotherm of 50° swings well poleward of the Arctic Circle over most of Asia and Alaska, coincides reasonably well with it over lowland Europe, and lies to the south of it over much of eastern North America and Greenland. Large inland bodies of water, the cool Labrador Current, and the Greenland icecap cause summers in eastern North America and Greenland to be distinctly cooler than in Asia. In the Southern Hemisphere, the only extensive land area with polar climates is ice-covered Antarctica. North of the equator, it is the Arctic Sea borderlands of Eurasia and North America, extensive island groups north of both continents, and ice-covered Greenland which are classified as F regions. In both hemispheres the lands with polar climates are important source regions for the polar air masses which so powerfully affect the weather of middle latitudes.

The Arctic and Antarctic serve the same thermodynamic function of maintaining the earth's latitudinal heat balance. Vast quantities of heat are transported by atmospheric and oceanic circulations from low latitudes to the polar regions, where it is dissipated to space in the form of long-wave radiation. In polar regions where the water vapor content is low, as it is over Antarctica, which has only about one-tenth the atmospheric moisture that the middle latitudes do, the escape of long-wave earth radiation is very rapid. It is less rapid in the Arctic, where the air's moisture content is somewhat higher.

The Antarctic is essentially a seagirt land which takes the form of a high ice plateau. By contrast, the Arctic is almost a landlocked frozen sea, whose marginal lands are mainly lowlands in Eurasia and North America, though they also include the high ice plateau of Greenland. Naturally the different configurations of the two polar regions result in important climatic differences between them. Because its single land mass is centered near the pole and surrounded on all sides by extensive oceans with uniform temperatures, the Antarctic shows much greater uniformity and simplicity in its climate than the more complex Arctic. Pressure and wind systems are symmetrically developed about the South Pole, so that Antarctica is dominated by a strongly zonal circulation, and there is only modest change in these elements throughout the year. The Arctic has far less symmetry, and greater seasonal variation, in pressure and winds, and also a stronger meridional component in the circulation. It is characterized by more frequent sporadic outbreaks of polar air toward lower latitudes.

Mean Arctic sea-level pressure in January is dominated by four great cells: two continental highs (Siberia and northwestern North America), and two oceanic lows (Iceland and Aleutian). It is noteworthy that there is no Arctic high as such on the mean winter map. In July, a continuous ring of low pressure encircles the ice-covered polar sea. Over the pack ice, pressure is nearly flat. Like winter, summer has no Arctic high. Because of the asymmetry and eccentricity of the sea-level pressure field, polar easterlies are not well defined. Moving disturbances, both cyclones and anticyclones, are numerous at all seasons and penetrate all parts of the Arctic. Many cyclones enter from outside. Because of the great synoptic activity, mean pressure and circulation patterns are not very useful in a description of the climate; irregular weather occurrences are the rule. As a consequence there is a high degree of interdiurnal temperature variability. Along the margins of open water, such variability may be associated with advection; over the inner-core frozen area, it is largely due to changes in wind and cloud and their effects on the prevailing surface temperature inversion.

Temperature and precipitation. Polar climates have the distinction of producing the lowest *mean annual,* as well as the lowest *summer,* temperatures for any part of the earth (Figs. 11.5 and 11.6). Temperatures remain low in spite of the long days of summer, for the sun's rays are too oblique to be genuinely effective. Moreover, much of the solar energy is either reflected by the snow and ice or consumed in melting the snow cover and evaporating the meltwater, so that neither the land surface nor the air adjacent to it becomes warm. Winters are bitterly cold, rivaling the severest in boreal regions. In spite of the cool summers, winter cold is so extreme that annual ranges are large. One of the most conspicuous features of polar climates is the intense low-level temperature inversions. In the

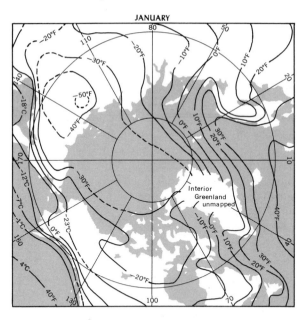

Figure 11.5 Mean daily surface temperature of the Arctic region for January. (*After Hare and Orvig.*)

Figure 11.6 Mean daily surface temperature of the Arctic region for July. (*After Hare and Orvig.*)

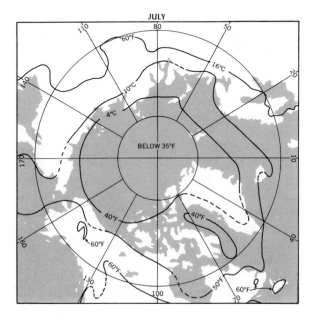

Arctic these are less common in summer than in winter.

Precipitation is meager throughout the very high latitudes: less than 10 in. over large parts of the land areas. But in spite of its meagerness, the low evaporation permits some runoff, part of it in the form of glaciers. Because of the low evaporation and the small amount of melting, great permanent snow and ice fields several thousand feet thick have accumulated on Greenland and the Antarctic continent. The scantiness of polar precipitation is not surprising in view of the low specific humidity which must accompany the low temperatures. The reservoir of water vapor is small at all times. Moreover, in these latitudes there is a general settling of the cold upper-air masses, a process which stabilizes the atmosphere and creates conditions unfavorable to condensation. Precipitation is usually heavier in the warmer months, when the air's moisture content is most abundant.

Tundra and icecap climates.   Polar climates are subdivided here into two types, with the *warmest-month* isotherm of 32°F (0°C) serving as the boundary between them. Where the average temperatures of all months are below freezing, the growth of vegetation is impossible, and a permanent snow-and-ice cover prevails. These are the *icecap climates.* Where one or more of the warm-season months has an average temperature above 32° (but not over 50°), so that the ground is free from snow for a short period and a sparse and lowly vegetation cover is possible, the climate is designated as *tundra.*

TUNDRA CLIMATE (*Ft*)

Type location.   Tundra climate is transitional between the icecap, or region of perpetual snow and ice, on the one hand, and middle-latitude climates, usually boreal, on the other (see Fig. 7.2 and the climate map). Its accepted equatorward and poleward boundaries are the warmest-month isotherms of 50 and 32°, respectively—which, as mentioned above, approximately coincide with important vegetation boundaries.

The isotherm of 50° for the warmest month seems a fairly satisfactory boundary for tundra climate in continental regions. However, in a few strongly marine areas (the Aleutian Islands, part of Iceland, and the southernmost tip of South America), the consistently cool (below 50°) but mild year-round climate permits tree growth in locations that are protected from strong winds. If it is desired to eliminate such minor areas, the definition can be expanded to include the further requirement that the coldest winter month must have a mean temperature of 20° or lower, so that the mean annual range will be over 30°.[1]

Tundra climate on land areas is almost exclusively confined to the Northern Hemisphere. In the Antarctic, open ocean occupies the latitudes where tundra would normally develop. Only some of the most northerly fringes of the Antarctic continent, the southernmost tip of South America, and certain small Antarctic islands might be included. The most extensive tundra areas are the Arctic Sea rimlands of both North America and Eurasia. Most of North America's Arctic archipelago, as well as the coastal fringe of Greenland, is likewise included. According to definition, the ice-covered Arctic Sea must also be classed as having a tundra climate, since the inner pack ice is uniformly cold, with a surface temperature of about 34°.

Temperature

Summer.   Since the land area occupied by marine tundra climate is negligible, it can be said that continentality in temperature characteristics is a distinguishing feature of almost all tundra regions. Long, bitterly cold winters and short, cool summers are the rule (Figs. 11.7 and 11.8). By the definition given

[1] James A. Shear, "The Polar Marine Climate," *Ann. Assoc. Amer. Geographers,* Vol. 54, pp. 310–317, September, 1964.

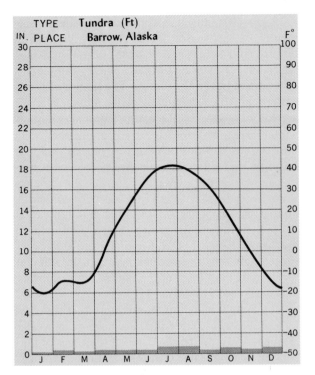

Figure 11.7 A tundra station of the severe continental type. Large annual range of temperature and meager annual precipitation are characteristic.

for tundra climate boundaries, the average temperature of the warmest month can be no lower than 32° and no higher than 50°.

Raw and chilly, the warmest months of the tundra resemble March and April in southern Wisconsin and January in the American Cotton Belt. Usually only 2 to 4 months have average temperatures above freezing, and killing frost is likely to occur at any time. Summer cool waves in middle latitudes are associated with air masses moving southward from the tundra and boreal source regions. Along coasts, where water, ice, and land are in close proximity, fogs are very common. These fogs may last for days at a time and are extraordinarily depressing.

Under the influence of unusually long summer days, the snow cover begins to disappear in May, and the lakes are usually free of their ice cover in June. Because of the permanently frozen subsoil,

called permafrost, subsurface drainage is deficient, and bog and swamp are prevalent (Fig. 11.4). Myriads of mosquitoes and blackflies make life almost unbearable for both men and animals during the summer period of wet earth.

At Ponds Inlet, Canada, a tundra station at 72°43′N, the average July temperature is 42°, with the thermometer rising to about 49° during the warmest hours of the day and sinking to an average of 35 or 36° at "night." A striking feature of tundra climate is the small diurnal temperature range even though there is a large annual range, a feature typical of continental climates (Fig. 11.9). At Sagastyr in Siberia, where the annual range is 85°, the daily range in July is only about 6°. This is because of the continuous daylight beyond the Arctic Circle in summer. No frost occurs on most July "nights" in

Figure 11.8 Annual march of temperature at a marine tundra station located on an island in the high-latitude Atlantic Ocean. A cool summer, and a remarkably mild winter considering the latitude, result in an unusually small annual range of temperature.

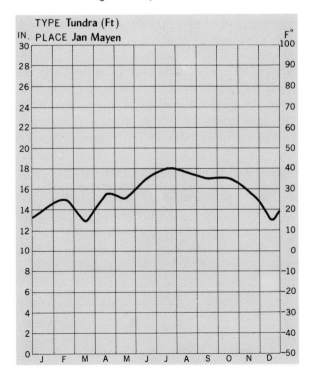

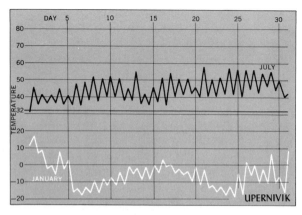

Figure 11.9 Small diurnal temperature ranges, in both winter and summer, are typical of this tundra station in Greenland. Nonperiodic temperature changes are relatively large in winter.

tundra climates, although it is not an unusual event when the thermometer slips a few degrees below freezing (Fig. 11.9). Warm days occur now and then. On at least one occasion, Ponds Inlet has recorded a temperature of 77°, and Chesterfield Inlet, another tundra station in Canada, has had a temperature of 84°. However, such high temperatures are a rare exception and not the rule.

Winter. While summer temperatures are not much different from one tundra region to another, there are greater variations in the winters. Along the Arctic coasts of Siberia, average January and February temperatures are in the neighborhood of

−35 or −40°, and it is appreciably colder farther inland. At this season winds are mostly from the bitterly cold boreal region to the south, and their advections of cold air further intensify the severity of temperatures in the tundra. The tundra of northeastern Siberia, where the winter-month averages are below −40°, represents the extreme condition; winters are not quite so severe along the Arctic borderlands of North America. A coastal station in Labrador has a January mean of −8°; Ponds Inlet in Canada records an average of −28° for January, −30° for February, and even −24° for March. At Ponds Inlet 5 months—November through March —have average temperatures below zero, while 9 are below freezing. Daily temperature ranges are exceedingly small: even smaller than in summer, for in midwinter most of the tundra lies in constant darkness.

The annual march of temperature is represented by a profile whose crest and base have much weaker gradients than the flanks. Thus at the times of both constant daylight and constant night the temporal change in temperature is not large. It increases in the intermediate seasons, when there are rapidly changing proportions of light and darkness (Figs. 11.7, 11.8, and 11.10).

Precipitation

Over most of the tundra lands, precipitation probably does not exceed 10 or 12 in. (Fig. 11.1). In portions of eastern arctic Canada (particularly the Lab-

Climatic data for representative tundra stations (*Ft*)

	J	F	M	A	M	J	J	A	S	O	N	D	Yr	Range
Sagastyr, Siberia, U.S.S.R. (73° N, 124° E)														
Temp., °F	−34	−36	−30	−7	15	32	41	38	33	6	−16	−28	1	77
Precip., in.	0.1	0.1	0.0	0.0	0.2	0.4	0.3	1.4	0.4	0.1	0.1	0.2	3.3	
Upernivik, Western Greenland (73° N, 56° W)														
Temp., °F	−7	−10	−6	6	25	35	41	41	33	25	14	1	16.5	50.6
Precip., in.	0.4	0.4	0.6	0.6	0.6	0.6	0.1	1.1	1.0	1.1	1.1	0.5	9.2	
Spitsbergen Island (78° N, 14° E)														
Temp., °F	4	−2	−2	8	23	35	42	40	32	22	11	6	18	44
Precip., in.	1.4	1.3	1.1	0.9	0.5	0.4	0.6	0.9	1.0	1.2	1.0	1.5	11.8	

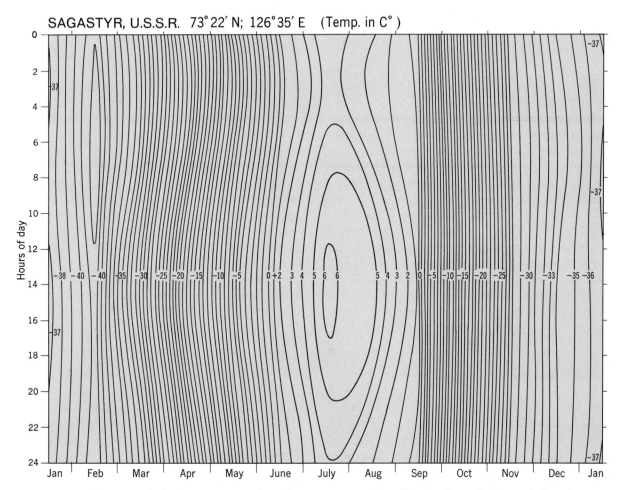

Figure 11.10 Thermoisopleths for a continental tundra station in northern Siberia. Exceedingly small diurnal ranges of temperature and large annual ranges are conspicuous features. Note the rapid change in temperature during the transition seasons. (*After Troll.*)

rador Peninsula) and a few other widely distributed areas, it is somewhat greater. Low temperatures and winter anticyclonic conditions are not conducive to much precipitation. In addition, convective turbulence induced by surface heating is weak. Summer and autumn, the warmest seasons, are the periods of maximum precipitation throughout the tundra as a whole, although in the more marine locations fall and winter may show larger totals than summer.

Precipitation is predominantly cyclonic, or frontal, in origin. In the warm season much of it falls as rain, with occasional wet snows. The meager winter snowfall is usually dry and powdery, so that it forms a very compact cover. It is only this very compact snow, a few inches of which may equal an inch of rain, that the Eskimos use in constructing their igloos. The actual amount of dry, sandlike snow that falls is not easy to measure, since it is often accompanied by strong winds which heap it up in depressions and on the lee sides of hills while they sweep all exposed surfaces bare. There are no forests, as in the taiga, to break the force of the wind and hold the snow cover. Stefansson estimates that 75 to 90 percent of the surface of Arctic lands is nearly free of snow at all seasons. As a result both of the small amount of snow and of its strong tendency to drift, sledging may be difficult.

Seasonal weather

There are conflicting reports concerning the character of *winter* weather in the tundra, undoubtedly because conditions differ from one part of the Arctic to another and because successive winters can be unlike. Certainly the variability of winters is much greater than that of summers. In some years clear, cold, anticyclonic conditions appear to dominate the weather, while in others, at least in some areas, cyclones accompanied by blizzards follow each other in fairly rapid succession. In general, however, winters in both the Eurasian and North American sectors probably have much anticyclonic weather. The dryness of the air causes rapid evapo-

ration from the human body, and explorers report the prevalence of torturing thirst. Blizzards on the treeless tundra are awesome weather phenomena, their low temperatures, gale winds, and driving snow combining to force all living creatures to seek shelter.

The transition seasons of *spring and fall* are somewhat different; autumn is a quiet dying away of nature, spring a more sudden awakening. Both are likely to be stormier than winter, however. Autumn is one of the worst seasons for severe storms, since the seas are still unfrozen, and their surface temperatures are markedly higher than those of the rapidly cooling lands.

Summer is a relatively quiet and uniformly cool season (Fig. 11.9). The wet, swampy ground makes the air damp and raw. Fogs are common, the sky is often gray and cheerless, and it is not unusual to have wet snowfalls.

ICECAP CLIMATE (*Fi*)

This least well-known among the world's climatic types is characteristically developed over the great durable continental ice plateaus of Antarctica and Greenland. Only fragmentary climatic data have been obtained from these deserts of snow and ice, where the average temperature of no month rises above freezing.

Circulation patterns

As noted earlier, polar circulation patterns are complex, and owing probably to contrasting surface features, they are not the same in the two hemispheres. Also, obviously they are not the same on and around the high ice plateaus of Antarctica and Greenland as they are at or near sea level (Fig. 11.11). Over Antarctica at stratospheric levels there exists a deep cyclonic vortex with high-velocity westerly winds. In summer this pattern weakens, permitting a greater influx of warmer air from lower latitudes. The Arctic cyclonic vortex circulation

at high levels is less persistent and is disrupted more frequently, in winter as well as in summer, so that great outbreaks of cold air pour southward over Canada and Eurasia.

Close to the ice surface of interior Antarctica and Greenland, persistent shallow anticyclones of thermal origin prevail. Within them steep temperature inversions extend upward from the ice surface for several hundred meters. Radiating outward

Figure 11.11 Hypothetical distribution of zonal pressure and wind in the South Pole region. (*After Meinardus, Mintz, and Dean.*)

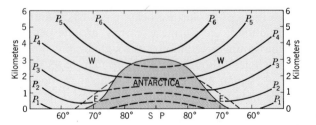

from the center of the anticyclone, and from the highest part of the convex ice plateau, a shallow layer of gravity winds drains downslope over the ice surface toward the lower marginal areas. Such downward-moving winds, called katabatic winds, dominate the circulation over the icecaps. At Eismitte in central Greenland near the crest of the icecap, the recorded wind velocity is only 10 miles an hour. But along the steep margins of the ice plateaus, winds may reach gale force in local areas. Subsiding air replaces this constant outflow, thereby probably strengthening the shallow surface anticyclone's circulation. Without the constant downslope drainage of cold air, a very cold and deep anticyclone would probably build up over the ice, with frequent surges of cold air from the interior toward lower latitudes. A steady downslope drainage, which eliminates the necessity for strong surges, may partly account for the fact that the Southern Hemisphere does not have such great polar outbreaks of cold air as the northern latitudes.

Temperature

Conditions on the icecaps all favor low temperatures. During a considerable part of the year the sun is completely below the horizon, and even during the period of continuous sunlight the solar rays are very oblique and deliver little energy per unit area. Because of the excellent reflecting properties of the snow and ice surface, probably 80 percent or more of the solar radiation reaching the icecap surface is sent immediately back into the atmosphere. A part of the remaining 20 percent is consumed in evaporating the ice and snow. On the other hand, the relatively dry air permits rapid losses of heat by earth radiation whenever the sky is clear. The result is a nearly permanent surface temperature inversion. Such an inversion prevails on over 80 percent of the days at the South Pole.

Both Antarctica and Greenland are ice plateaus with convex surfaces whose high interior parts rise to about 10,000 ft in Greenland and 13,000 ft in Antarctica. Hence any recorded air temperatures for the elevated core areas presumably would be

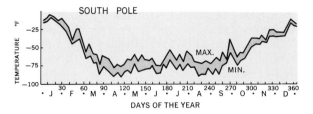

Figure 11.12 Five-day means of maximum and minimum surface temperatures, 1958, South Pole, Antarctica. (*After Sabbagh.*)

some 30° + higher if reduced to sea level. At Eismitte in high interior Greenland, the coldest month has an average temperature of about −53° and July has one of +12°, producing an annual range of 65°. The daily range in July, with constant daylight, is only 12 or 13°. In January there is no consistent daily range. At South Pole Station in interior Antarctica, the average monthly temperatures in 1958 remained below −70°F for the 6 months April to September (Fig. 11.12). The warmest month of the year averaged −10° and the coldest −75°. Certainly this is the lowest summer temperature on the earth, while the winter temperatures rival, or are somewhat lower than, those of northeastern Siberia. The annual range of 65° is continental in its magnitude. The lowest world temperature (−126.9°) and the lowest monthly mean temperature (−96.8°) were both recorded at Vostok in Antarctica.

Some, but not all, icecap stations have an annual march of temperature in which the profile based on month-to-month averages shows a broad, flattish winter minimum (Fig 11.13). At the South Pole, for example, monthly averages over the period April to September remain below −70°, with only minor fluctuations. Nonperiodic short-time temperature fluctuations over Antarctica are not uncommon, but their magnitude and frequency vary from station to station. Such fluctuations are associated with invasions of the inner polar areas by atmospheric disturbances in the form of frontal or nonfrontal low-pressure systems. Much of the temperature changes in these disturbances are related to their winds, which destroy the temperature inversion,

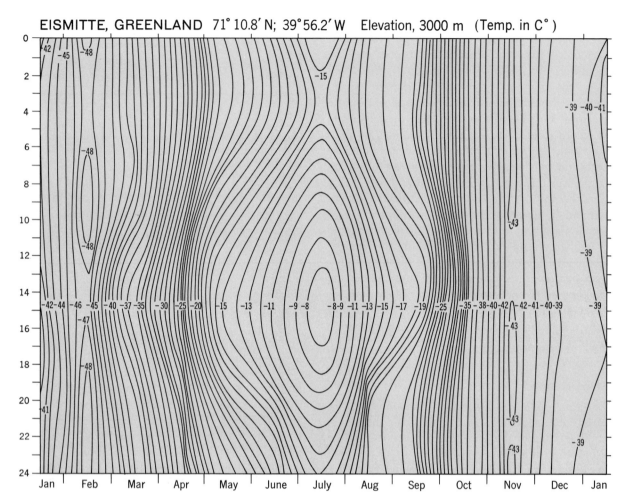

Figure 11.13 Thermoisopleths for a station on the Greenland icecap. Small diurnal ranges of temperature and large annual ranges are conspicuous features. So also are the rapid changes in temperature during the transition seasons of spring and fall. (*After Troll.*)

Climatic data for icecap stations (*Fi*)

	J	F	M	A	M	J	J	A	S	O	N	D	Yr	Range
Eismitte (Wegner), interior Greenland (70°54′N, 40°42′W, 9,941 ft)
Temp., °F	−42	−53	−40	−24	−4	+4	+12	+1	−8	−32	−46	−37	−22	65
Precip., in.	No data
Little America, coastal Antarctica (79°S, 164°W)
Temp., °F	22	(9)	(−7)	−24	−27	−29	−34	−34	−29	−14	9	24	−11.3	58
Precip., in.	No data

and their cloud decks, whose long-wave radiation back to earth may produce increases of 20° or more. According to Sabbagh,[2] at South Pole Station on June 28 and 29, 1958, the passage of a depression with a warm and a cold front first raised surface temperatures by 43° and destroyed the surface inversion, and then caused the temperature to drop by 23°.

Precipitation

If little information is available concerning temperatures of icecap climates, still less is known about their precipitation. There is no doubt that it is meager, or that nearly all of it falls as snow, mostly in the form of dry, hard, sandlike particles which are readily driven before the wind. The origin of the precipitation over icecaps is not well understood, however. Although there are almost no streams in such regions, some water is lost by evaporation from the ice surface, as well as by glaciers moving out to the sea in the form of icebergs. There must be enough precipitation to more than offset these losses. Yet conditions on the icecaps are generally opposed to precipitation: abnormally low temperatures, low specific humidity, extreme stability of the air as indicated by the persistent strong surface temperature inversions, and the infrequent occurrence of upslope winds—all act to inhibit snowfall.

No doubt a portion of the inland precipitation is produced by the cyclonic storms that pass along the margins of the ice plateaus. Much more originates in the smaller number of cyclones that pass in over the icecaps (Fig. 11.14). A little precipitation may result from condensation in the form of fine ice particles, or of hoarfrost, within the generally subsiding air as it reaches the intensely cold ice surface. The rate of frost deposit is exceedingly slow, no doubt; but since it is fairly continuous, the total amount may be considerable.

At Eismitte in interior Greenland (9,941 ft) the

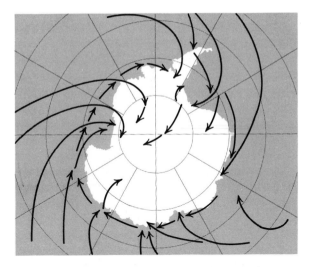

Figure 11.14 Winter storm tracks for the Antarctic region. They appear to swirl around the margins of the continent, moving inland mainly where continental elevation is lowest. (*After Rubin.*)

recorded average cloudiness in one study was between $\frac{5}{10}$ and $\frac{6}{10}$, with a maximum in the season of least cold. The cloud forms were predominantly stratus, cirrus, and cirrostratus. There were 204 days with precipitation, the larger part of which was cyclonic in origin. Considering the prevailing atmospheric conditions over icecaps, this number of days with precipitation seems unusually high. From a study of the snow layers marking the yearly accumulations of snow at Eismitte, it was established that the average annual snowfall over a period of 21 years was 12 in.—equivalent to 3 to 4 in. of water. Seasonal concentration was not conspicuous[3] (Fig. 11.15). It appears, then, that cyclones do cross the Greenland icecap, and they probably account for a large part of the snowfall. Certainly the weather element is a prominent feature of the climate, so that the concept of a permanent anticyclone is scarcely tenable.

[2] Michael E. Sabbagh, "A Preliminary Regional Dynamic Climatology of the Antarctic Continent," *Erdkunde,* Vol. 16, p. 99, 1962. See also Morton J. Rubin, "The Antarctic and the Weather," *Scientific American,* Vol. 207, pp. 84–94, September, 1962.

[3] Fritz Loewe, "Klima des Grönlañdische Inlandeises," in W. Köppen and R. Geiger, *Handbuch der Klimatologie,* Vol. 2, part K, Gebrüder Borntraeger, Berlin, 1935. Also by the same author: "The Greenland Ice Cap as Seen by a Meteorologist," *Quart. J. Roy. Meteorol. Soc.,* Vol. 62, pp. 359–377, July, 1936.

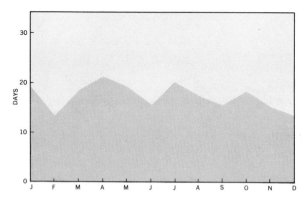

Figure 11.15 Days with precipitation at Eismitte on the Greenland icecap. (*After Loewe.*)

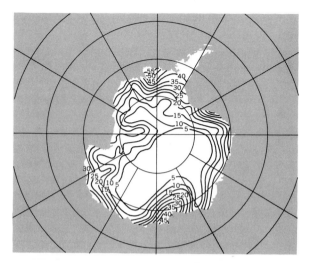

Figure 11.16 Annual accumulation of precipitation on Antarctica, expressed as water equivalent in centimeters. The mean value for the whole continent is about 14.5 cm. Most of the accumulation is along the marginal parts. (*After Rubin.*)

At South Pole Station in high interior Antarctica, there were only 17 days during 1958 with *measurable* precipitation, but 248 when some snow fell. A great majority of these had only a trace of snow. The total snowfall amounted to only 0.48 in. of water equivalent. There were 100 overcast days and 165 that were clear. It is believed that the whole Antarctic Continent receives an average of less than 4 in. of water equivalent in annual precipitation

(Fig. 11.16). The least snow falls in the higher, colder, anticyclonic interior; the most occurs along the continent's seaward margins.

HIGHLAND CLIMATES (*H*)

Altitude and exposure as climatic controls. Next to the distribution of land and water, elevation above sea level is probably the most important cause of differences in climate in similar latitudes. The climatic effects of elevated land masses such as mountains and plateaus are expressed through the two factors altitude and exposure.

There is no such thing as a *highland type of climate,* however; not in the same sense that there is a tropical wet type or a boreal type. Almost endless varieties of local climates exist within a mountain mass: the atmospheric conditions change markedly with altitude and exposure, and of course with latitude as well. An enclosed valley or upland is climatically very different from an exposed peak.

Weather conditions on windward slopes contrast with those on leeward sides, while flanks inclined toward the sun are unlike those lying more in the shadow. Each of these in turn is different at various altitudes and latitudes. Representative temperature and rainfall curves for highland climates as a class do not exist, and only the most flexible generalizations are broadly applicable. One of the most valuable of these generalizations is that highland climates to a considerable degree are low-temperature variants of lowland climates in similar latitudes.

Methods of classification. It is impossible to indicate the world's almost limitless variety of highland climates on a small-scale map like the one inside the front cover. Not only are there very few weather stations in such regions, but the profusion of local climates makes it impossible for the weather data of most stations to be representative of anything but a very restricted area.

Because highland climates have a third, or vertical, dimension, it is difficult to fit this group into a classification intended for horizontal arrangement. It is true, of course, that temperature decreases both poleward and upward. As a consequence, the temperature of, say, latitude 40° should be duplicated at some altitude closer to the equator. Thus Quito, Ecuador, almost on the equator at 9,350 ft, has a mean annual temperature very similar to that of St. Louis, Missouri, in the middle latitudes. Actually, however, the two stations have totally different climates, for St. Louis has a range of 47° between its warmest and coldest months, while the range at Quito is less than 1°. Yet in some climatic classifications the two stations are included within the same type.

A unique feature of highland climates is their large difference in temperature between day and night—a difference caused by the intense solar radiation during the day and the equally rapid loss of heat by earth radiation at night. Throughout much of the tropics, the cool climates of the high altitudes show far greater temperature changes between day and night than they do between the extreme seasons. One is forced to conclude that a system of climatic classification designed for lowland climates is not especially applicable to highlands.

There appears to be no simple satisfactory way of representing the variety of highland climates on a small-scale map. Up to an altitude of about 4,000 ft, the climatic peculiarities due to altitude are not so noticeable. But above about 6,000 ft they become very prominent. So in the climate map inside the front cover, a compromise based on this fact has been worked out. Where there are extensive highlands of only moderate elevation above the surrounding lowlands, these have often been included within the general climatic type characteristic of the lowlands, even though they represent a modified form of the lowland climate. Highlands of greater elevation have been included within the general group of H climates. It is the distinctive characteristics of this group that are described here.

Atmospheric pressure in mountains

At low elevations the minor changes in air pressure from day to day, or from season to season, are not directly perceptible to the human body. Consequently it is as a climatic control rather than a climatic element that pressure has been discussed in the preceding chapters. In highland climates, however, the rapid decrease in the atmosphere's weight with increasing elevation, and the low pressures found in high mountains and plateaus, cause pressure as an element to be somewhat more important. At an elevation of about 17,500 ft above sea level, pressure is reduced to approximately one-half its sea-level value. The highest human habitations are found below this level, although there are said to be settlements in Tibet and the Bolivian Andes located fairly near it. Most people feel the physiological effects of decreased pressure (faintness, headache, nosebleed, sleeplessness, nausea, weakness) at altitudes above about 10,000 ft. Usually "mountain sickness" is a temporary inconvenience which passes away after a week or so of residence at high altitudes.

Solar radiation

Intensity of sunlight increases aloft in the cleaner, drier, thinner air of mountains. This is because dust, water vapor, cloud particles, and other principal reflecting, scattering, and absorbing elements of solar radiation in the atmosphere are much more abundant at lower elevations. On a clear day, probably three-fourths of the solar radiation received at the outer atmosphere penetrates to 6,000 ft, but only one-half to sea level. The great relative intensity of the sun's rays is usually noticeable by people arriving at a high-altitude location. On Mont Blanc (15,781 ft) the intensity of solar radiation is approximately 26 percent greater than at Paris (200 ft). At the time of the summer solstice, the amount of solar energy received by Tibet is nearly one and a half times as great as that falling upon the neighboring lowlands in India.

Solar radiation is not only more intense in the higher altitudes, but it is also proportionally richer in the shorter wavelengths of energy at the blue end of the spectrum. People therefore burn and tan quickly in mountain sunlight.

Soil temperature.   Associated with the greater intensity of solar radiation at higher elevations is the excess of surface or soil temperatures over air tem-

peratures. Although the thin, dry mountain air is incapable of readily absorbing and retaining either solar or terrestrial energy, the land surface easily absorbs the intense solar radiation. Thus it attains a relatively high daytime temperature compared with the cool air. The effects upon plants are striking.

Air temperature

Probably the most fundamentally important of the climatic changes resulting from increased elevation is the drop in air temperature (about 3.5° per 1,000

Figure 11.17   Thermoisopleths for a highland station near the equator. Temperature changes much more during the 24-hr diurnal period than it does during the 12 months of the year. (*After Troll.*)

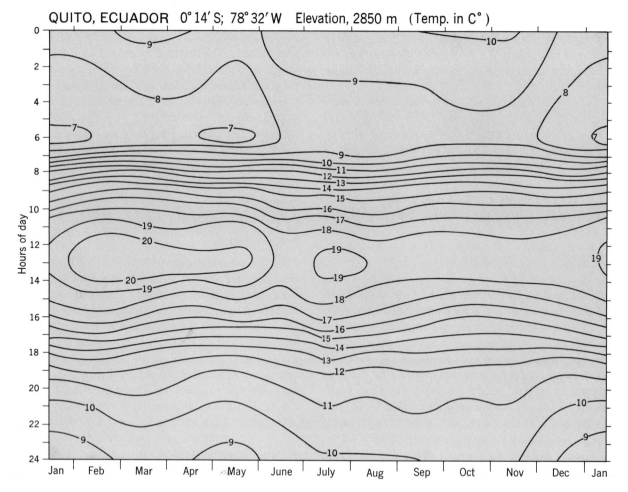

QUITO, ECUADOR   0° 14′ S; 78° 32′ W   Elevation, 2850 m   (Temp. in C°)

Climatic data for a high plateau station in the tropics

	J	F	M	A	M	J	J	A	S	O	N	D	Yr	Range
					Quito, Ecuador (9,350 ft)									
Temp., °F	54.5	55.0	54.5	54.5	54.7	55.0	54.9	54.9	55.0	54.7	54.3	54.7	54.7	0.7
Precip., in.	3.2	3.9	4.8	7.0	4.6	1.5	1.1	2.2	2.6	3.9	4.0	3.6	42.3	

ft)—this in spite of the increased intensity of solar radiation. Quito, Ecuador, on the equator at an elevation of 9,350 ft, has an average annual temperature of 55°, which is 25° lower than that of the adjacent Amazon lowlands (Fig. 11.17). But although the clear, rarified air at that elevation remains chilly, since it is incapable of absorbing and retaining much energy, the sunlight is intense. It is a climate of cool shade and hot sun. Viscount Bryce writes of the Bolivian plateau:

The keen air which this elevation gives has a fine bracing quality, yet there are disadvantages. One is never warm except when actually in the sunlight. . . . The inhabitants get accustomed to these conditions and shiver in their ponchos, but the traveler is rather wretched after sunset and feels how natural was Sun worship in such a country.

Vertical temperature gradients along mountain slopes are many times steeper than the most continental winter gradients in a horizontal direction on lowlands. In the low latitudes, a railroad trip into the mountains which takes only a few hours can transport the traveler from tropical to polar temperature zones. The steep vertical temperature gradients in highlands are particularly significant in the tropics, where people can escape the oppressive heat by going to the mountains. Partly because of their lower temperatures, tropical highlands commonly become centers of population concentration. In tropical Latin America, for instance, the capital cities of Venezuela, Colombia, Bolivia, Mexico, and five of the Central American republics are on highlands. In India, the so-called "hill stations" of the sub-Himalayas, at elevations of 6,500 to 7,500 ft, become havens for residents from the lowlands during the long hot season.

Vertical temperature zones in tropical highlands. Several altitude zones of climate, each with its characteristic wild vegetation and crops, are found in tropical highlands (Fig. 11.18). In mountainous parts of tropical Latin America, four such zones are commonly recognized: *tierra caliente* (hot lands), *tierra templada* (temperate lands), *tierra fría* (cool lands), and *tierra helada* (land of frost). Naturally these belts do not have identical altitudes throughout the tropics.

The lowest zone, or *caliente*, normally extends from sea level to 2,000 to 3,000 ft (the annual temperature is roughly 83 to 75°). Where precipitation is abundant, this belt is characterized by a luxuriant vegetation cover of trees or of trees and tall grass and by such crops as rubber, bananas, and cacao.

The *tierra templada* lies above the *caliente* and extends up to 6,000 to 6,500 ft (temperature is roughly 75 to 65°). A great variety of crops—among them coffee, maize, tea, cotton, and rice—is produced here.

Tierra fría, lying above the *templada*, reaches up to 10,000 to 11,500 ft (temperature is 65 to 54°). Middle-latitude crops, such as wheat, barley, apples, and potatoes, grow there, and the pastoral industries are frequently important.

Still higher, the *tierra helada* is above the tree line and beyond the agricultural zone. Here the alpine pastures lie, terminated along their upper margins by the permanent snowfields. Close to the equator, where a dry season is either absent or very short, the grass of the *tierra helada* is relatively thick and remains green throughout the year. This is known as the *paramo*. With increasing distance from the equator there is a longer dry season, so that the alpine grasses are dry for a part of the year and are burned over by native farmers. This is the

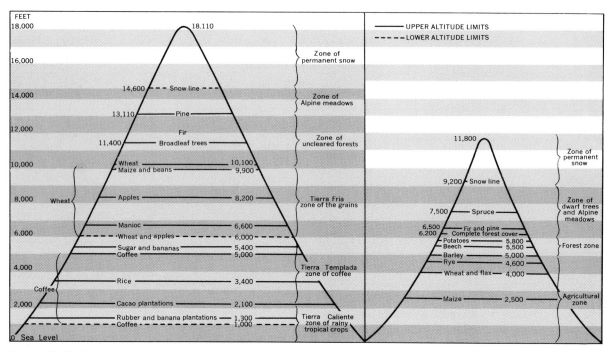

Figure 11.18 Vertical temperature zones and approximate altitudinal limits of selected crops and vegetation types on a tropical mountain (left) and a middle-latitude mountain (right). (*After Sapper.*)

Horizontal and vertical arrangement of the climatic vegetation belts in the tropical Andes

Number of humid months	*Tierra caliente*	*Tierra templada*	*Tierra fría*	*Tierra helada*
12 11 10	Tropical evergreen and semideciduous transition forest	Tropical mountain forest	Tropical altitude-and-fog forest	*Paramo*
9 8 7	Tropical moist savanna (forest and grassland)	Tropical moist valley vegetation (forest and grassland)	Tropical moist sierra vegetation (moist sierra brush)	Wet *puna*
6 5	Tropical dry savanna (forest and grassland)	Tropical dry valley vegetation (forest and grassland)	Tropical dry sierra vegetation (dry sierra brush)	Dry *puna*
4 3 2	Tropical thorn savanna (forest and grassland)	Tropical thorn valley vegetation (forest and grassland)	Tropical thorn sierra vegetation (thorn sierra brush)	Thorn *puna*
1	Tropical semidesert	Tropical valley semidesert	Desert sierra	Desert *puna*
0	Tropical desert	Tropical valley desert		

Source: After Troll.

wet *puna.* As the dry season lengthens with increases in latitude, the grass cover becomes less dense, and the wet *puna* changes gradually to dry *puna,* then to thorn *puna,* and finally to desert *puna.* Thorn and desert *puna* are characterized by thorny shrubs and cacti. Grazing is the principal form of land use in the *paramo* and *puna.*

Above heights of 14,000 to 15,000 ft the zone of perpetual snow usually begins. On these tropical mountains local trade of considerable importance is fostered by the temperature zonation of products.

Middle-latitude highlands. Although mountains and plateaus within the tropics may be climatically desirable because of their lower temperatures, this same characteristic causes highlands in the middle latitudes to be climatically inferior to lowlands. After all, tropical lowlands have an excess of heat, so that any reduction of temperature with altitude usually is an advantage both for human comfort and for the greater variety of products that can be grown. In the middle latitudes, on the other hand, even the lowlands are commonly none too warm. Thus reduction of temperature with altitude, causing a cooler summer and shorter growing season, materially decreases the opportunities for agriculture. In other words, there are fewer *utilizable* temperature zones in middle-latitude highlands (Fig. 11.18).

Diurnal temperature changes. Mountains and high plateaus have been called the radiation windows of the earth, since the thin, dry air facilitates the entry of strong solar radiation by day and the loss of heat by terrestrial radiation at night. Rapid daytime heating and nighttime cooling are the result, so that large diurnal ranges of temperature are characteristics of highland climates (Fig. 11.19).

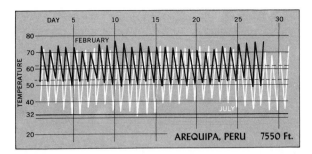

Figure 11.19 Daily maximum and minimum temperatures of the extreme months at a tropical mountain station of moderate altitude. Note the diurnal regularity of temperature change, indicating sun control. Diurnal range is greater in July, the drier season, when there is the least cloud.

In tropical highlands this marked temperature change between day and night stands in great contrast to the very slight temperature changes between the averages for the months and the seasons. At high altitudes in tropical highlands, especially in the *tierra helada,* the large diurnal range of temperature results in a very large number of days with night freezing and daytime thawing (Fig. 11.20). Such a frequent oscillation between freeze and thaw has major effects upon weathering processes, soil formation, and vegetation characteristics. In summary, a distinctive feature of the climate of high tropical mountains is the combination of large *diurnal* temperature variations and small *seasonal* ranges.

Seasonal temperatures and annual ranges. The lower temperatures in highlands have led to the statement that mountains in the tropics have perpetual spring. Quito's annual temperature of 55°, for instance, is not greatly unlike the May average at Madison, Wisconsin. However, the great variety

Climatic data for a representative high-altitude station in middle latitudes (*H*)

	J	F	M	A	M	J	J	A	S	O	N	D	Yr	Range
Longs Peak, Colorado (8,956 ft)														
Temp., °F	23	22	26	33	41	51	55	55	48	39	31	24	37	33
Precip., in.	0.7	1.2	2.0	2.7	2.4	1.6	3.6	2.2	1.7	1.7	0.9	0.9	21.6	

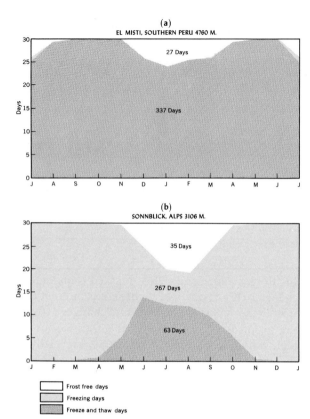

(a)
EL MISTI, SOUTHERN PERU 4760 M.

27 Days

337 Days

(b)
SONNBLICK, ALPS 3106 M.

35 Days

267 Days

63 Days

☐ Frost free days
▨ Freezing days
▨ Freeze and thaw days

Figure 11.20 Annual number of freeze-and-thaw days on a tropical and on a middle-latitude mountain. A large number of days on which night freeze and day thaw occur is characteristic of high mountains in the tropics. This climatic feature expresses itself strongly in the nature of the wild vegetation, in weathering processes, and in soil characteristics. Middle-latitude highlands have many fewer freeze-and-thaw days and many more freezing days. (*After Troll.*)

and coolest months is under 1°, which is even smaller than that of the Amazon lowlands in the same latitude. Mexico City, at 7,474 ft and farther poleward than Quito, has an *average annual temperature* 17° below that for Veracruz on the coast; yet their *annual ranges* are almost identical—11.5 and 11°, respectively. One climatologist has aptly described both the difference and the similarity in the annual march of temperature between lowlands and highlands in the same latitude in the statement: "The pitch changes; the tune remains the same."

As a general rule, seasonal temperature contrasts, or mean annual range, increase with latitude in both highland and lowland stations. Also, the annual ranges for highland and lowland stations in similar latitudes are of the same general magnitude. Thus high-altitude regions in the tropics present the unique feature of a cold climate with a small mean annual range of temperature. This is quite in contrast to cold climates in middle latitudes. The small annual ranges in tropical highlands have some resemblance to those of marine locations farther poleward (Fig. 11.21).

Temperature inversions in highland climates. One of the characteristic phenomena of mountain regions, especially those of middle latitudes, is the larger diurnal and seasonal ranges of temperature in the valleys compared with the slopes. On summer

of elevations within a tropical mountain mass obviously results in all gradations of temperature.

And although the temperature is lower on a tropical mountain than on an adjacent lowland, both locations have a similar uniformity in average monthly and daily means. Small seasonal ranges, and the same monotonous repetition of daily weather, belong alike to tropical highlands and tropical lowlands (Fig. 11.21). At Quito, for instance, the temperature difference between the warmest

Figure 11.21 A comparison of the annual march of temperature at Iquitos, a tropical lowland station, and at Quito, a tropical highland station, both in equatorial latitudes. Note the generally lower temperature at Quito. On the other hand, a small annual range of temperature is characteristic of both stations.

ANNUAL MARCH OF TEMPERATURE

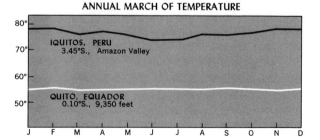

IQUITOS, PERU
3.45°S., Amazon Valley

QUITO, EQUADOR
0.10°S., 9,350 feet

days the protected valley receives much reflected radiant energy from the surrounding slopes and may become warmer than the slopes above, where winds provide greater ventilation. But at night, especially in winter, the valleys become reservoirs of cold air draining from surrounding slopes. In mountainous regions, with their uneven surfaces and varied exposures, extensive air drainage causes local temperature inversions to be unusually well developed. This is further aided by the briefer daily period of sunshine, as well as the calmer, more stagnant air in the protected valley. The basins are not only colder but foggier. A pall of gray fog may shroud the Swiss foreland for a week at a time.

In descending into a mountain valley on a warm summer evening, one does not need an instrument to note the increasing dampness and coolness of the air. From the valleys of Carinthia in the Austrian Alps, where temperature inversions are well developed, comes the proverb, "If you climb in winter up a stair, one less coat you need to wear" (Hann). It often happens that on a winter day one can ascend from damp, cold, dark, sunless weather in the valley and come out suddenly on the slopes above, into a realm of sunshine and beauty where the air is clear, mild, and dry.

Highlands as temperature divides.   Since highlands function as barriers to the free movement of air masses, they commonly act as a shelter to areas on their leeward sides. Steep horizontal temperature gradients may be the result. Thus the cold continental air masses from central and northern Asia, which dominate the winters of eastern Asia, are prevented from invading Hindustan in winter by the great highland mass of the Himalayas and Tibet north of India and Pakistan. The protective effect of the mountains is made clear by a comparison of the January temperatures of stations in India-Pakistan and in China in similar latitudes:

Lahore, Pakistan 53°   Calcutta, India 65°
Shanghai, China 38°   Canton, China 50°

The northern highland rim of the Mediterranean Basin likewise blocks the free movement of cold winter air into southern Europe. Consequently while Bucharest and Uskub in the Balkans have January temperatures of 26° and 29°, Salonika south of the highlands records 41°, Athens 46°, and Trieste 39°. See the accompanying table for the same kind of temperature effects caused by the Cascade Mountains.

The Cascade Mountains as a climatic divide

	Windward side (Tacoma)	Lee side (Yakima)
Temp., °F		
Mean winter	41	31
Mean summer	62	69
Mean daily range	15	29
Mean annual range	25	45
Absolute range	91	128
Rel. humidity, % mean, 1,630 hr	67	46
Sunshine duration, % possible, yr	43	65
No. of clear days, mean annual	73	113
Precip., in., mean annual	38.7	7.2

Source: After Landsberg.

Precipitation

Increased precipitation in highlands.   On a mean annual rainfall map of the earth, mountains ordinarily stand out as "islands" of increased precipitation. The additional precipitation in highlands has a multiple origin, a topic which was discussed in Chapter 4. The patterns of precipitation increase with altitude are somewhat different in low and in middle latitudes. In tropical mountains, total annual rainfall shows an initial increase at lower altitudes which continues up to about 5,000 ft (around 1,500 m). At higher elevations there is a continuous decline. Outside the tropics, however, total annual precipitation continues to increase, at least up to the levels of high peaks.

It is for dry climates, no matter in what latitude, that the heavier rainfall of highlands has critical importance. In regions of lowland drought, highlands are areas not only of heavier precipitation, but of heavier vegetation cover, and usually of more abundant agricultural production as well. In both arid and semiarid lands, highlands frequently bear a cover of forest in contrast to the meager grass-and-shrub vegetation of the adjacent drier lowlands. The Black Hills of western South Dakota are "black" because the color of their dark-green forests is such a contrast to the tawny-hued steppes surrounding them.

Not only are settlements in dry lands attracted to the humid slopes of mountains and to the well-watered mountain valleys, but streams descending from the rainier highlands carry the influence of highland climate far out on the surrounding arid lowlands. The Yemen Highlands in southern Arabia, and the adjacent lowlands watered by its rivers, are a garden spot as well as the principal center of population in that otherwise largely desert country. In eastern North Africa, the Ethiopian (Abyssinian) Highlands are a similar "culture island." The Nile floods have their origin in this same mountain knot. The waters of the Colorado River, whose principal sources are in the Rocky Mountains, make agriculture possible in the dry Imperial Valley of southern California over 700 miles away. From the Andes come the 50 or more small streams that, crossing the Peruvian coastal desert, nourish the irrigated strips of what is otherwise mainly wasteland.

The heavy precipitation associated with highlands is also significant in terms of power resources, for as the accumulation of water (including snow) at high elevations flows to lower levels, its energy may be harnessed to produce hydroelectric power. The amount of potential water power depends upon two factors: the volume of water (precipitation), and the extent of its fall, which in turn is directly related to the height of the mountain.

Windward and leeward slopes.   As already discussed, highlands usually have wetter windward slopes, and their drier leeward side is described as the *rain shadow*. On the leeward side also, however, precipitation is likely to increase with elevation, just as it does on the windward side. This is because the ascending current on the windward side does

not begin to descend immediately upon reaching the crest of a mountain range, but continues rising for some distance beyond the crest. As a consequence the heavy windward precipitation spills over onto the higher leeward slopes.

Moreover, the lifting effect of a highland barrier upon approaching air masses, and hence the increase in precipitation, begins at some distance out in front of the marked change in slope. For example, there is a strong increase in rainfall within the flat lowlands of northern Java 25 miles or more away from the mountains. Lowlands just leeward of highlands are likely to be much drier, as shown in the table on the Cascade Mountains (page 365).

In summary, the windward sides of mountains are cloudier and rainier and have smaller temperature ranges, while the climate on leeward slopes is drier and sunnier, shows more variability in temperature, and has a tendency toward increased continentality.

Snowfall and the snow line.   Because of lower temperatures in highlands, snow falls more frequently and abundantly, and remains on the ground for a longer period, than on the surrounding lowlands. It is the slow melting of deep accumulations of snow in highlands that gives many lowlands a large and continuous supply of water throughout the warmer seasons.

Considerable attention has been given to the permanent, or year-round, snowfields in highlands and to the changing elevation of the snow line, which marks the lower boundary of permanent snow. As a rule, the snow line becomes increasingly higher with decreasing latitude, a fact which reflects the decreasing temperatures away from the equator (Fig. 11.22). But as the table on page 367 shows, the highest snow line is not at the equator, where precipitation is heavy, but in two zones 15 to 25° to the north and south of it, where precipitation totals are smaller. Thus although latitude, or zonal temperatures, largely accounts for the general latitudinal variations in the altitude of the snow line, there are bound to be large departures from the zonal average caused by differences in amounts of precipi-

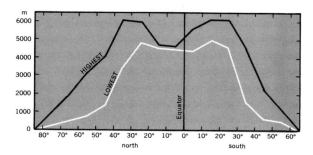

Figure 11.22 Highest and lowest limits of the snow line in the different latitudinal zones. In general, heights decline with latitude. But the greatest heights are in the subtropics, which have less cloud and precipitation than regions close to the equator. (*After V. Paschinger.*)

tation, distribution of precipitation throughout the year, and degree of exposure to the sun. The fact that the snow line on the warmer southern slopes of the Himalayas is 2,500 ft lower in elevation than on the cooler northern slopes reflects the much heavier precipitation on the former. As a rule, the snow line is lower on windward slopes, where precipitation is heavier, than on drier leeward slopes. It is also lower on shadier slopes inclined away from the sun. A winter maximum of precipitation tends to lower the snow line too. In some places these controls are cumulative in their effects; in others they counteract and oppose each other.

Winds

On exposed mountain slopes and summits, where ground friction is small, wind speed is high. Mountain valleys, on the other hand, are more protected against violent winds.

Owing to the great variety of relief and exposure

in highlands, there are a number of local winds characteristic of mountainous areas. The gravity wind, involving a downslope movement of cold, dense air, is one type. Another is the diurnal reversal of wind direction, upslope by day and downslope by night, which was discussed in the section on mountain and valley winds in Chapter 3. Most are unnamed.

Foehn or chinook.   The foehn is a warm, dry, gusty downslope wind generated by a passing cyclone or anticyclone. In the western United States and Canada it goes by the name of chinook. Such local winds are fairly common in most highland regions which feel the effects of large-scale traveling disturbances. They are especially well known in the northern valleys of the Alps and along the eastern slopes of the Rocky Mountains from Colorado northward. When a well-developed cyclonic storm is positioned over the High Plains just east of the Rockies it acts to draw air down the lee slopes toward its low-pressure center. The warmth of the chinook may be due exclusively to heating by compression as the air descends the eastern slopes. But commonly this source of heat is supplemented by heat of condensation as air is drawn up the windward western slopes and over the crest of the range (Figs. 11.23 and 11.24).

Usually the temperature of the chinook in winter is not much over 40°, but 60 to 70° temperatures are not unknown. These appear very warm—by contrast, at least—after a spell of frigid anticyclonic weather. The warmth is made more noticeable by the accompanying desertlike relative humidities of 10 to 20 percent. If snow lies on the ground, it vanishes as if by magic before the warm, dry blast

Mean altitude of the snow line (Elevation in ft)

	Latitude							
	0–10°	10–20°	20–30°	30–40°	40–50°	50–60°	60–70°	70–80°
Northern Hemisphere	15,500	15,500	17,400	14,100	9,900	6,600	3,300	1,650
Southern Hemisphere	17,400	18,400	16,800	9,900	4,900	2,600	0	0

Source: After Landsberg.

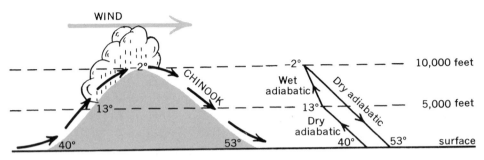

Figure 11.23 Diagrammatic representation of a chinook (*left*), and lapse rates associated with the chinook (*right*).

of the chinook. A rise in temperature of 40° within 24 hr is not unusual. Kipp, Montana, has the extraordinary record of a 34° rise within an interval of 7 min.

Foehns or chinooks have a number of conflicting economic effects. In the western parts of the North American High Plains, the chinook meliorates the winter cold and makes the snow cover less persistent, so that livestock can be grazed throughout the winter on the open range. An offsetting factor is the serious depletion of soil moisture, together with the evaporation of the snow mantle before its meltwater can penetrate the soil. Chinooks following spring planting may seriously damage the sprouted seeds.

In the northern valleys of the Swiss Alps, the average number of foehn days may be as high as 45 to 50 per year, with a minimum in summer and a maximum usually in spring. Some of the foehn valleys become climatic oases in winter. In spring the foehn valleys are freed early from their winter snow mantle, thus hastening the beginning of farming operations. Autumn foehns help advance the ripening of grapes and so lessen the danger from freeze. During a vigorous foehn, however, great precautions must be taken against the fire hazard associated with the excessive dryness and the strong winds.

Daily weather

In highlands the weather changes within the 24-hr period are likely to be greater than on adjacent lowlands. Striking contrasts between hot sun and cool

Figure 11.24 Barograph, thermograph, and humidity changes during a foehn at Altdorf in Switzerland. (*After Walter.*)

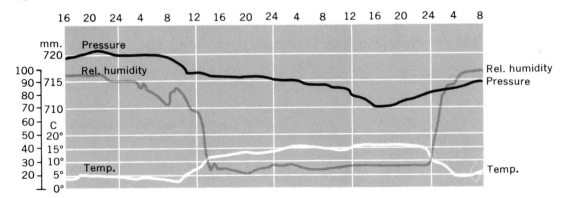

Average monthly frequency of the foehn at Sierre, Switzerland

	J	F	M	A	M	J	J	A	S	O	N	D	Yr
Average number of days	2	2	5	7	6	3	2	1	2	3	2	2	37

Source: After Landsberg.

shade, rapid shifts from chilly winds to calm, sudden gusts of rain or possibly snow, changing again to intense sunlight—such is the erratic nature of the daily weather. Even within tropical highlands, the complex sequence of daily weather contrasts with the uniformity of temperature conditions between the months.

At Quito, Ecuador, nights and early mornings are cold and raw, but the strong sun causes temperatures to mount rapidly. By noon it may be hot in the sun, though still cool in the shade. About midday or before, convectional clouds begin to form. In the afternoon there may be a violent thunderstorm, with heavy rain or snow showers, sometimes accompanied by hail. Storms and clouds die away as night approaches. The early mornings are fine, with clear air and good visibility. But in the afternoons clouds hang low over the gloomy landscape, so that the mountain peaks are ordinarily hidden and distant views are rare.

SELECTED REFERENCES FOR FURTHER STUDY OF TOPICS IN CHAPTER ELEVEN

American Geographical Society, The Antarctic atmosphere: climatology of the surface environment, Folio 8 of the Antarctic Map Folio Series, plates compiled by National Weather Records Center and W. S. Weyant, text by W. S. Weyant, 1968.

Antarctic Meteorology: Proceedings of the Symposium Held in Melbourne, Pergamon Press, New York, 1960.

Dorsey, Herbert G., Jr., "Arctic Meteorology," in Thomas F. Malone (ed.), *Compendium of Meteorology*, American Meteorological Society, Boston, 1951, pp. 942–951.

Hare, F. Kenneth, "Some Climatological Problems of the Arctic and Sub-Arctic," in Thomas F. Malone (ed.), *Compendium of Meteorology*, American Meteorological Society, Boston, 1951, pp. 952–964.

——, *Studies in Arctic Meteorology*, Publ. Meteorol. No. 10, Arctic Meteorology Research Group, McGill University, Montreal, 1958.

—— and Svenn Orvig, *The Arctic Circulation*, Publ. Meteorol., No. 12, Arctic Meteorology Research Group, McGill University, Montreal, 1958.

Rubin, M. J., "The Antarctic and the Weather," *Scientific American*, Vol. 207, pp. 84–94, 1962.

——, "Antarctic Weather and Climate," in *Research in Geophysics*, Vol. II, *Solid Earth and Interface Phenomena*, The M.I.T. Press, Cambridge, Mass., 1964, pp. 461–478.

Sabbagh, Michael E., "A Preliminary Regional Dynamic Climatology of the Antarctic Continent," *Erdkunde*, Vol. 16, pp. 94–111, 1962.

——, "Seasonal and Regional Variations of Temperature over the Antarctic Continent during 1958," *Geog. Ann.*, Vol. 45, pp. 52–75, 1963.

——, and Reid A. Bryson, *An Objective Precipitation Climatology of Canada*, Tech. Rept. No. 8, The University of Wisconsin Department of Meteorology, Madison, Wis., 1962.

Schneider-Carius, K., "Klimazonen und Vegetationsgürtel im tropischen und subtropischen Gebirge," *Erdkunde*, Vol. 2, pp. 303–313, 1943.

Shear, James A., "The Polar Marine Climate," *Ann. Assoc. Amer. Geographers*, Vol. 54, no. 3, pp. 310–317, 1964.

van Rooy, M. P. (ed.), *Meteorology of the Antarctic*, South African Weather Bureau, Pretoria, Norsk Polarinstitut, Oslo, 1957.

Wexler, H., "Seasonal and Other Temperature Changes in the Antarctic Atmosphere," *Quart. J. Roy. Meteorol. Soc.*, Vol. 85, pp. 196–208, 1959.

CHAPTER TWELVE

DRY CLIMATES (B)

The five groups of humid climates described in Chapters 8 through 11 are defined in terms of temperature. Only one of the great climatic groups, the dry type, has its boundaries fixed by rainfall values. Because it is the exception, this group is treated after the five humid groups, even though its letter, *B*, seems to place it earlier in the discussion. As mentioned in Chapter 7, *B* was Köppen's label for the dry climates, and his letter is retained here because the Köppen classification is widely known and used among American geographers.

Definition and boundaries.   The essential feature of a dry climate is that the annual water loss through evapotranspiration at the earth's land-water surface exceeds the annual water gain from precipitation. (In a humid climate, of course, the reverse is true.) Thus dry climates do not have a constantly replenished groundwater supply, and permanent streams cannot originate within dry regions. However, permanent streams can cross areas with dry climates—as do the Nile, the Colorado, and the Indus, for instance—provided they have their sources in more humid regions.

Logically the boundary separating dry from humid climates is located where, on the average, annual precipitation equals annual evapotranspiration. Notice that since two variables are involved, no specific amount of annual rainfall can serve as the universal boundary of dry climates as a group. The amount of rainfall which is permissible will always vary with the amount of water lost by evapotranspiration.

But to compare water gains and water losses over the earth is not easy. The rain gauge measures precipitation with fair accuracy, so that rainfall distribution, at least over much of the land surface, is relatively well known. But no adequate instrument has been developed for measuring evapotranspiration. As a consequence much less is known about the distribution of water losses from the land-water surface to the atmosphere.

Because there are no actual measurements of evapotranspiration for large areas of the earth, the only alternative is to discover a relationship between potential evapotranspiration and other climatic elements for which more abundant world data do exist. Since the rate of evaporation depends upon the vapor-pressure difference between the surface and the air immediately above, and also upon turbulence which carries the moistened air upward, it has been determined that there is a fairly close relationship between air temperature and wind speed on the one hand and potential evapotranspiration on the other.

Thornthwaite and Holzman have developed the following formula for computing evaporation:

$$E = \frac{17.1 \ (e_1 - e_2) \ (u_2 - u_1)}{t + 459.4}$$

where

E = evaporation in inches per day

e_1, e_2 = vapor pressure in inches of mercury at the two levels 1 and 2

u_1, u_2 = wind speed at the two levels in miles per hour

t = temperature in °F

Unfortunately, data on vertical gradients of vapor pressure and wind speed are rare, so that the formula is not very helpful for showing the distribution of the earth's dry climates. Other evaporation formulas based on more commonly measured quantities have been developed, but the usefulness of these too is impaired because of meager observational data.

There are cruder but more widely applicable evaporation formulas, often referred to as moisture indexes or indexes of aridity, that relate potential evaporation to air temperature alone, since temperature is the major control of evaporation potential. Lang's index of aridity, $I = P/T$, indicates that the effectiveness of precipitation varies directly with precipitation and inversely with temperature. De Martonne's moisture index, $I = P/(T + 10)$, and Köppens $I = P/(T + 7)$, are slight refinements of Lang's. All these use annual values of precipitation (in millimeters) and temperature given °C.

No such formulas seem to be entirely satisfactory or universally acceptable, however. They all do show that in the warmer lower latitudes, where the losses due to evapotranspiration are great, less of the total rainfall is effective for plant growth than in the cooler middle latitudes. It is quite possible that an amount of precipitation sufficient to produce a humid climate in regions with moderate temperatures might be classed as dry in a region of great heat. Paris, France, has an annual rainfall of only 23 in.; yet in that cool marine climate it produces a distinctly humid landscape. The same amount in tropical Africa could result in semiarid conditions. Moreover, if a large amount of the total annual rainfall comes in the warmer months, much more is lost through evapotranspiration than would be in a region where precipitation is evenly distributed over the 12 months or concentrated in the cool season.

Köppen's method for determining the amount of annual precipitation that defines the boundary between dry and humid climates, or the outer margins of the semiarid steppe, is expressed by three formulas:

$r = 2t + 14$ rainfall evenly distributed   (1)

$r = 2t$ rainfall concentrated in winter   (2)

$r = 2t + 28$ rainfall concentrated in summer   (3)

where

r = annual rainfall in centimeters

t = average annual temperature in °C

From the formulas it is obvious that the amount of rainfall r defining the humid boundary of dry climates will be greater where mean annual temperatures (and hence losses through evapotranspiration) are high, and less where the temperatures are low. Also, r will be highest where rainfall is concentrated in the warm season (formula 3), and least where the maximum is in winter, when evapotranspiration is least (formula 2). From the table below it can be seen that in a climate with a mean annual temperature of 50° (provided rainfall is well distributed seasonally), a yearly rainfall of only 13.5 in. or over is required to produce a humid climate; but where the annual temperature is 80°, the comparable figure is just about doubled, or 26.7 in. Of course, Köppen never meant his formulations to be definitive and exact boundary values, but only convenient approximations.

Köppen designed formulas 2 and 3 to be applied only in situations where there are marked seasonal contrasts both in rainfall and in temperature. In places without important seasonal temperature differences, winter rains obviously can be no more effective than summer rains. Köppen is never very definite concerning the exact meaning of "summer concentration," "winter concentration," or "even distribution" of the annual rainfall as used in his formulas. Some writers have used the figure of 70 percent to mean a concentration as applied to the

Boundary between humid and dry climates according to Köppen (no dry season)

Temp., °F	Precip., in.
50	13.5
60	17.9
70	22.3
80	26.7
90	31.1
100	35.5

summer (April through September) or winter (October through March) half-year. If less than 70 percent is concentrated in either 6-month period, the rainfall is said to be evenly distributed. Others choose the same definition of summer rain and winter rain that Köppen uses to identify w and s in his C climates, i.e., ten times as much rain in the rainiest summer month as in the driest winter month and three times as much rain in the wettest winter month as in the driest summer month.

When the three formulas given above are converted into their nearly exact equivalents in English units of measurement (R = annual rainfall in inches, T = average annual temperature in °F), they appear as follows:

$R = 0.44T - 8.5$

  rainfall evenly distributed   (1)

$R = 0.44T - 14$

  rainfall concentrated in winter   (2)

$R = 0.44T - 3$

  rainfall concentrated in summer   (3)

But in their transliterated form they tend to give a false impression of the degree of accuracy which Köppen intended for his formulas. Patton[1] suggests substituting three transliterated formulas with simpler constants which approximate their metric counterparts closely enough:

$R = \frac{1}{2}T - 12$ rainfall evenly distributed   (1)

$R = \frac{1}{2}T - 17$ rainfall concentrated in winter   (2)

$R = \frac{1}{2}T - 6$ rainfall concentrated in summer   (3)

Moreover, he continues the simplification process by transforming the three formulas into the single one

$R = \frac{1}{2}T - \frac{1}{4}Pw$

in which Pw is the observed winter percentage of rain at a particular place. From tests applied, this

[1] Clyde P. Patton, "A Note on the Classification of Dry Climates in the Köppen System," *Calif. Geographer*, Vol. 3, pp. 102–112, 1962.

single formula, simpler to use and to learn than three, gives results which do not depart significantly from those obtained by using the three standard Köppen formulas.

Dry climates are the most extensively developed over lands of any of the great climatic groups—occupying, according to Köppen, 26 percent of the continental area. Of this total, 14 percent is steppe, or semiarid, and 12 percent is desert, or arid. As might be expected, dry climates occupy a much smaller proportion of the earth's water surface—probably between 4 and 5 percent.

Temperature.   Since dry climates are found in such a wide variety of latitudes and continental locations, few valid general comments can be made concerning their temperatures. On the whole, however, their characteristic interior and leeward locations on the continents, and their clear skies and dry atmosphere, tend to make them severe *for their latitude,* with relatively extreme seasonal temperatures and thus large annual ranges.

Their large daily ranges, however, are even more marked. Clear, cloudless skies and relatively low humidity permit an abundance of solar energy to reach the land surface by day, but likewise allow a rapid loss of earth energy at night. Large diurnal ranges in deserts also are associated with the meager vegetation cover, which permits the barren surface to become intensely heated by the sun. The surface of dry ground may reach a daytime temperature of 200°F. It is a physical law that the higher the temperature of a body, the more rapid is its loss of heat by radiation, and consequently the more rapid its reduction in temperature.[2] Deserts therefore not only acquire heat quickly, but also lose it very fast.

On the other hand, in humid regions with a relatively complete vegetation cover, more of the solar radiation reaching the earth's surface is utilized in evapotranspiration. A large part of the energy consumed in this process is taken from the moist soil surface or the transpiring plant cover. Thus evapotranspiration is a heat regulator, preventing excessively high surface temperatures. As a consequence, humid regions with a vegetation cover are unlikely to have such extreme ground and air temperatures as deserts.

Based upon temperature, two main subdivisions of dry climate may be recognized: that of the tropics-subtropics, or *hot* dry climate (*Bh*), and that of temperate-boreal latitudes, or *cold* dry climate (*Bk*)—"cold" meaning cold in winter.[3]

Winds.   Dry regions are inclined to be windy places, since there is little frictional retardation of the moving air by the lowly and sparse vegetation cover. In this respect they are like the oceans. Moreover, the rapid daytime heating of the lower air over deserts leads to strong convectional overturning, and this interchange of lower and upper air tends to accelerate horizontal surface currents during warm hours when convection is at a maximum. "In the desert the wind is almost the only element of life and movement in the domain of death and immobility. A journey in the desert is a continuous strife against the wind charged with sand and, in moments of crisis, a painful physical struggle" (Gautier). Nights are likely to be much quieter, which is a partial explanation of the rapid nocturnal cooling of surface air in dry regions.

Because of the strong and persistent winds, desert air is often murky with fine dust which fills the eyes, nose, and throat, causing serious discomfort. Much of this dust is carried beyond the desert margins to form the loess deposits of bordering regions. The heavier, wind-driven rock particles, traveling close to the surface, are the principal tool of the wind in sculpturing desert landforms.

---

[2] The amount of heat radiated by a body is directly proportional to the fourth power of its absolute temperature.

[3] Köppen uses the mean annual isotherm of 18°C (64.4°F) as the boundary between the two main latitudinal subdivisions of dry climate. Many American geographers have substituted the January isotherm of 32° (0°C). In the classification employed here, the isoline of 8 months with a temperature of 50° (10°C) or above is accepted as the boundary between hot and cold dry climates. It is identical with the boundary separating subtropical and temperate climates.

Precipitation and humidity. Average annual rainfall in the dry climates is always deficient. In addition, it is extremely variable from year to year, so that the average is not to be depended upon (Fig. 4.34). One of the general principles of climatology, already discussed in Chapter 4's section on precipitation distribution, is that dependability of precipitation usually decreases with decreasing amount. Thus the handicaps of meagerness and unreliability of rainfall seem to go together. No part of the earth is known for certain to be absolutely rainless, although at Arica in northern Chile, the rainfall over a period of 17 years was only 0.02 in. During the whole 17 years there were only three showers heavy enough to be measured.

With a few exceptions, relative humidity is low in the dry climates, 12 to 30 percent being usual for midday hours. Conversely, potential evaporation is extremely high. Absolute humidity, on the other hand, is by no means always low, for hot desert air usually contains a considerable quantity of water vapor, even though it may be far from saturated. The amount of sunshine is great, and cloudiness small. Direct as well as reflected sunlight from the bare earth is blinding in its intensity.

Based on annual rainfall, two subdivisions of dry climate (which include both hot *Bh* and cold *Bk* types) are commonly recognized: the arid, or desert, type (*BW*), and the semiarid, or steppe, type (*BS*). In general, the steppe is a transitional belt surrounding the desert and separating it from the humid climates beyond. The boundary between arid and semiarid climates is an arbitrary one, which is defined by Köppen as one-half the amount separating steppe from humid climates. For example, if for a specified temperature, 19 in. of rainfall marks the outer, or humid, boundary of dry climates in general, then for a similar temperature, $9\frac{1}{2}$ in. may be taken as the boundary between steppe and desert. Thus in the three Köppen formulas given previously for determining the boundary of steppe and humid climates, the right-hand side of each equation must be divided by 2 in order to represent the boundary between desert and steppe. The same arbitrary treatment may be applied to the single Patton formula. A. Austin Miller, who has suggested the formula $r = t/3$ as representing the boundary between steppe and humid climates, proposes $r = t/5$ for defining the boundary between desert and steppe.

TROPICAL-SUBTROPICAL DRY CLIMATES (*BSh, BWh*)[4]

Type location. The heart of the tropical dry climates (see Figs. 7.2, 12.1, and the climate map) lies in the vicinity of latitudes 20 or 25°N and S and the average positions of their margins are at approximately 15 and 35° +. Thus they coincide fairly closely with the dry, subsiding air masses of the subtropical anticyclones. Subsidence and drought are not confined to the crests of the anticyclonic cells, for these characteristics extend out onto the equatorward slopes of the highs into the trade winds.

Ordinarily tropical dry climates do not reach to the eastern margins of the continents; humid climates characteristically take their places on the windward margins (Fig. 7.2). Along west coasts in these latitudes, by contrast, dry climates extend not only down to the sea margins, but even far beyond them over the eastern parts of the adjacent oceans. They also thrust abnormally far equatorward along some tropical western littorals (e.g., Peru-Ecuador and southwestern Africa).

As discussed in Chapter 7, this asymmetrical development skewed toward the west sides of continents is related to several factors: (1) the greater stability of air masses in the eastern as compared with the western parts of oceanic subtropical anticyclones, (2) the smaller number of atmospheric

[4] As shown in Chapter 7's list of definitions, the letter *h* indicates a hot, dry climate—8 months or more with an average temperature of 50° (10°C) or above.

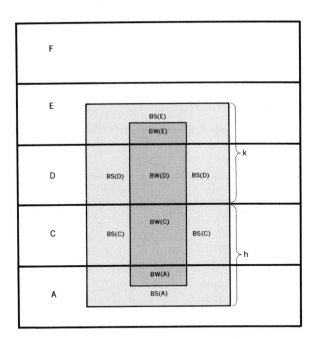

Figure 12.1 In this diagram, dry climates (*B*) are seen as intersecting four of the five great thermal zones (*A, C, D, E*), producing four subsets, *BA, BC, BD,* and *BE*. Two levels of aridity, steppe (*S*) and desert (*W*), are then added to produce the basic types shown in the diagram. *BA* and *BC* may be combined to form the hot (*h*), or tropical-subtropical, dry climates; and *BD* and *BE* to form the cold (*k*) dry climates. (*After James A. Shear.*)

disturbances along the eastern parts of tropical oceans and the adjacent western coasts of tropical continents, and (3) the general humidity contrasts between windward and leeward coasts in the tropical easterlies. Along tropical west coasts, no doubt the principal drought maker is subsidence in the subtropical anticyclone. But the cool ocean currents, fed by upwelling, which usually parallel these west coasts may further intensify the aridity. Some of the more extensive deserts, particularly the Sahara and the Australian desert, are important source regions for tropical continental air masses.

It appears to be a general rule, then, that humid tropical climates extend unusually far poleward along the eastern (windward) sides of continents (eastern Brazil, eastern Central America, eastern

Madagascar), while dry climates are carried equatorward beyond their normal latitudes along some western littorals. Low-latitude dry climates are characteristically bounded by *Aw* climates on their equatorward sides and by middle-latitude *C* (usually *Cs*) and *B* climates on their poleward and interior margins (compare Fig. 7.2 with the climate map inside the front cover).

The difference between type locations of desert and steppe is that desert climates are situated in the core area of subsidence, divergence, and temperature inversions within the subtropical anticyclone. These features are opposed to the development of fronts and atmospheric disturbances. Even when the intense surface heat of summer develops seasonal low-pressure centers over some of the low-latitude deserts, such convergent cyclonic circulations in the lower air are relatively shallow, and anticyclonic circulation still predominates aloft, damping any tendency toward convective overturning. Too far equatorward to be reached by the equatorward advance of middle-latitude fronts and cyclones on the poleward side, too far poleward to be affected by the ITC advancing from the low latitudes, and too far inland from eastern littorals to be affected by the humid onshore winds and the disturbances in the western oceanic trades, these low-latitude deserts lie outside the realms of the usual rainbringing winds and storms (Fig. 7.2).

Steppe typically surrounds the desert, except possibly on its western side (Fig. 7.2). It therefore constitutes a transition belt between desert and humid climates. Because steppe is less at the heart and more on the margins of dry, settling tropical air masses associated with the subtropical high-pressure cells, and is consequently one stage closer to the humid climates than the desert, steppe areas are encroached upon for a short period of the year by winds with rainbringing disturbances. It is this brief period of seasonal rains which causes them, although still having a dry climate, to be semiarid rather than arid.

In the case of North Africa, which may be taken as a fairly typical example, the climate map shows that there are two large and separate areas of tropical steppe, each occupying a representative location. One borders the Sahara on the *north* and lies between it and the subtropical dry-summer (*Cs*) climate. This steppe region is encroached upon by the westerlies with their cyclones and fronts in winter, the time of their maximum equatorward migration. Consequently winter is the season of maximum rainfall. Other subtropical steppes with this same type location are found in southern Australia; in Mesopotamia, Arabia, and southern Iran, in western Asia; and in northwestern Mexico and adjacent parts of the southwestern United States.

The second steppe region of northern Africa lies along the *equatorward* margins of the Sahara, separating the desert from the *Aw* type. This steppe receives its meager rainfall at the time of high sun from the disturbances accompanying the poleward-displaced ITC. The semiarid regions in northern Australia, much of dry southwestern Africa, and northwestern India-Pakistan largely belong to this group. In Australia the two typical belts of steppe, one on the poleward and the other on the equatorward margins of the tropical desert, are connected by a crescentic belt of steppe along the eastern side of the arid area. It is only on the western sides of continents, therefore, that the tropical deserts usually extend down to the sea margins and have no semiarid transition belts.

Precipitation

Annual amount.   Although no exact amount of rainfall can be accepted as defining the outer or humid margins of tropical-subtropical dry climates, the figure usually lies somewhere between 20 and 30 in. Half these amounts are more characteristic of the humid margins of deserts. Over much of the Sahara precipitation is under 5 in., as it is also in large parts of the other low-latitude deserts: the Kalahari in South Africa, the Atacama-Peruvian desert in western South America, the Australian desert, the Thar in northwestern India-Pakistan, and the Sonora in northwestern Mexico and the southwestern United States. At Cairo, Egypt, the annual rainfall averages 1.2 in.; at Lima, Peru, 2;

William Creek, Australia, 5.4; Yuma, Arizona, 3.3; and Port Nolloth in southwestern Africa, 2.3. In parts of northern Chile, rain may not fall for 5 to 10 years in succession. At Calama in northern Chile, located back of the Coastal Range, it is said that no rain has ever been recorded. Averages are of little value in giving a correct impression of desert rainfall, however, for not only is it small in amount, but it is also erratic. Over most low-latitude deserts, rainfall variability shows a 40+ percent departure from the normal (Fig. 4.35). It is therefore almost impossible to speak of a *typical* rainfall curve, or an *average* annual rainfall, for desert stations. At Iquique in northern Chile, for example, no rain fell during a period of 4 years. Then in the fifth year, one shower produced 0.6 in., which made the "average" annual rainfall for the 5-year period 0.12 in. On another occasion, 2.5 in. of rain fell in a single shower.

Rainfall in the steppes is also highly variable. Its undependability is probably more dangerous in semiarid than in arid lands, for in the desert there is not enough precipitation to tempt settlers to depend upon it. But the somewhat greater steppe rainfall, especially in more humid years, may lure the agriculturist into taking chances. For the most part it is only where irrigation supplements the variable rainfall that crop farming is reasonably safe. Animal grazing consequently takes on greater importance in steppe agriculture.

Seasonal distribution.   Desert rainfall is so meager and so erratic in its time of fall that its distribution throughout the year is of almost no consequence. But the larger annual total characteristic of steppes makes its distribution vitally important to settlers. As noted in an earlier section, tropical-subtropical steppes with contrasting type locations have different rainfall regimes.

Steppes with low-sun rainfall (BShs).[5]   These belts of steppe, which lie on the poleward sides of tropical deserts and close to *Cs* climate (see Fig. 7.2 and the climate map), have nearly all their rain

[5] The letter *s* indicates summer drought.

Climatic data for representative stations in tropical-subtropical deserts (*BWh*)

	J	F	M	A	M	J	J	A	S	O	N	D	Yr	Range
						Jacobabad, Pakistan								
Temp., °F	57	62	75	86	92	98	95	92	89	79	68	59	79	41
Precip., in.	0.3	0.3	0.3	0.2	0.1	0.2	1.0	1.1	0.3	0.0	0.1	0.1	4.0	
						William Creek, Australia								
Temp., °F	83	83	76	67	59	54	52	56	62	70	77	81	68	30.5
Precip., in.	0.5	0.4	0.8	0.4	0.4	0.7	0.3	0.3	0.4	0.3	0.4	0.3	5.4	
						Phoenix, Arizona								
Temp., °F	51	54	60	69	77	86	91	89	84	72	59	53	70	40
Precip., in.	0.7	0.8	0.7	0.3	0.1	0.1	0.8	1.1	0.7	0.5	0.5	0.8	7.2	

in the cool seasons. Like the *Cs* climates they border, they receive their rain from fronts associated with cyclonic storms, which travel more equatorward routes in winter than in summer. During the warmer part of the year, however, *BShs* regions are dominated by the dry settling and diverging air masses of subtropical high-pressure cells. Because rainfall is concentrated in the cool season, evaporation is less, and consequently the modest amount that falls is relatively effective for plant growth.

At Benghazi in the steppe region north of the Sahara, 3 midsummer months—June, July, and August—are rainless, while December and January are the rainiest months (see the table given below). The mean annual precipitation is slightly less than 11 in., but this is derived from such totals for single years as 22 in., 24 in., 6.8 in., and 7.1 in.—all of which occurred within a span of 7 years. Variability is not so great, however, as in steppes which have a high-sun rainfall maximum.

In steppe lands with a low-sun rainfall, spells of cloudy, rainy weather associated with passing cyclonic storms are not unusual in the winter season.

Not only cloud and rainfall are involved, but changes in temperature as well: Air of tropical origin with higher temperatures precedes the low center, and higher-latitude, cooler air is advected following the storm. It is obvious from the climate map that these regions are far enough poleward to feel the effects of modified polar air masses. In spite of the fact that winter is the rainiest season, it is not a time of predominantly overcast skies, for a considerable part of the cool-season rain falls from cumulus clouds and has a short duration.

Steppes with high-sun rainfall (*BShw*).[6] Tropical steppe lands occupying the equatorward margins of deserts, and therefore lying between them and the *Aw*, are likely to have a very brief period of relatively heavy rains at the time of high sun, when the ITC is farthest poleward (see Fig. 7.2, the climate map, and the table of climatic data for Kayes, Mali). Seasonal rainfall periodicity is like that of the *Aw*, except that the dry season is longer and the total precipitation less.

[6]The letter *w* indicates winter drought.

Climatic data for a representative tropical-subtropical station with low-sun rainfall (*BShs*)

	J	F	M	A	M	J	J	A	S	O	N	D	Yr	Range
						Benghazi, Libya, 32°8'N (marginal)								
Temp., °F	56	57	60	65	71	75	77	78	76	73	67	59	68	22.5
Precip., in.	2.7	1.6	0.8	0.2	0.1	0.0	0.0	0.0	0.1	0.7	1.8	2.6	10.5	

Climatic data for a representative tropical-subtropical steppe station with high-sun rainfall (*BShw*)

	J	F	M	A	M	J	J	A	S	O	N	D	Yr	Range
Kayes, Mali, 14° 20′N														
Temp., °F	77	81	89	94	96	91	84	82	82	85	83	77	85	19.2
Precip., in.	0.0	0.0	0.0	0.0	0.6	3.9	8.3	8.3	5.6	1.9	0.3	0.2	29.1	

At Dakar in Senegal, 6 months—December through May—are nearly rainless, while 86 percent of the year's total falls (principally in convectional showers) during July, August, and September. Since the rain arrives in the hot season when evaporation is at a maximum, less of it is effective for vegetation, and consequently these steppes bordering the savannas usually have more total rainfall than their poleward counterparts described above. This convectional rainfall is also more variable. Temperatures are not greatly different from those of the adjacent desert. As shown in the accompanying table, Kayes, a station with abnormally high temperatures, has its time of greatest heat preceding the rainy season. Since cloudiness is greatest during its rainy summer months, its highest temperatures do not coincide with the time of highest sun.

Intensity of rainfall. Tropical dry climates, like those of low latitudes in general, are characterized by convective rains that fall as heavy local showers from towering cumulonimbus clouds. Seven single convective storms brought nearly one-quarter of the total rain (30.7 in.) that fell at Helwan in the Egyptian Sahara in a 20-year period. In one of these storms 1.8 in. of rain fell, causing torrents to sweep down the wadies and do much damage to buildings and crops.

These sudden heavy downpours may cause much more harm than good. The wadies, which are entirely without water during most of the year, can become muddy torrents filled with debris after one of these flooding rains. In an earlier period, army regulations forbade French troops in the Sahara to pitch their overnight camps in the bottoms of dry wadies because of the danger of sudden floods—and this in spite of the fact that the high banks of the wadies give protection against the disagreeable winds. After a serious desert flood, settlements suffer, roads, bridges, and railways may be damaged, and irrigation systems are often clogged with debris.

Because of the violence of tropical desert rains and the sparseness of the vegetation cover, temporary local runoff is excessive, and consequently less of the total fall becomes effective for vegetation or for the crops of the oasis farmer. This "dash" character of hot-desert showers, plus their local nature and their erratic seasonal distribution, makes them of little direct use for agriculture, so that no immediate dependence is placed upon them as a source of water. Much of the precipitation that reaches the earth is quickly evaporated by the hot, dry desert air, but some sinks in to replenish the underground water which appears at the surface in the form of springs or artesian flows.

Long-continued general rains, falling from an overcast cloud deck, are almost limited to steppes located on the poleward margins of tropical desert (*BShs*). In these, the winter rains are derived from cyclonic storms of the westerlies.

Cloudiness and sunshine. Skies are prevalently clear in the low-latitude deserts, so that sunshine is abundant. In the Sonoran Desert of the United States and Mexico, 75± percent of the possible sunshine is received in winter, and 90± percent in the other seasons. Yuma, Arizona, averages 88 percent of the possible sunshine for the year: 95 percent in May, 97 percent in June, and 78 percent in January. Over much of the Sahara, December and January have a cloudiness of only 1/10, while from June to October it drops to about 1/30. The pitiless glare of sunlight in the tropical deserts is such an essential characteristic of their landscapes that the occasional dark or rainy day, being so unusual, is said to be particularly depressing.

Strong surface heating, due to the intense solar radiation and the nearly bare ground, must give rise to vigorous surface convection currents. But because the stability associated with subsidence aloft is so great and the relative humidity so low, it is only infrequently that the heated surface air rises high enough to produce thunderheads. Dark cumulonimbus clouds do form occasionally, sometimes accompanied by thunder and lightning; but the streamers of rain that can be seen descending from them usually are evaporated in the arid atmosphere before they reach the earth. However, even though the air may be physiologically dry and may have intense evaporating power, there is usually a moderate amount of moisture in it. All that is lacking is a way to cause it to be condensed and precipitated. Thus the air at Yuma, Arizona, contains nearly as much moisture in July, and twice as much in January, as that at Madison, Wisconsin, in the same months. However, the relative humidity at Yuma (January, 47 percent; July, 34 percent—8 P.M. readings) is only one-half to two-thirds as great in either season. In spite of the low relative humidity, nocturnal surface cooling in the deserts frequently is sufficient to produce valley fogs and dew.

Owing to the high temperature and low relative humidity, potential evaporation is excessive, often twenty or more times the precipitation. At Yuma the average evaporation during the 5 hot months is 55 in., while the average rainfall during the same period is not quite 1 in. Relative humidities as low as 2 percent, with temperatures over 100°, have been recorded in the Egyptian Sahara. It was the extraordinarily dry air which allowed the Egyptians to mummify their dead.

Temperature

Annual and diurnal temperatures.   Annual ranges of temperature in low-latitude dry climates are larger than in any other type of climate within the tropics, for 20 to 30°+ is usual (Figs. 12.2 and 12.3). Aswan in the Sahara has mean temperatures

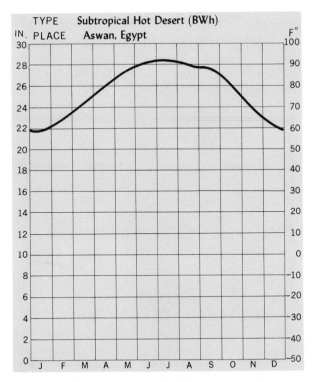

Figure 12.2   Average monthly temperatures for a hot-desert station in the Egypitan Sahara. Note the large annual range for a latitude of about 24°. Precipitation is not appreciable.

of 61° in January and 95° in July, resulting in an annual range of 34°. Such ranges, which even exceed those of some middle-latitude climates, reflect not only the clear skies, bare earth, and low humidity, but also the higher latitudes of the deserts and somewhat greater seasonal extremes of solar radiation compared with most of the *humid* tropics. Remember that in the tropical dry climates it is the excessive summer heat, rather than the winter cold, which leads to the marked differences between the seasons. This is the only tropical climate where annual range may occasionally equal daily range.

Daily ranges, however, are usually larger, averaging 25 to 45° and in rare instances even reaching 60°. The same conditions—dry air, cloudless skies, and bare, dry earth—that make for moderately large temperature differences between the extreme

TOMBOUCTOU, MALI (Temp. in C°) 16°49′N; 2°52′E

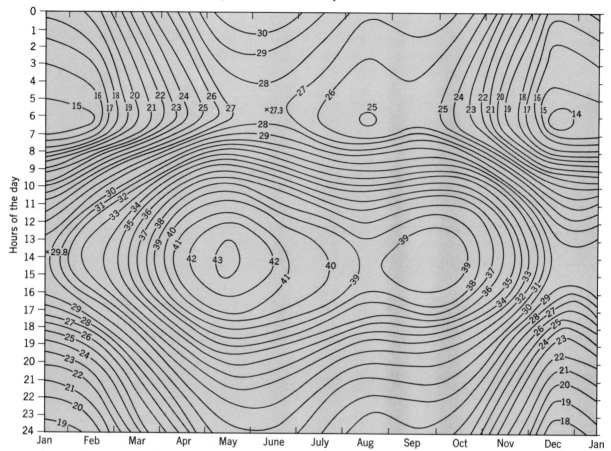

Figure 12.3 Thermoisopleths for a representative hot-desert station in the Mali Sahara of North Africa.

months are likewise conducive to wide differences within the diurnal period. At Bir Milrha in the Libyan Sahara, a minimum temperature of 31° and a maximum of 99° have been recorded on the same day.

The hot season. During the high-sun period, scorching, desiccating heat prevails. Hot-month temperatures average between 85 and 95° (Yuma, 91°; Tombouctou, 94.5°; Nullagine, Australia, 90°), and midday readings of 105 to 110° are common at this season (Fig. 12.4). In the western part of the Australian desert, temperatures have exceeded 100°

on 64 consecutive days and 90° on 150 consecutive days. At Greenland Ranch in Death Valley, California, the daily maxima in 1960 reached or rose above 100° on 136 consecutive days. At this time of year, although the lower night temperatures are a distinct relief by contrast with the days, they are by no means cool. At Phoenix, Arizona, the midsummer daily maxima usually exceed 100°, and the minima are close to 75 or 76°. In the northern Sahara, average daily maxima of 99° are followed by minima approximating 71°. At Azizia, 25 miles south of Tripoli, 136.4° has been recorded; this is the highest air temperature in the shade ever registered under

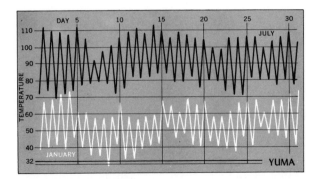

Figure 12.4 Daily maximum and minimum temperatures for the extreme months at a hot-desert station, located on the northern margins of the subtropics in Arizona. While solar control is dominant, modest nonperiodic air-mass effects associated with passing cyclones and anticyclones are present at this latitude, especially in winter.

standard conditions of thermometer exposure. The highest official air temperature ever recorded in the United States is 134°, in Death Valley in the California desert.

The low-sun period.   During the period of low sun the days still are warm, with the daily maxima usually averaging 60 to 70° and occasionally reaching 80° (Figs. 12.3 and 12.4). But nights are distinctly chilly at this season, with the average minima in the neighborhood of 50°±. The station In Salah in the Sahara during January has average daily maxima of about 70° and minima of around 40°. The average annual extremes there are 30° and 122°, and the temperature has been known to go as high as 124° and as low as 26°. There may even be occasional frosts in low spots in some subtropical deserts. A Saharan traveler gives the following description of the cool season in that arid region:

In truth the days are generally very trying, for there is either a blazing sun which burns through the thin cotton (clothing), or a bitter wind which pierces every bone in one's body. Sometimes there were both together, and then one side of one is frozen and the other baked! One's skin split and blistered under this treatment, but

there was only one hour I shall never be able to forgive the desert. This was the moment when, at 5 A.M., one crept shivering out of one's warm flea-bag into pitch darkness, placed one's feet gingerly on icy cold sand, fumbled with numb fingers for a candle and matches, and proceeded to drag on cold, stiff garments from each of which fell a shower of sand.[7]

Daily weather

As is true of the rest of the tropics, the sun very much controls the weather in the low-latitude dry climates. Diurnal regularity is pronounced, so that there is a great deal of sameness between successive days. This is especially true of the summer season in the dry climates. But on their poleward margins, which lie close to the middle latitudes, they have occasional invasions of polar air with associated fronts and cyclonic storms, which now and then may cause spells of weather. This happens particularly during the winter season, when the westerlies and the cyclone belt are farthest equatorward.

The daily march of temperature at Yuma, Arizona, clearly indicates these nondiurnal oscillations of temperature in winter (Fig. 12.4). On the front of the cyclone, southerly winds of tropical origin advect higher temperatures. These are followed by several days of cooler weather as the winds swing around to the north on the rear of the low. Occasional gray days with some rain may result from a few of the cyclones, whose centers are usually well beyond the poleward margins of the dry climates.

On the equatorial margins of tropical dry climates, it is the high sun or summer period that has the most "weather." As the ITC shifts poleward with the sun, various kinds of tropical disturbances bring spells of showers, particularly to the steppes. The effects of these disturbances are chiefly confined to precipitation, although their clouds are likely to reduce temperatures somewhat during the brief rainy season.

[7]Rosita Forbes, *The Secret of the Sahara: Kufara,* Doubleday & Company, Inc., New York, 1921, pp. 168–169.

COOL WESTERN LITTORALS (*Bn*)[8]

Temperature

The usual characteristics of tropical deserts—high temperatures, large diurnal and annual temperature ranges, low relative humidity, and little cloud—are significantly modified along the littorals (usually western) of several of the low-latitude deserts, especially where cool ocean currents parallel the coasts (Fig. 12.5). The influence of cool water is especially marked along the desert coasts of Peru and northern Chile from about latitude 4 to 31°S, and the west coast of Africa from 8 to 32°S. Cool currents also have a noticeable effect on climate along the Atlantic coasts of the Moroccan Sahara from Casablanca to Senegal, Somali in northeastern Africa, and northwestern Mexico. (Some of these regions are steppes rather than true deserts.)

The low temperatures of the ocean waters are partly the result of advection from higher latitudes, for the currents are driven equatorward by the spiraling winds about the eastern end of a subtropical anticyclone. In part also, they are due to upwell-

ings of colder subsurface water along these coasts. The land margins adjacent to the cool waters are unusually cool, with temperatures 10° or more lower than normal for the latitude (Fig. 12.6). Thus Callao on the Peruvian coast has an annual temperature of only 67°, and Mollendo 65°, while Bahía on the east coast of Brazil, in a similar latitude, averages 77°. The hottest month at Callao is only 71° (similar to July at Madison, Wisconsin), while the coldest is 62.5°. At Port Nolloth, a coastal desert station in South Africa which is paralleled by the cool Benguela Current, temperatures of the warmest and coldest months are 59 and 53°, while

[8] In the Köppen symbols, *n* signifies frequent fog (*Nebel* in German); *n'* high relative humidity with haze and therefore low visibility, but not actual fog.

Figure 12.5 Distribution of cool coastal dry climates (*Bn*) in tropical and subtropical latitudes. Here fog and low stratus are common. Characteristically this subtype of tropical-subtropical dry climate is located along coasts which are paralleled by cool ocean currents fed by upwelling and which are affected by strong anticyclonic subsidence.

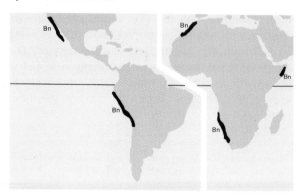

Figure 12.6 Average monthly temperatures for a marine desert station located on a coast paralleled by a cool ocean current. Temperatures are abnormally low, and the annual range is very small. Compare with Fig. 12.2. Precipitation is not appreciable.

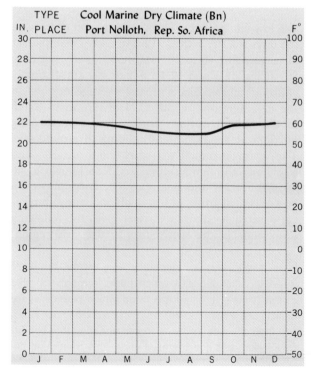

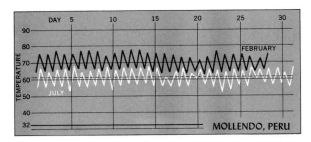

Figure 12.7 Daily maximum and minimum temperatures for the extreme months at a low-latitude desert station located on a coast paralleled by a cool ocean current. Note the abnormally low average temperatures and the small daily ranges. Compare with Fig. 12.4.

at Durban, across the continent on the east coast, comparable figures are 76 and 64°.

From the temperature data given above, it may be noted that the annual ranges of temperature are unusually small. The temperature difference between the extreme months is only 8.5° at Callao and 6° at Port Nolloth. These ranges should be compared with 34° at Aswan, Egypt, and 40° at Jacobabad, Pakistan. Diurnal ranges are also very small in these cool marine deserts of the low latitudes (Fig. 12.7). *BWn* regions are thus characterized by (1) lower-than-average annual temperatures, (2) distinctly cooler summers, and (3) smaller annual and diurnal ranges than are normal for most tropical dry climates.

Precipitation and fog

Annual rainfall along these cool coasts is extremely low (2.3 in. at Port Nolloth, 1.2 in. at Callao), and the drought conditions may extend to within a few degrees of the equator. Yet even so, these are regions of high relative humidity and abundant fog. Their intensified aridity is chiefly attributable to the very

stable air and low-level inversions characteristic of the eastern side of the subtropical anticyclone, which is strongly developed along these tropical and subtropical west coasts. Perhaps the cool coastal waters have a further stabilizing effect upon the *mT* air and hence may be an auxiliary cause for the decreased precipitation. In Peru, this cool, stable air mass must be forced upward along the flanks of the Andes to an altitude of about 5,000 ft before reaching the zone where there are dependable annual rains.

The fog and low stratus so frequent on these cool-water coasts are related both to advection from the cool water and to the low-level temperature inversion. Turbulence near the surface usually is sufficient, especially during the day, to prevent the fog from reaching to ground level, so that much of the time it hangs in the form of a low, uniform stratus deck. It is kept from rising and dissipating by the temperature inversion. In winter the fog and stratus lower and are more continuous, often reaching down to ground level at night. Occasionally the stratus produces mist and even a fine drizzle. At Swankopmund, South-West Africa, fog is recorded on 150 days during the year. In Peru the heavy fog, or "wet mist," is sufficient to create a meager showing of vegetation on the coastal hills. Darwin, in his book *The Voyage of the Beagle,* describes these Peruvian mists as follows:

A dull heavy bank of clouds constantly hung over the land, so that during the first sixteen days I had only one view of the Cordillera behind Lima. It is almost become a proverb that rain never falls in the lower part of Peru. Yet this can hardly be considered correct, for during almost every day of our visit there was a thick drizzling mist which was sufficient to make the streets muddy and one's clothes damp. This the people are pleased to call "Peruvian dew."

Climatic data for a representative desert station on a cool-water coast (*BWn*)

	J	F	M	A	M	J	J	A	S	O	N	D	Yr	Range
						Lima, Peru								
Temp., °F	71	73	73	70	66	62	61	61	61	62	66	70	66	12.8
Precip., in.	0.0	0.0	0.0	0.0	0.0	0.2	0.3	0.5	0.5	0.1	0.0	0.0	1.8	

MIDDLE-LATITUDE DRY CLIMATES (*BSk*, *BWk*)[9]
(Temperate-Boreal)

Type location.   Unlike the dry climates of low latitudes, middle-latitude steppes and deserts are not primarily a consequence of location within drought-making pressure and wind systems. Instead they are typically found in the deep interiors of the great continents, far from the oceans, which are the principal sources of the continental atmosphere's water vapor (Fig. 7.2 and the climate map). In both Eurasia and North America the aridity of the deep continental interiors is further intensified by highlands, which surround extensive regions in the interior and act to block the entrance of humid maritime air masses and rain-producing storms. Where high mountains closely parallel a coast, as they do in the western United States, arid climates may approach relatively close to the sea. Asia, the greatest land mass in middle latitudes, has the largest area of dry climates; North America is next in order.

Although tropical deserts characteristically extend down to the ocean margins on the leeward (western) sides of continents, the leeward (eastern) sides of land masses in the middle-latitude westerlies are far from dry. Eastern North America and Asia, for example, have mostly humid climates. This shifting of middle-latitude dry climates inland from the leeward coasts is associated with the presence of monsoons and cyclonic storms along the eastern sides of land masses in the westerlies. Owing to an unusual combination of circumstances, dry climates do reach the east coast in Patagonia (Argentina), but this is the exception. Outside of South America, no other Southern Hemisphere continent occupies sufficiently high latitudes to permit the development of extensive middle-latitude steppes and deserts. As in the tropics, steppe climates surround deserts, forming transition zones between them and humid climates.

Temperature

Although dry climates of middle latitudes duplicate the arid and semiarid climates of the tropics in their meager and undependable rainfall, they differ from them in having a season of severe cold. On the other hand, they resemble continental *humid* climate (*Dc*) of middle latitudes in their temperature and weather characteristics; they simply receive less rainfall.

The interior locations of most middle-latitude dry climates assure them of having relatively severe seasonal temperatures and thus large annual ranges (Fig. 12.8). Because their latitudinal spread is so wide (15 or 20° in both North America and Asia), it is difficult to speak of *typical* temperature conditions. For example, southernmost Colorado and

Figure 12.8

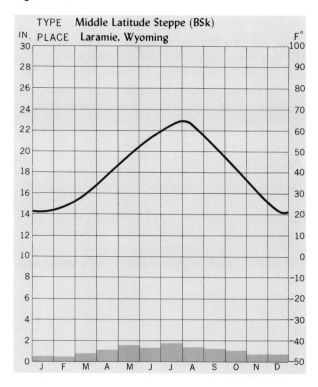

TYPE   Middle Latitude Steppe (BSk)
PLACE   Laramie, Wyoming

[9]The letter *k* indicates a cold (in winter) dry climate—less than 8 months with an average temperature of 50° (10°C) or above.

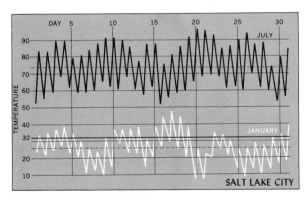

Figure 12.9 Daily maximum and minimum temperatures for a middle-latitude steppe station (*BS*). Note the strong nonperiodic air-mass control, especially in winter.

southern Alberta are both included within these climates; yet one is crossed by parallel 37°, while the other lies mostly poleward of 50°. Although naturally their temperature features are very different, each station has relatively severe temperatures for its latitude. Summers are likely to be warm or even hot, while winters are correspondingly cold. Tashkent in the U.S.S.R. at 41° N ranges from 32° in January to 81° in July, while for Ulan Bator, Mongolia, at 48°N, the comparable figures are −16 and 63°.

Because the ground is usually dry, the arrival of spring is relatively sudden, and the warm season advances rapidly. The quick rise in spring temperatures is much greater than in more humid continental climates, where a large part of the sun's energy is expended in melting the snow and evaporating the water rather than in heating the ground and the air. Diurnal ranges are apt to be large, for the same reasons given in the discussion of tropical steppes and deserts (Fig. 12.9).

The narrow Patagonian desert has seasonal temperatures quite unlike those of dry interior Eurasia and North America. Understandably, marine rather than continental conditions prevail, so that winter cold and summer heat are both largely absent and the annual range is small. No month's average temperature is as low as 32°, and none is as high as 60°.

Precipitation

Annual amount. Two factors chiefly account for the meager precipitation of middle-latitude dry climates: (1) They are either in the deep interiors of large continents or separated from the ocean by mountain barriers. (2) A well-developed seasonal anticyclone is characteristic of all but their subtropi-

Figure 12.10 Wide fluctuations in the location of the annual boundary separating dry from humid climates over a period of 5 successive years in the semiarid-subhumid region east of the Rocky Mountains. (*After Kendall.*)

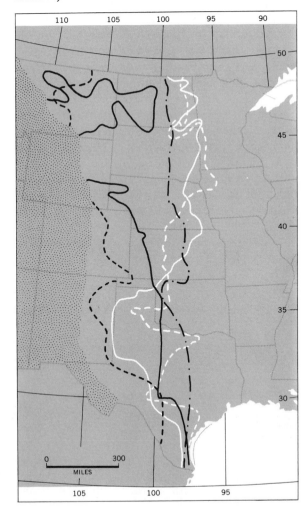

cal margins in winter. Moreover, the regions of most severe aridity are located in basins surrounded by highlands. Unlike the dry climates of the tropics, those of middle latitudes receive a portion of their precipitation in the form of snow, although the amount is characteristically small, and the winter snow cover is not deep.

Because of their generally lower temperatures, and therefore reduced evaporation potential, the humid boundaries of middle-latitude dry climates ordinarily have somewhat less rainfall than many tropical dry climates. This does not mean they are necessarily more arid. In fact the opposite is more often the case, for as a rule middle-latitude deserts are not so nearly rainless as some tropical ones.

Like rainfall in dry climates generally, that in middle-latitude *B* types varies greatly from year to year (Fig. 12.10). And in the middle as in the lower latitudes, this undependability has graver consequences in the steppe than in the desert. Parts, at least, of the steppe have enough rainfall to attract agricultural settlement. Moreover, a succession of more humid years may tempt settlers to push the agricultural frontier nearer to the desert. But drought years are sure to follow, bringing crop failures and economic disaster. In 30 to 40 percent of the years over a considerable area of the semiarid country in the United States, rainfall is less than 85 percent of the average. Over a period of 38 years at Minot, North Dakota, average annual rainfall was 15.7 in., but the most humid year had 24.3 in. and the driest only 7.2.

Seasonal distribution. It is not easy to generalize concerning seasonal distribution of precipitation in the dry climates of middle latitudes. In the more interior and continental locations poleward of about 40°, summer is usually the period of maximum precipitation (see the data for Ulan Bator and Williston, and also Fig. 12.9). This is related to the higher surface temperatures and associated convectional overturning, greater specific humidity, and tendency toward an inblowing system of monsoonal winds in summer. In winter the low temperatures and the predominantly anticyclonic circulation are opposed to abundant condensation. Most of interior Asia and the Great Plains region of North America are dry lands with a distinct summer maximum in their precipitation curves. Ulan Bator, Mongolia, for example, receives 84 percent of its average annual 7.6 in. of rainfall in the 3 summer months. Most middle-latitude dry climates do have a summer maximum of precipitation.

But those dry climates which lie close to subtropical latitudes, and especially to *Cs* climate, are likely to have somewhat more rain in winter than in summer (see data for Fallon, Nevada). This is caused by the same controls which produce subtropical dry-summer climate. Southern Turkestan in Soviet Russia and the southwestern part of the

Climatic data for representative stations in middle-latitude deserts (*BWk*)

	J	F	M	A	M	J	J	A	S	O	N	D	Yr	Range
Santa Cruz, Argentina														
Temp., °F	59	58	55	48	41	35	35	38	44	49	53	56	47.5	24
Precip., in.	0.6	0.4	0.3	0.6	0.6	0.5	0.7	0.4	0.2	0.4	0.5	0.9	6.1	
Kuche, Sinkiang, China (3,182 ft)														
Temp., °F	10	26	45	56	65	71	76	73	65	54	35	19	49	66
Precip., in.	0.1	0.1	0.2	0.1	0.1	1.3	0.7	0.3	0.2	0.0	0.1	0.3	3.4	
Fallon, Nevada (3,965 ft)														
Temp., °F	31	36	41	50	56	65	74	72	61	51	40	32	50.6	42.7
Precip., in.	0.6	0.5	0.5	0.4	0.6	0.3	0.1	0.2	0.3	0.4	0.3	0.6	4.7	

Climatic data for representative stations in middle-latitude steppes (*BSk*)

	J	F	M	A	M	J	J	A	S	O	N	D	Yr	Range
Williston, North Dakota (marginal)														
Temp., °F	8	12	24	42	55	63	71	68	57	46	28	16	40.9	63
Precip., in.	0.6	0.5	0.7	0.9	1.4	3.3	1.9	1.5	1.1	0.7	0.6	0.5	13.7	
Ulan Bator, Mongolia (3,800 ft)														
Temp., °F	−16	−4	13	34	48	58	63	59	48	30	8	−17	28	79
Precip., in.	0.0	0.1	0.0	0.0	0.3	1.7	2.6	2.1	0.5	0.1	0.1	0.1	7.6	
Saratov, U.S.S.R.														
Temp., °F	11	13	21	43	60	69	74	69	56	42	28	17	43	63
Precip., in.	1.1	1.0	0.8	1.0	1.3	1.8	1.2	1.3	1.1	1.4	1.4	1.2	14.5	

Great Basin in the United States both have a winter-maximum regime. Such regions are simply poleward extensions of the tropical *BShs* steppes with their low-sun rainfall maximum.

Seasonal weather

As a rule, the nonperiodic weather element associated with passing cyclones and anticyclones is not so well developed in the continental dry climates as in the continental humid types. In *winter* the dominant influence in dry climates of the higher middle latitudes is the continental anticyclone, whose settling air and diverging winds produce much clear sky and cold weather. Even so, the weather element is stronger in this season than in summer. On the whole, winds are not vigorous in winter, although violent winds sometimes do occur, chiefly with the passing of an occasional cyclone or with an anticyclonic surge from higher latitudes. The anticyclonic surge is known on the North American plains as a *blizzard,* already described in Chapter 10.

Summer weather is largely sun-controlled, and consequently the diurnal element is conspicuous in temperature, wind, cloud, and precipitation. Winds are often unpleasantly strong during the daylight hours, when convectional overturning is at a maximum.

REGIONAL FEATURES OF DRY CLIMATES

Probably in no other group of climates are there so many instances of local and regional departures from the world pattern.[10] A number of these consist of rainfall deficiencies in locations which, in terms of broad-scale circulation patterns, might be expected to be humid. Local and regional controls appear to be particularly effective in producing arid-ity. Many of the regional arid anomalies are not at present well understood. Significantly, a majority of them are located within tropical latitudes.

Africa. Some of the earth's most striking drought anomalies are in Africa. One is the unusual extensiveness of the Sahara, both in a north-south and an east-west direction. Obviously the Sahara's size is made possible by the great breadth of the continent north of the equator. Still, this is not the only reason, for broad South America south of the

[10] For a more complete analysis of the dry anomalies than this section provides, see Glenn T. Trewartha, *The Earth's Problem Climates,* The University of Wisconsin Press, Madison, Wis., 1961.

equator in Saharan latitudes has only a minimal amount of dry climate. In northern Africa, with no terrain barrier such as the Andes to break the continuity of the subtropical anticyclone, a divergent, subsident circulation prevails across the entire land mass and on into Arabia, southwestern Asia, and northwestern India-Pakistan. Dry Saharan air pushes far south, and as a result humid climates are able to extend northward only to about 13 to 15°, even though the surface ITC reaches a mean July-August position of 20–21°N. Here, however, the vertical structure of the air is such that the surface ITC is situated well within the Sahara. Hot, dry, northerly Sahara air overruns a thin wedge of humid maritime southwesterly air, but the Saharan air is so dry that in spite of slow lifting it yields no rain. Only as the wedge of maritime air deepens toward the south are convective showers possible, and this condition is not reached for several hundred miles south of the surface ITC.

Probably the most impressive single climatic anomaly in all Africa is the widespread rainfall deficiency in tropical and equatorial East Africa (see the rainfall map inside the back cover). It seems as if this region's location on the eastern or windward side, together with its elevation, should cause it to be wet. Since North Africa has no oceanic east coast north of about latitude 13°N, it may not be so surprising that desert climate there reaches down to the Red Sea margins. The real puzzle is why Somali, fronting on the Indian Ocean (also southern and eastern Arabia, fronting on the Arabian Sea), should be so dry, for east-side deserts in the tropics are rare. Moreover, along this east side, dry climates extend right across the equator and for nearly 10° into the Southern Hemisphere. And much of what is designated on the climatic map inside the front cover as tropical wet-and-dry climate is so distinctly subhumid that it is actually close to being semiarid.

The explanations for such an extensive development of dry and subhumid climates in tropical East Africa are complicated. Contributing factors are:

1. Both the northerly (November-February) and southerly (June-September) circulations crossing the area are divergent and subsident over extensive areas. Evidence of this is the frequency of above-surface inversions of temperature.

2. Both of these so-called monsoons have a strongly meridional flow, so that they do not advect oceanic moisture deeply into the interior. Not infrequently they closely parallel the coastline, or in places may actually have an offshore component.

3. North of the equator, Somali (also Arabia) is dominated year-round by stable subsident air of anticyclonic origin. There is no Indian Ocean–Arabian Sea anticyclone whose western margins might provide unstable or neutral mT air.

4. The southwest winds paralleling the Somali coast in summer result in upwelled cool waters, which may act to intensify the coastal aridity and produce coastal fog. This is the only important east-side Bn climate.

A striking feature of the Kalahari dry region in southwestern Africa is its Namib coastal section. Within the Bn class of deserts, the Namib is distinctive in that next to Peru-Chile, it is latitudinally the most extensive and also the most arid (Fig. 12.11). An annual rainfall of under 4 to 5 in. is maintained along a narrow coastal strip for about 15° of latitude. Three stations along this section of coast record less than 1 in. Lowest precipitation amounts appear to coincide with the coastline, and there is a slow increase inland. Fog, low stratus, and mist are prevalent.

The controls operating to produce this climatic combination are associated with a locationally stable anticyclone with a maximum subsidence along the coast at about 25°S. There is a low and persistent inversion. Since the cell's eastern end terminates abruptly at the coastline, smoothly curved southerly atmospheric and oceanic circulations develop along the coast, with an accompanying upwelling of cold water. As long as the coast bends westward, so that it maintains contact with the atmospheric and cool oceanic circulations around the eastern end of the anticyclone, drought prevails. Where it bends eastward, so that contact with the air and water circulations is weakened, rainfall increases. Still, the effects of these circulations in terms of greatly re-

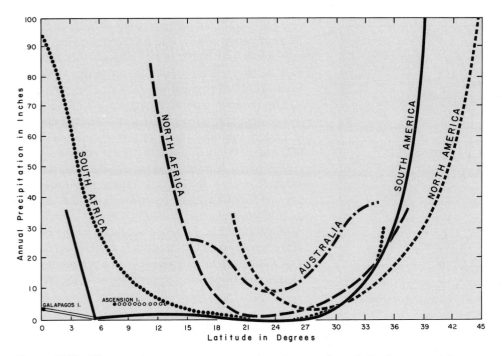

Figure 12.11   The annual precipitation curves plotted against latitude for five coastal deserts in tropical-subtropical latitudes. Note that the desert of Chile-Peru exhibits the highest intensity of aridity maintained throughout the greatest span of latitude. (*After Paul Lydolph.*)

duced rainfall are carried to within 5° or less of the equator along the coast.

The small enclave of semiarid, or subhumid *Aw*, climate in Ghana-Togo along the Guinea coast was referred to earlier in Chapter 8's discussion of tropical wet- and dry-climates.

Australia.   Here the chief anomaly within the extensive dry climates is the absence of any *Bn* involving a cool and intensely dry western littoral with a high frequency of fog and low stratus. Lowest rainfall along the west coast appears to be about 9 in., although it may decline to 6 in. in the deep interior. The reduced coastal aridity compared with similar locations on other continents probably is related to the absence of a strong, fixed anticyclonic cell whose smoothly curved easternmost circulation coincides with the Australian coastline. Consequently there is no cool current with upwelling of cold water. Instead of a positionally stable anti-

cyclone, western Australia is influenced by a succession of migratory high-pressure cells moving eastward, with occasional showers occurring in the troughs between individual cells.

South America.   Nowhere else on the earth is there a coastal desert of such intense aridity which spans so many degrees of latitude (25°±) as the Chilean-Peruvian desert (see Fig. 12.11 and the rainfall map inside the back cover). It is the *Bn* climate par excellence. From northern Peru, at about 5°S, to 30°S in northern Chile, the highest coastal rainfall is probably under 50 mm (2 in.), and a number of stations in northern Chile have recorded no rain over periods of a decade or more.[11] Even northward from Peru, dry climate in less intense form is con-

[11]Wolfgang Weischet, "Zur Klimatologie der Nordchilenischen Wüste," *Meteorol. Rundschau*, Vol. 19, pp. 1–7, 1966.

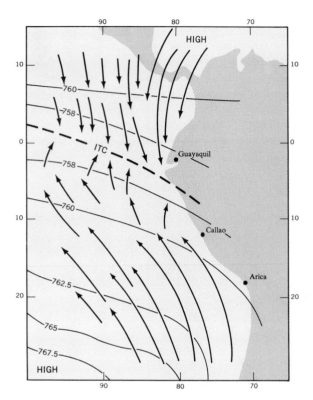

Figure 12.12 Pressure and wind patterns during one of the infrequent rainy episodes in the Peruvian desert. Note that the ITC, followed by northerly winds, had advanced to a position south of the equator along the coast of Peru. (*After Schott.*)

circulation and cool current are temporarily displaced by an invasion of ITC and its accompanying northerly winds and warm ocean current, the northern part of the coastal desert is suddenly converted from aridity to tropical wet climate (Fig. 12.12).

The desert-steppe of Patagonia has the distinction of being the only extensive east-side dry climate in middle latitudes (refer to the climate and rainfall maps). What is more, the driest or desert parts are on the seaward side, where annual rainfall drops to 4 or 5 in. In view of the narrowness of the continent in these latitudes, with consequent marine control, the prevailing aridity is all the more remarkable. Its origin is related to the effects of the Andes upon the broad-scale westerly wind flow. The Andean terrain barrier sets up a system of long, meridional, upper-troposphere waves in the wester-

Figure 12.13 Annual march of precipitation at a subtropical desert station. Note the primary maximum in summer and a secondary maximum in winter.

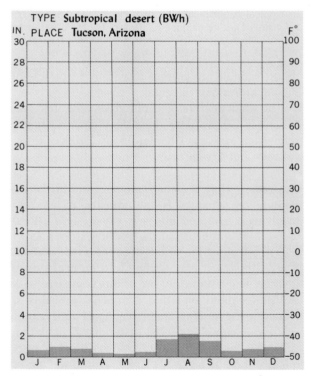

tinued along the Ecuador littoral to within a degree or less of the equator.

The combination of controls producing this phenomenal Peruvian-Chilean desert resembles that of southwestern Africa, except that in South America the drought makers, including anticyclonic circulation and cold current, maintain their effectiveness farther equatorward. This in turn is related to the concave coastline which continues to thrust westward to within a few degrees of the equator, so that the smoothly curved anticyclonic air and water circulations are held close to the coast. The high Andes also contribute by abruptly terminating the anticyclonic cell almost at the coastline. On rare occasions in northern Peru, when anticyclonic lies. These include a meridional anticyclonic ridge positioned over the narrow continent and a trough situated farther eastward over the ocean. Subsidence under the anticyclonic ridge acts to stifle rainmaking processes and damps the activity of cyclonic storms. If the continent were wider, so that its eastern parts were located underneath the trough, rainfall there would very likely be heavier.

Two other anomalous dry regions, one in easternmost Brazil and the other in coastal Colombia and Venezuela, already have been mentioned in the discussion of tropical wet-and-dry climates.

North America. The unexpected semiarid area in northwestern Yucatán (Mexico) may result from the fact that in summer, the rainy season, winds parallel the coast or blow slightly offshore. An offshore wind would result in coastline subsidence because of increased wind speed over the sea, where frictional drag is reduced. Paralleling winds would likewise result in divergence and subsidence, and also in the upwelling of cool water.

Along the west Gulf Coast both in northeastern Mexico and in adjacent parts of Texas, there is a semiarid region which appears out of place. Other parts of the Gulf Coast in both Mexico and the United States are wet. No adequate explanation for this dry region exists.

A distinctive feature of the dry intermontane region in the United States is its biannual rainfall maximum (Fig. 12.13). One maximum consistently occurs in winter. The second is more variable in its time of occurrence; in some parts it falls in spring or early summer, while in others it is a feature of mid- or late-summer. This dual maximum is in the nature of a transition type situated between the strong winter maximum of the Pacific Coast and the marked summer maximum of the Great Plains.

SELECTED REFERENCES FOR FURTHER STUDY OF TOPICS IN CHAPTER TWELVE

Bailey, Harry P., "A Simple Moisture Index Based upon a Primary Law of Evaporation," *Geog. Ann.*, Vol. 40, pp. 196–215, 1958.

Blumenstock, D. I., "The Humid-Arid Boundary Problem," *Geog. Rev.*, Vol. 29, pp. 681–682, 1939.

Bryson, Reid A., and Peter M. Kuhn, "Stress-differential Induced Divergence with Application to Littoral Precipitation," *Erdkunde*, Vol. 15, pp. 287–294, 1961.

———, and William P. Lowry, "Synoptic Climatology of the Arizona Summer Precipitation Singularity," *Bull. Amer. Meteorol. Soc.*, Vol. 36, pp. 329–339, 1955.

———, and David Baerreis, "Possibilities of Major Climatic Modification and Their Implications: Northwest India, a Case Study," *Bull. Amer. Meteorol. Soc.*, Vol. 48, pp. 136–142, 1967.

Lydolph, Paul E., "A Comparative Analysis of the Dry Western Littorals," *Ann. Assoc. Amer. Geographers*, Vol. 47, pp. 213–230, 1957.

———, "The Russian Sukhovey," *Ann. Assoc. Amer. Geographers*, Vol. 54, pp. 291–309, 1964.

Meigs, P., *World Distribution of Arid and Semiarid Homoclimates*. UNESCO Reviews of Research on Arid Zone Hydrology, Paris, 1953, pp. 203–209.

Patton, Clyde P., "A Note on the Classification of Dry Climates in the Köppen System," *Calif. Geographer*, Vol. 3, pp. 105–112, 1962.

Sawyer, J. S., "The Structure of the Intertropical Front over N.W. India during the S.W. Monsoon." *Quart. J. Roy. Meteorol. Soc.*, Vol. 73, pp. 346–369, 1947.

Sewell, W. R. D., Human Dimension of Weather Modification, Research Paper No. 105, Department of Geography, University of Chicago, Chicago, 1966.

Thornthwaite, C. W., and J. R. Mather, *The Water Balance*, Publ. Climatology, Drexel Institute of Technology, Philadelphia, Vol. 8, no. 1, 1955.

Trewartha, Glenn T., *The Earth's Problem Climates*, The University of Wisconsin Press, Madison, Wis., 1961, pp. 22–33, 35–39, 50–54, 59–64, 70–71, 80–82, 93–96, 106–110, 123–134, 144–148, 166–169, 260–270, 274–275.

White, Gilbert F. (ed.), *The Future of Arid Lands*, Publ. No. 43, American Association for the Advancement of Science, Washington, D.C., 1956.

KÖPPEN'S CLASSIFICATION OF CLIMATES

Köppen recognizes five principal groups of world climate which are intended to correspond with five principal vegetation groups. The five climatic groups, each designated by a capital letter, are as follows: *A,* tropical rainy climates with no cool season; *B,* dry climates; *C,* middle-latitude rainy climates with mild winters; *D,* middle-latitude rainy climates with severe winters; and *E,* polar climates with no warm season. Each of these in turn is subdivided into climatic types based upon the seasonal distribution of rainfall or the degree of dryness or cold. The small letters *f, s,* and *w* indicate the seasonableness of precipitation; no dry season (*f*); dry season in summer (*s*); dry season in winter (*w*). The capital letters *S* and *W* are employed to designate the two subdivisions of dry climate; semiarid, or steppe (*S*), and arid, or desert (*W*). Capital letters *T* and *F* are similarly employed to designate the two subdivisions of polar climate; tundra (*T*), and icecap (*F*). The table on page 396 shows the Köppen scheme of five main climatic groups and eleven climatic types. The parentheses indicate that the combinations *As* and *Ds* rarely occur, and for this reason they are not recognized as among the principal climatic types.

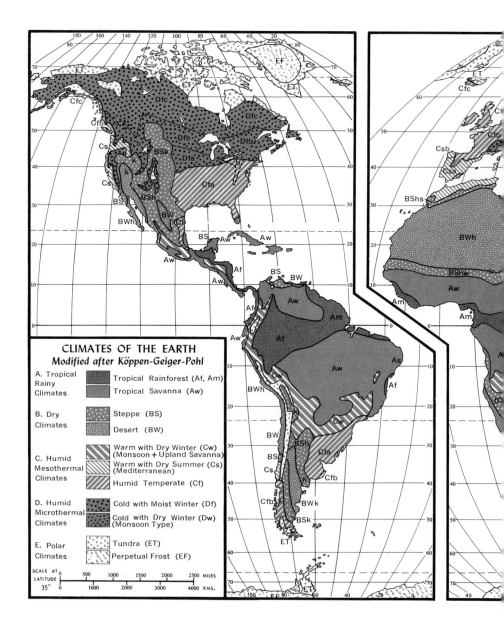

CLIMATES OF THE EARTH
Modified after Köppen-Geiger-Pohl

| A. Tropical Rainy Climates | | Tropical Rainforest (Af, Am) |
| Tropical Savanna (Aw) |

A. Tropical Rainy Climates
- Tropical Rainforest (Af, Am)
- Tropical Savanna (Aw)

B. Dry Climates
- Steppe (BS)
- Desert (BW)

C. Humid Mesothermal Climates
- Warm with Dry Winter (Cw) (Monsoon + Upland Savanna)
- Warm with Dry Summer (Cs) (Mediterranean)
- Humid Temperate (Cf)

D. Humid Microthermal Climates
- Cold with Moist Winter (Df)
- Cold with Dry Winter (Dw) (Monsoon Type)

E. Polar Climates
- Tundra (ET)
- Perpetual Frost (EF)

SCALE AT LATITUDE 35°

| 0 | 500 | 1000 | 1500 | 2000 | 2500 MILES |
| 0 | 1000 | 2000 | 3000 | 4000 KMS. |

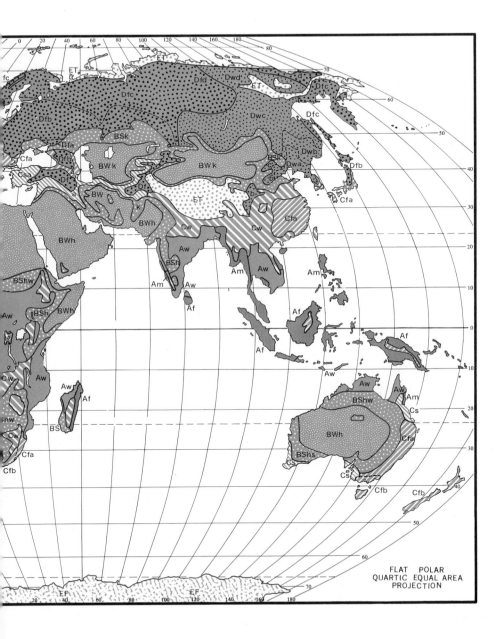

FLAT POLAR
QUARTIC EQUAL AREA
PROJECTION

Köppen's climatic groups and types

Climatic group	Symbol	Dry period	Degrees of dryness or cold	
Tropical rainy climates	A	f (s) w		
Dry climates	B		S	W
Mild temperate rainy climates	C	f s w		
Cold snow-forest climates	D	f (s) w		
Polar climates	E		T	F

A CLIMATES

A = Tropical rainy climates; temperature of the coolest month above 64.4° (18°C). With monthly temperatures lower than 64.4° certain sensitive tropical plants do not thrive. This is the realm of plants known as megatherms which need continuously high temperatures and relatively abundant precipitation. Within the *A* group of climates two main types are recognized: one has adequate precipitation throughout the year, while the other contains a distinctly dry season which affects vegetation adversely.

Af = Tropical wet climate; *f*: rainfall of the driest month is at least 2.4 in. (6 cm). Within this climate there is a minimum of seasonal variation in temperature and precipitation, both remaining high throughout the year.

Aw = Tropical wet-and-dry climate; *w*: distinct dry season in low-sun period or winter. A marked seasonal rhythm of rainfall characterizes *Aw* climates; at least 1 month must have less than 2.4 in. (6 cm). Temperature is similar to that in *Af*.

Other small letters used with *A* climates are as follows:

m (monsoon) = short dry season, but with total rainfall so great that ground remains sufficiently wet throughout the year to support rainforest. *Am* is intermediate between *Af* and *Aw*, resembling *Af* in amount of precipitation and *Aw* in seasonal distribution. In both *Aw* and *Am* the rainfall of the driest month is below 2.4 in. (6 cm). Whether it is *Aw* or *Am* depends upon the total amount of rainfall and the amount occurring in the driest month. For example, when the total annual rainfall is 50 in. the boundary between *Aw* and *Am* is 1.94 in. for the driest month; less than this is *Aw*; more than this, but less than 2.4 in., is *Am*. At 60 in. annual total the *Am/Aw* boundary is 1.55: at 70 in., 1.15; at 90 in., 0.34. The boundary between *Am* and *Aw* is expressed by the formula $a = 3.94 - r/25$, where *r* is the annual rainfall in inches and *a* the rainfall during the driest month. If with a given annual rainfall the rainfall of the driest month is greater than the value of *a* as obtained by the preceding formula, the climate is *Am*; if smaller than *a*, it is *Aw*.

w' = rainfall maximum in autumn.

w'' = two distinct rainfall maxima separated by two dry seasons.

s = dry season during high-sun period (rare).

i = range of temperature between warmest and coldest months less than 9° (5°C).

g = Ganges types of annual march of temperature; hottest month comes before the solstice and the summer rainy season.

B CLIMATES

$B =$ Dry climates, in which there is an excess of evaporation over precipitation. No surplus of water remains, therefore, to maintain a constant groundwater level so that permanent streams cannot *originate* within B climates. The amount of precipitation that falls is not sufficient data with which to determine the B climate boundaries, since the effectiveness of precipitation in providing moisture in the ground for plants is dependent upon the rate of evaporation, which in turn varies directly with temperature. Rain that falls during a hot summer obviously is less effective than the same amount falling in a cool winter. Köppen's formulas for identifying arid and semiarid climates, therefore, involve not only the annual temperature and the total annual rainfall, but likewise the season of maximum precipitation. There are two main subdivisions of B climates, the arid, or desert, type BW (W from the German word, *Wüste,* meaning "desert"), and the semiarid, or steppe, type BS (S from the word *steppe,* meaning dry grassland).

$BW =$ Arid climate or desert.

$BS =$ Semiarid climate or steppe; for precise definitions of steppe and desert boundaries see formulas at end of this section on B climates.

Other small letters used with B climates are as follows:

h (*heiss*) = average annual temperature over 64.4° (18°C). BWh and BSh therefore are low-latitude, or tropical, deserts and steppes.

k (*kalt*) = average annual temperature under 64.4° (18°C). BWk and BSk therefore are middle-latitude, or cold, deserts and steppes.

$k' =$ temperature of the warmest month under 64.4° (18°C).

$s =$ summer drought; at least three times as much rain in the wettest winter month as in the driest summer month (see footnote under Cs climate).

$w =$ winter drought; at least ten times as much rain in the wettest summer month as in the driest winter month (see footnote under Cw climate).

n (*Nebel*) = frequent fog. BWn and BSn climates are usually found along littorals paralleled by cool ocean currents.

Formulas for identifying steppe (BS) and desert (BW) margins ($r =$ annual rainfall, in., $t =$ average annual temperature, °F)

	Boundary between BS and humid climates	Boundary between BW and BS
Rainfall evenly distributed	$r = 0.44t - 8.5$	$r = \dfrac{0.44t - 8.5}{2}$
Rainfall max. in summer; at least ten times as much rain in the wettest summer month as in driest winter month	$r = 0.44t - 3$	$r = \dfrac{0.44t - 3}{2}$
Rainfall max. in winter; at least three times as much rain in the wettest winter month as in driest summer month	$r = 0.44t - 14$	$r = \dfrac{0.44t - 14}{2}$

C CLIMATES (MESOTHERMAL)

C =   Mild temperate rainy climates; average temperature of coldest month below 64.4° (18°C) but above 26.6° (−3°C); average temperature of warmest month over 50° (10°C). The average temperature of 26.6° (−3°C) for the coldest month supposedly roughly coincides with the equatorward limit of frozen ground and a snow cover lasting for a month or more. Within the *C* group of climates three contrasting rainfall regimes are the basis for recognition of three principal climatic types: the *f* type with no dry season; the *w* type with a dry winter; and the *s* type with a dry summer.

Cf =   no distinct dry season; difference between the rainiest and driest months is less than for *w* and *s,* and the driest month of summer receives more than 1.2 in. (3 cm).

Cw =   Winter dry; at least ten times as much rain in the wettest month of summer as in the driest month of winter.[1] This type of climate has two characteristic locations: (1) elevated sites in the low latitudes where altitude reduces the temperature of the *Aw* climates which prevail in the adjacent lowlands, and (2) mild middle-latitude monsoon lands of southeastern Asia, particularly northern India and southern China.

Cs =   Summer dry; at least three times as much rain in the wettest month of winter as in the driest month of summer,[2] and the driest month of summer receives less than 1.2 in. (3 cm).

Other small letters used with *C* climates are as follows:

a =   hot summer, average temperature of warmest month over 71.6° (22°C).

b =   cool summer; average temperature of warmest month under 71.6° (22°C).

c =   cool short summer; less than 4 months over 50° (10°C).

i =   same as in *A* climates.

g =   same as in *A* climates.

x =   rainfall maximum in late spring or early summer; drier in late summer.

n =   same as in *B* climates.

D CLIMATES (MICROTHERMAL)

D =   Cold snow-forest climates; average temperature of coldest month below 26.6° (−3°C), average temperature of warmest month above 50° (10°C). The average temperature of 50° (10°C) for the warmest month approximately coincides with the poleward limits of forest. *D* climates are characterized by frozen ground and a snow cover of several months' duration. Two principal subdivisions of the *D* group are recognized: the one, *Df*, with no dry season, and the other, *Dw*, with dry season in winter.

Df =   Cold climate with humid winters.

Dw =   Cold climate with dry winters; characteristic of northeastern Asia, where the winter anticyclone is well developed.

Other small letters used with *D* climates are as follows:

d =   average temperature of coldest month below −36.4° (−38°C).

f, s, w, a, b, and *c* are the same as in *C* climates.

[1] Alternative definition: 70 percent or more of the average annual rainfall is received in the warmer 6 months.

[2] Alternative definition: 70 percent or more of the average annual rainfall is received in the winter 6 months.

E CLIMATES

E = Polar climates; average temperature of the warmest month below 50° (10°C). In the higher latitudes, once the temperatures are well below freezing and the ground frozen it makes little difference to plant life how cold it gets. Rather, it is the intensity and duration of a season of warmth which is critical. For this reason a warm-month isotherm is employed as the poleward boundary of *E* climates. Two climatic subdivisions are recognized: one, *ET*, in which there is a brief growing season and a meager vegetation cover, and the other, *EF*, in which there is perpetual frost and no vegetation.

ET = Tundra climate; average temperature of warmest month below 50° (10°C) but above 32° (0°C).

EF = Perpetual frost; average temperature of all months below 32° (0°C). Such climates persist only over the permanent icecaps.

INDEX

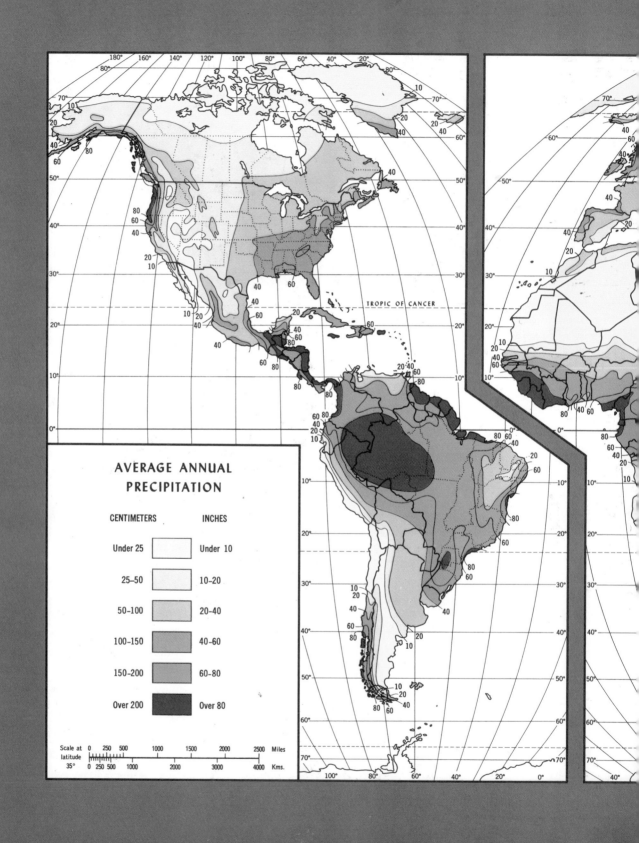

AVERAGE ANNUAL
PRECIPITATION

CENTIMETERS		INCHES
Under 25		Under 10
25–50		10–20
50–100		20–40
100–150		40–60
150–200		60–80
Over 200		Over 80

Scale at latitude 35°

0 250 500 1000 1500 2000 2500 Miles

0 250 500 1000 2000 3000 4000 Kms.

TROPIC OF CANCER

THE AWKWARD AGE

The Awkward Age

Francesca Segal

Chatto & Windus
LONDON

1 3 5 7 9 10 8 6 4 2

Chatto & Windus, an imprint of Vintage,
20 Vauxhall Bridge Road,
London SW1V 2SA

Chatto & Windus is part of the Penguin Random House
group of companies whose addresses can be found at
global.penguinrandomhouse.com

Penguin
Random House
UK

Extract from 'Poem for a Daughter', from *Poems 1955–2005*,
by Anne Stevenson (Bloodaxe Books, 2005)

First published by Chatto & Windus in 2017
penguin.co.uk/vintage

A CIP catalogue record for this book
is available from the British Library

ISBN 9780701187002

Typeset in India by Thomson Digital Pvt Ltd, Noida, Delhi
Printed and bound in Great Britain by Clays Ltd, St Ives plc

Penguin Random House is committed to a sustainable future
for our business, our readers and our planet. This book is made
from Forest Stewardship Council® certified paper.

For GMA

Why does a mother need a daughter?
Heart's needle, hostage to fortune,
freedom's end. Yet nothing's more perfect
than that bleating, razor-shaped cry
that delivers a mother to her baby.
The bloodcord snaps that held
their sphere together. The child,
tiny and alone, creates the mother.

A woman's life is her own
until it is taken away
by a first, particular cry.
Then she is not alone
but a part of the premises
of everything there is:
a time, a tribe, a war.

Anne Stevenson

PART ONE

ONE

The teenagers would fuck it up. Certainly they always tried; it was the only impulse Gwen and Nathan had in common, besides their hostility to one another. This morning the thought of waking her daughter filled Julia with a particular foreboding, despite her own excitement about the weekend.

They were all going to America, to James's hometown, which Julia had imagined since meeting him. They had given one another their futures but she was greedy for his past, too; she would never know him young, but knowing Boston seemed the next best thing, a way to make up the impossible, inconceivable deficit of all the wasted days spent not loving him, before they'd met. She wanted to see the places that had mattered; to visit Harvard where James had turned his tassel, had become a doctor, a husband, a father, had grown from unknown boy into the cherished man who now lay beside her, breathing steadily, face down in his pillow, in their bed, on the top floor of what was now their home, a narrow Victorian terraced house in Gospel Oak. She was looking forward to Boston. On the other hand, this holiday meant three intensive days with Nathan, who would no doubt take every opportunity to needle her with casual reminiscences about the halcyon days during which his father had been married to his mother. Meanwhile Julia's own daughter, Gwen, would be dependably more difficult. Such had been the way.

James stirred, smiled sleepily up at Julia, and hooked an arm round her waist. He drew her back to the horizontal, and began to mumble into her hair. A muscled thigh fell over hers, hot and marble heavy, and she was pinioned.

'The cab's in an hour, we've got to get the kids up. I have to do the dog.'

He shook his head, without opening his eyes. 'Send the kids without us, let's stay here. It'd serve them right for being pains in the rear end.'

On cue, a thudding bass began beneath them, too loud for the rest of the terrace at this or any hour. Nathan was awake. Impossible to rouse most mornings he was home from boarding school, it seemed he could spring up before daylight when Boston – and an escape from her house, Julia suspected – lay ahead of him. Predictably, dispiritingly, Gwen's voice now rose, shouting a sleep-slurred obscenity. At the sound of so many humans unexpectedly awake during his early shift, Mole began to bark with joy. The thump of tail on wooden boards was followed by a frantic scrabble outside their bedroom door. 'Shut *up*!' they then heard, and the dog and the rest of Gwen's complaint were drowned out when Nathan turned up the volume.

'When will they start to be nice to each other?'

James had tipped forward and was fishing on the floor beside the bed for last night's T-shirt, bare buttocks in the air. 'Probably never,' he said cheerily from this position. 'But we can get rid of them soon. College. The army. Sell them into service.' When this got no reply he sat up again and said more gently, 'Give it time, it hasn't been very long. It's a big change for both of them.'

'Saskia's been civilised. Why is your daughter an angel when mine is being such a nightmare?'

'Saskia doesn't have to live here,' James pointed out. He was squinting at his watch. 'Cab's in an hour and twenty. Have I got time for a run? I'll take the dog.'

He was now out of bed, flexing and yawning, and Julia paused to look at him. It was extraordinary that this man now shared her bed. He was broad-chested, solid, beautiful. At fifty-five he was still mostly blond. He was tall, and square in the way that only Americans are square – as if raised, corn-fed and free range, on strong sunshine and red meat and the earnest and deliberate pursuit of happiness. Her English imagination placed him in dungarees on a tractor, a piece of straw between white teeth, or tugging on the brim of his cap as he swaggered up to bat on a sun-bleached baseball diamond, a mixing of metaphors inspired mostly by her admiration for his height, and his shoulders. This visit to America would begin to set her imagery straight, and that he was, in reality, a Jewish obstetrician from a working-class neighbourhood of Boston would remain a delightful incongruity. In surgical scrubs he looked outsized, and vaguely alarming. He saved women's lives. He saved Julia, every day.

When they met she had been bringing up Gwen alone for five years, with the volatile intensity of hostages long held together. He had come to Julia for piano tuition and she had found, over time, that her weeks began to shape themselves around his lessons. He had an easy charm, and made her laugh. With a series of caveats she eventually agreed to coffee, ostensibly to discuss his musical progress (which was poor, if dogged). On their first date, timed to coincide with Gwen's geography field trip to study glaciated landscapes around Keswick, Julia had sat, prim and awkward and resistant, had spoken little but had drunk a great deal of red wine and had eventually launched herself upon James in the taxi home with an alarming and volcanic hunger, and had spoken her first honest, unguarded words to him, hungover and ashamed the next morning. This was an English first date, as she remembered it. To James, its speed affirmed his growing conviction that they were meant to be together. For they were meant to be together. He was all she'd never dared to want.

Until then, Gwen had been absently polite when James arrived each week – just another of her mother's students traipsing to the first-floor music room with Chopin nocturnes and a mediocre handspan – but overnight had sworn him mortal enemy; blood-deep rival; her father's bitter adversary and her own. She had lost one parent, and would not yield up her mother without a fight. Julia feared Gwen and feared for her, and had never before withstood her daughter's rages. But she had uncovered a new, accidental source of strength: she had fallen in love. Despite the obstacles James brought sunshine and she had begun to believe, with his help, that her own happiness could start to heal her daughter. This new relationship was entirely different from her marriage, and for that she was grateful. It made it simpler, somehow, to find for James a chamber in a heart that had for so long been only Gwen's. James encouraged Julia to relax, to take him for granted, to believe that he was hers to grow old with, but she would not. Such wasteful complaisance would be unforgivable when their luck was too extraordinary. That their two fragile human hearts continued to beat each hour she knew to be a miracle. Joy was a passing alignment of stars; a flash of sun burning gold flames on water before the clouds came. Julia knew life to be a series of calamities. She waited for the piano to fall, the tornado to strike, and in the meantime her own pure happiness thrilled and frightened her. If only Gwen didn't hate him so much.

Julia came down to find both children already in the kitchen, still in pyjamas, still deftly, stubbornly ignoring one another. Nathan stood spooning porridge into his mouth before the open fridge door, staring into its cavern with steady interest, as if watching television. He had not yet styled his hair, which meant a lengthy tenure in the bathroom lay ahead. It now stood electrified in thick dark tufts above his dark brows, and a milky complexion slightly roughened by excessive unnecessary optimistic shaving. Julia had not yet grown accustomed to the boy's minute interest in and attention to his own appearance, which far outstripped her daughter's daily maintenance. The other day she had come upon him sprawled on the sofa while his girlfriend, Valentina, iced and plucked his eyebrows. He had waved in lordly greeting, unembarrassed.

Gwen lay extended on the tiled floor beside Mole, stroking one of the Labrador's black silky ears and whispering apologies for the upcoming disturbance. Mole yawned hugely in reply, black wax lips contracted, long pink tongue extended and curling upward. Gwen took this to be the end of the conversation and stood up. She was taller than her mother, taller even than Nathan. She had the alien, angular proportions of a fashion model, Julia knew, and desperately hoped the idea would never occur to her. In any case, Gwen moved not with grace but with clumsy, gangling awkwardness. It would be charitable to believe that she had yet to learn her own proportions, that she'd simply grown too quickly, but she had been almost six foot tall since she was thirteen – three years, now – and still she bumped into walls, and tripped over invisible objects, and banged her knees beneath tables. Today she had piled her exuberant red curls on her head and skewered the fat knot with a striped black-and-yellow pencil. She bent to brush her knees, vigorously. Her glasses slipped down her nose and she pushed them back up with her knuckle.

'Must you?'

'Must I what?'

'Dolly, you're getting dog hair all over the kitchen.'

Gwen gave a last swipe at her pyjama bottoms. 'It's not my fault he sheds. Oh! So listen, I found my black jeans, they were – duh, duh duh! – in my school bag. The mystery is solved.'

Behind her Nathan had begun to whistle 'Yankee Doodle', softly, out of tune. Julia carried the kettle to the sink, fantasising about coffee and silence. 'Good morning, Nathan,' she said, in his direction. Then to Gwen, remembering, 'Have you got the dog stuff together for Grandpa?'

Gwen nodded towards the door. 'Daunt bag, by the door. He said just bring food and tablets, he'd use his own bowls.'

Nathan was still gazing into the fridge. Misty, cold, expensive air reached Julia. Eventually he extracted a punnet of raspberries which he then began to plop one by one into the saucepan of remaining porridge, now bubbling over on the hob. Julia averted her eyes. She had stayed up late last night, cleaning the kitchen.

'Oatmeal?' he offered, extending the saucepan towards her.

'No, thank you.'

'I might have some,' said Gwen, freed by her mother's presence to speak to him directly. 'But you're meant to wash raspberries, they're covered in stuff.'

'I wouldn't take undue risks in that case,' said Nathan, tipping the contents of the pan into his own bowl. He scraped, and set the empty, encrusted pan back down on the hob. Their methods varied but on balance the children were equally rude to one another, and James had told Julia he thought they could be safely left to duke it out between themselves. Privately, she was inclined to blame Nathan, who goaded.

Julia sipped scalding coffee and went through her list again. The windows had been checked; she had taken out the rubbish but there would be more generated by the children; something needed to be done about the heating. James would happily do it all when he returned, but she had grown used to running her household alone, and could not bring herself to tempt fate by depending upon him. They were really leaving, and it would soon become clear whether this idea of a family trip had been foolhardy or inspired.

Nathan took out a chopping board and announced his intention to make a vegetable omelette, following this with the news that he had never attempted an omelette before but how hard, after all, could it be. It was important to travel on a good, square meal. He was back in the fridge again, taking out eggs, butter, milk, tomatoes, several courgettes and the whole cheese drawer, which Julia knew from experience was almost impossible to get back onto its plastic runners once it had been removed. Had James been here he would have put a robust and efficient kibosh on this plan as Nathan was unlikely to starve between Gospel Oak and Terminal Five, and had not yet finished packing. But James was not back from his jog, and Julia had so far avoided disciplining or even advising his son. She looked at her watch. The morning was slipping from her grasp, and they still had to drop the dog with Philip.

TWO

All this cohabitation was new. The house in Queen's Crescent had been home to Julia Alden since before Gwen's birth; she and Daniel had bought it when she was heavily pregnant, moon-faced and cumbrous as she unpacked boxes and helped Daniel to paint the baby's room in pale willow and stronger mint greens, a grassy landscape against which their tiny, red-faced, orange-haired daughter would resemble a furious, insomniac leprechaun, demanding and bewitching in equal measure. When Daniel died five years ago, succumbing in six months to the efficient liver cancer he had once long ago managed to beat with such misleading ease, Julia could not bring herself to move. Queen's Crescent was where he was, or wasn't, and his palpable absence had been all that she and Gwen had of him. She was no longer on speaking terms with her own bitter and disappointed mother but Daniel's parents, Philip and Iris, had helped her with the practicalities. How they felt about this latest development was an uncertainty that made her anxious; asked directly, they were unfailingly elegant and generous. Iris Alden had for some time been suggesting, hinting, commanding that Julia ought to 'move on'. It was unhealthy for Julia and Gwen to live in such intense and inward symbiosis, Iris had reproved her daughter-in-law, and each now needed a man around, for different, equally valid reasons. But 'moving on' was abstract, where 'moving in' was concrete, deliberate and unavoidable. Julia had first met James through Philip Alden, who had befriended him at an obstetric conference. This ought to have eased her conscience, but didn't. Philip had recommended her to James as a piano teacher, not a life partner. When she found the time Julia worried for her in-laws, in between worrying about everything else.

Along with five suitcases, several crates of expensive red wine, twelve cardboard boxes of books (many of which proved to be the US paperback editions of novels already in the house), an elaborate sound system with large, free-standing speakers, and a cherished American coffee maker, James Fuller and his son Nathan had arrived one afternoon in the balmy golden light and warmth of early September, and for the eleven weeks since then, the household had been black with tension and thunder. Gwen was constitutionally incapable of concealing her loathing and distress; Nathan, a year older and slightly more socially sophisticated, was equally unhappy but would not admit it. To Julia he was obsequious and detectably patronising.

Alone with Gwen he mostly ignored or bullied her, idly, correcting her grammar or mocking the blog she kept, on which she recreated key scenes from her week with miniature plasticine figures staged in elaborate shoebox sets, photographed and posted online. James was represented by a sculpted figure of Darth Vader, black-helmeted, sinister, wreaking destruction. Nathan appeared in clay, always hand in hand with his girlfriend Valentina, a polished and imperious little sprite who stayed over whenever he was home for the weekend from boarding school. Gwen had made Valentina beautiful, had faithfully rendered the girl's silky blonde hair and prominent bust, but she always made the couple's clothes match, and put them both in sunglasses, even inside, even at night. This was a clever and irreproachable way of making them look slightly ludicrous. Julia, Philip and Iris made frequent use of this blog to gauge Gwen's mood. Once upbeat and sunny, it was now unfailingly despairing, since her mother had fallen in love with Darth Vader.

'I just wanted to say *bon voyage*, darling.'

Julia wedged the phone between ear and shoulder and continued to do battle with the zip of her holdall. Poised and unflappable, imperiously judgemental of those who were neither, Iris had an unerring instinct for Julia's most chaotic moments.

'Thank you. The *voyage* part might be a bit stressful – we're late already, nobody's downstairs. You'd think we were preparing to go away for a month.'

'Under the circumstances three days may come to feel like a month. Have you and Thing planned anything *à deux* while you're there? A little breathing space?'

'No, I don't think it's possible this time. It doesn't seem fair to the kids.'

After a heavy silence Iris observed, 'Travelling with babies can be so wearying.'

'Iris –' Julia tried once more and the zip slid effortlessly up to its hilt, several fine threads of her favourite wool scarf snared halfway down between its teeth. She lowered her voice to a whisper. 'I took on board what you said. I'm trying not to infantilise her, but there will be a lot happening for her –'

'There will be a lot happening for you, too. Last time I checked you were meant to be having some fun.'

'We will.'

'Well do, please. No martyrdom while you're there, it would be very unfashionable, Americans don't believe in it. Channel the national spirit. Be plucky and aspiring.'

Julia promised to try. Neither of these characteristics came easily to her, though they were the twin peaks dominating Iris's own natural territory. Julia poured the remains of the milk down the sink, scanning the surfaces for anything else that might turn into a disaster in three days of neglect. When the doorbell rang she was squeezing a perfunctory spray of kitchen cleaner onto the hob where light splashes of Nathan's porridge had already set, hard as concrete. Iris was now describing her own most recent trip to America, and a production of *Indian Ink* on Broadway. Julia of all people really ought to get tickets to the BSO, and Thing loves music too, doesn't he? Couldn't they sneak off to the Symphony Hall? Didn't Julia think she might deserve it?

'Oh, God, sorry. Cab's outside, I'd better go. Oh, wait! Iris?'

'Yes, I'm still here.'

'Are you sure Philip can handle the dog? I know how much he loves him, but Mole's just so big . . .'

'Philip Alden will be just fine, it's good for his knees to walk. He's always threatening to rescue some abandoned scrap from the pound, you know how dotty he is about anything with four legs. They'll be two *alte kakers* together.'

Julia bit her lip. An image arose of the dog bolting after an insouciant London squirrel, pulling slow-moving Philip to the pavement and thence to broken ribs, pneumonia, death. She suppressed this. Mole had not bolted for many years, and his cataracts occluded large items of furniture, so he was unlikely to spot squirrels. His arthritis rivalled Philip's own.

Julia turned her attention to the thermostat. It had a holiday setting, she was certain of it. She pressed buttons, experimental, pessimistic. Iris interpreted her silence, and responded.

'You want me to say I'll take him if it doesn't work out. Julia, that animal reeks. In fifty years I've never let a stinking beast into my beloved house.'

'Only if something goes wrong? If Philip seems tired?'

'Nothing will go wrong, but yes, if it makes you feel better, I'll take him should it seem necessary. Now go, and have a lovely time. Don't let the ex-wife intimidate you. Remember she's ex for a reason.'

James had come in and was miming his intention of taking her bag out to the idling taxi.

'Mmm. I can't really discuss that right now.'

'How subtle you are, darling, a veritable Enigma code. *Bon voyage*. And *bonne chance*. And for the love of God have some fun.'

'Thank you. Lots of love, Iris, thank you.'

From upstairs Gwen shouted, 'Is that Granny? Can I speak?'

'The cab's here! Sorry Iris, one sec, Gwen's yelling at me –' Mother and daughter met in the hall where Gwen, still shoeless, was extending her hand for the phone. Her hair was in a fat and sopping plait from which a halo of drying curls escaped, glinting copper and gold; she held three packets of polymer modelling clay in white, cherry red and peacock blue. Nathan thundered down the stairs, flung open the hall cupboard and began throwing out items, like a dog turning up garden dirt. A pile of hats and gloves and scarves grew behind him.

'Mum, are these "gels or liquids", d'you think? Can I carry them on the plane?'

'Please put some shoes on. Iris, sorry, I'll call you when I'm back.' As she was speaking she heard Nathan, his head deep between coats, muttering, 'I think it ought to be fairly clear they're not liquids, given that they're solid.' It was going to be a long weekend. 'Found my scarf!' Nathan added, in triumph, and disappeared outside to the waiting car.

Gwen put a sharp little chin on her mother's shoulder and bellowed, 'I'll call you from the airport, Granny! Love you!', handed her deafened mother the plastic-wrapped clay and then slid off down the hall in search of her trainers while Julia poked in hopeless uncertainty at the thermostat. It now said ++ENTER SUMMER MODE?++. That would have to do.

In her kitchen in Parliament Hill, Iris poured herself a second cup of coffee and dialled Philip Alden. Someone in the family had to listen to sense.

When the phone rang, Philip had been napping. Since his eightieth birthday sleep had been an evasive and unsatisfying business and he now rose each morning at five a.m.,

unable to bear the racing of his mind while trapped in stiff and supine immobility. Better to be in physical motion, however tentative and ponderous. By now – just after eight a.m. – he could sometimes manage forty winks in a chair.

His basement flat was touched by brief morning sun, thick yellow beams that poured in through high windows and showed, briefly, the motes of dust that swarmed and rolled in dense clouds around the battered furniture. Otherwise the living room was murky, illuminated only by a pair of fringed, tangerine silk bedside lamps that had been re-homed on the large and middle-sized segments of a nest of laminate tables on either side of the sofa, a low-backed cube upholstered in threadbare, milk-chocolate velvet that had been the proud centrepiece of the Aldens' living room in the seventies. An Anglepoise stood beneath the bookshelves, raised off the floor only marginally by four hardback copies of the *Physicians' Handbook of Obstetric Intensive Care, VI Edition*, edited by Philip. Last summer Gwen had taken quilting lessons in a Kentish Town church hall, and her only quilt now lay across her grandfather's knees, a garish herringbone of purple and mustard cotton stuffed with a sheet of thin foam. 'I love you, Grandpa' was embroidered in its centre, surrounded by glittering, cross-stitched hearts pierced by glittering, cross-stitched arrows. In his lap a printout of a short story by Stefan Zweig, emailed to him by Iris with instructions to analyse it so they could disagree about its intention.

By the time Iris had swept into his life Philip was a confirmed bachelor of thirty-six, a new consultant in the Obstetrics and Gynaecology department of University College Hospital, his limited spare time spent overseeing

a clinical study of the use of forceps in persistent occiput posterior births. Iris was interviewing physicians for a feature on the first anniversary of the Pill. She had whisked Philip to the Pillars of Hercules, fed him whisky, made him laugh. She had sharp grey eyes and glossy hair, carbon black, that slipped like satin through his fingers. She was furious, vivid, fearless, young. He had awoken, and learned happiness. Iris had brought a wonder and confusion that had thrilled and dizzied him, but he had never trusted that it could be his, lifelong.

When after three decades their marriage had finally ended, when Iris had decided that Philip ought no longer to ignore her long-standing affair with Giles Porter, her section editor, Philip had acquiesced without great protest. He bought a modest basement flat on Greencroft Gardens, off the Finchley Road. It was a return, in some senses, to a familiar routine. He knew life to be quiet, to be a serious and solitary business. His late son's family, as well as his friendship with Iris, were precious beyond measure and more than he had ever hoped for, or expected.

Iris remained in the house in Parliament Hill, with Giles. The three had maintained a cordial relationship, and Philip had still, on occasion, come for dinner, or to cocktail parties, or for drinks on the terrace of the garden he had planted. It was Iris and Giles who had started to argue almost as soon as they had begun to live together, and three years later Giles retired permanently to his house in France after which the fighting had stopped, aided by the civilising separation of the Channel. When Giles had died not long after his move to Provence (a maddeningly predictable heart attack, Philip felt, after years of taking dogged, perverse

pleasure compounding atherosclerosis with bacon butties and unfiltered cigarettes), Philip had been genuinely saddened and sorry. If Iris had had other relationships since then they were not discussed, and though he visited Iris often, Philip had seen no evidence.

Many nights on call had trained him; the phone would be at his ear, the other hand dutifully taking dictation of a patient's name, her complication, the state of the baby, before the fog had fully lifted. He sounded awake, professional.

'Iris?'

'Gwen is still bullying the American. And I have a bad feeling about this Boston business.'

Philip considered. 'Surely not bullying.'

'She barely speaks in his presence, and she still won't touch his cooking, or even Julia's cooking if he's served it to her. And now apparently she pretends she hasn't understood anything he's said because of his accent. That part is rather ingenious, actually, but it can't go on. And now they're meant to be going for a jolly weekend jaunt with the insufferable son.'

'I really don't think James can be bullied. He trained under Steingold at Harvard, after all.'

'But she can't get a taste for it. These early days matter.'

'He's got teenagers of his own, he must know she's having a hard time. He's a very nice man, Iris. I liked him long before – before all this.'

'Yes, well. I'm not interested in him,' said Iris primly. This was an outrageous lie. Iris was consumed with

curiosity about James Fuller and his family. 'I'm interested in Gwen's happiness, and she can't be allowed to behave so badly he finds her intolerable. People have long memories for that sort of thing. And now they're going to be piled on top of one another, and this evening they'll be fresh off the plane and going to Give Thanks at his ex-wife's house. It's a thoroughly bizarre expedition. If they wanted a romantic break then Julia and Thing should be off frolicking in a country hotel somewhere, not forcing their warring children to pretend to be civilised.'

'I think he wants to show her a little of Boston.'

'Yes, well, that's one thing, but showing her the ex-wife is quite another. Why do they have to see her?'

'She's Nathan and Saskia's mother. And they're apparently on very good terms.'

'It's distinctly odd,' Iris declared, with finality. Neither alluded to their own long years of devoted and easy friendship, risen as it was from the ashes of their intermittently tempestuous marriage. It had long been agreed that they were the exception. Instead, Iris moved swiftly to the purpose of her call. 'I want Gwen to come to the Puccini with us next week, not that her taste for melodrama needs encouragement. I plan to stage a subtle intervention.'

'Your interventions are never subtle. Will you ask her, or shall I?'

'You'll ask her. They're en route to you as we speak, to deliver the slavering beast. Now listen, I know you adore that creature but if Mole wears you out, stick him in a taxi to me. And don't invite. Insist.' She rang off.

THREE

It was James who knocked on the door of Gwen's hotel room and announced they were ready to go. She presumed it had also been James earlier, tapping a maddening military tattoo on the interconnecting wall, which she had ignored. The fight, for the moment, had gone out of her, but she would not join in with the pretence that they were all together on some sort of fun-filled summer camp. So far there was nothing sunny about being here – needles of icy rain had stabbed their faces on the short dash from the airport terminal to the taxi, and the early evening sky was not promising. Nathan's complaints about London weather did not, on first sight of Boston, make any sense whatsoever.

Gwen stepped into the hallway where thin floral carpets met elaborately panelled, dark green walls, and pulled the door shut, not quite a slam. Julia stood behind James looking apologetic and, on second glance, unexpectedly stylish. While getting rid of James was her own, ultimate goal, nonetheless Gwen did not want her mother bested by the mysterious Pamela. She knew James's ex-wife was English (James obviously had a fetish) – but this did not stop her from picturing her as American, and therefore sophisticated. Nathan had once hinted that his parents

had divorced due to an unmanageable excess of sexual chemistry, and that he would not be surprised if in the future James and Pamela were reconciled. Gwen had not shared this threatening information but had protected Julia from it, and acted on her behalf. She felt a twist of guilt and tenderness for her mother, who seemed vulnerable without her layers and folds of cocooning wool and denim and ancient, sensible silk vests. Instead she was in a black silk shirt with a wide, soft collar, and a black wool pencil skirt that almost, but not entirely, revealed her knees.

Julia had a neat, wiry figure, and a clear, very pale complexion. Everything about her was pale – her veins showed grass-green through translucent skin, her eyes were palest blue, and her eyebrows and lashes were almost invisible, a defect that she had long ago given up bothering to correct. Her thick hair was a forgiving ash blonde, the right shade to camouflage, for the moment, the streaks of grey that had appeared by stealth over the last few years. She wore it too long, because she rarely felt strong enough to argue with her hairdresser about highlights and layers, and the other age-appropriate measures he wished her to take, and so avoided going as much as possible. Once employed only for actual hiking, her ancient boots had, somewhere along the way, been appropriated for daily wear, practical both for arch support and for signalling, as clearly as a sign hung in a shop window, that she had closed for business. At forty-six she had known her romantic life was over, and to dress as if she hoped otherwise felt pathetic, and unseemly. Then James.

Julia found herself attired to do battle. Her legs, so long concealed beneath thick, bobbled tights, or shapeless

trousers, or sometimes a practical layering of both, were now required to compete. They must look not only amazing, Gwen had decreed, but more amazing than Pamela's, and as neither of them knew what Pamela looked like they could not know how high the bar was set. Gwen had insisted that they go shopping, and had folded herself cross-legged on the floor of the small changing room in Whistles on Hampstead High Street, hunched over her phone, tapping, looking up only to issue brief, strongly worded and – Julia had to concede – accurate assessments of various garments. Of the outfit they had eventually chosen Gwen had pronounced, 'With heels it will make your calves look amazing. Shoes next,' and had marched her mother up the road to Hobbs. This was the closest Gwen had come to supporting the relationship, and it had at first moved Julia and then seduced her into a *folie à deux* of anxiety. 'You have to wear the heels we got, it's what they're for!' Gwen had screeched when Julia, having second thoughts, had begun to pack a pair of black, lace-up flats, rubber-soled and sensible. 'Those are like nun shoes. You have to be sexy!' Gwen almost always addressed her mother in the imperative but had seemed even more urgent than usual, and this anxiety was contagious.

It was five p.m. on Thanksgiving and the hotel had not been able to find them a taxi. They could wait an hour for the hotel minibus to return from dropping guests in Belmont, the concierge said, otherwise they could walk. James had reached a pitch of vigorous, impenetrable enthusiasm. 'It's so close, we oughta walk!' he boomed, commanding the attention of the entire lobby. 'You guys don't mind, right? Mad dogs and Englishmen.' His nerves

were out of character and Julia, who in any case had no idea how far they were going, felt she must acquiesce. Even Gwen, who did not usually miss an opportunity to cross him, said nothing. She merely tugged the hood of her sweater out from beneath the collar of her coat, pulled it tight around her face, and followed him out into the blustery street.

It was a brief window of respite in a day of near-relentless, pounding rain, and the uneven sidewalks had become a hazard of icy gullies and slick, mulched leaves. Julia watched Gwen's long form bent against the wind, trudging obediently after James towards this odd, modern encounter. Her uncharacteristic compliance made Julia's heart hurt. She wanted to scoop up her gangling child and bustle her into the warmth of a taxi or better yet, back into the comforts of the hotel where they could have a quiet dinner, and then commune with the wondrous, vacuous numina of American cable television. In the lobby's adjoining restaurant she'd seen aproned waiters ferrying huge Cobb salads, thick, chargrilled burgers heaped with fat-sheened onion rings, and black skillets of steaming macaroni cheese. Gwen would love these dishes. Julia wanted to pore over the menu with her daughter, to order absurd portions that they could never finish, to compare them with their English imitations – to be, in short, a mother and daughter exploring the New World. It was her own first trip to America, after all, as well as Gwen's. Julia was filled with sudden regret for the holidays they hadn't taken in their years alone together and realised, with an unexpected pang, that she might have missed that chance, now that she had James. Ahead, James and Gwen's figures retreated down

the dark street. Badly dressed for the weather, Julia was given no choice but to follow.

They hurried down streets of South End brownstones, their broad, steep front steps intermittently decorated with fall paraphernalia. On one, a small scarecrow in overalls and a straw hat slumped drunkenly on a hay bale, rain-battered and sodden. Several stoops displayed a series of knobbly, unadorned pumpkins and squashes, lined like Russian dolls on one side of the front door. Fairy lights trailed like ivy around spade-headed railings. It was, indeed, a short walk, but the wind felt arctic, already beginning to freeze a thickening crust onto the black surface of the puddles.

Moments away from Pamela's house came the minor calamity. In England there is no weather with the muscle to warp and weft brick pavements into roller-coaster humps and valleys and so Julia, used to mild, English puddles polite enough to plunge only half an inch, stepped off the kerb and into a pool that engulfed her up to the ankle in a slurry of filthy, iced water. She screamed with shock.

James had been charging ahead, describing buildings and restaurants, encouraging a moderately responsive Gwen to tell him of the various gifts she planned to buy her grandparents. He hurried back to Julia looking shamefaced.

'God, I'm so sorry, we should have waited for the van. I'm a putz. I'm nervous. This suddenly seems insane, I've lost my mind dragging you both to Pamela's. We could have taken the kids and all gone to Mexico for Thanksgiving instead of – did you hurt yourself? Can I carry you the rest of the way? Should we ditch it and go for Chinese food?'

Julia shook her head. Her right foot was burning with the cold, and pain radiated up through her marrow. She kicked several times, and then began to limp onwards, leaning on James's arm. The shoes that Gwen had pressed upon her, undeniably flattering, horribly expensive soft grey suede, were ruined beyond repair, and even immediate use. Julia felt the right one loosen and slacken with every sodden step she took. She had lost all feeling in her toes, a welcome relief from the burning. It began to rain.

On the doorstep, Julia prepared for Pamela, carefully arranging her face into an expression of openness and enthusiasm, but it was an older man who opened the door. He was extending a hand to shake James's when he was pushed aside, rather violently, by a large woman wearing voluminous, autumnal robes. Pamela – blonde, buxom, a whirl of loose wraps and silken items and alarming glimpses of flesh through folds of draped fabric, came upon them. She wore Thai fisherman's trousers in raw plum silk, huge and flowing and tied in an elaborate bow at the waist, and a silk vest in bright tangerine. The sleeves were so deeply cut that when she raised her arms the side of her torso was visible almost to the waist, as well as the fold of a rather pendulous breast. A raw amethyst buried in silver hung on a formidable chain around her neck. Every surface, and she had many, was glistening faintly – the jewels, the raw silk, the loose blonde hair. Her face and décolletage shimmered faintly with sweat. Gwen, who had felt violent hatred for several people in recent months, took an instant, vehement loathing to Pamela. Her hair was too long for an old lady. She ought to have worn a bra.

Julia found herself clutched to Pamela's bosom and was immediately and unexpectedly distressed by the image of James, in earlier days, enjoying the comforts of precisely this musky declivity. The amethyst was pressed painfully into her clavicle. Pamela looked very young, the extra weight she carried smoothing and plumping her face into girlishness. She did not look like the mother of teenagers. Julia felt conscious of her rain-frizzed hair and of her sopping, painful foot.

'Sister!' Pamela cried, releasing Julia and holding her out at arm's length, as if she were a garment under consideration at a market stand.

'Not sister,' said Gwen involuntarily, louder than she'd intended, and saw a tired expression cross her mother's face. Pamela rounded on her, beaming. 'We're all sisters in the same fight, lovely girl. Gwendolen.' Gwen in her turn was embraced by Pamela, rescued by her height from the same suffocation as her mother. Over the top of Pamela's head she tried to catch Julia's eye, but caught only James's who smiled, looking rather manic.

'Julia needs dry footwear,' he told Pamela, who freed Gwen and spun round, silks flying, and bent over Julia's feet. Julia was afforded a clear view down the front of her shirt, beyond the swinging crystal.

'Boston's brutal. It's brutal. It took us two winters – you remember, two long winters? – to get it, really. You have to be dressed like Shackleton to survive. I did a whole winter the first year with a coat from Marks and Sparks, I nearly died, I was so unhappy and I kept begging James to go back to miserable old England with me, or transfer to Stanford or anywhere. And then he came home one day with a fur hat, and I thought, well, I might just about survive. Fur, I know,' she addressed the grey-haired man who had let them in. 'You'd have been shocked to know me then. But those creatures died so I could live. I still have that hat, I was going to give it to Saskia but perhaps I should bury it. Take those impractical things off immediately,' she commanded. Several other guests were visible through the open door of the living room and Julia was aware that people to whom she had not been introduced were now looking on with curiosity. 'James, you didn't tell her! Boston's not a town for pretty little heels. Come upstairs, there's no rush at all, everything's out. We were far too many to sit down, I've flung together a buffet. Start, people! Go, start!'

Julia was now in stockinged feet in the hallway and Pamela held her shoes captive, suspending them by their ankle straps like a pair of shot birds. 'Come up here, lovely lady,' she commanded, surging up the stairs, holding Julia by the wrist. 'I'll introduce you once you're sorted out. Jamesy, just man the bar till we get back.'

FOUR

Gwen stuck close to Saskia, who had ambled downstairs moments after Julia's kidnapping. This meant remaining regrettably close to James, who had not seen his daughter since the summer though they spoke, as far as Gwen could tell, nine million times a day. She ate sugar-coated peanuts, crossly, and waited for her mother. She had been promised family time in America; obviously she had misunderstood Julia's definition of family.

'I missed you. Let me see you.'

'Same as when you saw me on Skype yesterday.' Saskia pulled away from her father's bear hug and gave a lazy twirl, and then a slow dipped curtsey. She tucked her long loose hair ineffectually behind her ears, and it fell forward over her face again.

'You look beautiful, kiddo, you really do. Did your mom book your Christmas flights?'

'Not sure, I'll ask her. Is that sorted? Am I definitely coming?'

'You're coming. Tell me if Pamela hasn't and I'll do it, I need my girl back home with me for a few weeks. I tell you something, your brother's a pain in my ass. Enough with all this college and independence bullshit, come home already. How are you? How was the drive back? How did the paper go, did you turn it in on time in the end?'

Saskia rested her head on James's shoulder and smiled mildly. 'So many questions.' She yawned, as if merely hearing them had exhausted her. 'I told you stuff.'

'Tell me more stuff about stuff. Tell me about the term paper.'

Gwen gave her studied attention to a bowl of crisps on the mantelpiece, between a photograph of small Saskia and smaller Nathan on bicycle and tricycle respectively, and a burnished ebony statue of what looked like, but surely could not be, a vagina. She hoped James would take his revolting display of paternal concern elsewhere, but he had noticed her turn away and now took his arm from his daughter's shoulders and drew Gwen back into the conversation. 'If you're looking for some impressive small talk, that guy,' he whispered, raising a blond eyebrow towards the far wall where a round, white-haired man in frameless spectacles sipped a large tumbler of whiskey and studied Pamela's straining bookshelves, 'holds a gastroenterology chair at MIT. He's the world's leading expert in flatulence. Seriously. Enjoy.' He then strode off, promising to return with sodas.

Gwen had liked Saskia from the beginning, the single ray of pale sunshine to penetrate the bank of black cloud that James had cast upon their former life, and was slightly in awe of her calm and serenity in the face of life-altering family developments. Saskia was three years older, a solid girl with unkempt dark blonde hair, broad shoulders and a bust (an unimaginable asset to Gwen who hoped that her own might burgeon into noteworthiness when she reached seventeen). An entirely different creature from rangy, highly strung, flame-haired Gwen, she moved in languid slow motion. Her detachment was radical and thrilling. It wasn't that she didn't notice what her parents did but that, having noticed, she then returned, unfazed, to the concerns and interests of her own life. Gwen, in the active process of collecting characteristics with which to furnish her future adult self, coveted this one in particular. For as long as she could remember her mother had seemed in constant danger of error or accidental self-harm, and only Gwen's anxious vigilance and interference could stave off certain disaster. Wasn't this evening, coming to James's ex-wife's Thanksgiving, evidence of Julia's poor judgement? Gwen ought to have put a stop to it.

'It's awesome you're here.' Saskia put a plump arm around Gwen's waist and squeezed.

'Is it not super weird for your mum, having my mum here?'

'No way, Pamela loves having the house full of randoms, and FYI you are not the most random of randoms here. I think she dated that professor of farting. She's *beyond* that you guys are visiting. How's it been?'

'Weird. Whatevs. The same. Mum and your dad obsessed with each other, it's ongoing. It's beyond foul.'

'It's such a weird thing to study. Like, I think I'm going to study gas?'

Gwen gave an indistinct reply and returned to what pre-occupied her. 'They're literally *obsessed*.'

Saskia shrugged. 'But if they're happy together . . .'

'Also your brother hates me,' Gwen went on with her gloomy update, 'and Valentina hates me, and whenever they're back at weekends she's like, *there*, all the time, flicking her hair around and being evil. It's like a hate-fest, they officially hate me.'

Nathan came up behind them, startling Gwen who felt her cheeks flush. He was in skinny, faded jeans, grey suede sneakers and a large, bright purple hooded sweatshirt, bearing the same brand name across its oversized pockets as the black one she herself wore, which displeased her. He was gallingly attractive despite a painful-looking spot on his forehead, for which Gwen did not judge him, as she fought her own sebaceous battles. Unlike his sister's accent, which sounded enviably American, Nathan's hovered diplomatically mid-Atlantic, tending east or west depending on the company and his mood. To Gwen, this suggested fickleness, and a more general unreliability. A large set of neon-green padded headphones was slung around his neck, like a DJ off duty. He was always disconcertingly sure of himself. 'It's true,' he said, and as she watched he hung his head briefly on one side and passed a loving hand through his dark hair to encourage its wave. 'Officially. I filed paperwork to make it legal just this week. I officially hate you.'

'Shut *up*.'

'Aww, guys.' Saskia put an arm round each of them and drew them into a group hug. Both had to bend down to her height. 'Be friends! Feel the love!'

'I feel it.' Nathan dropped his head, overcome with the evangelist's fervour. 'I feel it. All is healed. Sas, listen,' he whispered, now they were close enough to confide, 'don't leave me alone with Wentworth again, he's seriously dry.'

His phone began to ring, and he broke free of the huddle. '*Amore mia*.' There was a long pause, then, 'Yes, can I call you later – you're right, I'm sorry, you're up very late. Can we Skype tomorrow? I know, I said I was sorry –' He stopped, now grasping a fistful of hair, holding it back from his forehead. A few moments later he murmured, 'I love you, *cara mia*. Saskia and Gwen send love. *A domani*.'

'Hiatus continues,' he told his sister in an entirely different tone, putting away the phone.

'What, you've broken up, you mean?' Gwen demanded. She was surprised. A recognised fact of teenage life was that relationships would end, and whether they lasted days or years did not change this expectation. Yet Nathan and Valentina had seemed exempt, their union entirely established and unalterable. Like adults. Valentina had talked openly about their wedding, had once even been heard to say that their first daughter would be called Fabia. This development was extremely interesting. 'Why were you calling her cara blara if she's not your girlfriend?'

'It's only a hiatus.' Nathan sounded irritable. He moved Gwen aside two steps to check his appearance in the antique mirror behind her. 'She wanted us to stay at your mom's house for the weekend while you all came here, which is classic Valentina insanity as obviously I'm going to visit my mother and sister for Thanksgiving. I'm taking some time to reconsider.'

'It didn't sound like you were on a hiatus. And we didn't send love.'

'I would have,' Saskia protested mildly.

'We're not just going to stop talking after two and a half years.'

'So basically you just decided not to see each other this weekend when you couldn't see each other anyway because you were on opposite sides of the Pacific. How radical.' She felt pleased by her appropriation of what she felt was his own, airy manner. 'And you literally spend more time looking at yourself than I do.'

Nathan made a final, invisible adjustment. 'I'm not sure that's anything to boast about. And it's the Atlantic, but don't let the details bog you down. Come, let's get food.'

'It was raining,' said Gwen crossly, trying to tame the frizzing corkscrews that she now saw had escaped from her ponytail. Admired and envied by older women, her hair was disobedient, far too thick and wiry, and an appallingly bright colour, but to master it and make it serve her would take a patience she lacked. Together with her height it made her obtrusive, and to be obtrusive at sixteen was the unhappiest of states. Nathan had departed in the direction of the buffet table and beside her in the mirror she saw Saskia shaking her head, looking sorrowful.

'You two are so mean to each other!'

'He's mean to me.'

Saskia held out a bundle of plastic cutlery wrapped in a paper napkin printed with prancing turkeys. 'Poor Valentina. It will be a major deal if they break up.'

'She's had a lucky escape, if you ask me,' muttered Gwen, but when she noticed Saskia's crestfallen expression she apologised, and resolved to save her abuse of Nathan for private moments with her mother, or her grandparents, or her friend Katy who simultaneously fancied Nathan and hated him, and therefore made a satisfyingly insatiable audience. They discussed him at length.

* * *

Gwen was distressed to see Julia descending the stairs bare-legged, and in sagging purple mohair bedsocks. She abandoned her plate on a sideboard and rushed over.

'Mum! You look so weird.'

'It's all she gave me, darling, I couldn't get out of it.'

'Take them off!'

'I took my shoes off, too, to be companionable,' said Pamela, appearing behind Julia with a flourish, her hand extended to clasp and squeeze Gwen's. Gwen looked down to see naked white feet, the toenails vermilion, a toe ring in black-stained silver shaped like a serpent and wrapped, sinuously, around the second toe.

It was the first sight of this toe ring that led Julia to understand that James had sold to her a picture of family harmony that was not wholly accurate, or possible. She and Pamela would not, she saw, be friends. Pamela did not seem the kind of woman who was a successful friend to other women, whatever proclamations she might make about sisterhood. It was unimaginable, and indeed now was not at all the time to be imagining, that James had married and had his children with this expansive, threatening person.

'I love that you're with us,' Pamela now whispered, as if Julia had been at death's door and had rallied bravely to attend her party. She linked her arm through Julia's and squeezed, like a confiding schoolgirl. James, who had been across the room helping himself to one of the many untouched M&S mince pies that Pamela had requested he ferry from London, hurried over to Julia's other side and took her fingers. Julia felt for an odd moment as if they were parents leading her towards an altar, possibly marital, possibly sacrificial. Pamela summoned over the man who had let them in.

'I'm going to introduce you to everyone. This is Wentworth.'

'Wentworth Hale.' He nodded and offered a hand to Julia for the second time, doffing an imaginary cap to Pamela. Behind one ear he'd tucked a roll-up, and a small white badge pinned to the breast of his leather waistcoat read 'STAMP OUT REALITY'. His grey ponytail was held back with a thick blue elastic band that looked as if it had once held together a bunch of asparagus.

'Wentworth is fighting the good fight with us, he's on our board at the clinic and he's done fantastic advocacy work for us, I've never known anyone make better use of their retirement, I can't even tell you. He campaigned and wrote letters for us when it looked like our local admissions privileges were under threat – he'll tell you all about it and I'll make some drinks. Gwen,' Pamela called, 'would you like a G and T?'

'I'm sixteen,' Gwen replied rather frostily, and then seeing a way to avoid Nathan at the buffet table added with marginally more warmth, 'I'll make them though, if you want.'

'Thank you, lovely girl, that would be marvellous. Limes in the Minton.'

Though Pamela had not grown up with Thanksgiving, as a hostess she had nonetheless managed to capture its essence: a day on which hard-working Americans are required to spend upwards of five hours on a freeway (one way) in order to eat turkey, very late, in the twilit company of family members avoided the rest of the year. With no nearby relatives of her own, Pamela ensured a little friction by populating her parties with ill-assorted friends, colleagues, and acquaintances from yoga who had in common only that each could think of nowhere better to go. Julia and James's journey from the hotel had been nothing compared to those of a recently divorced speech-and-language therapist who had driven from Amherst past three accidents and a two-mile lane closure, and a professor of paediatric oncology who'd been on an unsuccessful date with Pamela several months earlier, who had been on the I-95 since eight a.m. and now, slightly sickened by a large Dunkin Donuts pumpkin latte and a bag of powdered donut holes, was mutely nursing a Calvados and wishing he'd stayed at home. The most cheerful guests were twin toddlers currently chasing one another with peacock feathers, overdue for a collapse into sticky, corn-syrup tears.

Julia did as expected. She ate dry slices of turkey breast – cruelty free, Pamela assured her. She tasted sweet potatoes topped with blackened marshmallows, as cloying as imagined, and far more delicious. She compared gelatinous tinned cranberry sauce to Pamela's glossy home-made rendering and dutifully admired the latter (the recipe handed down through James's family). She sipped lukewarm too-sweet apple cider in which sharp shards of cinnamon bark bobbed, and in which there was regrettably no alcohol. She met midwives and doulas, a hypnobirthing expert and a drunken, florid acupuncturist. She listened while Pamela described to a widening circle of listeners the day that James, as a young resident, had stitched up a new mother with such assiduity that he had closed off her urethra and had then had to call her back into theatre to confess, and remove three stitches. Julia saw that this anecdote was intended to make James look foolish and that it succeeded, noting its effect upon James himself: a rigid tension in his jaw. 'Who really needs to pee, right?' he shrugged, as if telling a deprecating story himself, but it was clear he was not happy.

Though this visit had been his own initiative, James had seemed frantic to leave almost as soon as they arrived. Julia now understood that he and Pamela were friends only on the telephone or by text message, and in the reassuring narrative he told himself about the end of his marriage. They were amicable when the Atlantic lay hugely between them, but in person were irritable and competitive. James evidently found his ex-wife aggravating, but was too much a gentleman to say it. What he did say, coming up behind Julia, slipping his hands around her waist and speaking low and urgently was, 'I need to leave ten minutes ago.' She squeezed his forearm and promised to find Gwen. The visit had been instructive, and Julia was now glad they'd come.

She was scanning the room when she felt her phone vibrating and glanced down to see that it was Philip. It was, Julia calculated, quarter past one in the morning in London. Philip had never called her after half past nine.

'Are you okay?'

'Yes, *maidele*, please don't worry, I'm fine. Have you got a minute, though?'

'Of course.' She went up the winding staircase and closed herself in a spare bedroom, next door to Pamela's own boudoir where earlier, among gauzy scarves and crumpled piles of silky garments, she had been forced into Pamela's socks. Here hung the guests' damp coats on a cloakroom rail, and behind it various items necessary for attending home births. Three cylinders of oxygen were aligned against one wall, and beside these a tower of loose plastic packets of absorbent pads. A stack of kidney dishes stood on the bedside table. The large bed was made up with a crocheted blanket in shades of sage and umber and orange. Julia sat down, only to roll sideways. A waterbed, she realised, righting herself and feeling a liquid, undulating wave lift and fall beneath her. She stood up again feeling tricked and slightly foolish.

'There's nothing for you to worry about, but I just wanted to let you know that Mole hasn't been very well. He's with the vet now and they're taking good care of him.'

'Now? It's late, how did you get him there? What happened?'

'I took him in a little while ago but I wanted to stay and see what they said. He's dehydrated, primarily, so they've put him on fluids and they'll see what's what overnight.'

'Poor Mole. Poor you, I'm sorry.'

'By the time I left him just now he was wagging his tail. Dehydration does make one miserable. He looked better in half an hour. I wouldn't have bothered you, only I thought you might have spoken to Iris and worried.'

'Thank you. I'm so sorry it's kept you up. Are you okay? You must be exhausted.'

'Right as rain. How is it?'

Julia stepped out into the hallway and peered over the bannister to judge, swiftly, whether anyone could hear. Closed in the spare room once again she said, 'Pamela is quite a big personality, shall we say. I don't really think she's your cup of tea, she's written a book about orgasm in childbirth.'

'God help us,' said Philip, with a chuckle that turned, almost instantly, into a cough. 'As if birthing mothers don't have enough to worry about.'

'She's signed a copy for you.'

'I look forward to it. How's my granddaughter?'

'Good, I think. The girls get on so well.' This was her own favourite reassurance. She sat down again, gingerly, on the waterbed. 'I should probably go back, I'm lurking in a spare room with all her medical equipment.' She peered into a bag that lay open by her feet and saw a package of empty syringes and pink-tipped needles in sachets; glass bottles and tubes. She picked up a tiny vial that contained a coarse white powder and shook it, speculatively, and then returned it. 'I'd much rather hide in here talking to you, it's so lovely to hear your voice. Are you really not worried? Should I say something to Gwen? She'd be devastated if anything happened to him.'

There was a long pause. 'He is twelve, you know.' Philip said this very gently. 'But don't think about it now. Iris and I will go and see old Mole in the morning.'

Julia waited a moment before descending. Gwen had been very little when Daniel had come home with a puppy, and his decision had taken Julia by surprise as in those days they had still been trying for another baby. Perhaps he'd guessed it might take longer than they'd hoped; at that stage he could not have imagined that it would never happen. With hindsight, she thought, tiredly, he had probably been trying to force to a close that fraught and unlovely chapter of their marriage. In the early years Gwen had fawned over Mole, dressing him in hats and outfits and trying to draw him into her games, with mixed success. Later her enthusiasm had waned; for years he had seemed part of the furniture and had been, in truth, Daniel's dog, for it had been Daniel who'd walked and fed him, groomed him and planned their weekends for his amusement, choosing pubs that were dog friendly and walks that Mole might favour. He took after his father (Philip had almost become a vet, before choosing medical school). But after Daniel died, Gwen had turned back to Mole. They both had, Julia realised, and had each focused deliberate love and energy upon him as a proxy for Daniel himself. The warmth of the dog's rough fur had soothed her; at night when he lay next to her on the sofa Julia sought out the quick, steady gallop of his heart beneath her hand. She and Gwen had often agreed about Mole's wisdom, an impression that had deepened since the coarse fur around his eyes had turned from black to ashy grey. Mole's mortality, like Philip's, like Iris's, like her own, in fact, was just one more item on an extensive list of impossible, uncontrollable anxieties. They would all have to go on living because they simply had to, for Gwen.

She knew that Iris and Philip thought she'd coddled Gwen. That Julia failed to admonish small rudenesses, that she reflexively lifted responsibilities off Gwen's shoulders. But why deny any wish so easy to grant? Julia had never minded what they had for supper; so easy to let the little girl decide. Why care about report cards, or place emphasis on school work that frustrated or upset her when to build her own miniature refuge in clay brought a smile to her face, and connected her to an online world when she had been so lonely in the real one. All adult life lay ahead in which to do laundry and pick up crumpled jeans, to learn – as Julia's own mother had never allowed her to forget – about the sisyphean battle against entropy and chaos that was maintaining a household. What innocent liberty it was, to believe that a water glass left empty on a bedside table would appear, clean, back in the kitchen cupboard. So little magic remained for her. And so Mole could not be ill because Gwen would be unhappy, and Julia could not bear for her daughter to be unhappy again. Committed pessimism was supposed to offer this single, ultimate benefit – that one could never be side-swiped by sadness. It was only now that she realised her vigilance had slipped. She had stopped – so foolish! – she had entirely ceased worrying about the dog. And now look.

FIVE

Nathan and Saskia were staying with their mother and back at the hotel Gwen announced with greedy satisfaction that she was going to watch sitcoms and eat candy in the bath. James took Julia towards the river. It was still very cold but the sky was clear and he needed, more than anything, for Julia to see and understand the beauty in this fine, proud city. He had grown up in a spare, rented apartment on the top floor of a Dorchester triple-decker. Later a scholarship spirited him across the river, and he spent four years at Harvard as an undergraduate, followed by many more at the Medical School and then a residency and fellowship at Beth Israel. The deep, turgid black of the Charles River stirred his soul; in the words of the anthem bawled in the happy heat of Fenway Park, he loved that dirty water. He would play her the song, he thought, when they got back to the hotel. Holding her hand he felt like a boy, making a gift to her of every place he'd been happy. He wanted each site blessed by her gaze. He wanted her to see that he would always give her all he had.

'I understand why Pamela wanted to come back,' Julia said, leaning on the railings. They had walked to Harvard Bridge and stood looking down into blackness, halfway between the boathouses and jewel-bright polished cupolas of Cambridge and on their other side solid, honest Boston. There was a sharp wind coming in off the water and Julia pulled her collar up higher until only her eyes were visible. She had been quiet for some time and he had been waiting, patiently, to discover what it was she had on her mind. After a moment she added, 'You didn't want to move back when she did?'

He pulled her to him. In his arms she felt slight, even beneath the insulating layers of her winter coat. They had had similar conversations before but it felt different, in Boston. Here he heard the unspoken questions and understood her earlier silence. *Will you leave London? Will you leave me?*

'You look cold,' he said gently. 'Are you?'

'A bit.'

He began to lead her back towards Storrow Drive. 'Here, take my scarf. Let's go and have Manhattans in the lobby. Or something warm, maybe Irish coffee. You know, I do really love this town. But I love London also, and now London has you, which makes it the only place I'd ever want to be. I'm not going anywhere. You're my home,' he added, and smiled to himself at his unconscious appropriation of another lyric from Boston's defiant punk theme song. But he meant it.

'Thank you. I know, I think. Sorry. I suddenly saw just a glimpse into your life here, before we met, and I got jealous. Of a city. You had a whole life before I knew you, and I missed it.' Their gloved fingers were interlaced and she squeezed his hand.

'Truly, the only life I want is what's ahead, with you. It was all practice, before.' After a moment he added, 'Pamela is . . . an experience.' He felt that Julia had been graceful in the face of Pamela's assault. Once that theatricality and confidence had captivated him but this weekend, seeing the two women side by side, he had found his ex-wife more than usually enervating.

He had been a fourth-year medical student when they met and Pamela had intrigued him, British and bosomy, full of sexual and intellectual confidence. They had taken uro-gynaecology together and she had challenged a famously irascible surgeon day after day, asking questions that infuriated him, immune to his loathing while better-liked students were regularly reduced to tears. He had found himself in her busy and unmade bed, where he stayed for the rest of medical school. They had been, in that way at least, a good match.

In adulthood they were not well suited. He had felt perpetually unsettled, she, increasingly defensive and competitive as he relied less and less on bolstering infusions of her own self-belief. She had exhausted him, and they had irritated one another. The divorce, they agreed – sometimes amicably, at other times in the throes of an accidental, old, appalling fight – had been the best choice they'd made together.

Now he was fifty-five and truly in love, deeply in love, for the first time in his life. Tonight, above all, he was grateful Julia had trusted him and come to Boston. She had the generosity to see that to keep his family on civil terms was so very important to him. He pulled her closer to him as they walked. He felt expansive with love for her.

'She's very attractive. I was a bit intimidated.'

'You're so beautiful, Julia, that's crazy. Please don't be intimidated by anything at all, she's a friend now but we got divorced for a reason.' He tried not to speak ill of his children's mother but this statement was not disloyal to anyone, and was true.

'Why did you get married?'

He considered. He had told Julia a great deal about the separation, but had talked little about what had come before. In general he did not spend much time in retrospection. 'I was . . .' He considered 'overpowered' and then said, 'over*whelmed* by her. She was – is – brimming with confidence and social ease, and I wanted both of those things. She sort of . . . kicked me up the ass, I think. I wasn't super young but I was still pretty immature. I'd never really known anyone like that before. She was kind of the British equivalent of the Waspy girls who would never look at me. Except she looked at me.'

'And then?'

'And then I grew up, a little slowly I guess, and once I was more mature or self-assured we began to fight. We outgrew each other.' He had talked enough, and so returned to the far happier present. 'And now I'm with you, which is exactly where I should be.'

They had turned into the pedestrian mall at the heart of Commonwealth Avenue and walked in silence for a while beneath the canopy of yellow elms now looming black in the darkness. Before them drifts of fallen leaves lifted and skittered in the sharp wind.

'What did Philip say about the dog?'

'It's so hard to tell, he wouldn't want to worry me but it didn't sound good. I feel so awful he has to deal with it.'

James stopped and faced her, and took both her hands. He had been thinking for some time about how he could help. He watched her struggle with her guilt for distressing him, and for introducing a note of sadness into this first, small vacation. He could see she was anxious.

'Listen to me,' he said gently. 'When we get back to the hotel I'll look online for the best vet in London. I'll find the guy who looks after the corgis, just tell me how to help. Your people will be my people. And your dog, my dog.'

SIX

Last night they had not seen Boston at her best, but early the next day she welcomed them, awash with pale yellow sunshine beneath a blue sky, the air crisp, the light dazzling. On the broad black silence of the Charles the rowers rowed; along the esplanade the runners ran, in hats and earmuffs, in fleece and gloves and clouds of their own quick breath. The greedy stasis of Thanksgiving was behind them; busy Bostonians had returned to river life.

'Oh em gee –' Gwen bounded off the bus, scarf flying, and calling backwards to Saskia. 'This is unbelievable.' James had taken Julia and the girls to Cambridge to lead them through the leaf-strewn paths beneath the ivy-clad redbrick of his glorious alma mater, but Gwen's praise was in fact for a fire hydrant. She fell upon it with a cry of joy, a delightful reunion with this old friend known only from the quaint, unreal America she inhabited on television. She photographed it, and then crouched down beside it for Saskia to capture her looking at it. She measured its solid contours with her gloved hands. She would make one for the blog, she told them all. She giggled at the sign that offered instruction in case of 'SNOW EMERGENCY' and asked her mother to take another picture of her with Saskia, beneath it.

'Nathan's just getting off the T, he'll be here shortly. I'm not sure the Widener can compete after a hydrant and a sign. But there may be other signs in Harvard Yard. "No Smoking. Fire Exit". That sort of thing.'

Julia watched Gwen with anxious interest but Gwen merely grinned. 'Fire hydrants are cool. I like Americana.'

Not rude, Julia noted, just conversational. Progress.

James led them towards a small ice-cream shop. In the doorway Saskia paused, and she now gently poked her father's shoulder.

'I'm leaving, Dad. I'm meeting people for lunch.'

'We're people. We're people right here. Three people, who all live in England and who pine for you across the ocean . . .'

She patted his head mildly. 'Bye, Dad.'

'Have you got cash? Scarf? Bat phone? Call me if you need a ride from anywhere.'

'You don't have a car in this country, but thanks.' Saskia turned to Gwen. 'When you go into Harvard Yard, don't let him or Nathan tell you to rub John Harvard's toe, the students pee on it. 'Kay, bye. Get the black raspberry.'

Nathan was late, and they ordered without him. Gwen held out her cone of black raspberry to James, tentative, casual. James took it, tasted, considered with head cocked to one side, reviewed it favourably, returned it. He offered Gwen his own malted white chocolate. They agreed to swap and Julia watched in a state of rigid disbelief and fascination, breath held, as if willing a paused and watchful wild animal to approach a titbit held on offered palm. This would have

- 49 -

been unthinkable in London. It was Nathan's absence, surely, or it was Boston, or it was the alignment of the planets. In her pocket her phone vibrated, and she excused herself from the table, handing Gwen her untouched frozen yoghurt and stepping out into the noise and chill of Massachusetts Avenue.

'I'm so sorry, *maidele*,' Philip said, when Julia answered. She stood in the cold, numbed. 'It wasn't right. We couldn't let him suffer.'

A hope extinguished. Each change had come like this. Gwen's first day at secondary school. The rapid and murderous blight that afflicted the blowsy, salmon-pink roses that had always climbed their garden wall, flourishing over the years despite total ignorance and neglect. The transformation of their family's beloved local curry house into a fluorescent-lit, linoleum-floored nail bar. Each wave swept Daniel further from his little girl, a stronger tide even than the accumulated minutes since she had last seen his face. And Julia could do nothing but stand on the shore and watch, hopelessly, as he receded, alone with the wounded little girl he left behind. Gwen's longing for her father was why Julia would not get a new car, nor replace – of all the things about which to be sentimental – the unreliable microwave. Gwen had asked her not to. Through the glass she watched Gwen talking, gesticulating, eating the ice cream James had given her, opening up to him, possibly for the first time. And now she would have to be told and would suffer. It was on this duty that Julia fixed as she turned her face away from her family and into the biting wind, permitting herself only a short, silent weep before she returned to the café.

SEVEN

James was an optimist. He was determined that eventually Gwen would love him and, though at present it was challenging to imagine, that one day he would also love Gwen. There was no question that Gwendolen could be extremely trying and that Julia's guilty permissiveness had not helped. She would be a less demanding child, and more importantly would show greater fortitude, he thought, had she not been raised in such a spirit of compensatory contrition and apology. But they were family now and the only way to proceed was with positivity. Falling for her mother did not entitle him to a role in her upbringing, and he would keep his opinions to himself. *Primum non nocere.* And one did not need to be her parent to see that she was absolutely devastated about the dog. Julia had led her gently to the bathroom for privacy. They had been gone some time.

When they returned Gwen was even more hunched than usual, folded in upon herself as if she carried something fragile clutched to her chest. Her eyes were red-rimmed but she was composed, and she pulled her jacket tighter and huddled into the cocooning woollen mask of her scarf. Julia put her arm round her daughter and kissed her forehead, stroking back her red hair. At the last minute James decided to offer no eulogy, wagering – correctly – that Gwen would not like him to besmirch Mole's memory. Instead he squeezed her shoulder and she'd given him a brief, wan smile. They gathered up their belongings to go.

As they were pushing back their chairs Nathan loped up, drinking from a stainless-steel travel mug that James immediately identified as Pamela's. The ghosts of a dozen arguments rose from that mug like unwelcome genies – disputes about paper coffee cups 'choking our landfills', about disposable nappies and the reuse of plastic bags, and a particularly hysterical exchange about the 'poisonous and inhumane' chicken nuggets James had bought for Saskia on a visit to Sea World that had really been, he was convinced, about the fact that at that stage they had not had sex for almost three months. All their disagreements echoed in that mug: the petty, ludicrous, deathly serious battlegrounds of discordant – and subsequently divorced – parenting. He now considered they were mature and cordial, and yet he knew she would be working hard to undermine many of his choices this weekend. He couldn't blame her – he would begin his own exorcism at the airport by treating everyone to a McDonald's.

'Well, hello to all of you,' said Nathan, looking between them, perplexed. 'What an overwhelmingly enthusiastic welcome.'

'We're a bit sad, that's all,' said Julia, squeezing Gwen's arm. 'Gwen's grandpa phoned this morning and we heard the news that Mole died.'

Nathan exhaled through his teeth. 'Christ, you scared me, I thought something awful had happened. Well, look on the bright side,' he grinned and raised his coffee to

Gwen in a partial toast, 'at least you won't have to clear up shit in the kitchen any more.'

James had sensed this comment long before Nathan's arrival, he realised, had felt it in the air like coming rainfall, yet nonetheless he was momentarily floored by his son's misjudgement. He turned, but before he could address Gwen she was already outside and crossing back through the speeding traffic of Massachusetts Avenue. The lights were not with her and for one heart-stopping moment she had looked – he hoped Julia hadn't seen – the wrong way to check for oncoming cars. Julia stood and went after her daughter. With a hand on the door frame she paused and looked back, addressing Nathan. 'That was utterly uncalled for. That was crass and unkind.' She then departed, breaking into a run.

And now Gwen would need to be pieced back together all over again, James thought, frustrated. Why couldn't Nathan keep his mouth shut? Why was Gwen so maddeningly thin-skinned?

Nathan began to stir Julia's tub of melting frozen yoghurt, looking sullen. 'She's so hypersensitive.'

'Well, there's no concerns about sensitivity with you.'

'I was only joking. She's like a three-year-old, running off all the time and throwing tantrums.'

James had been about to protest this accusation, but then conceded. 'I know, she does. But can I explain something? I don't entirely blame you because I know you were trying to be funny and probably wanted to make everyone feel better. But we've come into a family that's very different from ours—'

'—too right.'

'Right,' insisted James, earnestly, refusing to be drawn at this moment by the temptation of disparaging collusion, 'but you've also got to understand that this is about her father. I don't want to ask you to imagine but can you just for a moment, imagine what that must be like to lose your dad? She misses him all the time. And it's been just the two of them for all those years, and it absolutely does not excuse her behaviour in other circumstances, I agree, and Gwen can be difficult, but that dog was her father's. He bought that dog and trained that dog, and probably spent a lot of time with Gwen and the dog, and she's probably thinking about her father today and feeling like she's lost a connection to him. She's really hurting. You have to think of things in context.'

'I'm sorry. I was kidding.'

James paused. His son had been, he felt, consistently mature and accommodating in the face of seismic family change. The divorce had been hard on both children, and Pamela moving back the following year had been a second loss. Now their little threesome had been disrupted, Saskia was in America, they'd sold their flat in Kilburn and moved in with two relative strangers. His own low-level guilt reminded him that his kids had not had it easy, either. They were beautifully mannered which hid their sadness, but the squeaky wheel shouldn't always get the grease.

'I think you're doing a fantastic job. I'm so proud of you and your sister. This hasn't been straightforward, and you've both made it so easy for me.'

'Unlike some people?' Nathan prompted.

'It's not a competition.'

'But if it was,' said Nathan, putting Pamela's thermos cup on the floor between his feet where James resisted the urge to kick it, 'we would win, right?'

There was no one to hear him; it was a relief, in that moment, to admit aloud that he preferred his own children. Of course he did – who wouldn't? It was tiring to pretend otherwise, the only lie he'd told or would ever tell Julia. She was the first woman with whom he could be entirely honest and with whom he felt entirely himself. Yet it had not been honest to say, *Your daughter is a bonus!* He wanted it to be true and tried to make it true by saying it, but Nathan too deserved some rare time alone with his father. 'I mean it, though. No one asks for a new sibling and a stepmother at seventeen. Let's walk, I can't sit here any more. We were meant to be doing all the Cambridge sights this morning, will you come with your old dad for a nostalgic walk around Harvard Yard? And then let's go down to Eliot House, I'll give you the James Fuller undergrad tour. First, I'll show you where I never managed to make out with girls in the stacks.'

'Dad, no.'

'No?'

'Just no.'

They entered the Yard beneath the Porcellian's carved stone boar head, hoisted blank-eyed and open-mouthed above McKean Gate. The freshman dorms on either side were empty, their inmates home for the first time since their arrival at Harvard, returned for Thanksgiving to behave imperiously to younger siblings, to have clothes laundered and stomachs filled, to oversleep in crisp new Harvard-branded sweatshirts and pyjama bottoms and H-logoed non-slip bedsocks, and to be bad-tempered with the parents they instantly resented for behaving as if nothing about them had changed.

Stripped of undergraduates, only tourists remained in Harvard Yard. The centres of the segmented lawns were still green but around their edges were balding and muddied, roped off to recover from heavy rain and heavy footfall. James and Nathan rounded the looming grey flank of Widener, down a path slippery with a mulch of oak and elm leaves and then further on, around the corner to the statue of a man who was not John Harvard, despite his label, slouched huge and complaisant beneath a vast flag that snapped and wavered in the wind like a mainsail. They waited, watching while a family from Germany took pictures of one another reaching up to rub the statue's polished bronze toe. Three blonde daughters, small, medium and large, in matching green-and-pink flowered anoraks and new Red Sox baseball caps each took turns to strain upwards for the top of the plinth. James offered to take their photograph together and they thanked him, handed him a huge-lensed camera and posed, smiling and squinting only slightly in the sharp bright chill. After they'd gone, Nathan put an arm around his father's waist, tenderly protective.

'You and Mom are obsessed with talking to randoms.'

'I know, our existence is excruciating. If you come here to college I promise not to hang out and talk to students. Go rub his toe, it's good luck for applying.'

'Dad. That last worked when I was about eight. So anyway, I've been meaning to ask you,' Nathan changed the subject, casually, 'before, you said "stepmother", but are you actually going to get married again?' He and Saskia did not agree, neither could they agree whether it mattered. Nathan refused to admit that a legal contract endowed a relationship with permanence, using their own parents' marriage as an example. But still, he felt, there would be an ineluctable shift. At present, whatever his father might believe, Nathan had neither stepmother nor stepsister.

'I don't think so,' James admitted. 'Julia doesn't want to, she's worried about Gwen. I think we're fine as we are. Come, let's walk to Longfellow's house.'

'I've been a million times.'

'Just to walk a bit.'

'But you think of her as our stepmother now in any case.'

'I can't think of alternative, unmarried terminology. We're in it for the long haul, marriage or not.'

''Cause you're happy,' Nathan observed. In Harvard Square, a busker in a Santa hat and mauve-and-yellow striped fingerless gloves was playing Feliz Navidad on the accordion. The wind picked up, and without thinking Nathan handed Pamela's travel mug to his father and thrust his hands into his pockets, happily unencumbered. James was reminded of his son as a much smaller child, absent-mindedly passing him the smeared wrapper of a candy bar or the fuchsia-stained stick of an ice lolly, or even his chewing gum, plopped into an open palm without thought so Nathan could race off ahead. No running with gum had been one of James's few rules. Pamela, for ecological reasons, had vetoed gum under all circumstances.

'Yes. I'm happy. Is that okay?'

'I suppose we can overcome our childish amazement that parents are people and allow you to have, shock horror, a life of your own. You can pay for our therapy later, if you like. Even Mom said you seem good together. She said you need someone unchallenging at this stage in your life.'

'Did she. Come on,' said James firmly. 'We're going this way.'

They passed the Coop, where the Harvard insignia crept like a pox across towels and bed linen and cufflinks and jewellery and soft toys and toothbrushes and commemorative pewter and glassware. There were Harvard bottle openers and ping-pong balls, baby bibs and pencil cases. They stopped to admire these wares. James offered to buy his son an Ivy League chocolate bar and tried, and failed, to imagine his own father in such a place. ''S'tempting fate,' Nathan told him solemnly. 'Buy me one when I get in.'

'When you get in you can have the engraved champagne flutes.'

'Thanks, Dad. Smile,' Nathan commanded, leaning backwards, inclining his head towards James's shoulder and extending his arm to take their picture. He seemed pleased with the results, zooming and cropping until it was just the two of them smiling, the burgundy-and-white 'VERITAS' banner prominent behind them. As they walked on Nathan captured them in various locations. Nathan making bunny ears behind his father outside the freshly painted cream-yellow clapboard of Longfellow's house. Sipping hot chocolate together outside Peet's Coffee. Both grinning with shy pride, arm in arm outside the closed gates of Eliot House. His children both documented their own lives obsessively. Where did all these photos go? When he asked for copies they laughed at him.

'You know, you guys aren't little kids, and you and Gwen will both go to college in the next few years,' said James, returning to the subject so he could conclude and move on to more congenial topics. The thought of Nathan leaving – possibly coming here, across the Atlantic – created a strange sad pressure in his chest. 'Let's cross and walk by the river a while. I don't think you should have to pretend you're siblings. But just – flatmates, maybe, all of us. Friends. It might take the pressure off.'

'Yeah, maybe. Look, cool picture of us.'

'Great picture, send it to me. I don't know why I say that, you never do. Will you make it up with her?'

'I promise. And with Julia, too. But may I just say, in the privacy of this conversation, that I'm not completely gutted about the future lack of giant elderly dog shit in the kitchen.'

'Nathan.'

'Okay, okay.' He grinned at his father, wide-eyed and deliberately, disarmingly, devastatingly winsome. 'Should we buy them another dog? What about a Siberian husky?'

EIGHT

It was only ten p.m., but they were all subdued and weary and Gwen, in particular, was longing for the day to end. Mole's absence was unthinkable, and so she would not think it. In the television's narcotic company she could stave off the truth, just for tonight, but the fragile membrane of her shield required solitude and so she had refused her mother's offer to stay with her, dismissing her almost frantically at the door of her hotel room. Until only a few months earlier Julia would not have offered to stay like a polite, concerned acquaintance but would simply have been there, holding her hand while they sat together, absorbed in a flickering, inauthentic reality and safe, warm silence. One being. In this manner they had staved off grief before. Offered, Gwen could not accept. And she did not want James to think her a baby, tempting though it was to separate them and be spared the nauseating and insistent image of their not-quite-marital king-size bed.

There was a rap on Gwen's door and she opened it to see Nathan, bundled up in his coat, a woollen beanie pulled down low over his eyes. She went to close it, and he thrust his foot out to stop her.

'Wait,' he whispered loudly. 'Just wait. One second.'

Her pyjama top was an old cotton running vest of her father's, and was almost certainly see-through. She crossed her arms firmly across her unimpressive chest and stared down at the chipping blue polish on her toenails. She became aware that her pyjama bottoms had ridden up, but she could not release her arms to adjust them for fear of exposing a breast. The shorts were puce, printed with a motif of repeating black moustaches and a less regular, overlaid pattern of bright lilac bleach-stains, and were not for public viewing. She hunched, awkwardly, and did not reply. He would not have the satisfaction of seeing her upset.

'I'm sorry. I mean it. I know you think I'm a dick –' Nathan began. Gwen started to speak and he continued hurriedly, 'I know, I know, what I should say is I know I *was* a dick.' He took a step and she began to protest again, but he did not come further into the room, merely reached for the door handle and began turning it slowly, back and forth, inspecting the mechanism. 'We never even had a goldfish or a hamster or anything, because Pamela thinks that animals shouldn't be enslaved to human needs, not that I'm saying Mole was enslaved, I'm just saying my mother's a little eccentric, which I'm guessing hasn't escaped your notice this weekend, but I just didn't think. Your mom got mad, which I totally deserved, and my dad said that Mole was your father's dog, and I didn't know that either. I'm not making excuses but – I, I just wanted to say that I can't imagine how sad it must be for you today.'

Gwen nodded fiercely. She turned aside in order to wipe her face with the back of her hand, noticing as she looked back that Nathan, too, wore an expression of genuine distress. He cleared his throat and repeated, more steadily, 'Anyway. I just wanted to notify you that the jury have returned a unanimous verdict of Dickhood, and sentenced me accordingly.'

'It's okay,' Gwen said, because it was expected. But now that he was here she could not help herself from inviting him to annul the other words that had hurt so much this morning. She wanted them not repented but somehow actually unsaid. 'Did you really not like him at all?'

Nathan missed this prompt. His sister was rarely angry with him and when she was forgave him in silence and without discussion. Valentina specialised in spectacular tantrums, in cancelled or aggressively terminated phone calls, and on the infrequent occasion she knew herself to be in the wrong she would ring repeatedly until he picked up, imperiously demanding his forgiveness. These fights had not equipped him with a sophisticated understanding of how to nurture or comfort. All he'd learned so far was to reassure women of their beauty and of their value to himself, neither of which seemed of use in this circumstance. In later years, in adulthood, he would have understood that he was meant to declare that Mole had been extraordinary and precious not only to Gwen but to humanity; had been the sweetest-tempered animal, the most intuitive, that there would never be another like him. Grief can be petty and voracious; it craves repeated assurance of the worthiness, the unique value of its subject. He would learn. At seventeen he did not understand the cue, and simply said, 'I don't really know about dogs.'

'He wasn't like other dogs,' Gwen said, let down, and started to cry again.

'Come and sit on the roof and have a drink. I've got whiskey, and they've got hot apple cider downstairs at the bar. It's only ten. If you get dressed I can get one and make us hot toddies,' Nathan offered, anxious to distract her, reaching into a capacious pocket to produce a hip flask. He wanted her to feel better, and to know that he had been forgiven. He was keen to win back Julia's approbation in order to deserve his father's.

'It's late. What is it? I don't really drink. And I only like Malibu.'

'That's probably because it's the only thing you've ever tried,' said Nathan reasonably. 'Whiskey's medicinal. It's why I picked it, it's reviving. Saint Bernards delivered it in the Alps. Or maybe that was brandy. Anyway.' Would this canine reference be enticing, or insensitive? 'Come up. Five minutes?'

She nodded her assent and elbowed the door closed, careful not to unclamp her arms from across her chest.

Ten minutes later they reunited on the roof beside a deep, square swimming pool. This had been drained for the winter, though the small round lights embedded into its walls still shone, filling the pool with overlapping rings of cold, turquoise light. A drift of tiny leaves had collected on the blue-tiled bottom, fallen from a thick climber that hung heavily over a box trellis near the diving board.

The sun loungers were stacked and shackled beneath tarpaulins for the winter so Gwen and Nathan sat down on the concrete lip of the deep end, cold seeping through coats and jeans. It was impossible to remain there and they both stood up almost immediately, casting around for alternatives. Nathan noticed a panel of switches by the elevator and began pressing them in turn, and eventually a large heater came on above the door. Gwen found two small aluminium coffee tables, icy to the touch and beaded with moisture from the damp air, and dragged these into the doorway where they could sit shielded from the wind and warmed, fractionally, by the buzzing fan. That morning James had presented her and Saskia each with a pair of yellow, faux-fur earmuffs, and she clamped hers tighter over her ears.

Gwen's few, tentative experiments with Malibu and pineapple juice had been uneventful. She had always mixed her own drinks at parties and, cautious about quantities, had used the tiny plastic screwcap of the lemonade bottle as her measure. She watched Nathan pouring long slugs of toffee-coloured liquid into two white paper cups of hot apple juice. Far below in the street, an ambulance wailed.

Her first sip made her cough. 'It's burning,' she said, recovering herself, but immediately tried again. 'It's so grim, how can people drink this?'

Nathan made a show of taking a swig straight from the hip flask. 'It is rather smoky, it takes time to acquire a taste for it. I took it from a decanter in my mother's house. The current man likes Scotch malts, apparently.'

'Is that Wentworth guy her boyfriend?' Gwen asked. Something in Nathan's careful enunciation of 'Scotch malts', a spitting quality, caught her attention.

'Who knows. My mother is quite liberal with her favours.'

Gwen giggled, shocked.

'I speak only the truth. Boyfriend, who knows? But I mean,' Nathan continued, forcing an unsuccessful innuendo, 'he keeps his *whiskey* at her *house*.'

'Won't your mum notice you took it?'

'I didn't take it. I used it for its proper purpose. I decanted it.'

Gwen's earmuffs were itching and she took them off, shaking out her hair. Nathan smiled.

'Those look absolutely ridiculous.'

'Take it up with your dad, he bought them.'

'Well, no one ever claimed he was a sartorial genius.'

'What does sartorial mean? Why do you speak like that?' she demanded, made bolder by the dark, and by this unexpectedly companionable transgression.

'You mean, with words? In sentences? It means "about or to do with clothes". It was the perfect word for the moment.'

'You could have just said, "No one ever claimed he knows about clothes."'

'Orwell would admire your commitment to simplicity.'

'I'm not simple!'

'I never said you were any such thing. You are quite complex, in fact. Like all women,' he added loftily.

She clamped the earmuffs back on, defiant.

'You look like a Fraggle with those things on your head.'

'I never watched it. Didn't the main one have red hair?'

'Yes. How come you're actually wearing a gift my execrated father bought you?'

'I'm not even going to ask you what that word means.' She shrugged, her hands in her pockets. 'My ears were cold. And I'm trying to *adjust,* isn't that what we're meant to be doing? Adjusting to our new family. My mum wants me to be nice to him, so I'm trying to be nice to him.'

'I wouldn't expend too much energy adjusting,' Nathan said. He was typing on his phone as he spoke, and did not look up. 'It'll last till it lasts, and then who knows.'

Gwen fell silent. She had never – not once – considered the possibility of the relationship 'not lasting'. Adult relationships lasted for ever or until someone died, which was precisely why James's appearance had been so devastating. The idea that it could just end and life could return to normal was thrilling. She and her mother could slip back into old, easy ways, the soft comfort of favourite jeans after this stiff, unnatural costume.

'Why d'you think it won't last?'

'I can think of a hundred reasons. First of all, I don't believe in marriage.'

'They're not married!' cried Gwen, horrified.

'You are terribly literal. I don't believe in lifelong monogamous cohabitation, then.'

'I don't think it matters if you believe in it, I think it matters if they believe in it.'

'Well, my father obviously doesn't either or he'd still be married to my mother.'

Gwen considered this – it made James sound rather threatening. 'Who broke up with who?'

'Whom. Who broke up with whom. In any case,' Nathan said easily, 'it was never all that clear. I think it's one of those absurdly passionate can't live with, can't live without things. When Mom lived in London Dad was always randomly staying over. She'd have chucked some boyfriend or other and then on Sunday morning Dad would be there, all jolly and making pancakes and wearing some weird old clothes that he hadn't bothered packing when he moved out. It doesn't bear thinking about. People over forty should be forced into celibacy. It's so wrong.'

'So why aren't they still married?'

'Oh, I'd not be surprised if they got back together properly at some point, when they're living in the same country again.' And then, as if discussing his own children he added, with indulgent fondness, 'I've given up second-guessing. Nothing with those two would surprise me. Don't look so freaked, it's not like he'd ever be unfaithful to your mother or anything. He's utterly besotted right now. I just don't believe anything lasts, that's all.'

Gwen's fantasy scenarios of getting rid of James involved her mother listening to reason and evicting him. She did not like to think of Julia being abandoned for a seductress who lured him back with pancakes and a restoration of his former family life. Then she remembered Mole, and to her dismay she felt a lump begin to form in her throat.

Nathan glanced at her. 'That girl Fraggle was quite hot. Red.'

'Being ginger's awful,' she said crossly.

'Red was her name, I mean. Red hair's pretty.' He moved the small table he was sitting on until it was immediately next to hers and reached out to lift a strand from her shoulder. Gwen thrust her hands deeper into her pockets. His face was very close to hers, inspecting a curl beneath the dull yellow light that spilled from the hallway.

'Not bad,' he said, and she felt his gaze, slightly unfocused, shift away from the lock of hair that lay in his gloved hand.

There followed a fraction of a second in which Gwen felt he might kiss her. And a fraction of a second later, she realised that she had misunderstood, but that this had been – just for one painful instant – what she wanted. She felt herself flush. Nathan's face remained inches away from hers but he was still, with a show of great interest, studying the colour of her hair. Then he looked up at her, but did not sit back.

'I like red,' he said quietly, so close that his breath tickled her lips. He was twirling the strand around his finger.

She looked back at him and thought, I'm drunk. I am humiliatingly drunk, on two thirds of a paper cup of lukewarm apple juice and whiskey. He is almost my stepbrother. And what if it's illegal? At that moment he lifted his hand to her cheek and drew her face towards him, and their lips met.

A border crossed. A new territory, and uncharted anxieties. His tongue, unexpectedly firm, was now in her mouth where it remained, probing her own. She did not know whether it was permissible to close her lips, briefly, now that they were parted, and wondered too when she might be able to pause for a moment in order to swallow. But if they paused they would have to speak to one another and that, when it came, would be excruciating. Their heads were tilted to the right – was there a prearranged moment at which one was expected to rotate ninety degrees and incline the other way, left to left? Nathan did not seem to want to stop, nor appear to suffer any salivary concerns.

So this was it. And it had not happened in the dark, buttered-popcorn recesses of a cinema, or years before, beneath the rolling swell of disco lights on the dance floor of a bar mitzvah, to a soundtrack of a power ballad and the envious whoops and giggles of spectating friends. It had happened in America on an icy hotel rooftop, with a boy much more experienced than she, a little older, very much cooler, who might or might not have a girlfriend and to whom she might or might not be related. It was possible she had been, until tonight, the only sixteen-year-old in London who had not yet kissed a boy but she already knew that this tale, when she recounted it to an envious Katy, would be worth the wait.

Nathan's hand was at the back of her neck, pulling her towards him with a new and surprising insistence. In a moment of tentative confidence she pulled away, swallowed furtively and performed her revolution, right to left, her neck relieved of its increasing tension in the chill. After the successful execution of this move she started to relax. The racing of her mind began to slow, and she found herself thinking, with a flash of new triumph, that her mother, James, Katy and Valentina would all be horrified, for different, precious, valid reasons.

NINE

Philip had lost his Andrew-and-Fergie commemorative mug, one of the treasured possessions of his recent years. Gwen had accepted his attachment to this object without judgement. Julia was bemused, while Iris found it risible, and an embarrassment. Philip didn't mind. If they wished to believe he had lately become an ardent collector of royalist memorabilia, so be it. Iris need not have the family monopoly on caprice, and it was considerably less humiliating than the truth: that he was a man whose surgeon's hands had been seized by arthritis and who hoped – correctly, it turned out – that a two-handled mug would mean he could once again drink tea first thing in the morning. He had happened to mention that it was missing, and Gwen had raced over to help him hunt.

'Well, where did you last have it?' Gwen demanded, her hands planted on her hips. She had painted a butterfly on the back of her left hand and every now and then glanced down at her own handiwork with admiration. She spun on her heels in place, scanning the room, and her hair, in two fat plaits, thumped against her back and chest as she turned. It was a pleasing sensation and she did this several times back and forth. 'Can't we put some more light on?'

'It is on. It really doesn't matter, darling,' Philip said, gesturing for her to sit down again. She peered around once more without moving and then flopped back on the sofa, pulling her phone out of the marsupial pouch of her sweater. 'Let's find another one on eBay, I'll bid on a few to make sure. Oh! Maybe they've got Charles and Diana?'

'Later, later. It must be somewhere. Tell me how you are, first. How have you been?'

'I'm okay.' Gwen shrugged, tucking her phone away again. 'School's boring. You know.'

'Your blog was very moving,' Philip told her. 'The portraits were beautiful. I don't know how you think of these things. Beautiful. You made your grandmother cry.'

'Really?' Gwen brightened. 'Is that possible?'

'It's possible. Not frequent, but it happens. You moved us both.'

Gwen had depicted herself and Julia hand in hand in the Museum of Fine Arts in Boston, beneath a gallery of portraits of Mole, tiny, recognisable Old Masters in which an elderly black Labrador had replaced those old familiar faces. Mole, peacock-blue-and-gold-robed in His Studio; an uncertain, white-turbaned Berber King Mole; Mole in the brass-buttoned, double-breasted uniform of the Arles postman.

The dog's final, rattling breath had slayed Philip, though he had remained calm and professional with the pretty, sorrowful young vet while she had wielded her terrible needle. He did not tell Gwen that when he had seen her portraits he had wept until fat tears had fallen onto his keyboard. When he had collected himself he had called Iris and they had agreed that their granddaughter was a genius. 'Memento mori,' Iris had said thoughtfully, and he had agreed, though these days he needed no such prompt.

Gwen was looking at him, her expression solemn. 'I wanted to say – thank you *so much* for taking care of him. I'm glad he was with you. You're the only person – you are very soothing, you know, Grandpa. I'm sure Mole loved you.'

'And I him. Thank you, *maidele*. I do promise you, I made the decision that felt moral –'

'Oh, I know,' Gwen said, with a decisive nod. 'I'd have felt awful if you'd kept him suffering for me. It would have been so selfish. You're a dog person, I totally trust you. And a *doctor*.'

'You're anything but selfish.'

'I dunno.' Gwen drew her brows together in a frown. 'I'm trying not to be but sometimes I just am, without realising. I get upset about things and then that upsets Mum, and then I feel bad, but I never know it's happening till after it's happened, you know? Suddenly we're having a huge fight and I don't even know *how*. And then I can't talk to her properly because we're literally never alone. Ever. We used to get ten milliseconds in the car on the way to pottery, but now James comes with, and they go to the gym together during my lesson. The *gym*. I mean, Mum in the gym is so beyond ridiculous, it's so try-hard, it's only because James is obsessed with it. She doesn't even have leggings, she goes in like, linen trousers. So we literally have to whisper in the bathroom or whatever, and I get upset and then she gets sad and worried and feels *torn*, and then I get upset she's upset. I'm not joking, I have to physically kidnap her to talk to her any more.' She had begun to look brooding. Philip saw his son's defiant dark eyes flash in his granddaughter's face.

'It sounds like you miss her. Have you talked about it?'

'Maybe a squillion times and she just says it's an "adjustment period". If I need to say something private I message her now, but she's so rubbish texting it's painful, I can see her across the room and she'll be spending five hours typing three words so it's actual parental abuse to make her do it. You text super quickly. You're amazing.' She said this with some pride.

'I use voice recognition. It's why my punctuation is sometimes a bit strange.'

'Punctuation's so not important, Grandpa,' said Gwen loyally and Philip, who wished to differ, held his tongue.

Instead he asked, 'And the rest of last weekend, apart from what must have been the very hard parts? How did you find Boston? Your mother says you get on well with James's daughter.'

'Saskia's awesome, she's coming for Christmas I think, because her mother, you know Pamela? She's coming over too, to visit her sister. She is a total and complete psycho. It literally scares me how mental she is. No wonder James is a total wet blanket, I think she ate his brain when they got married. She's like, terrifying.'

Philip laughed and began to reach forward, painstakingly, for the lemon biscuits Gwen had made him, and she sprang forward and handed him the plate. 'Terrifying in what sense?'

'She just throws herself around all the time, it's gross. Nathan is convinced it's because she's still in love with wimpy James, but I mean, good luck with that when he's clearly obsessed with Mum, which I said and he was like, I know, I know, *for now*.'

'So you and Nathan are friends now? That sounds like progress.'

Gwen opened her mouth to speak and then clamped it shut with such sudden contraction that he heard the hollow thock of teeth closing together. 'Not friends, he's lame. But we're stuck with each other, so everyone keeps saying.'

TEN

They had been to collect Gwen from a visit to her grandfather's, and when Philip had appeared at the threshold to wave goodbye Julia was moved by the warmth with which he'd greeted James.

The two men had met at a conference on neonatal health. Their rooms had been side by side in an isolated block at the far end of campus and each morning, Philip had reported, the blond American next door had knocked and invited him to walk to breakfast. Together they had crossed the neat triangular slices of lawn that lay between redbrick faculty clusters, and in the refectory Philip would find them seats while James had queued for their oily, lukewarm fried eggs. When the conference ended James had offered Philip a lift back to London, and over coffee in an M4 service station had mentioned that he was considering music lessons. There had been no music in his house growing up, he'd confided, only the low susurrations of financial anxiety and the dissonance of raised voices. Was it a foolish aspiration, in his fifties? Philip had carefully lowered his cup and felt in his breast pocket for a pen. A surgeon should take care of his fingers, he had counselled. James absolutely must learn to play the piano. He had urged Julia's email address into James's hands.

James was a terrible, determined pianist, combining exuberance with Julia's first true experience of a tin ear. He strode in tired from the hospital but in lessons seemed inexhaustible. He claimed to practise relentlessly, yet made no progress. He grinned, and swore, and hunched over to redouble his efforts. When a phrase defeated him he played it louder. He charmed her, but she knew he did not see her.

And then for his fourth or fifth lesson he'd arrived to find her stapling programmes for her students' winter concert. The youngest, only five, would open with 'When the Saints Go Marching In'; Susannah Gowers, who at twelve was the eldest, was rounding off the night with Mozart's Sonata in F Major, K. 332. James had picked up a stiff white card.

'A recital.'

'Yes.'

'How many students playing?'

'All of them. Sixteen, in total.'

He'd run his finger down the list, frowning. Bach, Brahms, Chopin, Mozart, Bach again. 'When am I?'

She willed away the bubble of laughter rising in her throat. It was a four p.m. children's concert in a school hall, on a sticky Pearl River upright. There would be orange squash and pink wafers. There would be proud parents filming, most of whom themselves were younger than James Fuller.

'Don't worry at all, and definitely don't waste paper printing them again, you can just pencil it in. Perhaps I should perform the Schubert we've been working on? Or something new? I think you should decide what would work best for me. What about "Für Elise"?' He was grave, respectful. He regarded her unblinking.

'I –' She was defeated into acquiescence by her own bitter disappointment. She had liked him, and he was deranged. 'If you like,' she said weakly.

'Great.' He sat down at the piano and began to murder the first few bars of the fantasie. 'And I've been thinking,' he called over his shoulder, jaunty, like a music-hall entertainer, 'I'm going to sit for my grade three. I think I'm almost ready, what do you think?'

Julia had made a strangled noise, and it was then that James had laid his forehead against the music stand and begun to shake with silent laughter. He gasped out, ' "Für Elise"!' and she caught up. He was not deranged. He was wonderful and foolish, and he had spectacular muscled shoulders, and she was smitten. Later that day he had called, between patients, and suggested coffee. She did not know whether the life-altering generosity of Philip's introduction had been deliberate, and she could never ask. The belief shimmered in and out of certainty. She wondered whether she would ever be able to sense if Philip found it painful or distasteful to see them together.

Julia entered the kitchen to find Nathan and an apparently reinstated Valentina sitting at the table, playing cards. This weekend there had been no trace of her, an unprecedented period of serenity in the household. Under normal circumstances if she wasn't at their dinner table she was interrupting it with calls and text messages, and it had been a relief to be free of her pouting and huffing, her air of bored pretension. She batted sooty lashes at James, addressed Julia as if condescending to a member of household staff, and rarely deigned to speak to Gwen at all. Julia had felt cautiously hopeful that without her Nathan might be a nicer boy, and so it had proved. He had been more relaxed, able to act his age and to drop his air of world-wearied, supercilious cynicism. It could not be a coincidence that Gwen and Nathan had been getting on so much better. On Friday night the children had volunteered to go shopping together for supper, and later Nathan had sat with them watching at least ten minutes of one of Gwen's favoured reality shows without once suggesting that the devoted followers of such programmes must be lobotomised morons. James had heard from Pamela (who had heard from Saskia) that Nathan and Valentina had broken up. If true, this would have been radical, and auspicious. But now it was Sunday evening and here she was, barefoot and back in their kitchen.

It was Valentina's pointed look towards the refrigerator, accompanied by a stifled, fey little giggle, that first attracted Julia's attention to the blackboard on the fridge door. When the fancy took her Gwen would write notes on this board, or practise her various calligraphies, or paint rainbows or self-portraits with chalk-dusted fingertips. Frequently she drew elaborate illustrations of the shopping list. 'Grapes', Julia would write, and the next day a vine would climb and twine around the letters, heavy with misty bunches. If Julia reminded herself to pick up some cottage cheese, she might find a drawing of a thatched and rose-wrapped little chalet perched upon a wheel of generously perforated emmenthal. Julia had always treasured these artworks, begun, like so much else, in the months after Daniel's death, another form of silent communication, and another small way in which they worked to make one another smile. Family traditions could go some way towards making two people feel like a family. Gwen's rendering of a winsome, smiling anchovy had remained in one corner for months.

Today, a new, tertiary commentary had appeared. In Julia's handwriting it said, 'Olive oil, mushrooms, cheddar'. James had written 'Spuds', which Gwen had then rubbed out and replaced with a drawing of a potato. She had made her own additions to the list but two of these – 'MAYONAISE' and 'TOMATOS' – had since been amended in thick red chalk to their correct spelling by a third, unknown hand. A drawing of an anthropomorphised fish finger that had been there for days had been wiped away and in its place, in ornately serifed upper case the words, '5/7. TRY HARDER NEXT TIME.'

Julia frowned at Nathan but from his face it seemed he too had only just noticed. Beside him she saw Valentina widen her eyes and pout. She snapped a card down on the table and looked back at her hand with an expression of rather camp, exaggerated innocence, then raked her fingers through her long hair and pulled it forward over her shoulders, and stretched. 'Hello, Julia,' she said sweetly.

James came in, unzipping his coat, and betraying no surprise at seeing Valentina in the kitchen, for which Julia admired him. She moved to get a damp cloth to wipe the blackboard, but at that moment Gwen appeared. She stopped short in the doorway, looking startled.

'I'm so sorry for your loss,' Valentina cooed, with an exaggerated expression of regret.

Gwen appeared to struggle with a series of conflicting emotions but then said, rather stiffly, 'I haven't lost anything.'

'She means Mole,' Nathan explained, looking embarrassed.

Gwen appeared not to hear him. 'I haven't lost anything I actually *wanted*.'

While this indecipherable exchange was taking place, Julia edged forwards and tried to conceal the horrible, unsolicited little spelling test by standing in front of it. This drew everyone's attention.

Only Julia had a vantage place from which to see Gwen's expression of bewilderment collapse into raw new shame. Gwen opened the fridge, extracted an apple and then left, slamming the door only marginally harder than necessary. Her footfalls up the stairs receded. To follow would compound the humiliation, Julia felt, though she longed with a magnetic pull to go to her daughter. James glanced at her and then turned and ambled out again. 'I'm going to do a little work,' he said, as he left. 'I'll see you guys.'

Julia noticed, unmoved, that Nathan was glaring at Valentina. 'It's late,' she said finally. 'I'm going to start dinner. Do you two mind shifting to the living room?'

'Val's not staying for supper,' said Nathan, smearing his hand over the scattered playing cards and pulling them towards him on the table with the satisfaction of a Vegas dealer. 'Anyway, she's given up eating till next year. Nil by mouth till she's the size of the square root of minus one. Imaginary.' He sounded blithe but looked guilty, Julia noted. In truth, she thought, it wasn't on to let him make fun of Valentina either, and James would have pulled him up on it, but Julia did not feel inclined to defend her daughter's assailant. Policing all these delinquent and unrelated teenagers was tedious. She took two aubergines from the newly denuded refrigerator and began to chop them. Behind her she heard Valentina saying, 'Forgive me for thinking we had major things to talk about,' and then in a lower voice, 'What? She won't actually care. They don't believe in stuff like spelling at her school, anyway, do they? It's too rigorous and constraining. Who needs to be able to spell when you can draw such a jolly, friendly little *fish finger*?'

Julia pulled open a lower drawer and clanged several saucepans on her hunt for the colander. If Nathan replied she couldn't make it out, and the next she heard was Valentina adding, petulantly, '*E ho già detto che,* don't call me Val.'

So that, Gwen thought, was that. Shame twisted within her. Valentina might be odious but she, Gwen, was something far worse, for she was stupid. Whatever peculiar Bostonian wormhole had yawned open and deluded Nathan into finding her attractive had now resealed, and the natural order of the universe had been restored.

All week she had been summoning the courage to message him at school to ask about Valentina; silent rehearsals of phrasing and rephrasing in which she tried to balance the desire to know with her more pressing wish not to seem invested in his answer. It had been a waste of energy. They were obviously back together, if indeed they had ever broken up.

But then why, why all the kissing? Alone in her room she flushed, reliving it. He'd been home from school for the weekend and they had kissed for nearly two cumulative hours, she had calculated, all of it initiated by Nathan.

It was true that he had never attempted to approach her in the house, but this had surely been appropriate caution under highly unusual circumstances. If they were going to be boyfriend and girlfriend – and this had been her sustaining and most cherished fantasy from that first fraction of a second, on the roof in Boston – if they were going to be in a serious relationship then a certain degree of tact would be required of both of them. She had planned it all out.

On Friday he'd already been kicking about in Belsize Park when she'd got off the bus from school, when he usually spent Friday nights at Westminster. They had walked home together through the nature reserve where he had turned and pulled her to him almost in the middle of a sentence, stumbling with her off the path and pressing her up against the broad, rough trunk of an old oak, and on the way out had even held her hand, their fingers interlaced until they'd emerged into the familiarity and exposure of Lawn Road.

And there had been other developments. When it first happened, the night of their return to London, she had fended off his hands as they'd snaked their way beneath her sweater. On Friday in Belsize Wood, she had waited a third and then a fourth beat before pushing him away. The cold of his fingertips had shocked her but there had been something else, too, and though it had begun to rain and the wintry, late-afternoon darkness had long fallen she had felt a clenching low in her belly, a knot of sudden hunger, and had wanted to let him continue. Even to contemplate it was impossible – it thrilled her that a boy like Nathan would make these attempts but it was impossible to succumb to them. Her first kiss had been only a week ago; it was far too soon for anything further. In any case, she had privately resolved, his hands would go nowhere until he had clarified his position with Valentina. She would have told him of this stipulation had he asked.

It had become clear that Nathan was a two-timing weasel and a liar. Home was now officially and comprehensively unbearable – there would be nowhere to which Gwen could escape except her own room, and even that would be no liberation if Valentina started staying over again. It was not only in the movies, she'd discovered, that headboards banged against walls with rhythmic and unequivocal insistence. Valentina had read Dante in Italian, and she was not dyslexic and she would definitely be accepted to read English at Merton, which was – Gwen had heard it discussed as a fait accompli so often she might scream – what she planned to do after graduating from Westminster. Not hoped. *Planned.* Gwen did not know who or what Dante was, though she knew it to be the name of a character on an American television drama. Alone in her room, her cheeks flamed. She wanted to open her new polymer modelling clay, a deep indigo that she'd hoped would be perfect for rendering denim, but Valentina's mere presence made her art feel foolish and for that she hated her more than anything. It was the anchor of her identity without which she was undifferentiated and unremarkable, and it was childish and pointless.

There was a cheery rap, and James's head appeared round the door.

'Your mom sent me psychic vibes that she wanted me to come and check you were okay. She'd have come herself but she's busy lacing arsenic into the dinner.'

'Good. Tell her to make it a double dose for me.'

'Not for you. But I think she's ready to dispatch our visitor.' James advanced a little into the room and opened the door wider behind him. He always did this when they were alone together, Gwen had noticed with exasperation, shuffling away on sofas and adopting modes of ostentatiously monkish propriety that he had no doubt learned from a book of pop psychology. *How Not to Make Your Stepdaughter Think You're a Perv, Volume I*. This was the first time he had ventured alone into her bedroom and so he must have been on high alert. He needn't have bothered. James did not have it in him to be anything so interesting as a pervert. Of all her objections that, thankfully, was not a concern. His self-conscious behaviour merely drew attention to the idea that he could have been an incestuous paedophile, but wasn't. Still, if he was willing to insult Valentina he could stay.

'Your son,' Gwen said, with slightly wobbly scorn, 'is a total douche.'

'He has it in him,' James conceded. 'But I think that particular little nastiness was someone else's handiwork. I saw his face, I really think he hadn't seen. Do you want to come back down and show them that you're a bigger person?'

'Is that some kind of joke?' Gwen demanded, ever attuned to anything that could be construed a reference to her height. 'You think I should like, stand on her, or something?'

James looked bewildered and then briefly horrified. 'No! I wouldn't make personal – no, no. Retake. Do you want to come back down and show them you are a *more mature person* than she?'

'I'm not. I'm a retard who can't spell.' Gwen promptly burst into tears. James would never attempt to hug her unchaperoned, and she felt fleeting gratitude for this consideration before sinking back into the partial relief of misery and self-pity. And her mother hadn't even come up. She'd sent her new proxy, as if she and James were interchangeable. Gwen's companionship no longer necessary, her requirements no longer paramount. Gwen had no one. James sat down in the open doorway and pulled his knees up awkwardly.

'You know, nowadays we have spellcheck,' he mused. 'I'd say on balance I'd rather be you.'

Gwen shook her head, mute with unhappiness, but just then a message arrived.

'SORRY ABOUT V. SHE'S MAD BECAUSE IT'S TOTALLY OVER, THAT WAS LAST TALK. YOU'RE MY GIRL? XXX'

Gwen gave James an unsteady smile that broadened as she reread. She said he could go, thanks. She would be okay.

ELEVEN

Christmas had always been presumed a point of tension between Julia and Daniel but had been, in reality, quite the opposite. Before they'd married they had felt obliged to visit Julia's mother every year on the grounds, put forward by Julia's mother herself, that Daniel's parents were Jews and it was not 'their day'. 'They can't have everything,' she had said, dark and obscure. Julia had sat in shame and misery while her mother scorched a crown of turkey, refused Daniel's help with anything but taking the bins out and instead sat, slashing deep scores into the bottoms of tough sprouts and alternately ignoring or interrogating him on the subject of his religious beliefs. Unearthing his agnosticism, layered on top of the already unacceptable Judaism, had been the final insult. They had gone one final time when Gwen was tiny, teething, battling an unfortunate coincidence of pinkeye and impetigo, not a celestial Christmas cherub but a blotched and irritable tyrant. Julia's mother had refused to hold the baby but instead had sat back, arms crossed defensively across her chest, and offered the bewildering adage that 'a redhead aboard a ship brings bad luck', implying that both Gwen and Daniel might have had the same ill effect upon National Rail, opined that it had been wicked to take the child on a crowded train spreading all those germs, and had then gone on to suggest that they had done so only because Daniel (and wasn't it always the case with his sort?) was too tight-fisted to pay for the petrol. Julia had not repeated the mistake, preferring to visit alone, and at less charged points in the calendar. Christmas had offered too much tantalising material, too many baubles of obvious conflict and star-points of attack.

Since Daniel died, they had not visited. She had fought hard to forget that final conversation, to lock it away, sealed very tightly out of sight, in the dark, where it could no longer hurt her. Daniel would have dismissed it, would have laughed and told her to forgive, would have said that hell didn't exist anyway so how could a fanciful evocation matter; he knew Julia didn't believe fairy stories, nor that he'd face lakes of fire or unquenchable flaming pits. But she could not forgive, and even to contemplate it burned like a betrayal. Gwen had never asked to go back, and the birthday cards she received, containing five pounds and the unvarying and unpunctuated message in blue biro, 'MAY JESUS KEEP YOU FROM GRANDMOTHER', were never mentioned. Julia had embraced Daniel's family traditions with relief.

Gospel Oak: a pleasingly ecclesiastical name at Christmastime. The Queen's Crescent lights as scanty and ineffectual as a weak torch in daylight and lit, not by a minor local celebrity but instead by whichever council-employed electrician has garlanded the lampposts in perfunctory and partially functioning strings of white bulbs. Stiff felt Santa hats and last year's Dairy Milk advent calendars appear on market stalls, added to the usual array of tissue multipacks and plastic children's shoes and individual batteries on sale in a clear plastic washing-up bowl, the tartan-print vinyl shopping trolleys, nesting Tupperwares and carousels of polyester headscarves. In December a regimental bank of small, potted poinsettias stand on proud display beside the usual buckets of wearily opening lilies. The market itself takes on a genial air and here, for the last ten years, Julia bought tinsel and wrapping paper and boxes of reliably cheap and unreliable fairy lights. She joined in with Christmas in the scrappy and defiant local style. And this year there was James, her family and his, around a single table. Thrilling. Terrifying.

He had set her free. Julia had never before considered retiring. Give up teaching for what? More hours of solitude? But James would retire in ten years, and was already full of ideas. He had a colleague supervising a training programme for community midwives in Sierra Leone and he wanted to spend three months a year there, teaching. He'd always thought he'd move back to New England but now he talked of Sussex, 'Lewes or some other absurdly beautiful British town,' and learning to cook on an Aga, and walking together, if not by the icy western Atlantic, then on the quieter shores of the English Channel.

What did she want? She hardly knew, and she'd never dared consider. Growing up she'd wanted a mother who wasn't always angry; whose love did not feel conditional upon being unobtrusive, or upon the meek and tireless execution of chores. James asking allowed her to wonder, and to fantasise. She would adore the opera at Verona, to go to JazzFest in New Orleans, and now wanted to go walking with James in the northern Appalachian mountains he'd described to her so vividly. They would wake up together in Maine and New Hampshire and Vermont. A new phase ahead, when their hours were freed only for one another. Whispered to James as they fell asleep, these wishes did not sound foolish. Instead, now, they sounded like plans. She no longer need dread the loneliness and silence of her daughter leaving home but instead could look forward to the new world that Gwen's growing up would enable. If they left London and moved to Lewes, she could buy a better piano. Gwen would visit – with a degree, a boyfriend, with stories, with laundry – and then return to her own life. James and Julia would have one another.

But in the meantime, all must coexist in closer quarters. And no doubt Gwen was dreading every moment of Christmas lunch today, Julia thought, swallowing down the hard bead of guilt that had lodged in her throat. She would find time alone with her on Boxing Day. Maybe they could go for a long tramp on the Heath together as they had last year, and the year before. They no longer had Mole, but she hoped Gwen knew they still had one another.

Upstairs, James was folding the laundry and examining his own sense of faint unease, probing it like a sore tooth. He had felt almost instantly at home in this house, he reflected, and had only realised it with hindsight, now that his sense of belonging was unexpectedly undermined. Each meeting with them had been characterised by generous goodwill and decorum, but Daniel's parents had not visited the house since he had moved in, and he was surprised by the degree of his own discomfort. He knew he was not a usurper. Nonetheless he intended to remain upstairs until Iris and Philip had arrived to avoid the insensitive accident of welcoming them into a hallway that they knew better than he.

Since the divorce he and Pamela had managed to spend the holidays together in relatively amicable coalition. (Usually in Boston and once, less successfully, in Barbados – in the course of that week they had reunited intermittently for angry late-night sex, the pleasure of which had been entirely undermined by the magnificent violence of their daytime arguments. Afterwards they'd agreed to celebrate chastely, and in Boston again.) He had readily agreed to host the Aldens for Christmas lunch, but this would be the first year his children would not have their parents together and he knew, though they would not admit it, that they minded. Both had spoken to their mother several times already, and he'd overheard Nathan, in particular, sounding wistful and slightly guilty. Pamela had flown over with Saskia the day before, and was having lunch with her own sister and extended clan in Sussex, and the kids would join her on Boxing Day. They were shuttling, in the time-honoured tradition of broken homes. It turned out they were not the rule's exception.

Nathan appeared, looking conspiratorial. Then he re-arranged himself, cool and collected again, and drawled, 'They're here. Jeez, how boring. But at least now we can eat.' He tossed the hair from his eyes and grinned, winsome, devilish, spearing James's heart with love, and then was gone again, footsteps thundering heavily down the stairs.

James followed and joined them all in the hallway. Julia looked up and gave a quick nervous smile. He willed her to understand: They're yours, and I shall learn to cherish them as you do, or try. *I will love them*: another tender, necessary lie.

'Really, you're going to have to help us,' Iris was saying, 'I've booked tickets for the whole series and I'm just not sure that I can face them every week.' She was shrugging off a black fur coat, silky, heavy, and Philip stood behind her attentively to receive it. Iris raised a leather-gloved hand to James in greeting. 'I was just telling Julia I've booked a thousand and one tickets for a series at the Wigmore. You two are going to have to take a few off our hands, my ears were bigger than my stomach. Take the Borodin Quartet Shostakovich in February.'

Philip had hung Iris's coat over the end of the banister, and was slowly unwinding his own scarf. 'I sometimes find Shostakovich rather exhausting,' he mused. He took off his glasses slowly, and began to polish them on the corner of his cardigan, smiling blindly towards James.

'Which is precisely why I am offloading him. I'm saving us Brahms and Liszt.'

'Thank you,' said Philip humbly. Glasses replaced, he extended an unsteady hand to James. '*Chag sameach*. Thank you for having us.'

'Right, exactly. Christmas *sameach*. Come in, come in.' This invitation was just what he had intended not to say, and with nerves he had somehow said it twice. Come in, make yourselves at home. Too late. He stood back, allowing them past him and into the living room. Philip patted his arm.

From the kitchen came a loud clattering, and then Gwen skidded in, red hair loose and flying. She threw joyous arms around her grandmother, who recoiled. 'Darling, you reek of fish, get off me immediately!'

Gwen pushed a curl from her eyes with the back of her wrist, and then sniffed her hands. 'Yuck. Sorry, I've been making smoked salmon rosettes. I should have rubbed lemon on them.'

Saskia followed from the kitchen, and smiled vaguely around. 'Hey,' she said in general greeting, and then added, 'Does that really work? Mine stink too, I've been unwrapping. Gwen's cooking awesome stuff, come see.'

'Gwen doesn't cook, she presents,' Nathan amended.

'That's true. But I tell you something, my presentation is seriously *Off. The. Charts.* Granny, I've made a cream-cheese snowman, he's in the fridge, he's got poppy-seed hair and everything. There's not really cooking to do with Christmas bagels.' She pirouetted on socked feet, landing rather heavily on her heels.

In the last weeks James had detected a thaw between Nathan and Gwen – not an alliance, for that would be too much to ask, but a truce, perhaps. Late at night, he and Julia whispered about it with cautious optimism. Since Valentina's now firmly established absence, family life had steadily improved, and it no longer seemed unreasonable to picture them all coexisting in relative harmony, until the next years would send one and then both of the children to college.

They moved together into the kitchen where Julia peeled cling film from various dishes and James, glad to have something to occupy him, offered drinks, clinked ice into glasses, and then retrieved Gwen's snowman construction from the fridge. It was indeed very impressive, with eyes cut from scraps of black olive, rosemary twig arms and a tiny carrot nose. It was likely she'd spent more time on this edifice than she'd spend on a week's homework, but her academic future (or lack of it) was not James's business. An appreciative murmur went around the table. Julia moved a basket of bagels to one side and took a seat between Iris and Gwen.

'Not wanting to pit matriarch against matriarch,' Nathan began, offering Iris the platter of Gwen's elaborately rolled salmon flowers, 'but why bagels exactly? Pamela always makes goose on Christmas Day.'

'It's an Alden family tradition.' Julia pushed back her chair to retrieve the sliced lemons from the counter. She was feeling charitable, more relaxed than expected in this odd, mixed company. She took Gwen's hand and squeezed it, and Gwen squeezed back, and smiled.

'It was Iris,' Philip told him, pointing apologetically at a poppy-seed bagel in the basket that Julia held out. She took it and sliced it for him. 'It was entirely Iris's innovation. I was often at the hospital on Christmas Day —'

'—That is a total misrepresentation,' Iris interrupted. 'You were always at work on Christmas Day because you always offered to work Christmas Day.'

Philip shrugged. 'It's not our holiday, it seemed fair . . .'

'It seemed charitable to take them all bagels,' Iris shrugged. 'They were such a sorry bunch, nothing scheduled on the wards and these rather pathetic strands of tinsel over the nurses' station. And hospital food is just so revolting, and they did the most repulsive seasonally inspired muck. Horrid pale greasy sprouts, and slices of mystery meat with stuffing. It was an act of charity that turned into a tradition.'

'They still do the mystery meat,' James told her. 'I've grown quite fond of it.' To Philip he said, 'I forgot to tell you, you know we had the quad mother?'

'Did you manage to keep them in?'

'We had to section her yesterday. She was—'

'—Dad.' Saskia spoke very softly, but her voice was firm. 'No gross birth stories today, please. It's Christmas.'

'Christmas is all about birth stories,' said Nathan through a mouthful of lunch. 'In a barn or whatever, with nothing but herbs as pain relief. What do frankincense and myrrh actually do? It's right up Mom's street, it's like, the ultimate home birth.' He snorted, pleased with himself. Gwen giggled.

After a few moments hunched over his phone Nathan announced, 'Myrrh opens up the heart chakra.'

'So says the wisdom of the Internet.'

'No, so says Mom, I texted her. "Good for making one accepting and non-judgemental."'

'I'd need a hell of a lot of myrrh not to judge that utter horse shit,' James told him, and then looked to Iris, regretting the obscenity, but Iris was nodding in firm agreement.

TWELVE

'A success all round I'd say,' said Iris, coming up behind Julia. She was already in her coat, and pulling on long, tangerine leather driving gloves.

'You're a lovely hostess and this was perfect, but Philip Alden's terribly tired now, so we'll take our leave. He's used some sort of minicab application – a gentleman called Stu is, so I'm told, four minutes away.'

Together they peered through the doorway into the living room. James and Philip sat talking on the sofa, Saskia had sprawled in an armchair with a magazine and Gwen lay on the floor sketching Philip's profile on a lined legal pad. Nathan was also on the floor, sitting at Saskia's feet reading the same copy of *Swann's Way* that he'd been carrying around the house for weeks, unopened until today. As they watched, Saskia's phone rang.

'Hi, Mom . . . I don't know. Dad, is there any sherry? Mom's going to be driving past on her way back from lunch, she wondered if she could come by for a glass of sherry.'

'That's pretty specific,' James muttered, excusing himself from Philip and standing up. From the doorway Julia called, 'Of course Pamela must come for sherry.' Behind her she heard a heavy breath.

'This is presumption.'

'We hadn't said we'd see her today, but I suppose it's nice she feels so comfortable.' Julia spoke softly to encourage her mother-in-law to do likewise.

'Oh, what tosh,' said Iris in irritation, pulling at the fingers of her left glove. It came away, exhaling a rich, musky puff of Chanel No. 5. 'It's an imposition. Cancel Stu, please,' she commanded Philip from the doorway, as if barking orders at a court attendant. Julia watched Philip, unquestioning, reach into the inside pocket of his corduroy jacket and fumble for his phone.

'You don't have to stay.'

'Oh, for goodness' sake don't be so naive, we most certainly do. It's why she's coming, to inspect us all. Philip Alden shall simply have to have an espresso and look lively.'

Iris had reached the limit of her forbearance with these strangers and to extend it was almost unendurable. But Gwen had described Pamela in vivid detail, and it would do Gwen no good to see her mother trampled like a doormat once again. It was quite enough to suffer that cheery, insipid American so conspicuously failing to make his presence inconspicuous, but to have his ex-wife arrive and wreak unchecked havoc was insufferable. She would not have the Aldens so outnumbered in their own home.

All afternoon she had found James terribly trying, with his earnest smiles and reflexive nods of agreement as he danced attendance on herself and Philip like an obliging houseboy, his urge to be hospitable hampered by an obvious anxiety to avoid seeming proprietorial. Feigned imbecility did nothing to conceal the unpalatable fact that he now had the keys to, and possession of, Daniel's house. James was so bloody sensitive, and *careful*, and several times during lunch she'd wanted to smack him. Christ alive, man, she'd thought, you're screwing her upstairs every night, don't pretend you don't know where she keeps the ground coffee.

In the last years Iris had counselled Julia to put herself about a bit – she herself had always been a believer in the therapeutic powers of sex, and the nourishing balm of male attention. Men were necessary and had been necessary to Iris, often in the plural, for much of her life. What had stung, an unexpected betrayal, had been this insistence upon cohabitation and the intermingling of lives – love, she supposed they would call it. She had always suspected Julia would be too insipid to take casual lovers; still, it would have been more tactful, and less disruptive for the rest of the family.

But at lunch she'd been kept in check by Philip Alden's cautionary frowns, which she felt across the table like the soft glow of a heat lamp. His warning glance alone was enough to lower her blood pressure, and the monitoring eye he kept on her behaviour at all times relieved her of the burden of self-censorship. His silent reproof soothed her irritation, for she felt understood. I know, he assured her; I see.

Since Pamela's phone call they all sat arrested in expectation of her arrival. Saskia's magazine was now in her lap.

Gwen had stopped drawing and was on the floor beside Nathan, inspecting her split ends. Philip still wore his scarf and jacket. Julia, who had only just relaxed after hours of managing the afternoon's social lubrication, began to clear the debris and to gather in the colony of glasses and mugs that had taken over most surfaces. Foil chocolate wrappers and crumpled napkins decorated the spaces in between them, and beside Gwen was a square of kitchen towel piled high with tangerine peels. Nathan had recently made himself a third cream-cheese bagel, a post-lunch snack, and his discarded plate was also on the floor. Balanced on the arm of Saskia's chair was an empty Oreo packet. Rowan, an old school friend of Saskia, had come over on Christmas Eve, a tiny, angular and white-skinned girl with severely cut black hair and impeccable manners. She'd presented Julia with a tin of amaretti biscuits, and the wrappers from these, printed with text in rose pink, had accumulated on the coffee table like a drift of flushed magnolia bells. The house looked like the celebratory aftermath of precisely what it was, a gluttonous and pleasurable family Christmas and also, to the new visitor, a bloody mess.

Julia turned out every kitchen cupboard and had not unearthed a bottle of sherry, a foregone conclusion as she had never known a bottle to be in the house. But she had hunted nonetheless, if only to show James her attempts to be hospitable. He had been nothing but charming to Iris and Philip today which meant she did not feel she could say, *Why is your mad ex-wife descending upon my house?*

'Gwen?' she called lightly. 'Would you like to make some mulled wine for when Pamela arrives? We've got cloves and I'm sure there's some star anise somewhere. You could look up a recipe online.'

Gwen mumbled something to Nathan beside her, who laughed.

'I'll help if you like,' he offered. 'You may not be aware of it but I am an excellent mixologist.'

'You're an underage mixologist,' James called from the kitchen.

'My blends are purely in the interests of science, I assure you. Help me up, sous chef,' Nathan commanded Gwen, who crossed her wrists obligingly and hauled him to his feet, and Julia's free-flowing anxiety about Pamela's impending visit was momentarily staunched by this heart-warming camaraderie between the children.

THIRTEEN

Pamela did not arrive until six, for 'driving past' turned out to mean that she was en route from Sussex to her hotel in Ladbroke Grove. 'Glastonbury by way of Goodwin Sands,' Iris was heard to mutter, refusing James's offer of a fourth cup of tea.

When the doorbell rang it was Gwen, to everyone's surprise, who sprang to her feet and rushed to open it. Pamela swept into the hall, drawing in behind her a theatrically cold wind. Iris, never anything but ramrod straight, threw back her shoulders and lifted her chin a fraction.

'I'm just so thrilled we could do this,' trilled Pamela, as if answering an invitation extended months ago that had been fiendishly difficult to honour. She kissed Julia. 'I just couldn't resist the opportunity to see my babies on Christmas Day. Will you send one of them out with me to help bring pressies from the car?'

A pair of Nathan's trainers lay abandoned by the front door and Gwen slipped these on, laces untied, and trotted out after Pamela. Once introductions had been made Pamela arranged herself in an armchair and looked about with satisfaction, scanning the room until she had educed a tentative Mexican wave of returned smiles. Only Iris remained impassive, regarding Pamela as she might a stage on which an amateur theatrical production, of mixed reviews, was about to begin.

'Isn't this a lovely nest you have? If I miss anything from London it's these sweet little Victorian terraces. Now, shall I make my presentations?'

'It's commendable how well prepared you are for a spontaneous visit,' observed Iris, regarding the pile of gift bags and boxes that Gwen had obediently carried in behind Pamela, like a bellboy.

'Oh, everything was in the car for tomorrow in any case, but I was whizzing past and thought, Why not? A Christmas sherry with you all. I'm so pleased to meet you, I've heard such wonderful things about you from James. And you,' here she addressed Philip, 'of course I've read your papers on OP presentations and have so many enormous bones to pick with you, so I am utterly overjoyed we're meeting like this, I just have a hundred thoughts to share. Perhaps later I will sweep you off into a corner.'

'Pick swiftly,' advised Iris, 'our bones are going to have to go quite soon, I'm afraid.'

'No sherry, Mom, but we've been mulling wine in your honour,' said Nathan, coming in from the kitchen. Gwen followed behind him carrying a tray of mugs. She was being oddly obliging, Julia thought. Perhaps later she would begin a campaign to be allowed to go to Trafalgar Square alone with her friends on New Year's Eve, or to attend the overpriced, underage driving course she'd discovered in Elstree. It was possible she'd broken something in the kitchen.

'That accounts for the gorgeous smell. I can have half a glass, I'm sure, I've eaten enough mince pies to line my stomach for a week. Or I suppose I could be devilish and have a whole one and pick up the car tomorrow.'

'Why not have tea?' Iris suggested.

To no one's great surprise, Pamela outstayed her tentative welcome. Iris had long since abandoned any noble thoughts of outlasting her and had called herself a taxi, without the aid of Philip's app, and the two of them had gone home. After a nod of permission from Julia, Gwen had escaped to her room where she flopped on the bed with her laptop, relieved and exhausted and glowing from a series of audacious, snatched intimacies with Nathan – his hand on her knee beneath the lunch table; their socked feet touching, fleetingly but in plain sight, as they'd all watched the Queen's speech. Alone in the kitchen they had whispered while on the stove the neglected mulled wine reduced to a sticky, over-boiled syrup and they had to rescue it with a second bottle, one of James's better Pinot Noirs. There had been a sea change. The wrongness of family occasions with James, the pressure in her chest, the slight constriction of her throat during all festivities without her father – this was the sixth Christmas – were alleviated by the support and camaraderie of a boyfriend, even a secret one. And his weird mother seemed to like her.

'I really must get going,' Pamela was hooting, in an ever-increasing volume that suggested she was coming further up the stairs, away from the front door, 'but you must give me the tour before I go. Show me the kids' rooms.'

A light tread followed. 'Right at the very top is our bedroom,' she heard, 'really no need to go up there – it's a mess. My practice room is here, where I teach, this is where Saskia sleeps when she stays—'

'Wonderful!' Pamela boomed. 'You must be so inspired there.'

'Yes.' Their voices got louder as they came up half a flight of stairs and stood outside Gwen's door. 'That's Gwen in there, we won't disturb her, I think she said she was going to nap, then the bathroom across the hall, and this is Nathan's.' The door beside Gwen's creaked open.

'Isn't he a pig?' Pamela declared, with a hint of pride. 'And everything's just giant with boys, isn't it – giant stinking shoes, and giant stinking clothes just strewn about everywhere. You really are a saint to take all this on. He said you've been doing his laundry! When he's with me of course I insist he does his own. Still. Not long before he's off and this could be the baby's room, *inshallah.*'

Gwen, bewildered, stood and padded forward to listen more closely. Her mother coughed, and she heard Pamela barrelling onwards, 'Oh no, don't blush, I am sorry, I know it's none of my business, but it would be just so invigorating to have a new little one in the family, don't you think? And it's not yet *quite* too late if you were really determined. No. *Are* you? No. I could have sworn you were just a scrap of a thing! Are you really? What a complexion. Right, on that note – on that note, lovely lady, I'll be off. Maybe I'll scoop up Saskia to come and spend a girls' night with me at the hotel, then you can reclaim your peaceful music room.'

The footsteps descended once again. Gwen remained still, her heart pounding. She remembered a long-ago supper table and herself at six, nibbling at the tail of her dinosaur-shaped cheese on toast, on the single occasion she had asked her parents about siblings. Then too, it had been at someone else's prompting – another child at school with a brand-new baby brother had warned Gwen that the same fate could just as easily befall her own slim and attentive mother. 'We are perfect just us, don't you think?' Daniel had said, and Gwen had nodded, chewing steadily, and the three of them had held hands around the table. In childhood when friends had stayed over and Julia had kissed them each goodnight, first Gwen, and then the little girl beside her, Gwen would lie awake until long after her guest was breathing steadily, unable to sleep until she could pad downstairs alone to find and reclaim her mother. To see her kiss another child goodnight was a torment. Julia would look up, surprised, and explain that she had only wanted Katy to feel welcome. She would open her arms to her hot, distressed little daughter and Gwen would bury herself there, breathing away the horror of their last parting, and the memory of Julia's infidelity. She had only one mother; her mother had only her. Their devotion was balanced, and equal. Never, not once in all these last distressing, enraging, unprecedented months had she ever considered that her mother and James might have a baby. But anything was possible. Weren't there women in India having triplets at seventy-five, or whatever? She'd thought her mother too old for a boyfriend, and yet here was James. She remained by the door, winded.

Gwen picked up her laptop and sent Nathan a message. He was in the kitchen; too far away for her to hear his phone beep, but a minute later the door opened and he slipped in, closing it behind him and grinning.

'You are daring today,' he said, coming towards her and putting his arms around her bony shoulders. 'I thought we weren't taking undue risks.'

'I'm feeling daring.' And then emboldened she added, 'So what are you waiting for?'

Nathan needed no further encouragement. His mother and sister had gone; he had seen his father and Julia side by side in companionable industry, emptying the dishwasher. Encouraged by this new, indoor comfort and Gwen's uncharacteristic brazenness, he pushed her backwards, gently, onto the bed. She would not let him lie on top of her exactly, but he pressed beside her, one leg slung over hers, his crotch pleasingly close to her firm upper thigh. Every now and again he moved as if to readjust, and inched their bodies a little closer into alignment. And it was in this position, with one of his hands lost beneath the printed logo of her T-shirt, that Julia came in and found them.

FOURTEEN

'Fuck!' Julia shouted, startling all three of them. Gwen had never before heard her mother use the word and it sounded comical, and disconcerting. Julia clapped her hands across her mouth and looked, for a moment, as if she was about to vomit. 'What the fuck is going on in here?' But she did not stay for the answer and instead backed out, shaking her head. 'I can't believe you,' she kept repeating. 'I can't believe you. I don't believe this.' She turned on her heel and left. A moment later, while Gwen and Nathan were still straightening their clothing, the front door slammed.

'Nathan?'

'Here.'

James came in, surprised to see the children standing up in the middle of Gwen's bedroom, looking at one another in awkward, complicit silence. 'Hey, guys. Was that the door? What's up?'

'We've got something to tell you.' Gwen threw her shoulders back and went on, in a voice that managed to be both imperious and confiding, 'We were going to wait a bit longer but – Nathan and I are together.'

James frowned. 'What?'

Gwen bit her lip and looked to Nathan for reassurance but he was staring out of the window with his hands crossed behind his head, like a man before a firing squad.

'Together. Boyfriend and girlfriend. Dating.'

James was staring around the room somewhat fixedly, his gaze moving from Nathan to the bookshelves of magazines and trinkets and assorted dolls' furniture, the mobile of Polaroid photographs suspended with rainbow ribbons from two reshaped coat hangers, to the home-made beaded necklaces slung over the bedpost, to the colony of clay figurines in various stages of completion, guarding the expanse of her desk like a mismatched terracotta army. 'No. I don't even – I can't – I don't even know where to begin. This seems like a recipe for – *what*? You're not serious.'

Gwen, unable to help herself, began to giggle. It was gratifying, after diverse and concerted efforts, finally to see James unsettled.

'How long has this been going on? Nathan, will you turn around, please? Does Julia know? Is this why she just left, is she okay? Was she . . . hang on –' He pulled his phone out of his pocket. 'I expect to see the two of you downstairs, at the kitchen table, in five minutes. Do not – I repeat, DO NOT CLOSE THE DOOR OF THIS BEDROOM. Five minutes. Downstairs.'

When the children descended they were hand in hand, a brief chain gang of penitents. This solidarity seemed staged. Gwen looked mutinous and defiant with lifted chin and narrowed eyes, and appeared to be gripping Nathan as if leading an uncooperative child around a supermarket. Nathan was gazing at the tiled floor. A blush crept up his neck and cheeks. They were very sorry, he said, with an unmistakable smirk in his voice. Still, he did not move to free himself from Gwen.

'We're all going out,' James said shortly. 'Julia and I have discussed it. We're going to the pub and we're going to sit and talk like adults. Right now.' He gave Julia a small smile of solidarity before returning to face the children looking thunderous. Beside him she dug her thumbnails into the pads of her ring fingers. *Just breathe,* James had said. *I'll talk to them.* Nathan would soon be back at boarding school Monday to Saturday. Obviously he must stay away at weekends too, she thought, and in the holidays they could take him directly from Westminster to Heathrow. The children would not sleep another night under the same roof.

Gwen would merely have to be dispatched to a convent in the Hebrides. There were ways, she thought, to – what had James said just now? – *curb the insurrection.* He had offered castration, a chastity belt, sedation, bromide in the tea, digging a basement and locking them in it for eternity together to get on with it. *Or we could leave? Two weeks in the Caribbean? I bet Pamela would take 'em. A few days of a legume-only diet would kill the mood pretty quickly, I promise you.* He'd worked hard to calm her. Should James and Nathan move out for a month? Probably that was the best solution but – the idea of him leaving made her frantic. She had waited her whole life for him she thought fiercely, and if he left he might never return. To wake up alone another morning was unthinkable – if Gwen chased him from the house, Julia could not imagine forgiving her easily. Never before had she felt so assaulted by her daughter. And never had she come so close to slipping, and telling James what she thought about his son.

Nathan had taken out his phone. 'Why do we—'

'—I'm not interested in one syllable from either of you until we are sitting around a table like adults, in a neutral space.'

'But—'

'—and I have a beer in my hand. Seriously. Just zip it, Nathan. We've been in this house all day and I need air.'

'But—'

'Be quiet. You'll both do as you're told, for once. And you will leave your damn devices here and talk like civilised humans.'

Nathan fell silent and Julia rose from the table, fortified. She was too angry to look at Gwen, too angry to speak to Gwen, but James had taken charge and she sagged with inward relief, leaning heavily against the strength of his resolve. He would speak for them both, until she felt able. He could be calm, where she would have raved. He was a good father. He would stop this madness in its tracks.

Nathan and Gwen relinquished their phones sulkily, but without protest. James hesitated, about to set them on the coffee table, and then seemed to change his mind and slipped them into his own pocket. Coats were gathered in silence, and they all waited by the front gate while James switched on the alarm and double-locked the front door.

They set off down the road in single file – Nathan toggled tight into his hoodie, followed by Gwen, then Julia and James. The pavement was deserted, but light glowed between curtains and shutters. They walked down the terraced street, rich sand and ochre London stock beneath gnarled and naked winter-stripped wisteria. Functional, nuclear families inside home after home, Julia imagined, obedient, rosy-cheeked children bringing pride to their misty parents at the foot of sap-heavy Douglas firs. Gospel Oak, by Norman Rockwell. *I can't believe them*, Julia had said to James, moments earlier. He'd shrugged, his thumb moving gently across her knuckles and said, *Remember their ultimate aim in life is to piss us off. We don't capitulate to terrorists.* And she had found herself laughing – with disbelief at her undented happiness, at the power of James's voice to lift her heart, with gratitude that the sight of his face turned towards hers still made her throat catch, that his eyes upon her could make all the rest mute and fade into insignificance. Her daughter had launched a missile at her life and yet here was James, and so everything was okay, even when it wasn't.

The pub was closed. It was Christmas Day; their beloved, unrenovated local had bowed out of the race. Better to stay at home, its dark, etched windows advised; it would not compete with marked-down supermarket beer and glutted lassitude, and the rising screech of seasonal family tension. 'Merry Xmas', said a small sign on the door in red felt tip, and then on a sloping second line the assurance, 'Reopen BOXing Day'.

James swore. He caught Julia's eye, and she wondered if he was about to laugh, but when he faced the children he looked stern once again. He shooed them away, homeward.

'Back. Now.'

'That was what I was trying to say,' Nathan muttered, as they began to trudge back the way they'd come. 'Nothing'd be open.'

They had been out of the house for approximately three and a half minutes. As they turned back into their own street sloppy raindrops began to fall, landing splashily in shallow puddles from an earlier downfall. London seemed under water; it felt like the middle of the night. Back inside they moved by unspoken consensus into the kitchen. Julia put on the kettle, as if they'd been adventuring in the cold for hours. James went to the cupboard and took out two tins of baked beans. Julia went to the bread bin. Gwen opened her mouth to request a bagel, thought better of it, and closed it again. Nathan and Gwen sat side by side at the kitchen table, waiting and watching while their parents began to orchestrate supper. Gwen had begun to find the silence unbearable, which she suspected was the intention.

'What can I do?' she asked brightly. A new approach. Sunny and amenable.

'You've done enough,' said James. He sounded almost cheerful.

Nathan said, 'I think we should be allowed to put a case.' Beneath the table his knee pressed reassuringly against Gwen's. 'You can't sentence us without hearing the case for the defence.'

James began to spoon warmed baked beans onto the plates Julia had lined up beside him. 'This is a kangaroo court. I can do whatever I damn well please.'

'Can I have mine—' Gwen began, wanting to ask for her beans on the side, not actually touching her toast.

'Nope.' James was giving every indication of enjoying himself, but then said, in a different tone, 'You've betrayed our trust. I am deeply disappointed in you both.'

'But – thanks – we haven't,' Nathan explained, accepting the two plates that Julia had brought to the table and setting one down in front of Gwen. Julia turned back for the others. 'It's only been a few weeks, it didn't make sense to get everyone all upset if it was nothing.'

'It is nothing,' James told him, taking his place at the table, opposite his son. He cut into his toast with relish and said, with his mouth full, 'It's nothing whatsoever. Whatever it is or was, it's done. Finito.'

Gwen, who had been elongating and then releasing a single coil of hair, now raised her head, her eyes flashing with rekindled fury. 'It isn't nothing! You can't just say that – you don't know anything. You can't tell us what to do!'

Julia set down her fork with a clatter. 'Don't you dare shout at James like that. This is absolutely inappropriate, Gwendolen, and I forbid it.'

'Why do you even care what I do? You're such a hypocrite, you don't tell me anything about your life, you barely even talk to me any more except to tell me, "Be nice, be nice, be nice," and "Oh, by the way, a family of total strangers are moving in, 'kay, thanks, and I'm going to need you to be a totally different person now," and we're all meant to be best friends and you don't even notice or care that everybody's miserable except you two obsessed with each other, and now something nice has actually happened for literally the first time in my life and you only care what it means for you.' She was out of breath and paused.

'Well, sorry if it's not convenient. Nathan's my boyfriend. You didn't tell me when you first got together and you don't tell me *anything* about your plans for this family and I would have thought you'd be pleased to know I have someone who cares about me while you're busy replacing me in your new fabulous life. I'm a – a *superfluous person.*' She dropped her head and began to sob, her face now entirely concealed behind a mass of russet hair that had fallen forward, perilously close to her plate. Julia opened her mouth to reply, but closed it in stricken silence. That Gwen should feel safe, that Gwen should feel cherished; these objectives had been her life's work. Her anger began to drain from her like water from a pool.

'Can everyone please lower their voices.' James was speaking in a sing-song half-whisper, in the tone of one addressing much smaller children, at nap time. He picked up his remaining crust and began to mop up tomato sauce. 'One at a time, please tell us what's been happening. Calmly. Nathan?'

Nathan looked to Gwen and then back to his father. 'Can we please scratch everything that happened today, and can you listen as though we'd brought this to you ourselves?'

'No. Next question.'

'Okay, fine. Look, we like each other, okay? And I know it's a little weird that you guys are dating and now we're dating and we all live in the same house, but we both understood the ramifications of it all beforehand and considered it worth the risk.'

'You did, did you. How very mature. Well, we all live in the same house, as you so charmingly put it, because you are our offspring and we are your parents. This isn't a Noël

Coward play, it's not just some unfortunate coincidence in a boarding house. I do not allow it, and that's the end of the story.'

'We're not related, we never could be even if you guys – we were adults before you even met.'

Both Julia and James now began to laugh, which was enraging, and after a moment James set both his palms on the table and stood up, scraping his chair back loudly. 'Enough. I've had enough hilarity for one night. Nathan, I am phoning your mother with whom you will now stay this evening and in the meantime Gwen, please go upstairs. Take whatever sustenance you need for a good twelve hours, I don't want to catch sight of you again until tomorrow.'

Gwen, whose usual trick of storming to her bedroom had been whisked unexpectedly from her arsenal, looked wrong-footed, and then gave James a scathing glance. 'You're sending me to my room. Like someone from the olden days. *Fine*, I'm going. But newsflash, you're not my father. And you can't stop us seeing each other, we both live here.' She too now stood, clutching her plate in both hands as if in line at a soup kitchen. 'You can't lock me in my room for ever.'

James already had his phone to his ear. 'I will look seriously into the legality of it. Pamela? Yup. Yup. Minor change of plan. Can I deliver your son in half an hour?'

FIFTEEN

'Did you have to tell her? Couldn't you just have said he was coming to visit?'

Taking off his coat James paused, looking surprised. 'She is his mother.'

'Yes, but –' Julia could think of no good reason other than her own, visceral objection. Pamela's involvement was perhaps the only way to make the circumstances feel more calamitous. She could not get past the suspicion that this latest, repugnant development was due to Pamela's own unwelcome pheromones and sexually permissive influence wafting through the house. She felt an urge to burn sage leaves, or perform some other sort of occult, neo-pagan cleansing ritual and then, thinking that this was perhaps precisely what Pamela herself might do, wondered if she was actually losing her grip. She thought, but did not say, *I don't like Pamela.*

'Nathan would have told her himself anyway,' said James reasonably, dropping the car keys onto the coffee table and collapsing into an armchair. 'But also we have to be honest with one another. I'd be mad if something happened on her watch that she didn't share with me.'

'It wasn't "on our watch", we could hardly have known—'

'I'm not saying we could have stopped them – you know what I mean.'

'This is nauseating,' said Julia, laying her forehead on the arm of the sofa. She rejected the memory of Nathan's hand lost beneath her daughter's T-shirt, the pert denim globe of his backside aloft as he lay almost on top of her child. 'I quite literally cannot believe this is happening. It cannot happen. They've chosen the one thing that will make our family life impossible. It's genius really, when you think about it. It's the perfect sabotage.'

James moved to sit beside her and laid his hands on her back. The warmth of his palms seeped through her sweater to her skin. 'I think it's also teenagers doing what teenagers do.' She lifted her head slightly. Before she could protest he continued, 'But let's say you're right and there's a part of them trying to rebel and make things difficult or, what I think is more likely, looking for attention they might feel they've lost recently. It's still pretty new for them, seeing us together. That's twice the reason to show them what we're made of and to handle it like a team. We've done a lot of family stuff recently, so maybe it's time to go back to the beginning, making sure you get time alone with Gwen every weekend and I get time alone with Nathan. They're good kids.'

'But that's the point, they're kids. They have no idea what a mess this could be. I don't think they even really get why it's so totally and utterly wrong, and revolting. And all those things she said – I've been selfish and I've hurt her and—'

'Stop. For right now Pamela's happy to have him and that will give them time to cool off, or pretend it never happened or whatever. They're apart during the week when he's at school, so it's only weekends we have to just say no, obviously this is unacceptable. We'll put a stop to it and that's that. We'll figure it out, but you have not been selfish. You do nothing but think of her. There's still some mulled wine, if you want?'

Julia shook her head. 'It wasn't very nice, I don't know what they put in it.'

'Maybe they weren't concentrating.'

'Oh, don't,' said Julia, but she laughed in disbelief. 'This is actually appalling.'

'Yes,' agreed James. 'Let's fire them and get better ones. But you know what, I'm pretty confident it will be okay. Probably the entire point was for you to see them and now the point's made.'

'Loud and clear.'

'Yup. Loud and clear.'

For his part, Nathan felt hopeful. He had charmed his way out of stickier scrapes than this one. He understood why everyone was angry but it would not alter the course of his behaviour and now, safely across London, he had lost all traces of his own indignation and merely felt enlivened by the drama.

Gwen was not at all his usual type. Valentina, he'd known with pride, was a nine, a point docked for her high-strung madness. (His friend Edmund's scale did not even consider faces, let alone personality, merely the hardware on display from the neck down.) But Nathan had eventually become bored and exasperated by Valentina, and what security and confidence he derived from having a steady girlfriend had been undermined by their relentless rows. It had seemed passionate and romantic at first, but whatever her physical attributes, he did not want a girlfriend who was always angry. Gwen Alden was a solid eight to eight-and-a-half. She was catwalk tall and could definitely be described as willowy, and her red hair was so startling that it transcended the traditionally disparaging label 'ginger' and recategorised her as 'striking'. She had a beautiful face. He liked her laugh and her belief, however resentfully held, that he was an academic genius. It was worth a little heat from his father, and in any case, his mother was bound to take it in better spirits. As long as he furnished her with a few details, she usually said yes to anything.

Boxing Day came the nadir. Julia sat on the end of Gwen's bed, her head bowed, her fingers interlaced in her lap.

'I've been up all night,' said Julia softly, 'trying to comprehend why. I am very disappointed.'

Gwen almost laughed at this grave, teacherly cliché, for she too had been lying awake slightly manic with nerves, and a sense of guilty defiance. It would be a day of reckoning. She restrained the giggle and said, 'I'm sorry.' And then worried that this was a concession, added primly, 'I'm sorry you feel that way.'

'You cannot possibly have thought this was a good idea.'

'It's not an idea. I *like* him. It isn't like we planned it or anything.'

'It's not appropriate.'

Gwen sat up and flung the covers off. Shouting would be awkward as she still had in her retainer, but she was too cross to pause and remove it. 'Who says? You can't actually control everything we do, we're adults.'

'Adults! This is precisely the opposite of adult behaviour. If you can't see why this is fraught with awkwardness—'

'It's not like I didn't find it *awkward* when you started going out with James. It's not like I didn't find it awkward when he took over Dad's house. That was pretty bloody *awkward*, if you ask me.'

'Can you not see that's a little different?'

'No,' said Gwen stubbornly. 'I can't. In any case, it's done now.' To shore up her sense of dignity she removed her retainer at last, clicking it into the purple plastic case on her bedside table. She then padded over to her desk in search of her glasses, feeling vulnerable and at a disadvantage, with the world blurred.

'What's done? You mean it's over?'

'No, it's done. He's my boyfriend. There's nothing you can do.' She and Nathan had never actually discussed the status of their relationship but he hadn't contradicted her when she'd made her announcement the night before and this bolstered her confidence. And then on impulse she added, 'We've been together for ages.'

Julia looked startled. 'How long?'

'None of your business. You don't consult me with what you do with your love life.'

'Gwen, that's enough. Don't be rude.' And then in a different, quieter tone, 'Gwendolen, darling, what do you mean by "love life"? How serious has this become? Many things are not my business but what happens under my roof is my concern. Are you – are you sleeping with him?'

And suddenly a conversation previously unimaginable to both of them was taking place. Gwen felt a simultaneous sense of injustice and betrayal. Here was conclusive proof of how wretchedly little Julia understood – about what was and wasn't appropriate, about life in general, and specifically about her own child who had not yet removed a single item of clothing in the presence of any boy, Nathan included, and who did not even *want* to go to bed with anyone. She might as well have asked whether Gwen had taken up sky-diving. Clearly her mother had stopped paying attention some time ago. Gwen had become a stranger to her, capable of anything. Self-pity threatened, but Gwen forced herself to focus on what she had for solace. And so she swallowed the outraged, honest denial that had risen and gambled instead. 'Why is our sex life anything to do with you?'

As soon as the words were out a gulf opened between them, a lake of a lie. *It's not true!* she thought, as loudly as she could, but the lie lay between them now, an expanse across which it was impossible to hear one another. Already she ached to confess, and already knew she never would. Watching her mother recede into the distance with the steady inevitability of a departing ship she thought, hopelessly, one day it might be true. Sex was at present entirely unimaginable, but Julia had begun to cry, and then left in silence, and so it must be believable to her.

Gwen had felt known her whole life, known and cherished, and had, she realised, taken that charmed state entirely for granted. She now saw it for the flossy, muffling cocoon of naivety and infantile solipsism it must always have been. A delusion. Only her father had entirely loved and accepted her, and he would certainly never have let Julia spend the rest of Boxing Day charging around in derangement demanding that James write a prescription for the Pill, nor allowed her to leave a frantic and humiliating message on the GP's out-of-hours answering machine after James had said his own involvement would be inappropriate. Without her father, no one saw her. Except Nathan.

PART TWO

SIXTEEN

'I'm outside. What on earth is the delay?'

'I'm sorry,' said Philip, words he'd spoken to Iris so often that they had become a ritual of greeting. 'I need just another moment.'

Iris ensured that her heavy sigh was audible before hanging up the phone, and Philip returned to the shoes he had been laboriously tying. This adventure should have begun some time ago but he had been on the computer for most of the afternoon, hunting down and then printing out an essay on Beckett to read to her. It was a habit they had developed early on in their relationship, started in imitation of Philip's mother who'd been a determined autodidact and who, in her rare moments of liberty, would take herself off to the Swiss Cottage library. Her English had eventually been excellent but drama had always remained a hurdle, so if she took Philip to queue for returns it would be for a play about which she had already spent snatched moments reading. Denied so very many avenues of education by gender, circumstance and war; now, newly British, newly emancipated, she would not sacrifice a single drop of insight or pleasure by failing to understand a nuance, a reference, a history. At first amused when she'd discovered what she referred to as Philip's homework, Iris had then begun to depend upon him whenever they went to the theatre.

'Oh, Philip will tell us all about it,' she'd say idly. 'What do we know about the play, Philip?' And Philip would produce his notes from the inside pocket of his jacket, folded sheets of scrawls and citations, the fruit of an afternoon's study.

Today, it was true, he had lost track of time. It would not help to suggest that she come in and wait in the living room while he finished putting on his shoes and then found his scarf and located his other glasses (mysteriously absent from the coil pot Gwen had made to house them). Instead she would sit, idling in a taxi vibrating with the diesel engine and her increasing vexation, for as long as it took him to emerge. She was happiest when he'd anticipated her early arrival and was waiting for her on the pavement when she swept up, barely needing to stop before they could motor away from this scene of his embarrassing isolation. The existence of this modest flat irked her.

'What were you doing?' she snapped, when he joined her in the taxi.

'I thought you'd like Harold Bloom for the interval. On *The Lady with the Dog*.'

'Ever since the Lessing comment I've gone off him, though perhaps it's time to make up. Thank you for the James Wood, though, I read it this morning. Oh, and I've booked us smoked salmon for the interval.'

'Thank you,' said Philip humbly.

'How did you like the Rosamond Lehmann?'

'I've only read the introduction so far, I will get to it, I've been doing a little research that distracted me. Pamela Thing emailed me.'

She glanced at him sharply. 'Thing's wife?'

'Ex-wife. Yes.'

'I can't think of a benign reason to be emailing your former husband's new . . . what is she, girlfriend I suppose – girlfriend's former father-in-law.'

'It's professional. She's asked me to critique a paper she's writing. We're not former, Iris.'

'Oh, I know, I know. Christ, on what?'

'Orgasmic childbirth. I think she's decided I exemplify everything she hates about the – what did she call it? – medical patriarchy, and so she wants me to comment and show her the holes they'll all find when it's published so she can plug them in advance.'

'Was "holes" her word? She can't be a very rigorous academic if she can't find her own holes. Nor a very good gynaecologist, now I come to think of it.'

'She said something along the lines of never being able to anticipate the sly ways in which the Establishment seek to quash the revolution—'

'Oh, she didn't. Does she listen to herself?'

'I assure you she did. I think I embody The Man. Because of the forceps.'

'But that doesn't mean you actually have to do it,' said Iris, irritated. Philip's acquiescence to the exploitation of others made her own dependence upon him less comfortable, and also less a mark of distinction somehow. 'You can just say, "No, you crackpot, I'm retired." Also, it's perfectly obvious to anyone with half a brain that there are certain moments a girl doesn't want to be thinking about sex, and I need not tell you that childbirth is among them. Why does she think the so-called Establishment should be hell-bent on depriving women of their right to orgasm during childbirth in any case? Actually don't tell me, I really couldn't care less.'

'I'll send you the paper to read.'

'Please don't.'

'She also said something about Gwen and the boy.'

Iris's ears pricked up. 'What boy? Gwen's got a boyfriend? How unbearable that that busybody should know before we do. What did she say, who is he? Is he from school?'

'Not *a* boy, *the* boy, their son. Whatshisname. Nathan.'

They had drawn up outside the theatre, where the bright bulbs of the awning cast a gleam into oily, puddled gutters. Iris paid for the cab while Philip set about the awkward business of clambering out of it – on the one hand easier than the low-slung seats of a normal car; on the other more challenging for the larger step down to the pavement. Iris managed to stay occupied until he had succeeded and had straightened up, restored to dignity, and then slipped her arm through his. They made their way into the heat of the foyer.

'What did you mean?' she demanded, when they had settled in their seats, picking up where they had left off after various digressions and excursions for programmes, lavatory visits, procuring of reading glasses in order to see their phones clearly enough to turn them off, and some enquiries to ascertain in which bar Iris had booked the interval refreshments.

'She seemed to imply that there was some sort of romance going on between Gwen and her son. It seems rather unlikely.'

Iris stroked the glossy programme that lay in her lap and considered.

'It's horribly likely, when you stop and think,' she said eventually. 'You throw two teenagers together, curiosity and hormones flying about, and it suddenly seems obvious. They're tripping over each other, it's bound to cross their minds eventually.'

'You don't think it's true? Gwen's such an innocent.'

'If it hasn't happened already, we should warn them that it might, so they can head it off at the pass,' Iris whispered, as the lights fell. 'Despite Julia's best efforts, Gwendolen can't be expected to remain twelve for ever.'

SEVENTEEN

Sébastien Benaim was an obstetric consultant at the Homerton and his wife, Anne, a cardiologist at the Royal Free. Sébastien and James had worked together ten years ago when they were all new Londoners – James from Boston, the Benaims from Paris. The family lived a ten-minute walk away, on Hartland Road, a pretty terrace of ice-cream-coloured blocks in whose front gardens the Camden Town revellers regularly threw bottles and cigarette boxes, or nightclub flyers in acid pinks and greens, or intermittently relieved themselves through the spear-headed railings. 'If you live in Camden you must 'ave many parties,' Sébastien had told James when he'd invited him for New Year's Eve, 'ozzerwise ze parties everyone else is 'aving will drive you crazy.'

They arrived late and the kitchen was hot and crowded; five or six people were already dancing rather drunkenly in the darkened living room. The Benaim children, a boy and girl of seven and eight, were in their pyjamas and jumping together in a corner, giggling. Julia saw Claire, James's registrar, crouched on the floor over a laptop, controlling the music. She was a poor and impatient DJ, and two thirds of the way through a song would become enthused about her next selection and abruptly replace mid-eighties singalong

Madonna with harsh-edged euro electronica, or a sensual R&B anthem with the title song of a Disney movie. It was loud, and even in the kitchen people shouted at one another to make themselves heard. It was a real party, Julia thought, surprised by the stirring of pleasure and recognition within her. Not civilised canapés. Not dinner for three couples and a discussion of school policy changes and university application forms. A loud, messy, drunken, badly behaved party. The copious wine was excellent. Curls of smoke drifted in from the small back garden; a fat spliff circulating around a circle of cardiologists. The music grew louder. *I am not old*, Julia reminded herself, and found herself smiling, happy she'd dressed up, happy she'd thought to wear make-up, and to pay attention to her hair. She grinned at James, who grinned back, buoyed by the same remembered freedom. He handed her a champagne flute from the kitchen counter.

'And the best part,' he said, continuing a wordless exchange aloud, 'is that they're busy, they're apart, and we don't have to lay eyes on either of them till at least lunchtime tomorrow. Prosecco?'

Julia nodded and held up her glass, and they were toasting their liberty as Sébastien came over to them and put an arm around each of their shoulders. After a decade, he retained a preposterously extravagant accent. ''Ow are you, James?' He slapped him heartily and turned to Julia. 'I love zis man. 'E made me laugh every day. Now it is dull wizout him. 'Ow is the eye chlamydia? You did not know that James 'as chlamydia of the eye, but 'e does, I am convinced of it. One of the best moments of my whole life was in ze operating room –' James too was now laughing

and shaking his head, covering his eyes with both hands –
'when zis man decided to operate on an *énorme* Bartholin's
cyst wizout glasses.' He mimed a fountain, or explosion.
'And whoosh. Pus in ze eye. Even ze poor patient she was
laughing at 'im. Such joy, you brought us all. It was a sacrifice, you know?' Sébastien nodded approvingly at their
drinks and excused himself, just as Claire bounced over.

Julia had met her in passing several times before, a slim,
Chinese-American woman in her mid-thirties with short-
cropped hair, and a large diamond-and-ruby cocktail ring
slung on a chain around her neck. This evening she was in a
pair of black leather trousers and high-top white sneakers,
and looked, Julia thought with envy, about twenty-five.
She kissed Julia and high-fived James. Julia noticed that
Claire's nails were painted with a sparkly black polish
Gwen would have loved. *When did I stop wearing nail polish?* Julia wondered, watching the tips of Claire's fingers
flash prettily as she gestured. *Why?* The idea returned as if
from another lifetime, together with a memory of admir-
ing her own hands as they moved, claret-tipped, across the
piano keys. Gwen would howl with laughter at the very
thought of her mother so adorned. Can anything make a
woman feel more ancient than her own teenage daughter?

'When did you guys get here? You missed Rebecca and
Sam, they were going to another thing. You need to get
Rebecca to tell you about the amniotic band we had the
day before yesterday, I can't even. It *fell off*. On the *floor*.
I'm going back, this music's terrible. I'm saving Guns N'
Roses for later.' She pointed at James. 'We'll get the whole
disco break crew.'

'What's an amniotic band?'

Claire gave Julia a dark look. 'Truly – in this case, don't ask.'

'I've just been hearing about eye chlamydia, I'm not sure it can be worse.'

'Oh yes, but luckily your man is the world's only known sufferer. No one he's taught ever forgets glasses when they go near a Bartholin's cyst now, it's truly a cautionary tale. James is the only consultant to admit he's fallible, the others are too grand. Or too weird,' she concluded, and then handed Julia the bowl of strawberries she'd been holding and returned to her station on the floor. The song changed again, and there were whoops of appreciation from somewhere in the dark depths of the room.

It was different to be at a party together. Almost immediately they were pulled apart by conversational tides but she could look across at James and recall the stranger he had been, not so long ago. She talked to his friends and felt his eyes on her and stood taller. She saw Claire say something and laugh with her whole body angled towards his, her hand for a moment on his forearm and thought, that man chose me. It seemed impossibly good fortune. She alone would go home with James and, for tonight, there would be no children, no drama, no competition. Just the two of them, the way it had never been at the beginning. Second relationships are starved of precious, nourishing solitude, and second couples must snatch for it with jealous determination. They cannot put themselves first, but must not put themselves last. We will, she resolved, try harder to be alone.

Julia felt a hand on her waist and suddenly James was beside her. His eyes were bright. He took her wrist and led her down a corridor and into a dark spare bedroom, in which coats and bags were piled. James pushed the door closed, and pressed Julia against it.

'I missed you.' His hands were moving beneath her skirt. 'Don't run away with a boring cardiologist. Be with me.' For a moment his mouth was at her throat, but the door behind them began to open and they sprang apart. His eyes glittered at her in the darkness.

It was Claire, apparently amused to find them there. 'Just getting lip balm from my bag, don't mind me, lovebirds. Just so you know, it's almost midnight.' She rummaged in the pile of coats for a moment and then was gone, closing the door rather pointedly behind her.

Alone, they remained apart, looking at one another.

'We need to behave,' said Julia softly, with regret.

'I don't want to behave.' James took her hand in his. 'Let's go home.'

From the living room they heard the sound of a count-down. Ten! Nine! Eight! Seven! This would be the year. She would learn to be assertive with her daughter, she would fight for time and space with this man whom she loved so fiercely; at half term they would send Nathan to America and leave Gwen with Iris and they would book a holiday just the two of them. Six! Five! Four! A fresh start. No more guilt. She would remember that she was allowed to be happy. Three! Two! One! Happy New Year!

Across London, Gwen was queuing for a night bus. She had spent the early part of the evening with Katy and two other school friends at a pizza restaurant on Haverstock

Hill. At ten thirty, Katy's mother had arrived to take them all back for a sleepover and to see in twelve o' clock armed with ice cream and Maltesers, and cans of sparkling apple juice that Katy's father would later decant into champagne flutes for them, thereby mortifying Katy. Gwen, as arranged, had hidden inside the restaurant.

After the car had pulled away Gwen had tugged her hood over her face and walked down the hill to Belsize Park Tube station, where she'd got the train to Waterloo, an unexpectedly exhilarating adventure. She had never before been allowed to go out on New Year's Eve. Her mother would argue she was not yet old enough now, but in the last days Julia had proven that she knew nothing about her daughter, her needs or principles, and no longer cared to pay attention. She was too busy with her own repulsive romance. And it turned out that there was a camaraderie in London on New Year's Eve, a carnival air on the Tube encouraged by the jovial announcements of the driver, and the make-up and glad rags and mounting anticipation of the passengers. Gwen could not know this would later sour into a less benign atmosphere, a bright-lit, bristling tension charged with disappointed hopes, too much alcohol, furious energy as yet unspent. In this same train there would be fights, and sobs and jeers, and possibly vomiting. But for now, while the night still held promise, all was celebratory. The Mayor's drinking ban was openly flouted. A man in a rhinestone-studded denim jacket and gold sunglasses played music aloud. In high spirits and higher hemlines, a group of girls at the other end of the carriage called out song requests and one, beneath a towering, backcombed beehive, stood up and began to gyrate around the central pole. Gwen smiled to herself, and was rewarded with a fleeting grin from a woman who sat opposite, in the midst of applying her mascara. The plan was going easily, and well. Julia, who had dropped her off and had chatted to Katy through the car window before disappearing to her own, private, exclusive and excluding plans, would never learn that Gwen was spending the evening with Nathan. Last year Gwen and Julia had shared pizzas from the same restaurant and watched *Calamity Jane* till midnight. It was amazing how much her mother, who had once known everything, did not know.

Since the discovery on Christmas Day, the household had moved together through various phases. Acceptance would follow, Nathan had asserted, since they'd dwelt so exhaustively in rage and denial. He was waiting out his father's disappointment as if it was a rainstorm and he happily settled in the window of a café with a newspaper and a hot chocolate, nowhere special to be. The squall would pass and he would venture back into the pale, clean-washed sunshine. He would be forgiven – had probably been forgiven already. Gwen felt less secure. Julia's immediate fury, though it had been startling and uncharacteristic, had turned out to be the easiest to navigate. Gwen was accustomed to her mother's fierce devotion and so her mother in a fit of violent feeling was, at least, feeling violent feelings about her. In the quiet isolation of late December, that pocket of slow, padded time between Christmas and New Year when families turn in on themselves, hibernating or festering, Julia and Gwen had been forced by sheer exposure to return to a superficial approximation of normality. Julia's temper cooled to chill disappointment.

The household had grown steadily calmer, but the unaccustomed rift between mother and daughter remained in place. Gwen had no choice but to cleave tighter to Nathan, and to stand resolutely by her choice.

The bus came, bright and busy, and from it poured a steady stream of revellers. Out came the pac-a-mac tourists heading for set meals at chain restaurants booked months ago, online; she pushed her way on, her height for once an advantage, and a text from Nathan pinged through. 'WHERE RU? DON'T LIKE YOU WANDERING THE STREETS. CAN I COME GET YOU SOMEWHERE? RU SAFE?' She began to feel the rends in her cocoon slowly knitting back together. Wasn't this growing up? Moving on, forging new bonds, and graduating into independence? If so, perhaps this desperate sadness and longing for her mother that she felt was usual too, and would pass, in time.

'ON THE BUS,' she wrote back.

Instantly he replied, 'PARTY'S LONG. I'LL MEET YOU. LET'S GO JUST US TO THE RIVER, BABY, CAN GO LATER TO CHARLIE'S. BISOUS.'

The parents did not expect them home (nor care, Gwen told herself, the taste of new, bitter cynicism on her tongue). She had said she'd stay with Katy; in her bag a pair of clean knickers, a toothbrush, trainers for tomorrow morning, the contact-lens case she'd painted with nail-varnish rainbows. Nathan had told the truth: he was sleeping at Charlie's with a mixed group of fifteen other school friends, only omitting the additional information that Gwen would join him. The night would offer little privacy but that afforded by darkness and a sleeping bag but this, already, was an improvement upon the late-night tiptoeing and furtive anxiety of home. Around them would be other teenagers with sympathy, and romantic concerns of their own.

'K,' she wrote back, and then almost as an afterthought – for though she'd never told him, she knew he already knew – 'LOVE U.'

EIGHTEEN

This time, Philip prepared by standing quietly to recall the name of James's son in advance, as well as the name of the play that he and Iris had seen together when the subject had arisen, and the name of the current book he was reading, just in case. It was not possible to consider all contingencies, but with this cache he felt able to ring Iris and inform her, 'I believe it's true that a romance has begun between Gwen and Nathan,' with the easy, conversational flow of a late-night radio host. His memory was not getting worse, thank God. But, despite online Sudoku, it was not getting any better.

'Well, I suppose it's not incest.'

'Don't be ludicrous, of course it isn't.'

'Aren't we relieved she's finally having a romance of any sort? Perhaps there are wiser places to look for it, but since when have teenagers been known for their wisdom?'

'This is a little different,' Philip told her. 'Imagine what will happen when they fall out.'

'Well, why should they fall out? What if it all ends happily ever after and we can throw the four of them a cosy double wedding in a few years' time? One of Julia's students can play the "Wedding March".'

Philip sat down heavily in his armchair. 'I don't understand why you are being facetious about this, it's your granddaughter we are discussing. It's horribly inappropriate. And it will put terrible strain on Julia's relationship with James.'

'Julia's relationships are her own affair,' Iris said breezily, and he heard in the background the clamour and thumping bass line that betrayed she was in Selfridges. 'Julia and Thing threw two teenagers into one another's paths and no doubt instructed them to be nice to one another, so in a sense they're only following instructions. Meanwhile it is really about time that Gwen had some romantic interest, even if she might have been a little more discerning. It was becoming peculiar.'

'She's sixteen!'

'Oh, don't be such an old woman. Sixteen is the new thirty, according to the papers. Of course, it's none of it rational when we are meant to believe that sixty is the new thirty-five, but still.'

'Those headlines are appalling. I'm content to be old. One of the privileges of being old is that I get to behave as if I'm old.'

'Well, I used to write those headlines so they don't appal me in the slightest. What is the source of your information? By the way, I'm buying you a polo shirt as we speak.'

'Gwen's blog. I don't need anything. I don't wear polo shirts.'

'Sales. Dregs. Very nice, though, it's a sort of slub cotton. Bit see-through but it's for under things. I looked at the blog a few days ago.'

'This went up today. They're arm in arm, and Julia and James are in the background with their hands to their ears in paroxysms of a very Munch-like horror. She's made a public declaration.'

'I hardly think public, I'm sure we're the only people who read that thing.'

'Well, I was phoning to ask about the party line, whether you think we ought to know or not to know. When we speak to her mother.'

'Oh, it's always better not to know. Never know anything at all, you taught me that. See no evil, and all that. In my case it was the truth as well as the party line, until you telephoned. Ought someone to put her on the Pill?'

Alone in his dusky living room, Philip covered his eyes with his hand. 'Iris. I sincerely hope it's not necessary.'

'If you don't want to hear my opinions I don't know why you always solicit them. Navy blue or black? I don't see you in black.'

'Not black,' Philip agreed, and rang off, exhausted.

Nathan had been there, embedded in her family like a sleeper cell, and Julia had welcomed him. She ironed his school shirts and drove him to the dentist, and had recently risked hypothermia on the sidelines of a rugby match watching as Westminster, in startling salmon pink, played a dirty and tedious game against UCS. She kept the house stocked with imported American breakfast cereals, and fruit loaf. She had tried. And then he seduced her daughter.

Since Christmas Day she had found it difficult to address him with civility. He would make polite, ingratiating conversation and she would be assailed by an image of him, conniving and predatory, pawing at Gwen like a middle-aged office roué. The laundry nauseated her; she lifted an escaped pair of his boxer shorts into the washing machine between clenched toes. Their existence was an affront. That he put them on, and took them off, in her house was appalling. She had not voiced her fantasy solution – that Nathan should move back to America to live with his mother – but on Boxing Day she had suggested to James that Nathan stay at school full-time instead of coming back for weekends, thinking it seemed not only the obvious but also the most desirable solution. But James had frowned and said that he couldn't ban his son from home. They would simply have to stay strong, and keep saying no. Yet allowing them under the same roof, even two nights a week, even after a family meeting in which James had reiterated their absolute and unwavering opposition, seemed a tacit permission.

The depth of her initial distress had startled her, as had the white rage that followed it. How dare they? *How dare they?* And the relationship persisted, flourishing against the odds, and against the express wishes of all but its participants. On and on it went, from strength to strength, however much Julia demanded they stop. It was high treason to recall that Nathan had not long ago been equally devoted to Valentina, whom Gwen, with flamboyant geographic inaccuracy and conflation, had taken to calling the Demon Barber of Seville. The new allegiance had wiped out all that had come before.

Yet since that first awful discovery the children had done little to which she could reasonably object. Unprompted, they began to spend Sunday afternoons doing homework together at the dining table. Gwen developed academic aspirations, in direct contravention of her previously asserted philosophies. Julia more than once overheard Nathan meticulously explaining a concept; once subtracting vectors, another time the factors that limit photosynthesis. He introduced Gwen to the programmes he watched, the podcasts he downloaded, and the two of them now spent hours glued to the screen of a shared laptop or listening together with a headphone splitter, deaf to the other members of the household. What could Julia say? How could she stop them listening to a podcast? Once indolent, Gwen was now industrious; once furious with James, she was now sunny and acquiescent. Beneath the heat of Nathan's attention she flourished like a hothouse plant, and after the third weekend during which Julia had exhausted herself lying rigid, listening for forbidden nighttime visits and had heard nothing, she had been forced to admit defeat. Not aloud – she could never give the children the satisfaction. But the truth was that forbidding feelings had got them nowhere. They could forbid only their public expression.

Since James had moved in Julia had suffered her daughter's resentment and unhappiness. Now, seeing Gwen's small, private smile as she hunched over her laptop typing messages made her heart hurt in a way that was harder to define. There was a new hauteur in Gwen's address; a new, polite formality that stung, even though it was almost certainly intended to sting. Blog readers were treated to a dramatic sequence of scenes in which Gwen and Nathan stood firm against the family's disapproval and finally won them over by making pancakes, and Gwen reported that the online community was thrilled by her new love, that several fans had only expected as much and had long been rooting for the cohabiting teenagers to find one another. Julia felt far away from her daughter, excluded for the first time from her confidence, punished for daring to betray that she was a woman, and not simply a mother. Yet only six weeks had passed – six exhausting weekends – and in that short time Gwen had unfurled, had stopped scowling, had started laughing at James's jokes, and once again helped to clear the table after dinner, even if James had cooked. And so Julia began to hold her tongue. She missed her child. She missed being needed, even when that need was expressed in baleful stares and tantrums. As a parent it was impossible to foresee anything but snares and brambles along this path, and almost certainly she ought to protect Gwen from her own foolishness by continuing to forbid, by creating obstacles, by allowing herself to be the enemy. But she needed James, and wanted him, and when Gwen was occupied and contented then he and she were granted space for one another. Harmony was hard to resist, however distasteful the price.

NINETEEN

To overhear Julia arguing with her daughter was an exercise in restraint, and took James back to the bad old days of early cohabitation. Only now did he realise how acquiescent Gwen had been of late and remembered, with an unpleasant jolt, how unappealing he found her when she wasn't getting her own way. Her wheedling, which veered from pleading to explosive rage and back to infantile beseeching again, wore on his nerves like tinnitus. And stamina was her secret weapon, for Julia would be exhausted and would run out of arguments, and seemed never to wise to this tactic. Instead, she followed her daughter down any conversational avenue she led, negotiating and reasoning and never drawing an end with a firm and final stand. 'You don't need to make a case, you can just put your foot down,' James would advise in their fraught post-mortems, but could say nothing when she explained that with Gwen it was more complicated. From this he was to infer that a dead parent was a trump card, and his hands were tied. Rarely sober, his own father had worked selling used trucks at a lot in Dorchester in Boston. His sporadic commission had kept the Fullers narrowly solvent and when he died James had won for it no special treatment, except the further reduction of the already minuscule possibility of his going to college. His mother, a paediatrician's receptionist, had adored and cherished her only child with an intensity he recognised, but she would not for one moment have stood for the kind of back talk Julia endured. It had all been long ago and in a land far over the sea, however, and would not, he knew, lend sufficient weight to his argument. He would have to pretend that he considered her judgements reasonable. Julia felt she owed reparations for allowing her daughter's father to die, and so Gwen continued behaving like a despot, and James had to watch as guilty Julia humbled and abased herself before her implacable little household goddess. They had their dance long choreographed; his past forays between them in an argument had ended, predictably, in both of them rounding on him, united and inflamed. Today, with Gwen deep into one of her campaigns, he hid behind his newspaper and did his best not to listen. He could not bear to hear his gentle Julia beleaguered.

'Please. Julia, *please*. You don't understand.'

'I do understand and I'm sad too, it's just bad timing. If it was any other night of course we'd go but James booked these Rossini tickets months ago. We've got flights. I'm so sorry, darling.' Julia reached to tuck a disobedient curl behind Gwen's ear but Gwen twitched away violently. She was frustrated, and increasingly desperate. This was not the first iteration of this exchange, not even the second or third, and preliminary attempts to reason with her mother had devolved to this – whining. It was fun for nobody, but it had won her bigger victories in the past. Across the room, James stifled the urge to stuff his fist into his mouth.

'But he's only here this one night! For the first time in *years*. It's Art Garfunkel, do you even understand?' Gwen flung herself down on the sofa. She glared across the room at the armchair in which James sat hidden behind his paper, and then hissed, 'If it was a weekend with me in Milan and James asked you to, you'd cancel.'

Julia felt a stab of pity at her daughter's wounded face and wondered, for a moment, whether this was true. She said, sotto voce, 'That's not the case at all. You can't possibly believe that.'

'It is. You put him first in everything. You guys go to boring classical music stuff all the time, you're going to that Verbier festival thing, and this is one single night. He's so old! You know he'll retire and this will literally be the last chance ever. I'll pay for it! And I'll pay you back for the other tickets, and the flights. I'll use my bat mitzvah money.'

The celebrated bat mitzvah fund – one hundred and twenty-five pounds deposited three years ago in a Post Office account – was always Gwen's last resort, the straw at which she clutched for independence. It had been 'used' to pay for hosting her Web domain and for a great deal of the expensive art supplies she needed for the early stages of her blog; it had been drawn upon again when she had so longed for a pair of white Converses that she claimed she could not survive another day. Julia fought a momentary smile, but her resolve was buoyed by the utter impossibility of what Gwen asked. James had booked the La Scala tickets almost six months ago – in the last days of

August they were to spend the weekend in Milan to see *Otello* which had not been staged there since 1870, perhaps because it needed not one but three spectacular lead tenors. The *Otello* seats made it easy to defend her choice. To be alone in Italy with James would be a dream – long private hours, Prosecco, the heat and the music. She would not yield it for anything. Of all the nights for Art Garfunkel to come to London this was the only one, all summer, that was out of the question.

Gwen was looking hopefully at her mother. 'I'll pay you back, I *promise*. And you can go to the thingy thing concert another night. It's months and months away, you can just change it.'

'Dolly.'

'I don't even get it, it's so pathetic. You're obsessed with us not being left alone together even for five minutes and then suddenly today I find out you've got summer plans to go to Italy for a whole weekend. So it's totally fine for us to stay here by ourselves if you get to go to the opera and Verbier, or whatever. It's like, insane double standards. So we *are* allowed, now.'

'I'm afraid,' boomed a disembodied voice from behind a newspaper, 'that I'll be here when your mother is in Verbier, and for Milan we'll find a suitably obtrusive chaperone. The arrangements predate the current regime. Don't get too excited, kiddo.'

'Maybe you could go with Nathan,' Julia suggested, and felt cheapened even as she said it. To her astonishment Gwen simply gave a melancholy shrug. Then she said softly, 'Mummy, I don't want to go with Nathan. The whole point was to go together,' and Julia's heart fractured, yet again.

TWENTY

Swiss Cottage library did not become more romantic in miniature, but Gwen could think of no other way to represent the day's events. Certainly she had no desire to record the morning's argument, in which her mother had made it clear, once and for all, where her traitorous priorities lay. *Maybe you could go with Nathan*, she had suggested, not simply missing the point but readily giving up custody or care of her daughter and forgetting, erasing, a precious long-ago memory. Gwen did not usually like old people's music but when she was eleven they had gone to hear Simon and Garfunkel, and it had been a magical evening in a dark, hard year. The concert, held outdoors in Hyde Park, had been hot and dry and perfect, and the first glimpse of a possible future in which they might once again, one day, be happy. Gwen had shut her eyes tightly and tried to feel the passion her mother felt for this strange, folksy music, had tried to let the simple melodies, the unexpected rhythms of the language, move in her blood. At eleven she was already the same height as Julia but she had hunched over and drawn closer under Julia's arm and had felt safe, and hopeful. Couples stood around them interlocked, swaying, and her father wasn't there to sway and sing alongside her mother but she was there, she told herself, and after a while she had straightened her spine and stood up to her full height and put her arm, instead, around her mother. In the days that followed, Gwen taught herself the words to every song they'd heard, and learned to love them. They would be okay. They would be a family again, just the two of them. But now Julia had made it clear that James was her only priority.

Her mother had needed a vessel for her love and energies, and now no longer needed to be needed. But it wasn't fair – she had lulled Gwen into believing that she would always be there. Gwen had offered up her life, her sorrows and pleasures, her preoccupations and requirements, had worked busily to keep her mother fulfilled and contented, and her being had formed around this belief, moulded like ivy around a solid trunk. Now, Julia had withdrawn. Without her mother at her centre she wavered. If she had seemed sturdy, it had been Julia firm beneath her.

She already had several sets of small bookshelves usually used for scenes in her mother's music room, and these now just needed populating with cardboard concertinas, decorated with some fine cross-hatching to imply the microscopic titles on the folded projections of tiny spines. She set up a shoebox to be the reading room and assembled all the paraphernalia to scatter on her tiny desk and on Nathan's – mobile phones, some pens and pencils and even a lined and ring-bound notepad she had painstakingly constructed long ago for use in an imagined, flashback scene showing her grandmother at work as a journalist. All that remained to construct were some textbooks to indicate homework, and the subtle nod to the real incident – the tiny paper aeroplane on which she had written her explosive missive and, heart pounding, sent it sailing over the wall between their carrels like a Kamikaze. It was time, she'd decided, to grow up.

She wanted the blog to capture the formative events in her life, good or bad, while as much as possible sparing the humdrum, or repetitious. This was not the way her friends depicted themselves on the Internet but she had no interest in varnishing her life as they did, glamorous moments threaded one after another like an endless string of glossy and identical fake pearls. That, after all, was not brave, and was also definitely not Art. She wanted wit, or poignancy, or meaning. This was her coming-of-age story, after all, and one day when the story was over and life had acquired stability – perhaps when she was twenty-five, or twenty-six – its coherence and powerful narrative thrust would be united into a book, or possibly an animated television programme, her own history re-enacted by tiny clay figures in shoebox worlds. It would be an album of memories. It would be proof that she had been, and felt, and lived.

But tonight something had happened and though it was momentous, she was at a loss as to how to honour it. Her grandfather read her blog. Her traitorous mother read her blog, and in any case thought this landmark long behind her. Meanwhile, she had a more pressing and practical problem for it was very late, and she did not know what to do about the bed sheets.

Already the night's events seemed distant. She examined her own feelings and found only deflation, and a sense of anticlimax. If she thought too long she could summon a quiet, mawkish grief for her own innocence.

The true secret turned out to be that there was no secret. She had thought that sex would be something else, yet already could no longer articulate what that something else could have been. Instead it was what it was – the putting of parts into other, tighter parts. She had wanted to advance their intimacy, to elect Nathan as the central person in her new, adult life; she had wanted them to cleave together conclusively and could think of no more conclusive way than this. He had been loving, and gentle, and tender. He had whispered endearments, had held her face and looked into her eyes, and had shown he thought of no one and nothing but her. But when it was over she had felt weepy, and though Nathan had stroked her hair and told her he loved her and that she was beautiful, she had needed more reassurance than he could give. She had expected the intensity of his focus upon her in those few, vital moments to be the way he'd always look at her now, for ever, and when his breathing had slowed and eventually his talk had gone back to normal she felt crushed. It was all meant to be different now, and wasn't.

The bleeding had been a surprise. She was not a demure and sedentary Victorian maiden. She had done school gymnastics and ridden horses; her own fingers had never encountered resistance. But there had been a great deal of blood, in disproportion to the pain, which had – a relief – been less than she'd expected. They had drawn apart and it had actually gushed from her, warm and shocking. This was not the pale spot of new womanhood. Hung outside the window in another place and time, these sheets would suggest the groom had dismembered, not deflowered, his new bride. Nathan had looked stricken, and his concern that she had not been truthful about it hurting had made it all the more embarrassing. 'My poor baby,' he had whispered, his hand on her heart, and his pity had made her feel pitiable.

The sheets were now stuffed into the kitchen sink and soaking in an improvised solution of washing-up liquid and peppermint hand soap and hot water, and the contents of a sachet of something she had found in the back of a cupboard, that claimed to restore net curtains to a wafting summer purity. Scrubbing had seemed to make it worse. While they soaked, she sat at the dining table in semi-darkness, recreating the watershed that had come hours before, when she had told Nathan she finally felt ready. *Maybe you could go with Nathan.* Well, maybe she would.

TWENTY-ONE

You must come to Paris, the email commanded, *and be part of the conversation. We'll bring you over. You must come.* Pamela then forwarded the details of a travel agent in Stanmore named Joan Perelman whom, she said, would be in touch in due course. Joan was organising a group booking for all nineteen of the conference attendees and had instructions to ensure that Mr Alden be given the best room in the small hotel on the rue Christine. Joan would pop the information through Philip's door.

Alone in the half-gloom of his flat Philip chuckled, and then launched a damp spluttering cough, and then, recovered, laughed again. Pamela almost certainly wished him to go to Paris not to converse with her biennial assembly of trainee holistic midwives, but to be paraded as some sort of animated fossil dug out of the obstetric field. He would be both pitied and pilloried, specimen of a genus they hoped to drive into extinction. Pamela had stepped up her campaign by offering first Eurostar tickets, then this hotel room, and finally a small honorarium, as well as the chance to attend as many of the lectures and seminars as he pleased. He did not please. He would not have gone, even had it not felt disloyal to Julia, who was at this moment on her way over, delivering what she claimed was a spare fish pie.

At my age it would be irresponsible to commit to anything so far in advance, he wrote back, *but thank you for thinking of me.*

Philip had last been to Paris in 1974, when the Fédération Internationale de Gynécologie et d'Obstétrique had offered him a fellowship and he had spent six weeks living alone, teaching a series of courses at the Pitié-Salpêtrière hospital. Iris and ten-year-old Daniel had stayed in London, aided by a homesick but willing Italian au pair. The final weekend of his tenure, after their long separation, Iris would join him, and two days later the au pair would deliver Daniel to Paris on her way home to Naples. Then the three Aldens would travel down to Nice for a week's holiday.

For those humid August days, he'd had his wife's sustained, unbroken attention. He alone, perhaps for the first time since they'd married. They had walked in the Jardin des Tuileries and – though Iris, unlike Philip, had not grown up in a particularly religious household – had eaten their first shellfish together, the tight, slippery mussels flavoured with transgression and daring. Iris had gone further and tasted dainty snails in garlic butter, while Philip had sipped a cold beer and told her about his teaching, and she had listened. Philip read *le Monde* to her, translating Watergate coverage badly, on the hoof. On Monday morning he had a brief return to reality, a final series of administrative meetings at FIGO, while Iris had gone to meet Daniel's train, and to deliver the au pair into a second train that would take her home – for ever, it turned out, for she did not return to them as she'd promised. When Philip had left the office on Monday afternoon, his wife and son had been waiting for him on a sunny street corner, and the next morning they boarded the train for Nice, where the precious bubble of happiness had miraculously held. In gold kaftan and Roman sandals, Iris had been the most elegant woman on the beach. The most elegant woman, Philip thought, that he had ever seen. She would drift for idle, solitary walks along the shore, disappearing sometimes for hours, and each time as she receded into the distance he ached for her as if she was slipping from him for ever, like Euridice. This ache was at its most acute when he saw her returning. In those moments, when she was approaching but not yet close enough to hear his voice, he feared his heart might break with longing. Approaching, but not near enough. Never near enough. No, he would not go back to Paris.

'I tried a different one,' Julia explained, shuffling the empty ice-cube trays and half-crushed foil takeaway containers in Philip's freezer until she'd cleared space for the fish pie. 'It's got ketchup in it which sounds suspicious but we had it last night and it wasn't bad, if I do say so myself, I just made a bit too much. You can put it in the oven frozen.'

'Thank you, *maidele*. Whatever you make is always wonderful. Now tell me, you said you're finally going back to Verbier this year, I'm thrilled. Who is playing in the festival?'

'Everyone worth hearing, I just wish James could come. He's on call that weekend but in any case now, with everything . . .' she drifted off. 'My lovely Emmeline Whitten has a masterclass on the Sunday morning which is the only reason I'm still going, and we'll all have dinner that night, and I'll fly back Monday.'

'I think the last time I heard Emmeline was when you took us to the Wigmore.'

'She's doing so well in Moscow, Vera's pleased. I wish James could hear her. Next time she's playing nearish I'd love us to go together. It's quite hard to imagine at the moment but – anyway. Gwen made shortbread so I grabbed the last bits for us, it's very good. She's taken to baking for Nathan every Friday.' She was able to say this neutrally, though everything about it was irritating.

She sat down at the kitchen table, averting her gaze from Philip's unsteady journey from kettle to sink to mug cupboard, and began to unwrap the foil parcel of biscuits. She had not known, on her way here, whether she wished to discuss Gwen and Nathan. It was all so sordid. Repellent. Worst of all was perhaps the small part of herself that found her daughter's new disposition a welcome change. No more resentment or black moods. And, Gwen continued to make clear, no more interest in spending any time with her mother. Seeing them whispering, heads together exchanging confidences, stung like a deliberate, personal rejection. It made Julia feel excluded. It made her feel very, very old. But – Gwen seemed happier. 'It's all ongoing, you know,' she told Philip now, snapping a piece of shortbread in half and handing him the larger piece, 'the romance of the century. She keeps telling me I *just don't understand*. It's true. I don't. She was utterly incensed that I forbade them from carrying on with this relationship, she actually tried to lecture me on *human rights*, she gave me a horrid little speech that sounded precisely like Nathan. In any case I've stopped trying to forbid it because it wasn't getting me anywhere. I just want her to *think*. I've never denied her anything I thought would make her happy, and you know I've always tried not to say no unnecessarily, all I want is for her to think through her decisions. What happens when they break up?'

Philip sat down heavily opposite her, the wicker kitchen chair creaking ominously beneath him. 'And what does she say?'

'She'll just say, "What happens if you and *James* break up?" and then I may as well be talking to a wall because it's the same conversation over and over, she just equates the two. It's all about proving that they're just like us. Just as important as we are, just as committed, just as much entitled to be together. She's desperate to prove she doesn't need parenting any more. I'm apparently no longer required. I've been replaced.' She gave what she hoped would seem an easy, self-deprecatory laugh. 'And now she's taken to calling me *Julia*, the way Nathan and Saskia call their mother Pamela, which I've always found odd in any case, so now I'm not even her Mum any more.'

'She was *very* cross about James.'

'So this is a revenge attack, you mean? I thought . . .' She trailed off. 'It was so much pressure, always, all those years she felt responsible for me and I wanted her to just be a child now. Carefree, a little. I thought this would be a good thing for both of us, she was meant to feel *liberated*.'

'And part of her must, I'm sure. Your happiness is good for her.'

'I know, you and Iris both keep telling me but do you really think so?'

Philip considered. 'Certainly your unhappiness wasn't good for her. Or you. But you must remember, you're in charge, not the children. You say you don't feel you can stop them but – I suppose I don't quite understand why not. I know you find it hard, but perhaps you might try putting your foot down harder, even so?'

'She can't push me away for ever.' This had begun as a question, but she tried to turn it into a statement of her own confidence.

'What does James say?'

Julia shrugged. She and James had not had very satisfactory discussions on the subject, lately. As long as Nathan's schoolwork wasn't compromised and the children obeyed his basic rules – no canoodling in front of the parents, no overnight room-sharing or closed bedroom doors – James now seemed willing to make the best of it. He was content to catch up on patient notes in the living room while in the kitchen his son and her daughter made dinner together, and giggled loudly. He was happy to accept that for the moment, under admittedly peculiar circumstances, Gwen was being friendly to him. Valentina had been allowed to stay over, and the thought of his son as a sexually active being did not affront or appal him. Julia had wanted his outrage to endure as hers had, and felt let down that it hadn't. He listened to her when she confided in him. He'd held her when, a few nights earlier, she'd succumbed to tears that she could not explain. She could not bring herself to admit to him that the intensity of her daughter's need had been precious in those years alone, and that she ached for it now that it was over. But she had brought this rejection upon herself, for she had reached outwards for James, shattering the covenant of their solitude. She could not regret it – James had brought her back to life. Gwen was only doing what Julia herself had already done.

'Nathan's incredibly ambitious, and James is incredibly ambitious for him which maybe explains it – he can actually put quite a lot of pressure on him, I think, without meaning to. James was the first person in his family to go to university so he's quite obsessed with it, and Pamela's just as bad for all her hippy-dippy nonsense – but anyway Nathan studies very hard, and now Gwen's started to work whenever he works. She just really wants to please him. Her teachers are certainly thrilled with her, and of course that's good for her confidence, but it's hard not to feel . . . I hate that she wouldn't feel good enough as she is, for anyone. She ought not to have to contort herself to please him. I'm just holding my breath, waiting for it to implode.'

Philip said, after a moment's thought, 'Do you think it might implode imminently?'

'They're very settled, not that that means much with teenagers. Gwen's happy as a clam, and he was with the last one for two years. There's not much we can do, in practice. We can't lock them into their rooms after we're asleep, so we've had to just settle for stating our position and – it's nauseating, we've had to absolutely forbid them on the tacit understanding that they'll – I can't actually bear thinking about it. Don't you think she's far, far too young to be sexually active? Thank God he boards on school nights, I just wish I could convince James he should stay all term.'

'I don't know, *maidele*, it does seem very young to me but a great deal has changed since my day.'

'I'm utterly exhausted. When he's at home I find myself staying up later and later, as if I could somehow stay up late enough to make it impossible. I know Verbier is weeks away and it's only two nights but I can't bear the idea of leaving them. I'm longing to cancel.' Julia frowned. 'I miss her like, like *a limb*. But all I've ever wanted was for her to be happy, and she keeps telling me how happy she is. Endlessly.'

TWENTY-TWO

Gwen could not remember a time when she'd worked with more deliberate, sustained exertion. Revision went by in a strange, feverish blur during which she sweated through light cotton tops like a boxer and ran dry a series of brand new ballpoint pens with the manic vigour of her practice papers. Nathan was home for the Easter holidays and she thrilled at his pride in her. Among Nathan's friends it was cool to work hard, and the competitive indifference that Gwen imbibed at her own school had backfired unexpectedly when she'd tried it on him. 'I did *nothing* for my GCSEs last year,' she'd once said to him, casually, and he'd looked at her oddly and said, 'That was dumb. Why not? You're a more focused person than that.' It was gratifying to be observed and then described as any sort of person, even if the portrait wasn't always immediately familiar or recognisable – it made her feel seen, and reminded her that he was close enough to see her. So when he told her that he knew she didn't only prioritise 'clay and shit', she believed him. She did not yet know what sort of person she was becoming, and was happy to take his word for it. Inside she sometimes feared she was no sort of person at all, only a wisp, and Nathan's observations were reassuring anchors, giving solid boundaries to her self.

Now it felt good, and the AS exams would all go fine, she felt. Tests were a different proposition if you had prepared for them; when the answers were not mysterious but obvious, and merely had to be transcribed from brain to page. She sat down to dinner ravenous each evening and meanwhile she was even getting the hang of sex. They had now done it eleven times. Now Nathan was home she was barely sleeping – the parents policed them, and it was usually long after midnight before it was safe for him to sneak in undetected. Yet during the days she felt wired, inspired, and as if she'd slammed back five espressos instead of the single mocha frappuccino with whipped cream that she allowed herself each afternoon, at their three o'clock study break.

And then she ground to a halt. On the final weekend of the holidays she found herself listless and exhausted. It was as if she had paced a perfect marathon only to be told over the loudspeaker as the finish line approached that the new goal was thirty miles, and the final leg must be sprinted. The fuel tank, once bursting, was empty. It was all she could do to get out of bed late on Saturday morning, and this she did only when Nathan sat on the floor outside her bedroom door playing an old reggae tune filled with sunshine and goodwill, on repeat. With the pillow over her head she bellowed at him to go away but he merely increased the volume. A rumour had swirled that this year's French oral questions were about the environment – possibly vivisection, possibly carbon footprints – and Nathan was insisting she prepare the relevant vocabulary.

When she finally came down Julia was sitting at the dining table reading the newspaper, and James was making blueberry buckwheat pancakes as brain food for the final push.

'You're being an arsehole,' Gwen said to Nathan, who was still whistling snatches of the song with which he'd eventually roused her. 'None of you get how tired I am. You try revising hours and hours every single day and see how you'd feel.'

'I did,' Nathan told her, 'I do. I've already done an hour of stats while you were snoring. It was awesome, I rocked it.'

'Please don't bicker this morning.' Julia was keen to launch the day in an atmosphere of studious calm. 'And Gwen, please don't swear.'

'"Arse" isn't swearing.'

James ladled more batter into the frying pan. 'And yet the British way does sound more offensive. "Ass" is somehow more innocent.'

'That's because it means donkey,' Gwen told him, and then laid her forehead on her crossed arms on the kitchen table, and closed her eyes.

'I think "asshole" has become the pan-Atlantic standard. "Arsehole" is for sure on the decline. It's inevitable.' Here Nathan paused to spear a pancake from the stack beside his father and transfer one edge of it directly to his mouth. 'With the dominance of American vernacular in the media I think "arse" is over.' Gwen burrowed her face deeper into the crook of her elbow.

Nathan had stayed up the night before doing a series of practice physics papers and it had been four a.m. before he'd made it to bed. Despite this, he had been awake bright and early to help his girlfriend. He tried again. 'Come on, baby, *allons. Effet de serre*?'

'Dunno.'

'You do, you knew it yesterday. When you fart you contribute to the –' He gestured for someone, anyone, to complete this prompt.

'You're so close to the end, darling, and you've done so well,' Julia coaxed, putting a plate down in front of her daughter, though Gwen felt she could not have been clearer that she did not want to eat. She pushed it towards Nathan.

'Just think, in a month or two they'll all be over and you'll be free. You can have a lie-in every single day this summer, you're almost there, Dolly. Can I make you something else? Do you want eggs?'

'Not hungry.'

'Do you want to walk to Starbucks for an early frap?' Nathan asked. 'I'll test you while we walk? I need a break from my stuff.'

But Gwen shook her head and drew the hood of her sweatshirt down low over her forehead, pulling tight the toggles to cover her ears, and to shield her eyes from the lights which this morning seemed offensively dazzling. The sweet indolence of the summer lay ahead, Nathan would no longer be away on weeknights, and they could be together every day. She had succumbed briefly to his results-obsessed propaganda and had expended needless energy tearing after the bloodless electric hare of senior-school success, but in truth academic qualifications did not matter. They were all deluded. She could not summon the energy to tell them of their misconception, however.

TWENTY-THREE

All afternoon Gwen followed her mother around as she packed, wearing the mournful expression of an abandoned puppy dog but, quite unlike a puppy, making no attempt to be appealing. In response to Julia's enquiries she would only offer such valuable contributions as, 'Who cares what you wear with a bunch of musicians?' Her sullen unpleasantness had been increasing since breakfast, when she had told James his aftershave made her want to vomit, and had even snapped at Nathan, complaining the eggs he had scrambled with much fanfare were slimy, under-cooked, and generally offensive. She was now standing in the hallway while Julia dithered over whether or not to bring a coat for the festival. Julia was indecently excited about this small, solo trip.

'If you change your mind I'm sure James will pop you round to Katy's party later. What have you planned for the rest of the weekend?'

'Weekends don't matter now it's Easter,' said Gwen, who had taken deep offence at her mother's evident eagerness to go, and would not give an inch before this treacherous departure. 'All days are the same. I'm tired, I don't want to see a bunch of randoms.'

'Have you and Nathan got anything planned?'

'Why are you interviewing me?' Gwen whined, sitting down heavily on the stairs and slumping over her knees. 'You don't need to plan play dates for me while you're away, I'm perfectly capable of taking care of myself.'

If she hadn't had one foot out of the door – or had James overheard – Julia might have felt fortified to check this latest discourtesy, but instead she raised her hands in surrender. Gwen laid her head on her crossed arms, the embodiment of bleak despair. Moved despite herself, Julia stroked back her daughter's tangled hair. 'No third degree, I just thought you might be doing something.'

'What, like a super-fun classical music festival?' Gwen mumbled into her knees. 'Woohoo, par-tay.'

Surely this mood couldn't be attributed to her own, brief departure, Julia thought, perplexed, and then with a thrill of disloyalty, reflected that in about half an hour this state of affairs would all become Nathan's problem. He wanted to be with her daughter? He could take her as he found her. The festival in Verbier had begun to take on the honeyed glow of a recuperative spa weekend. She was even looking forward to the drive to Heathrow.

'Mummy.' Gwen looked up, suddenly plaintive. 'Mummy, I don't feel very well.'

Julia laid the back of her hand on her daughter's cheek. It was cool and dry. 'What's wrong, Dolly?' she asked softly. 'I'll be back before you know it. What's going on?'

Gwen shook her head, hopeless. 'I don't know.' She began to cry. 'I feel dizzy.'

Julia bent to kiss Gwen's forehead. She looked down at the mass of loose, fox-red curls escaping and unravelling into a halo of fine frizz, the bursts of psychedelic swirls and flowering creepers that Gwen had drawn in blue and red biro across one forearm and then, above the loose cotton neck of an ancient vest of Daniel's, she saw the blue-veined marbling of her daughter's swollen breasts. She bent down suddenly and gripped Gwen's shoulders.

'Gwendolen.' Her voice was steady; as steady as an ambulance dispatcher's; as steady as due north. 'Gwendolen.' Behind her she heard a key scrape in the front door but she did not turn. 'Gwen. Look at me. Right now. Are you pregnant?'

Gwen looked up, her pale face striped with glossy tear stains. She shrugged.

'I'm home!' called James, from the doorway. He held many straining plastic shopping bags and had slung several others around each wrist, so that beneath their weight his hands had turned first white and then puce with temporarily arrested circulation. He edged the door open with his knee. He had determined to consider the weekend with Julia's daughter an opportunity, rather than a nuisance. Certainly he had made sure to tell Julia this was how he saw it, and he wished to make it true.

'Now,' he said, slamming the door shut behind him with a violent jolt of the hip and dumping the groceries at his feet before remembering the eggs, too late, 'I have big news, kiddo. And the news is this – we're making veggie pizza. Your mom's away so you get to be the queen around here.'

He crouched down to investigate. To his relief, the eggs were all unbroken. Now he looked up, one hand still buried in a Waitrose carrier bag. Two stricken faces met him in silence.

'What's happened? Where's my boy? Where's Nathan?'

This was not the right way. She should have taken a test alone, to prove that she was responsible. She should have presented the facts in a calm and considered manner, so that Julia would admire her solemn maturity and initiative. *These things happen*, Gwen imagined her mother saying, stroking her hair. *I can't believe how grown up you've been, my brave girl.* She should have gone online and found herself a doctor; should have made her own appointment to take care of it, and the magnitude of the decision and the stoic dignity with which she'd taken it would have filled both Julia and Nathan with awe. *These things happen.* She did not want to be pregnant. It was inconceivable that she could be a mother. But she knew she had not been foolish – in her head she had been courageous and responsible. She just hadn't had time to prove herself. How could you test for a pregnancy in which you didn't quite believe? Now it had all gone wrong, for her mother looked as if she hated her. They were together in the bathroom while James paced the hallway outside.

'I don't understand,' Julia kept saying. 'I don't understand how this happened.' She had not yet raised her eyes from the plastic window of the newly purchased pregnancy test which lay on the side of the sink, its message unequivocal. Her knuckles had whitened from her grip on the basin. And then the worst words, 'How could you be so *stupid*?'

Gwen shrugged hopelessly. Hot tears spilled down her cheeks, but she could not yet speak. She felt flushed and dizzy and slightly sick, from fear or pregnancy or possibly both. No fate, in that moment, could have felt worse than her mother's disappointment. She yearned for sympathy, for gentleness. She longed to be small, and to be taken care of.

'It wasn't on purpose,' she whispered.

This had been the wrong thing to say.

'On purpose? On *purpose*? I never for one moment imagined it was anything other than, than damn *foolishness*. How long have you suspected? How many weeks – oh, God. This is a nightmare.' More softly, to herself, 'This is a living nightmare.'

'I was going to deal with it. I was going to fix it so you didn't worry and then tell you . . .'

'But have you seen a doctor? Do you know if you even have time to *fix it*? Does Nathan know?' This last was shouted, in a crescendo of rage.

'No.'

'No, what? No, you haven't seen a doctor? No, you don't know? I don't understand how you could have allowed – we trusted you. You asked me to trust you. You promised me I could trust you, and you've let me down. You've let –' Gwen had a sudden instinct to cover her ears against the next words – 'you've let your father down.'

Gwen felt her last hope collapse within her. She would be abandoned for this, and would never be forgiven. Now, when she needed more than ever to be restored to the full beam of her mother's love, to that deep, old intensity, they felt further apart than ever. She fell to her knees like a penitent, laid her head against the cold edge of the bath and began to sob. *'Don't talk about Daddy!'* she begged, gasping for breath. Her shoulders heaved, and she waited for warm arms to enfold her. She longed to lay her head in her mother's lap and sob, *You used to love me – love me now.* But though she cried harder and harder nothing happened, and when she looked up Julia was shaking her head in disbelief, and there was something new in her eyes that frightened Gwen. Hatred, maybe. What happened now hardly mattered.

TWENTY-FOUR

Julia stayed up very late with James, talking. Just before midnight the evening's silence had been briefly broken by shouts and scuffles as the pub around the corner disgorged its Friday-night punters, and intermittent caterwauling as these liberated drinkers carried their singing from the bar into the streets. Tonight, though this was not always the case, it sounded spirited but good-natured, out of sight behind the sturdy Victorian terraces. Julia and James stood at the window, intertwined and unmoving, frozen in their bubble of shock. The solidity of James's arm around her waist was, quite possibly, the only thing that kept her standing. Disbelief came crashing back over her in waves, and each time it receded left a shoreline sullied with debris. Strands of anger and guilt. Empty shells of self-reproach. She felt a hundred years old.

'Maybe that's what we should have done this evening,' Julia said. 'Maybe we just should have walked out and gone to the Lord Southampton and drunk ourselves into oblivion.'

'What, take up binge-drinking? Sing our troubles away on a karaoke machine somewhere?'

'Yes, exactly. It would have been cathartic. Or numbing. Oh –' She turned and laid her head against the broad solidity of his chest. 'Let's run away. Let's just go. I've got a hotel room in Verbier ready and waiting, right now, that I'm meant to be in. We could conceal ourselves among the violinists.'

'We could pay our way across Europe giving recitals. You can play and I'll . . . dance. South of France? Tuscany?'

'We could start a vineyard.'

'Let's make buffalo mozzarella.'

'I think you might need buffalo to make buffalo mozzarella.'

James considered. 'So you'll look after the buffalo. I'll make the wine. I really think we're on to something, it will be more economical to make our own if we're going to become full-time alcoholics.'

'Not alcoholics,' Julia amended. 'Binge-drinkers.'

'Right. Tuscan binge-drinkers.' James sat down on the bed and pulled her hand gently until she was sitting beside him. 'It's a real shame about your masterclass, as well as everything else. I know it's not . . . this does happen, you know. I see a lot of kids at work—'

'Everyone you see at work is pregnant, it's not representative.'

'True. But what I mean is . . .' He trailed off. 'I don't know what I mean. I'm in shock, I think. I'm sorry, I won't quote statistics at you.'

'We should have stopped all of this, the whole thing. The sex. The unprotected sex. The utter stupidity of the relationship itself. How could they be so bloody stupid? How did this actually happen?'

James could not reply to this question for in truth he blamed Gwen, and was so angry that he did not think he could ever again be civil to her. Pamela had waged a relentless sexual-health campaign with their own children since long before it had been relevant or even appropriate, and despite these assurances, James himself had given Nathan stern reminders about the importance of condoms ever since Valentina's first appearance. Each of these unsatisfactory discussions had ended with a withering dismissal of, 'It's all taken care of, Father,' or more tastelessly, 'Dad, this ain't my first rodeo.' But it had now been established that they had not been using condoms, and that this current debacle was therefore entirely due to Gwen's laissez-faire attitude to taking the Pill. Nathan, James judged, had done his medic parents proud. He had taken himself off to the Royal Free for a full sexual-health screening before trusting to the hormonal contraception alone, which was mature and considerate, especially given his rather limited sexual history. Nathan had been gentlemanly, principled, irreproachable. Gwen, by contrast, was a spoiled, selfish and irresponsible little airhead. Despite tonight's earlier display, in which she had been the embodiment of abject misery and contrition and bewilderment, James thought it more than possible that she had done it on purpose. To share her mother's attention made her frantic, and with a single move she had commandeered it all, trapping Nathan in the process. Regardless of her insecurity, Gwen was a girl accustomed to her own way and now she had created such a tornado of dramatic tension around herself that it was possible she would once again get it. She had behaved indefensibly towards his beloved son. His beloved son who was staying over at Charlie's house after a gig, whose phone was still off, and who had absolutely no idea of the bedlam that awaited him at home.

He had stood outside the bathroom while the stupid girl had peed on a stick that would reaffirm what, with a little hindsight, ought to have been perfectly obvious, and by the time the three minutes of waiting had elapsed he had regained outward mastery of himself. Nathan would need his father to be calm. In any case, amid the howling and shrieking, someone had to remain clear-headed.

He now saw that he had been too cautious about discipline, too careful not to undermine or challenge Julia's rule, and far too deferential to the other, absent man of the house. Once they had all recovered from this unpleasantness he would assert himself, by Julia's side, at the helm of this family. He would dispatch Gwen to a grief counsellor. He would insist that they all see a family therapist. He would fix what was broken around here.

'I promised Daniel,' Julia was now saying, and he summoned his mind back to the present, back to her serious, pale face. 'I promised I'd take care of her. I promised I'd be two parents.'

'Even kids with two parents can get pregnant.'

'I know, but when we talked about her life, and the support she'd need to get through his loss – he felt so guilty about leaving her, you know, she was only ten and he knew how she would suffer. Can you imagine? She was just skinny arms and legs, and this huge bushel of mad red hair, and all sunshine and energy. He said it was like throwing a beautiful, porcelain plate high in the air – you can see it flawless and unbroken as it arcs upwards and descends, right until the moment you know is coming when it hits the ground and smashes. And he was going to be the one to hurt her like that. He was so angry he'd never see her grow up. And you know, we'd talk about what she'd be, who she'd become, we'd try and imagine it together, and I promised I'd do my best to protect her and give her a good life.'

James did not, in this instance, think that a father's death years ago offered sufficient excuse or explanation. He never usually acknowledged her daughter's bad behaviour, but with this silence, he now judged, he had also let Daniel down. He had pragmatic feelings about Daniel. He rarely chose to think of him at all, and when he did it was as a vague, benign presence, abstract as an ancestor, and with this unthreatening distance between them the two men could and ought to be brothers in arms. He imagined Daniel's love for Julia as his own – epic and sweeping as the prairie; broad and generous as the pale sky above it. When he thought of Julia he always saw this same image – vast, open spaces; the pallor and splendour of soothing, infinite skies. He would take care of her. He would not let her be bullied by an unhinged, manipulative teenager. A teenager whose attack had wounded his son as collateral damage. He could give voice to none of this. Instead he said, 'You have given her a good life. You are giving her a good life.'

'Maybe, but seriously, I considered making it through secondary school without an illegitimate pregnancy as the bare minimum.'

'No one, no one could love their daughter more than you love Gwen. And we will all get through this together and be fine. It's horrible, it will be horrible for both our kids, and then it will be over. We found out early, which makes everything vastly less complicated.'

Julia tucked her legs up beneath her and began biting the nail of her little finger. 'What exactly will they do?'

'You never had one?'

'No!' She looked scandalised. 'Why, did you? I mean, did you ever get someone pregnant by accident?'

'No,' James admitted. 'My knowledge is purely professional. Pamela had one, just before we started dating, in fact. She was characteristically robust about it. I don't think she was entirely sure who had helped her into her condition in the first place, which would make imagining an alternative outcome more abstract. Hard to picture a baby's face if you're not sure which dude it might resemble.'

'That's the bitchiest thing I've ever heard you say,' said Julia, briefly cheered.

'Well, there you go. I'm allowed a slip every now and again where my ex-wife is concerned. I should call her but, Christ, I really can't deal with her tonight. And I don't want him to hear it first from her on the phone. Or she'll tell Saskia, or arrive on our doorstep or – I just don't want to handle it right now.'

'So, what will they do?'

'If she's right about her last period then it's very early, she won't need a surgical abortion and can do it with mifepristone. It blocks progesterone, which then makes the uterine lining break down. Then she'll go back for misprostol which causes contractions, bleeding, and everything hopefully passes out after that. It's not a party, I will tell you, but it's pretty quick, they'll give her pain relief and antibiotics and if all goes smoothly that's it, just a check-up and then back to normal. Codeine, hot-water bottle, good TV, distraction.'

'Okay.' She nodded, her fingernail still between her teeth. 'Can you imagine, just for a moment, if our children actually had this baby together?'

'Let's not go there, it's entirely insane. You would have a grandchild related to me and Daniel. And you and I would have a shared grandchild. It's pretty fucked up. It might end up looking like both of us.' He raised her palm gently to his lips. 'But you're my family now. And that means any baby Gwen has, any time, with any man, is going to be our grandchild. It doesn't have to – this isn't . . . isn't anything but an accident. Whoever our kids end up marrying and having children with, you and I are going to be a team and we'll share all those grandbabies between us, and when it happens it will be awesome. We'll look after them together and enjoy them and then give them back when they cry and go back to our gardening and our vacationing and – and shuffleboard. As long as Nathan doesn't marry the Demon Barber of Seville we'll be in clover. Give it a decade, decade and a half, and we'll see what's cooking.'

'I know. Thank you.'

'Don't thank me.' And then, to share her pain, to halve her responsibility, he offered a sacrificial lamb, an echo of the unreasonable resentment he knew she must harbour. 'It's my dumb son who knocked her up.'

'When can she not be pregnant again?'

'Pretty fast.'

'How fast? This weekend?'

'Not that fast. A week. Ten days, maybe.'

'I could literally strangle them both.'

'It's a legitimate solution.'

She was silent for a moment. 'Can we grow tomatoes too, and basil? And olives, for olive oil.'

'Then I think we need a donkey to turn the press. Or a mule, whatever that may be, I don't know, we didn't have mules in Dorchester when I was growing up, they might be a form of female footwear. You'll wear nothing but mules when you ride the donkey to press the olives. With our buffalo we'll have an entire farm devoted to the Caprese salad.' He looked at his watch. 'It's two a.m., baby, let's go to bed. This will still be godawful in the morning, I guarantee.'

She laughed, and his heart lifted at the sound, the promise of future recovery, the first new buds after a hard winter.

'Okay. Do you swear?'

'I swear. You'll have hours and hours of misery and stress tomorrow. Days, until it's resolved. Let's go to sleep now so we can really appreciate it in daylight in all its sordid glory.' He took her face between his hands and kissed her deeply. 'I love you more than anything, and I promise you we will put this right together.'

TWENTY-FIVE

It was impossible that her mother had gone to sleep angry when Gwen so longed for her; never before had Gwen, in need, been left alone to cry. Her first thought on waking was that, despite evidence to the contrary, there must have been some mistake, half expecting to find Julia sitting quietly beside her bed, as she had so many nights in childhood. Her second realisation was that it was still only four a.m., and many hours lay ahead before she could make right what yesterday had gone so very wrong. She felt feverish and queasy. She needed her mother to understand – she could not be pregnant, she was only a child, she needed to be swept up, herself a babe in arms. Her unhappiness was abject and complete.

She lay in a mounting agony of indecision. Not once since James invaded had Gwen been up to the top floor. To enter their room was impossible. To wait, untenable. She found herself in a state of ferocious concentration, hoping her mother would sense her need and float downstairs, gather her into safety and rescue her. As a little girl she would remain in bed and shout, louder and louder, till the thud of approaching footsteps heralded relief; in later years she had realised that deliverance came faster if she flew to her parents' bedroom, though the mid-night flight itself held unknown terrors. She would gather her strength and run up the stairs and throw open the door into the moon-softened darkness. On the left would be her father, on the right, her mother. Always a space between them, Gwen-sized. Julia fast asleep was all wrong, for how could she guard Gwen in her own unconsciousness? Off-duty, vulnerable, her mind who knew where? Gwen would whisper for her over and over until Julia opened her eyes, and then her arms, and made right whatever was wrong.

How soon could this be made right so that her mother might forgive her, and how would it be? She did not know what abortions entailed but found herself picturing a high-necked white cotton nightgown, strawberry jelly and melting vanilla ice cream, the mint-green paper curtains of the hospital ward on which she had eaten these after the removal of her tonsils. Julia on a camp bed, by her side. Loving, ministering, proud of her brave girl. The thing now inside her was only the size of a poppy seed, far smaller than a tonsil, and could surely be shaken loose. A speck. She felt twitchy and restless, and to think of cells colonising and proliferating made her skin crawl. There was not a moment to lose; she must have freedom from it. She could not quite imagine Nathan's reaction but surely he would not be angry? He would support her, and they would come through it bound tightly together with the dark velvet bonds of a secret, but while her mother felt such paralysing disappointment Nathan remained out of focus. She couldn't breathe; she longed for absolution. One could not stay angry about a mistake the size of a poppy seed.

Upstairs she listened and hearing only silence, knocked softly. Nothing. After a moment she pushed the door open and took a single step into what once had been her parents' bedroom. As she adjusted to the gloom she could see Julia, sound asleep, not on the expected right but in the unimagined centre. Entwined with James, face to face, breathing one another's slow breath. A beefy bare arm slung over her delicate mother.

Gwen stared, arrested by curiosity and revulsion. What betrayal had filled the last waking moments before this easy, slumbering union? *I'm sorry about my daughter,* or perhaps, *Never mind, nothing matters as long as we have each other.* Sleep had softened her mother's face to girlish smoothness as she lay in her lover's arms; her brow was open, her hand resting upon James's bare chest. She did not look like a woman worried for her only child. She looked contented. She looked as Gwen had never known her.

Gwen backed away and closed the door softly. On the landing she stood very still, for a long time. She feared she might be sick. What truths had lain hidden in plain sight: she was alone. *Fuck you,* she thought, and then whispered it louder, to steady herself. She was drowning; she must evaporate her terror with burning rage.

Fuck you.
You didn't choose me.
You don't get to decide.

A series of thuds and scrapings brought Julia downstairs early the next morning. The night before, James had steadied and calmed her, and they had already taken decisive action. Falling asleep she'd remembered Claire, James's former registrar, young and approachable and direct, with an easy manner that Gwen would appreciate. She had asked James to email her and they'd received an instant reply, though it was almost three a.m. – Claire was on nights. She would go home to sleep and would then make herself available for a check-up, a scan, a chat, a cup of tea. Julia descended the stairs aching to put her arms around her daughter who must – now that anger no longer occluded her vision she could see it – feel so lost and frightened. Julia longed to tell her she'd taken steps to help. But overnight, Gwen had made radical alterations of her own.

Apparently unaided, Gwen had wrestled the mattress off Nathan's single bed, deconstructed the slatted base, and reassembled it in her own room. What had once been Nathan's room now resembled a university study, their pair of pine desks back to back on opposite walls. Gwen's room, the larger of the two, now contained nothing but an improvised double bed. Julia entered to find Gwen in a burst of furious energy, pulling taut a fitted sheet to unite the two single mattresses. She was red-faced and slightly damp with sweat, and did not look up as Julia came in.

'What are you doing?'

Gwen did not answer. She was on all fours, straining to tuck the sheet beneath the corner. Then she succeeded and sat back on her heels, satisfied.

'What the hell are you doing?'

'Moving a mattress.'

'You moved the mattress. And a divan.'

'Yup.'

Julia sat on the edge of the newly enlarged bed. 'Can you stop, please? I need to talk to you. I've made an appointment with James's friend—'

'Nearly done, one sec.'

'Gwen, stop right now.'

'*What?*'

'What the hell are you doing?'

'I'm *nesting*,' spat Gwen, with heavy irony. 'Can you stand up, please, I want to put the duvet down.'

Julia stood up, casting around for something on which to fix, and feeling faintly hysterical. 'You've lost your mind. This is not your house, Gwendolen. Darling, I know you're upset but you can't just— Help me, please, you will not believe this,' she told James, who had just appeared in the doorway with a tray and three cups of tea. He peered in, looking bewildered. 'What's going on in here?'

'Gwen moved the beds. Herself. She's apparently taken up weightlifting.'

'Did you have permission to do that?' James asked, and was ignored. He went to set his tray down on Gwen's desk, but Gwen's desk was no longer there. He cast around for another surface and then finally set the tray on the floor.

'She could have hurt herself, couldn't she? They're heavy. Please tell her. Gwen, sit down, you're upsetting me.'

'Moving heavy furniture alone is not smart,' James agreed. 'But also, and more to the point, there's no damn way in hell that you are sharing a room with my son. Are you out of your damn mind with this? And now? *Today*? Seriously?'

Gwen was shaking a pillow into a pillowcase and began to snap it violently, like a terrier breaking the neck of a small animal. Her teeth were gritted.

'Gwen,' Julia pleaded, 'please stop. Just sit down, darling. We need to talk. It's going to be okay.'

Gwen set down the pillow and began punching it violently into shape. 'I am not an idiot and I actually don't need to ask permission to share a room with the father of my baby. I'm fine, there's nothing wrong with me, I'm perfectly capable of moving a bed, I'm not a fucking *child*, and obviously we'll have to share a room when the baby comes so we can do nights together and you are not the only adults in this fucking house, you're not the only relationship that *counts* around here, and I don't have to ask permission to move things around in my own room. Why are you even in here?' She wiped away angry tears with the back of her hand.

'What are you talking about? Father of what baby?'

'*You don't control me! You don't get to decide every single thing that happens!*'

'Come on.' James rested a hand on Julia's shoulder. 'I don't know what the hell's happening but this is not productive right now. We'll be downstairs when you're ready to explain yourself like a civilised adult,' he went on, and Gwen wondered how he could still be standing there stolidly in her doorway, how his heart could continue to beat under the annihilating pressure of her hate for him. He had taken everything from her that counted, but what little remained to her, she would keep.

* * *

Late on Saturday morning Nathan came back from Charlie's house to find his family waiting for him in the kitchen. His father and Julia were pale-faced and grave, and before he'd had a chance to make a much-needed cup of sweet, strong coffee and address his ravenous hunger they imparted unimaginable news about his girlfriend – at that moment flushed and weeping noisily in the corner. Nathan made an odd, involuntary noise in response. A hoarse bark of a laugh; a single, mirthless staccato of irritated disbelief. He felt nothing except a surge of impatience that with their histrionics they were disturbing the warm afterglow of a perfect evening. The last big night out, they'd all decided, till summer. He was looking forward to fried eggs on toast, and then a long, hot shower to wash away the grime of the bar, and the two cigarettes he had accidentally smoked on the walk home. But everybody was now looking at him, expecting a reaction. In the corner Gwen's sobs grew louder and she surged forwards and fell upon his neck, her face blotched and swollen, snorting raggedly, as if she had been crying for hours and was only now clearing and loosening rolls of mucus from the back of her throat. He was alarmed and briefly repulsed by this transformation but he folded his arms around her narrow back to reassure her. It was only when over her shoulder he noticed his father's expression that his stomach twisted and tightened. This was not Gwen's solitary tragedy. Hot tears of panic began to rise and he held her tighter, for his own comfort.

He did not have time to speak to her. Almost immediately she was whisked away by her mother to see a woman who would talk to her about 'options' and the noise and drama departed, together with his unrecognisable beloved. The kitchen was silent and sun-filled. His father spoke softly. This must be a godawful shock. But Claire was calm and a pragmatist, James explained, and would inject a little reality into the situation. It would soon be resolved. Nathan felt his panic recede and a numbing wash of disbelief rise in its place. *A drowsy numbness*, he thought, *where do I know that phrase, or perhaps I've coined it myself? Worth remembering – though 'numbness' is a bit clunking.* His head throbbed. Gwen herself had only suspected since yesterday, James went on, and it was not enough time for anything but stubborn, reflexive posturing. She could not mean what she said, and in fact last night she had clearly wanted the opposite. Nathan must have so many questions – (Nathan did not) – but he was not to listen to or be terrified by any of the girl's wild assertions. A nightmare episode, uncomfortable, frightening, perhaps a wake-up call that one was not as mature as one believed. Nathan should know that James loved him and wasn't mad, even though it was a goddamn stupid needless screw-up. Things would change around here. Time now to knuckle down, refocus, re-establish priorities. Nathan must be so angry.

Nathan, who wasn't, pressed his temples. James fried him eggs and buttered him toast. Nathan meekly said, 'Okay,' and began his breakfast.

'It's just about attention, it's nothing to do with you,' James continued, battering the heel of the loaf into the narrow slot of the toaster with unnecessary force, 'and we'll figure it out.' Nathan took this statement at face value, and as all the explanation required. He had no wish to think deeper or further. He had taken up the reassuring, containing phrase 'nightmare episode' as an accurate description of the terrible five minutes during which his girlfriend had been wailing beside the refrigerator. That had been intense, but now he wished to burrow into his hood and sleep. It was a further unpleasant jolt to learn that before he slept he would have to help his father carry a divan and a mattress back to his own bedroom – the temporary theft of his single bed had been if anything a greater shock, and with it an attempt upon his autonomy and very *manhood*, he'd felt – but Gwen was obviously in distress, and would need careful handling until the nightmare episode was over. After the sheets had been restored he muttered, 'Keats!' rather sorrowfully to his father, and then fell into a dreamless slumber, without pausing to remove jeans or sweatshirt. James kissed his brow, reiterated softly that he loved him, and departed.

Nathan had surprised himself with his devotion to Gwen, for he had believed himself sincerely in love with Valentina and had since learned something deeper. With Gwen he was able to be himself, or at least, whichever version of himself felt truest at the time. She loved him without limits or conditions, and without apparent judgement. As he was, so she took him. Schooled by his friends to be quick and judgemental and to seize gleefully upon the slips of others, he was humbled by Gwen's simple, earnest loyalty. In their private spaces, she had made it safe for him to be sometimes wrong, or undecided. With Gwen it became less frightening to be fallible, because she resolutely refused to believe him so. If he were in trouble, he would not doubt her steadfastness. This weekend she was not rational, but his father assured him it was an episode, so he would stick by her until she had recovered. It was about attention, James had said, and once she's well and truly traumatised Julia there's no damn way she'll go through with any baby. Well, Nathan remembered what it felt like to be sidelined in a parental drama and was anxious to believe this explanation. No one his age could be pregnant. He was not such a statistic – he went to private school, for God's sake.

Nathan awoke in the afternoon to the return of the women, and of fear. By dinner time Gwen was vomiting copiously and pitiably, as if the revelation of her condition had unleashed her symptoms like hounds uncaged. She did not have anything resembling a glow about her but instead after only a few hours had begun to look haggard and almost feral; like something, he thought, swept in off the moors. Claire's celebrated pragmatism had had no discernible effect. During the brief moments she was not on her knees in the bathroom Gwen lurched from a soft-voiced, reasonable calm, stating her position with the deliberate, even tones of a well-trained customer-service agent, and a moment later would be unhinged by an imperceptible provocation, wild-eyed and snarling at James and her mother like Bertha Rochester. For Nathan she had only words of love, and of contrition, but through all of Saturday evening and most of Sunday they were alone for only fleeting snatches.

In the end it was decided on Sunday evening that when term began the next morning he would go to back to boarding, as planned. Regret could be stoked and fostered into a full-time activity but it was not a very constructive one and, as the stalemate continued, it became clear that there wasn't much Nathan could actually *do*. The baby about whom they all raved and ranted would be – an unimaginable hypothetical – his baby. And yet when mother and daughter clashed, eyes flashing, hands on hips, or more bewilderingly, crying softly in one another's arms, no oxygen remained. The tears and slammed doors, the ragged apologies and immediate retractions; Nathan had no place in these scenes. Neither Gwen nor Julia thought to ask him what he wanted. Instead he retreated behind his father. It became harder and harder to believe that it would all, as James continued to promise with grim determination, be okay. Gwen had lost her mind and so far showed no signs of recovering it. He missed his mother, and longed to be at home.

TWENTY-SIX

'Well, obviously she'll have to get rid of it,' said Iris equably, just as Julia had known she would. She waited for the rest of the address while her mother-in-law clicked sweetener tablets into her teacup. Julia felt almost giddy with relief to be in Iris's living room, awaiting judgement and a brisk shot of fortitude. In her mother-in-law's presence there was nothing that did not seem obvious or manageable. It was healing to be spoken to in the imperative.

Philip had been the one to tell Iris the news, and had therefore taken the unrestrained brunt of her wrath and disappointment. It was with Philip that Iris had also wept, once, briefly and in silence. Nonetheless, Iris did not understand the extended lamentations. She saw merely an unpleasant, regrettable expedient they would all hasten to forget once it was over. A young woman's future hung in the balance. On one side an education, choice, independence. On the other Iris saw the scale loaded with all the heavy, dark weight of the past. Biology as destiny: it no longer had to be. If that maddening child had any grasp of her generation's privilege she might have been more respectful of the sovereign miracle of contraception. She ought, Iris thought furiously, to have cherished it. Worshipped it. The Pill was golden liberty, deliverance from both the baby and the scalpel, and this needless mess was due entirely to Gwendolen's own stupidity and ingratitude. Never mind. It was not too late.

'She's got herself into a horribly foolish situation but all that matters now is that she be forbidden from doing something far stupider. If you don't like the place that Thing's pal found then that ex-wife of his will know the right women's clinic, surely. God's teeth, what I wouldn't give for a cigarette right now.' Iris took a prim sip of tea. 'If that girl undoes my Alan Carr she'll really learn what trouble looks like.'

Julia had not moved to speak, and so Iris continued, 'Look. Mistakes happen. This is truly one of Gwendolen's more spectacular balls-ups, I will give you that, but it can't possibly be allowed to dictate the rest of her life. You are her mother – no more fluffy Fabian philosophies and all that utter guff you thought would be so healing. *Trust the child.* I've always known it was a nonsense but I now see in serious circumstances it's positively dangerous. We've watched and we've said nothing till now but really, Julia, there must be limits. Teenagers have no impulse control, it's a neurological fact. What on earth does she know about anything? It's not at all the same as letting her choose her own bedtime or have marshmallows for dinner. You must save her from herself now, and you simply cannot allow this madness to proceed.' Iris gave a short, mirthless laugh. 'Julia? God help us, you're not suffering a sudden bout of Catholicism?'

Julia came to life. 'No! How can you even – no, of course not, you know I don't think there's any other sensible course, it's – she's just being so, so *intransigent*. Every time we talk she ends up screaming. She is absolutely deaf to sense.'

'Then you must be louder,' said Iris stoutly. 'Time is ticking.'

'Believe me, I'm well aware. I spent half the night writing her a letter, and I left it on her pillow yesterday and she came down looking sort of grave and pious and told me very calmly that she knew I only wanted the best for her but that she wasn't going to change her mind. Nathan was in tears this morning, he's frantic, Saskia apparently emailed her and even Pamela's spoken to her, not that she has any influence, but she's at least full of fire and statistics, and Gwen put the phone down on her. I don't know what to do, I can't *reach* her. I don't know how to make her see what she's doing to her future. And to my future, not that she seems particularly concerned about that. I can't actually force her, can I? Can I? You can't force someone. What if she really did regret it for the rest of her life? It would be unimaginable. But this – this is unimaginable. It's all unimaginable. I'd give anything to rewind, I'm longing to make it all just go away.'

Iris set her teacup and saucer down on a large, hard-backed copy of Le Corbusier's *The Modulor*, which sat at the top of a stack on a gold silk ottoman beside her. She began to speak more slowly, as if to a person of limited understanding. 'The "someone" in question is a child, and not a particularly mature or clear-headed one. Your language is problematic. Of course one can't *force someone* but one ought to direct one's minor children and take responsibility for their lives, it's a mother's job. If you want to discuss lifelong regret, I suggest you try imagining this – all her little girlfriends lining up in mortar boards to collect their degrees, or shouldering backpacks to binge-drink on Vietnamese beaches, or throwing their first dinner parties after a day in some jolly little graduate scheme, and I urge you to picture alongside it our young Gwendolen alone, for you and I both know she will be alone, these boys don't stick around for five minutes, *alone* with a screaming toddler at her knee, hanging up laundry.'

Julia nodded and said nothing, and Iris began to look mutinous. She had begun with her usual affectation of serenity but Julia was vexing her. 'Well?'

'I know,' said Julia quietly. 'It would be a tragedy.'

'Well then, for God's sake, stave it off! If you're all so worried about lifelong regret for this hypothetical infant then no wonder she feels she ought to keep it, you might as well start putting it down for schools. Not that it will be going to private school, of course, having grown up in ignorance and penury.'

'I can't actually drag her there by the hair! What am I meant to do? I've made the appointment and I'll try to find a way to get her there. There's only a few weeks left before it's too late. Oh, God. I should never have let this happen in the first place and then we wouldn't be here. I feel culpable. I've made an appointment to talk to a family therapist next week. I know we should have separated them, but the idea of James moving out again—'

'No self-flagellation, please, thank you very much, this is entirely Gwendolen's fault. But you can fix it.'

'And Nathan's,' said Julia, ignoring the second assertion. In the last days she had longed more than ever to dispatch James's monstrous, con artist, sex offender of a son to a life of hard labour in the colonies, or even to the lesser sentence of a life burying eggshells and peeing on compost heaps under his mother's permanent charge in Boston. She wished, with clear precision, to murder him. The vivid violence of her imagination shocked her. She saw house fires and gas leaks. She saw him jaunty and carefree, mown down into a cartoon two dimensions by a speeding bus. She was too angry with her daughter to allow herself safely to feel or even approach it; Nathan, therefore, received the full force of her fury. Fury was more bearable than sorrow.

'I will apportion him precisely twenty-three per cent of the blame. Nathan wasn't the one, after all, who "forgot" to take the Pill.' Iris left her hands frozen where they had risen on either side of her face, fingers held in drooping peace signs around the stinging, crucial word.

'I can't deal with accusations of deliberate idiocy right now. I do know what it looks like.'

'For the moment why it happened is irrelevant, now we find ourselves here. Listen to me. Do you know a single person in our milieu, a single girl of our acquaintance lucky enough to be from a privileged, educated north London family of means who has had a baby under these circumstances? Don't be so arrogant as to assume we're the only ones, it's statistically impossible that no one we know has had a daughter run into a bit of trouble. But they don't go leaving letters around like the tooth fairy, they *deal with it*, Julia. The parents deal with it. And the girls chalk it up to experience and go on to university and careers and marriages and there's *no harm done*.'

Composed until this moment, Julia suddenly covered her face and began to sob. 'I've lost her. I don't know how to get her back.'

'Oh, darling.' Iris's expression remained stern but her voice softened. She sighed. She felt less equipped to deal with Julia's grief; it was moving beyond her remit. 'Listen to me. You're very happy, in case you'd lost sight of it amid all this mess. You're happy for the first time since . . .' She abandoned this sentence, and began to readjust the gold watch that hung loosely on her left wrist, rotating it, checking and then re-checking the clasp. This was one of her forbidden paths of thought, leading only into snares and brambles. Back up, back out. Yet it was indisputable that Julia was in many ways better suited to this large, affable American than she had been to Iris's beloved son, and she was stung with sudden furious envy for Daniel. Daniel had been fiery and impetuous and brilliant – her captivating, flame-haired boy. Julia was unchallenging, far too passive for him, and they had argued, and she had not stood up to him as he'd needed. Her wilting would further aggravate him and they would then limp on for days in unresolved, unignorable tension while little Gwen, attuned and vibrating with every mounting bar of pressure, would prance between them like a court jester, exhausting herself in her efforts to effect a reconciliation. Daniel should have married someone with a bit of spice. Instead he'd chosen this pale flower and she had gone about looking harried. Now Julia had softened, and unfurled. Yes – Iris had talked herself free of danger – it was no insult to Daniel to concede that she and anodyne Thing were a better fit. She drew in a deep breath, and looked down at her hands. On the left a grape-coloured chip of ruby set in ornately engraved eight-carat plate that had once been Philip's mother's; the thin, scuffed gold of her wedding band now retired to her right ring finger, where Philip also wore his.

'My darling girl, I do know.' Here she paused, certain that Philip Alden would caution her not to sermonise. 'You won't lose her, the two of you are part of one another which is precisely why this must hurt so much. And you and Thing have enough on your plates. In not very long you'll be carefree together, and you'll be starting an entirely different sort of life. You cannot allow Gwendolen to sabotage everything and destroy her own life in the process. Believe me, that would do your relationship with her no good either.'

Julia wiped her cheeks, and nodded.

Enough, thought Iris, suddenly overcome with irritation and unwilling to mourn a catastrophe while it could still be headed off at the pass. All this ululating and rending of collars was simply wasted energy. 'Anyway. Your plans are your own business and are for you and Thing to discuss once the nest is actually empty. In the meantime,' she looked steadily at Julia, 'before the children go forth, you must forbid them from multiplying. Deal with it.'

TWENTY-SEVEN

'What about up here?' Nathan offered, pointing towards a patch of balding grass beneath a giant sycamore. It was less crowded than the larger clearing they had just passed, in which he'd spotted a group of local teenagers he half knew and urgently wished to avoid. A damp chill remained in the air, but an unexpected wash of pale April sunshine had drawn hopeful crowds to the Heath. Nathan's parents had given him a series of coaching sessions prior to this outing, and he had set out determined to act upon them.

'Ugh. You're *so* lucky you get to escape to school. I wish I could escape from Mum and – Julia and James. They're probably desperate to get rid of me anyway. I'm so sick of crying and being yelled at and grovelling and then crying again, it's not exactly relaxing.'

'I don't think the throwing up is majorly helpful. Maybe you should consider quitting that.'

'Okay, I'll think about giving up, but it's just been so much *fun*. I feel human again today, though.'

'I'm glad,' he said, with feeling. It had been dreadful to watch her heave, with the surreal guilt and awe that his own ejaculation could have such terrible power.

They sat down on the seam of shadow that fell across the grass, Nathan in the sun, Gwen in the full shade. She had showered and put in her contact lenses and looked pretty and fresh-faced again, in a pair of heart-shaped cerise Lolita sunglasses, and a denim jacket on which she'd long ago embroidered a seam of prancing, rainbow-tailed unicorns. She had been cheerful since they'd been alone together. Sucking intermittently on an orange lollipop, she looked the picture of youthful innocence. Here was someone he recognised.

'I'm sorry this has all got so crazy,' she said, after a while. The lolly clicked against her teeth as she removed it to speak. 'I just get so frustrated that they don't get it. And I know I'm super hormonal so it seems like I don't know what I mean because I keep crying but I do, I just express myself badly. It's like, insanely clear in my head. They're both so rigid, it's like they refuse to see that people can take different paths from them. From them? From theirs? Anyway. I think –' she paused to tuck the sweet back into one cheek – 'I think sometimes it can be very hard for parents to see signs that their babies have become adults.'

Nathan saw the truth in this statement, and also its dishonesty. Their parents were not upset because their children were growing up but because they had done something infantile. He had never felt less like an adult. This was most acute when he spoke on the phone with his mother, longing for the stifling warmth and reassurance of her soft arms around him. Last night he'd dreamed he had been entrusted with a minute baby in a jam jar. The jar had smashed, and the baby lay gasping and suffocating at his feet like a tiny landed minnow.

Gwen turned to him to speak again and he took the lollipop from her hand, crunched it between his molars and then grinned at her, handing back the remaining shard on its paper stick. She liked these small, exclusive familiarities, he knew, liked sharing his spoon or his toothbrush, enjoyed the ostentatious intimacy of licking a swelling drop of ice cream from his wrist, or passing chewing gum mouth to mouth. Or carrying his child, he thought, and found himself shaking his head involuntarily, as if the thought could be dislodged like water from his ears. He desperately needed her to listen.

'Tell me honestly what you want.' Gwen began to peel at the damp stick with a fingernail. 'I go mental when *they* ask because they're so judgemental and it's none of their business, but it's different just us. This is our decision.'

'Okay,' began Nathan slowly. 'Well, right now we're talking about, like, a grain of rice.'

Spoken by James or Julia, this would have tripped Gwen into a spasm of white rage, but alone with Nathan, she did not feel defensive. Nathan was not a threat. To compare it to a grain of rice did not reduce it to the insignificance of a grain of rice. Her chin lifted a fraction.

'But it's actually more like a grape by now than a grain of rice. So okay, what if you did cast the deciding vote? What if it was your body?' He noticed that her hands slipped beneath her jacket to her lower belly, still muscled, still firm. It was unimaginable that beneath the sleek concavity of her navel could be anything so sinister and alien. Then her hand moved from her own stomach to his, demonstrating, inviting.

He lay down on his back, though the hard ground was cold beneath him. It was easier to speak freely if he shut her out, and instead watched the crimson capillaries of his closed eyelids. 'We've talked about it. I think to have it would be a major-league mistake. I can't make you do anything.' This was the dutiful line, and he discharged it with feeling. 'But I think it would be a huge mistake. We're way too young. It's a nightmare. Neither of us has finished school, and I'd want any son of mine to have everything I have. We've been insanely privileged, really. And I'd want to provide my kids with what I've had, you know, educationally, and travel, I've lived in two countries already . . .' Here he tapered off because, apart from having a vague awareness that his parents had argued over his own monstrously expensive school fees, he was at a loss to articulate the innumerable ways in which he felt ill-equipped for parenthood. It came down only to this – he didn't want it. He *could* do it, he felt. If there were nuclear war, or the aliens came and it fell upon him to repopulate the earth with his bevy of flaxen-haired warrior-women, he would step up. But unless he found himself in those circumstances, where in any case he would have awesome weapons and iron-hard biceps and a life-and-death battle against evil forces, and the cameras never showed screaming infants but instead dwelt on the necessary and heroic adrenaline-charged trysts amid the rubble; unless it would be like that, he did not want children. Not now, maybe never. Panic like a trapped sparrow fluttered in his chest.

'I know,' she nodded in enthusiastic agreement, as if warming to an established theme, 'I know, totally. And we could have waited and got married first and been all organised and planned and – but I mean, this happened now, so plans change.'

It had not escaped Nathan's notice that she had begun to speak as if their lives together were inevitable, already planned and committed. Just weeks before, he remembered her saying something about a possible barbecue, if they were still together by summer. At the time he had been touched, and happy that she saw their relationship continuing. He was at his best with a girlfriend, fortified by the knowledge that there was one person who would dependably choose him first. But now the conditional tense had been entirely abandoned. He had, apparently without noticing, acquired a wife. Still, they could not talk sensibly if she was defensive. 'I never knew you wanted kids so young,' he said carefully.

'I guess I hadn't thought about it until this happened.' She had flopped onto her back beside him but sat up again, speaking urgently. 'And maybe some parts aren't ideal but it just feels right, it's like my whole life is clear suddenly, and makes sense. I know I probably sound crazy but it's like it was meant to happen. This is *everything*.'

He gave a dry chuckle, frowning and pinching the bridge of his nose, a position in which he looked, for a moment, exactly like his father. He sniffed. His eyes were stinging in the sun and watering, inexplicably. 'This was meant to happen, you think?'

'I know I sound insane. And even a few days ago I would have said it's the worst luck in the world but yes, really really *really* I think this is my good luck. I have never felt more certain of anything in my life, I was meant to have this little grape, I'm its mother already. I feel it. It wasn't what I planned but now it's happened.' She beat a small fist above her heart, tightly clenched. 'I feel it, this is who I'm meant to live for. I'm not against it or anything, if you'd asked me before I would have said I'd totally have an abortion and feel relieved and we'd plan our lives all neatly and go to university first, blah, blah, blah, but I don't think things happen like you plan, do they? And this way I'll take, like, six months or a year out now, and then go back to everything and go to uni a year late and just start my job one year later. It will be like, my gap year.'

'I don't think having a kid is much like a gap year. It's not like, I don't know, counting starfish on some eco mission in the Philippines. It's not hiking the Inca trail.'

'But I would never want to hike the Inca trail. Don't look at me like that, you're making me laugh and I'm being totally serious. I'm not that type, I'm a homebody. Compared to most of the country we're rich, really, and obviously I'll get a job part-time or whatever, but I know my mum will help look after it once it's here, because she'll want me to go back to school. They were probably going to have a baby themselves.' She lifted her chin, defiant, and an indecipherable expression crossed her face. Her eyes flashed. 'Now they won't have to.'

Nathan glanced at her oddly. 'Isn't your mother, like, fifty?'

'No!' Gwen looked wary. 'She's forty-seven.'

'I mean, it now seems fairly obvious the men of the Fuller family have supersperm –' here Nathan paused, dusting lint or perhaps falling confetti from his imaginary epaulettes – 'but I don't think even supersperm can do much with forty-seven. Why do you think they'd even want another kid anyway? In five years my dad will be *sixty*. There's no way. They're just getting rid of us and starting their new phase or whatever, it would be craziness. My dad goes on about whisking your mom off into the sunset to hear Scriabin or Messiaen or whatever. He can't wait to be done with school fees.' Nathan reverted to their own case. 'And what if taking the Pill has like, fried it in there?'

'They might have done. They *might*.' Tears threatened.

'Okay, okay, if you say so they might.'

'They won't any more!' She stroked his arm and her voice softened. 'We make such a good team. We've grown up more than our friends already, think about Katy or Charlie or anyone. We've had to.'

Nathan had no other way to get through to her, and could not raise his voice. She shifted slightly, and her shadow fell across his face so that after the dazzling glare of the sunshine he could see again, and with this fleeting clarity of vision he spoke, as frankly as he dared. 'I'm not ready for a baby. I'm not ready to be a father. I, I just don't want to. Please don't – I *can't*.'

'I think you're ready. I think you'll be amazing.' She lay down beside him again and inched closer, curled on her side, one leg slung over his, her hand resting lightly on his chest. After a moment he heard her breath change and realised, startled, that she had fallen heavily asleep.

When on the warpath both his parents were formidable in their own way, but his father's love for him was vast, he knew, and could conquer cities. James would always protect him. He had not felt able to present Gwen with some home truths, as his father had instructed, nor to threaten, as his mother had commanded, but at least all the adults were in agreement and he had only to survive down this topsy-turvy rabbit hole a little longer; parents were parents and ultimately she would not be allowed to go through with it. Surely there was no need for his throat to tighten like this; no need for the tears that now threatened, again, again.

The sun had moved and bright stripes now fell across Gwen's face. As carefully as he could, he manoeuvred himself from beneath her hand and sat up, leaning forwards so that the shadow of his back would protect her pale, unaccustomed skin. For the sake of the imaginary film crew he dropped his head into his hands, an exquisite picture of broken, masculine despair.

TWENTY-EIGHT

'Please don't even joke about deliveries. This obviously cannot happen.'

'Well, obviously not,' Pamela snapped, her voice made tinny by the speakerphone. 'Someone has to knock some sense into her. I can't believe Nathan was such a bloody wet blanket about it, I told him what to say.'

James and Pamela had been speaking every day for the last terrible fortnight, so she was well aware that there had been no change. Gwen had moved beyond the reach of all reason, as if beneath a dome of thick glass through which nothing, no sound, no sense, could penetrate. She had the blank-eyed conviction of the religious zealot, and the zealot's placid, maddening pity for those who didn't see the light. She was having the baby, she could do it, she'd been reading about it on the Internet, she had an instinct, a second sense, they just needed to have faith. James found it hard to look at her. How was it possible that one spoiled, angry teenager had wrested control of all their lives?

'Anyway,' Pamela went on, 'speaking of deliveries, you delivered our boy back to school. He sounds like a different child, you'd think he was at Disneyland. It's heartbreaking. My beloved little boy. I'm driving on the freeway in the sunshine and I was feeling such lightness thinking, Yes, he's going to be okay, my baby's going to be himself again, but now I'm questioning the wisdom of his absence. He should be processing, he's deeply in denial. It's dangerous. He should be fighting to prevent it before it's too late, that's the key here, isn't it? You can't do anything from a place of denial. For God's sake, he can be home a few weeks and then go back to boarding once it's dealt with – he's the only one with any influence, he's got to tell her as many times as it takes that she's being a bloody moron. I don't know what went wrong when they spoke on the Heath, I couldn't have prepped him any better but when I spoke to him just now he sounded manic and was wittering on about spending his gap year volunteering in a South African clinic. It's out of sight and utterly totally bizarrely out of mind.'

'Gotcha.'

'That's what Gwen said. Ha, ha. Anyway, so you see. I did mention that by the time this supposed gap year rolls around he'll have a six-month-old and won't be gapping anywhere, but it didn't seem to register. Total denial.' In the background James could hear the voice of the satellite navigation commanding Pamela to keep left ahead. 'But between us, I will say I hated making every word of that speech to him. I don't want to be Mean Mummy, the voice of doom and responsibility, but I was trying to scare him. Surely she'll listen to him if he's insistent enough, if he collapses when they talk face to face then he must email her from school like I've instructed. That is, assuming she can read. I've written him a draft. I want my baby travelling the world, carefree, with girlfriends in Argentina and Italy and Australia and Japan, learning his heart, expanding his horizons. I always tell him, if you call all your girlfriends "Darling" it will save you the trouble of keeping their names straight. You know something, he's having that bloody gap year if it kills me, whatever I said to him. If she wants it so much she can look after it. What was the point of – wait, what? One second, the road's – I need to read the signs. The satnav's saying north–south and the road's saying east–west. Okay, right. What was I saying? Oh, yes. I wanted him to fly. I did not envisage him trapped in the suburbs with a sulky little teen bride and a bawling bundle. It's not what I wanted for his *soul*.'

'I hope you didn't make teen-bride jokes with Nathan. We've had enough dumb moves.'

'Are you kidding? I told him I'd disown him for his stupidity. Luckily it hadn't crossed his mind, he sounded suitably horrified. Why the bloody bollocks is there an exit here? One second. I'm going to call you back, I've gone wrong.'

Something had gone wrong for Pamela lately, and not simply with her navigation. Her very identity was in conflict.

Her office at the clinic was a parlour. No hierarchical furniture arrangements, no barriers of desks or intimidating swivel chairs that spoke of diplomas and educational advantages and a disconnection from the common lives of those she sought to help. Instead, soft, womanish furniture – soft sofas, pairs of matching, soft egalitarian armchairs. And in this safe, cushioned space women cried and cried about men. About what had been done to them. About what had been sown in them by men. Biology itself dictated who was taking possession of whom; that was the oldest metaphor, the oldest reality. It was there in the syntax – women were never the subject, only the object, subject to a man. And yet two brains make a sequence of decisions; two bodies unite and two people should face the consequences. With the women in her office Pamela sympathised, and raged, and helped. The men must be made to take equal responsibility. They must.

But – when she thought of Nathan, when she considered her sweet son, his puff-chested naivety, his ebullience, his grin, she felt that something essential had been stolen from him that he had simply been too innocent to guard. Gwen, predatory and conniving beyond her years, had entrapped him. Some women did, we were not all passive, not all united in benign and supportive sisterhood, after all. Seeking revenge upon her mother, or a means to get her claws irretractably into Nathan (for he was manifestly out of her league, only available because of this accident of circumstance, of this Pamela felt quite certain), or perhaps just wanting a warm, responsive living dolly to cuddle, she had attacked – 'mugged' was the best word – had mugged Pamela's little boy. It was almost as if – she toyed with the word that had risen spontaneously to the surface. No, all right, she conceded, defensive against herself, it wasn't quite like that. But something like it. Certainly a violation.

She had not gone wrong. She found her exit and after leaving the slip road redialled James, who answered immediately and said, 'Look, maybe he should be around but you can't imagine how godawful it's been in the house with Julia and that girl at each other's throats, I just wanted him out of it. The boy deserves some peace and quiet to study now.'

Pamela whistled through her teeth. Ahead she saw a drive-thru Dunkin' Donuts and realised with a flash of grateful recognition that a large iced coffee would elevate this journey from tedious to transcendent. She slowed and turned, her mood already transformed. 'What a trip. Do you remember when he begged for that Japanese fighting fish? And then he forgot to clean it out and it suffocated. I retract what I said, I actually think it's a gift that he's away during the week and he can breathe. Charlie came into his room while we were on the phone and he sounded so happy to be with his friends again. They're good boys, with all their high fives and weird Masonic handshakes.'

'I asked the other day if he'd told Charlie about the baby and he looked at me like I'd lost my mind and I thought, You know what? Let him have his denial. If we can't change her mind in the next few weeks he won't have much longer to be a kid.'

'Oh, Jamesy,' Pamela breathed, back in the seductive tone she assumed when she felt he was no longer opposing her. He could picture her quite clearly leaning forward, steepling her fingers and offering beyond them the musky darkness of a substantial cleavage, and an outrageous pout of her lips. In fact she was idling at the mouth of the Dunkin' Donuts takeout lane, reading the menu with greedy pleasure. 'He'd still be a baby. He'd just be a baby with a baby. Which is precisely why you cannot let it happen. We're depending on you now, all these random people are your bloody responsibility. Please give your son a kick up the arse and get him to fucking deal with it.'

TWENTY-NINE

Philip had been disappointed in Julia before, saddened that in her guilty indulgence she succumbed to Gwendolen's rages. Gwen had been sent to a progressive school at which the delayed gratifications of discipline and academic success were sacrificed in favour of immediate comfort and cosiness, and which placed primary emphasis on the value of imaginative self-expression, time that elsewhere might have been devoted to the studying of parts of speech, or long division. Even so, Gwen had never been made to go to lessons, nor to do what little homework she had, nor to help her mother around the house. She had not been taught, or helped, to see her mother as a differentiated individual, for both Julia and Gwen found pleasure in the obsessive and intricate fulfilling of Gwen's needs, and this shared interest bound them. She had never been told no. Ever since Daniel's final diagnosis, Julia had devoted her life to smoothing away tiny quotidian discomforts like the ultimate, inexhaustible celebrity fixer, toiling to compensate for that one, huge, unrelenting sorrow. But giving Gwen what she wanted did not mean it was what she needed. 'Babies protest if one confiscates the steak knife they've grabbed,' Iris had observed, during one of their lengthy analyses. 'It doesn't mean one lets them play with weapons.'

Philip greed and had always agreed – Julia ought to have confiscated the knife long ago, and had the foresight and strength and conviction to withstand the howls. To parent well, sometimes one makes one's children unhappy, yet Julia had never had any ambition for her daughter's future besides a non-specific 'happiness'. *She doesn't have to be an astrophysicist, all I want is for her to be happy.* She spoke of it as though such a state somehow precluded hard work, or discipline, or focus. He and Iris discussed it interminably. Weren't there happy astrophysicists? But Philip had always dissuaded Iris when she announced her intentions of wading in, and for that he too now felt complicit. They should have spoken. He should have braved Julia's unhappiness by speaking out – he himself was guilty of the same indulgence.

It was Passover and Passover was somehow unavoidable, even for so lax and assimilated a family. James's suggestion that they 'pass on Passover' this year was tempting but was as unrealistic as cancelling Christmas. And so they were assembling at Iris's house for the first time, aping normality, just a fortnight after the bombshell. Iris would almost be choked by the commands she wished to issue, by the speeches she longed to give, and Philip alone would hear them all, over and over on a loop inside his head, for she was forbidden from challenging Gwen tonight. Julia had already warned them both, *It's not the place to attack her, if we want her to see sense then ganging up will backfire, if this really has to happen then let's just have a nice family evening,* but restraint was not Iris's forte. She would need an outlet, and there was no such edict in place against attacking Philip.

'You can spare me the sanctimony,' Iris told him sharply when he arrived, though he hadn't spoken. She signalled towards the kitchen with the paper-wrapped bunch of crimson tulips he'd presented. 'Go through. If you hush me again I shall go wild. I'll be shtum, as instructed, just don't repeat it. Don't even think it.'

It would not help for him to say, 'I didn't say anything.' She had heard his thoughts. Together, they had exhausted every iteration of every argument. So much of their map was covered in this old terrain; familiar pitfalls and ravines into which they fell and then revolved together uselessly. They were trapped in their old roles, and their own selves.

Gwen appeared behind her grandmother holding a bowl of cashews, which she was posting into her mouth with the regular swipe of a metronome. Her lovely hazel eyes were blackened with too much make-up, her freckles partially erased with something powdery and pale. 'Grandpa,' she said, smiling uncertainly from beneath her lashes, and wiped a salty hand on her jeans before coming forward to embrace him with her free arm. 'Cashew?'

'Not just yet, thank you. How are you, *maidele*?'

'Fine. A bit . . . have to keep eating or I feel sick.' She coloured.

Philip watched Iris drift upstairs without obvious purpose, repelled away from their granddaughter like a slow, elegant magnet. Keeping Iris silent would be impossible if Gwen kept referring to her pregnancy, even obliquely. Gwen barely seemed abashed. She was almost jaunty. He felt an urgent longing to go home.

In the kitchen he found James, laying the table. As they exchanged greetings Philip held out his hand for a bunch of cutlery, to help.

'No, it's almost done, thanks. How are you?'

Philip lowered himself into the chair he hoped Iris would permit him to occupy for the evening. She had strong ideas about seating plans and might well, though it was only family, have a configuration for this dinner scrawled on the back of a notecard. She was not above asking people to move, if they'd installed themselves somewhere that displeased her. 'Fine, thank you. How have you all been?'

James gave Philip a long look. 'Put it this way. Blood. Frogs. Pestilence. Cattle disease. Whatever. It all sounds better than twenty-four hours in our house. I must tell you, I'm ashamed. I feel I should apologise to you for my son's part in all this. You and Iris must have been very shocked.'

'Yes,' said Philip simply. 'But you have no need to apologise.'

'Well, I'm deeply sorry nonetheless. And now we must set it all aside this evening to contemplate the Exodus, so I'm told. I've been deputised as bartender, can I get you something? I intend to drink heavily, I advise you to join me.'

'Nathan's not here this evening?'

'No, we decided . . . he's studying at his friend's house for the night. I felt . . . Do you know where the corkscrew is? I just felt he needed . . .' James seemed unable to complete any of these sentences. It seemed likely that Nathan was avoiding Gwen, or all of them, and Philip found it hard to blame him. He too had dreaded this evening. He began the arduous process of standing from his seat and abandoned it with relief when James said, 'Here it is. There's only red, for the Seder.'

'Red,' Philip said. 'Thank you.'

Philip did know where Giles had kept the corkscrew, as well as the several other places between which it migrated in the time since Iris had reclaimed sole stewardship of this house, none of which were where he himself had filed it when he'd lived here, on the shelf beside the bottles. Giles and Iris had shared a disdain for his regime and though it had been many years since Giles had moved to Provence, much of the disarray he'd introduced still remained.

Giles had died shortly after moving to France full-time, and the two states – being dead and residing in a French farmhouse – had fused in the family lexicon so that between Philip, Daniel and Julia, one had become a euphemism for the other. It was not kind. Philip had in fact been friends with Giles, and Daniel had also been on cordial terms with him, but the term had nonetheless evolved and stuck. Philip could only hope that, as a man who'd loved the reassuring intimacy of a private joke, Giles would have been forgiving. Daniel had spoken of moving to France himself in the last months of his illness, and had studied his father's countenance, insisting, with his eyes, upon a small returned smile. Cool, insouciant, hiding his fear to spare them. His brave boy. *It's an obscenity that he is gone and I'm still here.* With effort, Philip recalled himself to the kitchen, and to James.

Philip liked James. James was likeable. He put Julia at ease, and made her laugh. This year she had become beautiful again, recalling the fragile, striking girl she had been when he'd first known her, where for years she had begun to look – it was Iris's uncharitable word, though he had had to admit a truth to it – slightly haggard. Now she looked young again, and luminous. James exuded a sort of Viking strength and vigour and, searching for a description, Philip found his first true use for the term 'in rude health'. He understood, choosing to steer his thoughts firmly away from his own son's swift waning and diminishing, why Julia would be drawn to such a man. Now, under extraordinary circumstances, James was proving himself over and over, tested in his kindness, his generosity, his understanding. He had found a clinic, he'd spoken to the psychologist in his department, he'd been the one to source online videos for Gwen to watch, to help her understand the realities of teenage motherhood. Not once, Julia said, had he raised his voice. He was kind to Gwen, and liked her. He understood that gentle steadiness was their only hope for persuasion. He was taking care of all of them. Still. Daniel.

'Pamela told me that she dispatched her travel agent to hunt you down. I'm sorry about that, she's not very good at taking no for an answer. I don't think the assembly will be for you, if that's okay to say. It's not for me, anyhow.'

'Yes, she sent along a great deal of unusual literature. I'm afraid Joan, the woman she sent, was rather misled to believe that I was simply a nervous traveller in need of a little coaxing so she was terribly embarrassed once she realised. I tried to reassure her that I was interested to hear the details nonetheless. Apparently –' he began to laugh – 'Joan's had terrible trouble finding a source of dairy-free croissants for the breakfasts. It's made the hotel manager very cross.'

'I think hearing about any of it would make me mad, too. Julia's just upstairs, by the way, fixing some sort of formatting issue on Iris's laptop.' James set a glass down before Philip, but at that moment everyone came in together, Iris shooing Julia and Gwen before her and demanding, 'Can we sit down, now?' as if it had been someone else occupied upstairs for the last half-hour.

They sat and raced through a perfunctory Haggadah reading led by Philip, prompted intermittently by Julia. Iris had forgotten the horseradish and they were forced to settle for the closest thing in the refrigerator, a squeezy bottle of yellow American mustard. It was then discovered that she did not have a shank bone either, but after scrabbling in the cupboard Iris presented Philip with an organic lamb-flavoured stock cube, wrapped in shiny purple foil. She had not cooked, but instead had bought lime-marinated chicken wings and red quinoa studded with tart currants, pre-made, in the Selfridges Food Hall. Philip had two helpings of salad, which he did not prepare for himself at home and so felt duty bound to consume, for its phytonutrients, when it was served to him elsewhere (and for the same reason, he had taken a punishingly large piece of parsley during the Karpas.) Work had seemed a neutral topic and he enjoyed a quiet discussion with James about a VBAC uterine rupture earlier in the day, called to a halt when Gwen, overhearing, said it was gross and could they stop, please, and he had then realised his own insensitivity. More than once he noticed James and Julia holding hands beneath the table. By contrast, Julia and Gwen did not speak to one another directly, except for a brief, bitter exchange overheard as they were ladling out soup together. He sensed Iris's mounting incredulity that Julia, while clearly seething, would not allow anyone to acknowledge the pregnant teenage elephant dominating the room. The evening had a hallucinatory edge – conversation was polite, brittle, utterly empty. Between Julia and Gwen hummed invisible electric wires of resentment, studiously ignored by everyone else. It was painfully, ludicrously English, and he wondered how James could stand it. James's praise for everything on the table irritated Iris, he noticed, though she demanded this same excessive flattery from her own family. Later James helped to clear the plates, and Philip observed Iris's disapproval of this, too, watching her dismiss it as both unseemly and overfamiliar. His son had compromised her granddaughter – he was implicated, and culpable, and entirely unwelcome at her dinner table. Philip wished sometimes to be liberated from his understanding of Iris – when they were in company together her feelings sometimes crowded his out; spoken in her rich and strident voice, they were frequently louder inside his head than his own mild thoughts and observations. He was tired.

THIRTY

The announcement, later in the evening, came as a surprise.

'We are all family here, after all,' said Iris, looking with undisguised irony from Julia to James who paused, arrested in the act of reaching for another macaroon. Her eyes slid over Gwen who was sitting primly, hands folded in her lap, and came to rest finally on Julia again, who was refilling Philip's water glass.

'As everyone's assembled I would like to say something important. I've decided I'm selling the house.'

'You always say that, Granny.'

'There's no need for you to move just yet, is there?' Julia asked.

'It's not a question of need. I'm moving. I've got a good buyer, a developer. She's the right person.'

'What do you mean, you've found someone already? When?'

'As it happens we exchanged this morning. She's happy not to dawdle, which was exactly what I asked for. There's really very little to do – if I'd known how easy it would be I would have done it years ago. I want options, and I want to be in a position to – who knows what the future holds.'

Nobody spoke. Philip, Julia saw, looked stricken. He said nothing, but was now gazing down at his hands, their joints stiff and swollen, though he would rarely admit they bothered him. She felt an urge to defend him but could think of nothing to say that would not diminish or shame him. He did not move or look up. Eventually Gwen said, 'But Granny, I really don't think it's a good idea for you to move, everyone loves your house, and you're so close to us.' More quietly, 'And it's where Dad grew up. Don't sell it. I think you should think more about it.'

'Where will you go?' James asked.

'I've found a flat in St John's Wood. Well, off the Finchley Road, in actual fact. Really, I don't know why you are all gawping at me, you can't have thought I'd stay in this enormous house for ever and I'm not waiting until I'm wheeled out of it. I want to be able to walk to Regent's Park. I want to be closer to town. I liked Giles's flat in Bayswater before he gave it up, it was convenient, and I want to have a management committee to deal with the roof and the hallway carpets. I want the financial freedom to be able to – I don't intend to spend my seventies enslaved to the running of a house, I have far better things to do.'

'But it's your seventies, Iris, not your nineties.'

'Regardless,' said Iris primly.

Beside her Philip still had not spoken. It seemed he'd known as little as anyone else. Surely this house was his, too? How could Iris just sell it without his consent? And why? Strolling through Regent's Park was not a convincing argument when she currently lived on Hampstead Heath. Gwen had not understood what it meant to exchange, Julia saw with exasperation, and it would have to be broken to her that her grandmother's house was all but gone, and further discussion pointless. Gwen needed support and stability to face the choices ahead, not further upheaval and insecurity. At that moment, Gwen scraped her chair back.

'I'm *desperate* for the loo,' she announced unnecessarily, and then trotted out into the hall, one hand now cupped against an invisible bump.

Iris tutted. 'What a mercy she reminded us all she's pregnant, we've been talking about something else for all of twelve seconds. How remiss of us.'

Julia caught James's eye and began, despite herself, to laugh. James shook his head; he too was fighting a smile. Just as Julia felt that giggles might overwhelm her Gwen returned and James straightened his face and stood up abruptly. 'It's been a great night, thank you. *Le shana haba'ah be* Finchley Road. And it's getting late. Philip, shall I give you a ride back?'

Julia and Iris looked up at him in surprise. Gwen stood in the doorway, yawning widely.

'That would be lovely, thank you,' said Philip. He had not joined in the laughter. He leaned heavily on the table and rose, slowly, to his feet.

When they were alone, back in their own kitchen, James asked Julia, 'Did you know she was doing that? Philip seemed stunned, in the car.'

'I don't understand, surely it's half his. She can't just sell without asking him. He bought it before they even married, I think.'

'It must be in her name.'

'But whoever's name it's in, doesn't common courtesy require you to at least ask your former husband about selling the family home? Your best friend, supposedly? She's been there –' she began to estimate – 'Giles lived there with her for a few years after he sold his flat, I think, before he moved to France –' She allowed herself a small smile here, at the phrase, but did not pause to explain and in any case, in this instance she was referring to his actual move to France – 'and before then all those years with Philip. Daniel was born in that house. What an awful thing to announce just like that. It's classic Iris. You know that for ages we didn't even know if they ever actually got divorced? They made it impossible to ask. And then in the end it turned out that the divorce came through exactly around the time she and Giles were breaking up anyway. It was all part of their act, you know, how unusually civil it all was. Oops! We almost forgot to divorce.'

'It's not very civil to make unilateral decisions.'

'No.'

At that moment the phone rang. 'It's Granny,' Gwen shouted, from upstairs. 'She wants you, Mum.'

Julia picked up the kitchen phone.

'You needn't have looked at me like I'd grown a second head this evening,' Iris snapped, without preliminaries.

'I'm sorry, I was just a bit surprised.'

'Well, lots of things are surprising. I was surprised to discover that my sixteen-year-old granddaughter thinks it's reasonable to have a baby, but I've adapted,' said Iris shortly. 'Now I'm equipped for bribery and corruption – art college, a gap year, whatever her little heart desires if only she abandons this insanity. And if she does have the bloody thing it won't have to be dragged up by its bootstraps, not that I will tell her that at present.'

'Oh, Iris, surely that's not—'

'I have several reasons, none of which I owe it to you to explain. It's my house, to do with as I wish.'

'Of course, I know that. But I really hope it won't be necessary—'

'So you say, and yet the days pass and nothing changes. I dearly hope I'm wrong. Thank you for coming this evening,' Iris finished stiffly. This formality was intended to be wounding. 'Tell Gwendolen I'll call her over the weekend. I sincerely hope this family-therapist person knows her onions.' She rang off and Julia shrugged, in response to James's look of enquiry. Her mother-in-law's self-righteousness, her generosity, her ominous prophesies – Julia could not face discussing any of them.

THIRTY-ONE

The gabled redbrick mansions of Fitzjohn's Avenue were built in the late nineteenth century for the great and the good of Hampstead; spreading Gothic piles with grand staircases at their hearts, down which the bustled daughters of ship-owners and silk magnates and wine merchants could sweep towards waiting carriages. Now, the great and the good of Hampstead trudge up these stairs to try and understand their own unhappiness, for these palaces have been carved into a warren of magnolia consulting rooms for Freudians and Jungians and Kleinians and, in the case of number 88, for three Independents, two marriage-guidance counsellors and one Dr Rhoda Frankel, clinical psychologist, family therapist, Wesleyan graduate and grandmother, she'd said on the phone, of seven. Her voice was warm, her accent broad Long Island, and Julia had appreciated the fact that, upon hearing that her sixteen-year-old daughter had recently been impregnated by a newly acquired de-facto stepson, Dr Frankel had not offered a non-committal, therapeutic 'mmm' but instead whistled through her teeth and said, 'Well, *that*'s not easy.' Her photograph on the Internet was of a bright-eyed woman in her middle sixties, broad-chested, and with a sharply cut bob of caramel hair that fell neatly either side of a pair of cherry-red plastic-framed glasses. She was all in navy, except for a long chain of complicated, interlocking lucite squares of neon green slung round her neck. Julia had looked into the eyes of this facsimile while on the phone to the original and, speaking as calmly as she could manage, yearned to collapse and weep like a baby in Dr Frankel's comfortably substantial arms.

Julia sat beside Gwen in the waiting room on a low, sagging, buttercup-yellow sofa before a glass coffee table tattooed with fingerprints, its stacks of curling *National Geographic*s long neglected now that passing patients instead hid their faces in their phones, busily online, resolutely pretending to be elsewhere. A spider plant cascaded dustily from a hanging basket in the window, above a vibrant aspidistra that was, on closer inspection, plastic. Gwen sat with her hands retracted into her sleeves and clamped between denim thighs. Her brows were knitted into a frown, her lips pushed out, her eyes fixed on a point somewhere in her lap. Her posture, her expression, her every movement conveyed, megaphone loud, that she had come on sufferance. *You are detestable*, Julia thought, *and you have ruined and continue to ruin my life, I should have had cats instead.* She noted with an anxious pang that Gwen looked woefully drawn and pallid – almost grey.

Julia found she was unable to break from the constant repetitions of her own case. The prosecution, or was she the defence? In planning this session she had appointed Dr Frankel as their saviour but was gripped by a new fear that the kindly American woman was to be her judge; that they were to receive not arbitration but a verdict and sentence. Gwen had gone back into their shared and precious past and had set fire to every room. *She's too young*, she rehearsed, *she has her whole life ahead of her.* And, without knowing for what she pleaded she returned to it over and over. *I fought with every breath to be two parents for you. Why are you so angry?* And – *Please. Please. Please.*

As she had been in her photograph online, Dr Frankel was all in dark navy blue, stouter than her image, her hair the same resolutely expensive caramel, her crimson glasses replaced with frameless ovals resting on the very end of her nose. She greeted them warmly by name, 'Gwen, Julia, do come in,' and gestured to a pair of narrow biscuit-coloured armchairs. She herself squeezed into an upright wooden chair opposite them, a ring-bound notebook on her crossed legs, an expectant smile for them as they settled. Gwen surprised Julia by arranging herself bolt upright, her hands neatly on her knees, an expression of anticipation on her face. Her head was cocked slightly to one side, as if listening for instructions. Dr Frankel turned to her.

'I'm sure you know, Gwen, that Mom and I had a brief chat on the phone when we set up this meeting, and so she's had a chance to tell me a little bit about what she feels has been happening, but I'm really interested to hear from you. I take it for granted that each of us has a different perspective, right?' Julia thought she saw Gwen offer the ghost of a nod. 'And I'm here to listen, and maybe to help everyone else find a way to listen too, in a way that might feel easier than when you're at home together. I'd like to hear why you're here, and what you hope to achieve. How did you make the decision to come today?'

'My mum wanted me to come.'

'Okay.'

There was a long silence. Julia's hope wavered.

'I understand. So it wasn't your plan to be here.'

Gwen shook her head.

'So then I'm thinking –' Dr Frankel leaned back and considered a point above their heads for a moment – 'I'm thinking then that it was quite a decision you made to show up, in that case.' Her gaze returned to Gwen. 'After all, you're here now. Our moms ask us to do a lot of things, and would you agree it's fair to say, as teenagers, we don't always do them?'

'I came today because you asked me to –' Gwen turned to address Dr Frankel – 'I came because she asked me to because it would show that I don't just *not do* stuff . . .' She blinked several times and cleared her throat but lapsed once again into silence.

Julia had not yet given her prepared speech. There had been so much she'd wanted to say in this hour – to Gwen, to Dr Frankel, perhaps also to herself. But something passed across Gwen's face that made her suddenly ask, 'Would you prefer to talk to Dr Frankel alone? I can wait outside?'

Gwen glanced up and met her mother's eyes for a moment. She nodded.

Julia stood. 'Okay,' she said brightly. To Dr Frankel, in her thoughts she whispered, *She's a baby*, and then one final time, *Please*. She slipped out.

Up Fitzjohn's Avenue on a late-spring afternoon, beneath the heavy spreading sycamores and horse chestnuts. At regular intervals are spaced several academies where north London's most privileged three-year-olds learn to read and write, are taught computer code and Mandarin in striped winter caps, or in summer beneath ribboned straw boaters. Today the little girls were in deep blue gingham dresses, woollen cardigans and navy elastic purse belts, the boys in miniature blazers and grey tailored trousers. Many emerged skipping, as yet unencumbered by their parents' weighty expectations. The pavements thronged with mothers and nannies. Where Gwen and Julia crossed, two black Range Rovers and a black Jeep were doubled-parked, badly, the traffic crawling up the hill behind this presidential convoy in their variously armoured vehicles. And babies were everywhere. In buggies and in slings, or toddling on reins attached to tiny backpacks, greeting older siblings at the school gates. Julia averted her eyes from this sea of tiny creatures, but as they walked she reached for Gwen's arm. This school uniform was royal blue. At primary school Gwen's had been red; almost, but not quite, as bright as her hair.

They were toiling up the hill towards the art-supply shop. Gwen had not known if her mother would agree to this extension of their outing, but she did not feel ready to go straight home, where nowadays they could never be alone. It had been Dr Frankel who'd suggested (in desperation, Gwen felt, after several other conversational dead ends) that mother and daughter spend more time together on activities that made them happy, and there was nowhere that brought Gwen as much joy as this paradise of pristine dyes and clay, and the promise of future projects. She did not know with any certainty which activities made her mother happy. Maybe playing the piano? A knot tightened in her stomach. Until recently, she had always believed that Julia's happiness lay simply in spending time with her, regardless of what they did – certainly that was what she'd always said. But in the last few days, Julia could barely look at her.

The remainder of the therapy session had not been an enormous success. Initially she'd felt her mother's presence hampered her ability to defend herself with any eloquence, but after Julia had gone Gwen felt a sudden tender home-sickness, and a longing to rush out to the waiting room and beg forgiveness for dismissing her. She hadn't wanted Julia herself to go away; only Julia's disapproval and disap-pointment. After that, guilt had stifled her and made her feel hot and snappish, and she had shut down the rest of Dr Frankel's valiant approaches. She had not deserved the professional kindness palpable in that room.

Now mother and daughter walked up the hill in silence. As they crossed Prince Arthur Road Julia reached out for her and they walked the rest of the way arm in arm, and though neither spoke, Gwen began to feel a slight easing of the pressure in her chest. She shuffled a little, shortening her gait to keep pace. On the threshold of the shop they separated. Gwen held the door open, shy, chivalrous. They made their way through Painting and Drawing, over to the temple's inner sanctum, Casting and Modelling.

'So what are we looking for?'

Gwen shrugged. 'Dunno. Just browsing.' She frowned over a package of 'skin tones' polymer clay with professional interest. She had been mixing her own flesh tones for years – this overpriced multipack was for amateurs. But next to it stood a tray of wire-tipped modelling tools with sleek wooden handles and on one of these she pounced, turning it over and over between her fingers as if rolling a cigar. It was sixteen pounds, an enormous sum. But it was double-ended and one tip, the needle, would be useful every day. Future promise lay in all these wares, the world a bit less lonely when she could sculpt and share it. She fished in the pocket of her cardigan for her purse.

'Mum.'

'Yes?'

'Do you still hate me?'

Julia looked stricken and Gwen felt fractionally heartened. Hope unfurled and blossomed when her mother reached to stroke her cheek.

'I could never hate you, my darling, you're the most precious thing in my world. You know that.'

Gwen nodded uncertainly, the cuticle of her little finger between her front teeth. After a moment she fingered a packet of frog-green modelling clay. 'I'm going to use this to make that massive green cactus thing in her office. I mean, that was so weird. It was like this giant looming *thing*.'

Julia smiled. 'It was rather phallic.'

Gwen began to giggle. 'And it had massive spikes!'

'I wonder what a Freudian would make of that.'

Laughter overtook them both, drawing looks of disapproval from the checkout girl. Julia covered her mouth, then turned away. A sob rose in her chest and she swallowed it down. Enough. For healing and for sanity, all that would have to end. She wiped her eyes, took a breath and turned back, resolute. Gwen's giggles petered out, uncertain.

Julia took Gwen's hand between her own. She raised it to her lips and kissed her daughter's dry knuckles, above the mulberry-coloured hearts and black stars that Gwen had idly inked upon the back of each finger.

'My darling, what do you really want? What does your gut tell you?'

Gwen looked down at her mother and blinked steadily. She said, no longer confrontational, but as calmly as she knew how, 'I have to keep my baby,' and her all-powerful condemning possessive made possible no other answer. Julia put her arms around her hunched, gangling little girl.

PART THREE

THIRTY-TWO

Iris swept Gwen and Katy upstairs into her bedroom where the bevelled-glass doors of the empty, lilac-papered wardrobes gaped open and the windows were now uncurtained. Bonfire heaps of clothing lay on the bed, on the floor, on the armchair; and on one bedside table stood a tower of small white boxes ominously printed in red with the words 'MOTH KILLER'. Each pile had been labelled with torn sheets of lined paper on which Iris had written queries and imperatives such as 'CHARITY?' 'KEEP!' 'DO NOT THROW!' 'MAYBE FOR SUMMER?' 'GWENDOLEN?' in her tense, sloping copperplate.

'You may take anything except from that chair – those I still wear. And if you would like anything from that heap by the wall then please show me first. There are a few pieces for your mother – the trousers would be far too short for you in any case. I can't wait to see the back of it all. I feel freer and freer as this exercise advances, I ought to have moved years ago.' She swept her arms out wide, a conductor acknowledging her orchestra. 'Anything you don't want just pop into that empty box over there to take to Norwood, with a few sachets of the moth murder.

I'm scrupulous but it would be mortifying to infect the charity shop.'

Gwen looked over at the cartons uncertainly. On each was printed a red bull's-eye and a rigid insect, various legs radiating in odd directions as it suffered electrocution, or rigor mortis. 'I don't think I should touch moth-murdering stuff, Granny, it might be toxic.'

'As you wish,' said Iris tightly. She turned to Katy. 'The world seems filled with gestational hazards these days. When I was pregnant with Gwen's father I was desperate to go to Vietnam and everyone was terribly difficult about it, worrying about stress and helicopters and gas, and nonsense like that. I'd never actually *been* a foreign correspondent – in truth, I don't really know what came over me but I was suddenly longing to go and it was still early days but it was clear that that was where the action was, especially after the Gulf of Tonkin. Of course the paper wouldn't have it. I told them, my husband is my obstetrician and he says there's no reason why not, women have babies in Vietnam, one's *brain* still functions after all, but then they gave me my column and that suited me far better in any case. And Philip Alden was awfully good about my wanting to go but of course men are always happier to have one stay at home, what-ever they say.'

Katy tucked her hair behind her ears, smiling in admir-ation and an evident fear that she might be required to respond intelligently about Vietnam, or pregnancy, or men. 'Yes,' she said, dark eyes blinking. 'Gosh. You were so brave.'

'Women must be brave, Katy darling, if we are to achieve anything at all. Cowardice and skinlessness are the enemies of female success. If one cares at all what others think one's done for. In any case, there will be crumpets in the bread bin when you pause. Assuming –' this to Gwen – 'that your mother hasn't done another wonderfully officious sweep around my kitchen and packed the bread bin. When you have a cache call me up.'

Alone in the bedroom, the girls exchanged incredulous glances. Iris had always had exquisite taste, even in the days in which she and Philip had been supporting his parents as well as managing their own mortgage, and she had kept almost everything. Already Gwen could see two Biba frocks, one in burgundy, the other lilac jersey and, from a still-earlier era, a yellow poplin blouse with an oversized Peter Pan collar. A vision of her future self arose – she could become stylish and eclectic and enviable, and could sashay to school next year in lace and silks. By then she would have an unimaginable new life, and a new, more sophisticated wardrobe seemed only fitting.

They began clearing the bed. Ruthlessly they discarded cotton shirts and office slacks. Then Gwen unearthed a boxy sweater in pale peach mohair and moments later Katy held up a slippery fuchsia blouse which Gwen, who did not wear pink, said she should keep.

'So how long will you be able to wear normal clothes?' Katy asked, folding the blouse with care. Gwen had confided in her only a week ago, swearing her to secrecy, and they had talked exclusively and exhaustively of the pregnancy ever since.

'Dunno, for ever probably, because I'm so insanely tall. I don't want to tell anyone at school till the end of term. My mum will tell the teachers then, and start planning next year and stuff.'

'Today's bump-watch, please?'

Gwen lifted up her jumper and Katy peered speculatively.

'Nothing, you're still super skinny. It's just so crazy. I think it will feel more real once you *look* pregnant. Is Nathan getting excited?'

'It's a bit early for all that,' said Gwen, suddenly vexed. She pulled down her jumper and returned her attention to the bed. This was a provocation from Katy, she felt, who was well aware that excitement had been thin on the ground in the Alden–Fuller household. In any case, how could any-one be expected to get excited about something more than half a year away? She dropped a belt into a pile of rejects.

'I'll take that if you don't like it.'

Gwen handed her the belt, and then returned in silence to her own heap. Katy's questions always pertained to Nathan. How did he feel, what did he want, would he 'stand by her' – closed-minded Katy had instantly reverted to the language of another century. Gwen had had to explain that pregnancy happened to two people, it was not for a woman to be 'stood by' or otherwise, and that she and Nathan were in total accord. This last may have been a slight exaggeration for he had so far resisted her attempts to bring him round to the idea of fatherhood, even in the abstract. The last few times they'd talked he'd grown panicked, twice had cried, and each time, to comfort and convince him, she assumed a depth of conviction she did not feel. But unlike the parents he never seemed angry, nor did he appear to blame her. Something had befallen them both, and he said he believed she was trying to make the best of it, even if his best and hers were not (yet?) in concert. He was still her boyfriend. Relations between them improved when she realised that all he wanted was to discuss it as little as possible; if she adhered to that stipulation everything continued between them, if not exactly, then almost as before. That morning she had taken time away from her own work to bake raspberry-and-white-chocolate muffins that might fuel his; he had eaten three and lifted her heart by declaring them (and herself, she inferred, by proxy), 'awesome, thanks'. When he was home he no longer chided her nor even seemed to notice if she played with her phone or doodled blog designs on the corners of her notes and this, conversely, encouraged her to focus in order to win back his notice. At first his disengagement had unsteadied her but she knew him, and knew how it would be. He would be incredible, once it became necessary for him to be incredible. The male instinct was to deal with what lay immediately ahead; he had exams and university decisions and these were all-consuming. The pregnancy would take them to Christmas; it was now only May. Katy had sworn secrecy and support and undying friendship, but today she was filled with irrelevant, childish questions, and Gwen had begun to wish she had not told her.

'It is actually ages, isn't it. I guess you found out majorly early.' Katy was twirling a glossy lock of dark hair round and round the end of her nose, thinking. Then she ventured, 'Aren't you scared? You must be, a bit.'

'I'm really not. I'm just excited to meet my baby.'

An opportunity offered, and rejected. Katy recognised the lie, for behind her eyes Gwen saw a willing empathy shut down; instead disappointment that she, long-trusted, wasn't to be trusted now. Katy would have said, *I know*; she would have stroked Gwen's hair and said again, stoutly, *You'll be wonderful, you're doing the right thing. It's natural to have wobbles, it doesn't mean you're making the wrong choice.* No one else would offer this reassurance. But how could Gwen confess that she struggled to focus upon what would inevitably follow this pregnancy? It was there in her peripheral vision, but when she turned her head it slipped away like a phantom and her mind would skip elsewhere, distracted, relieved. Far easier to daydream about how her classmates might react upon finding out, about how she might look by late summer, a neat, startling bump, a badge of distinction; a commanding unequivocal sign of adult womanhood. It was the pregnancy for which she had fought. What must come next – a baby, motherhood – was hazier, and harder to comprehend. Ludicrous, even. But to admit fear was to admit doubt, and if she admitted her doubts aloud, she knew, her outward conviction might crumble.

Katy held up a polka-dotted handkerchief, a peace offering. 'This is mega cute – maybe you could put this on the baby's head, like a bandana. It's all just so crazy. You have to tell me everything. I want to know every single thing.'

'So stop being so serious,' said Gwen crossly, but then relented and said, 'Obviously I'll tell you everything. But you'll see, so you'll know it all anyway.'

'I told you I'll come every day on my way home. I'll be, like, the fun auntie. And I want to come with you when you have scans, and help you buy things and get ready and everything.'

'I feel sick again, I'm sitting down. You can hold stuff up and show me.' Gwen sank heavily into the armchair, on top of an untouched pile of coats. It helped to imagine a future with Katy always there, involved. With her friend by her side it would be far less frightening to do whatever needed doing.

They worked on, exclaiming intermittently about gems found and horrors unearthed. At the back of a wardrobe Gwen spotted a small, scratched leather suitcase and she humped this onto the duvet. Katy was holding up a pair of white silk trousers when Iris herself appeared, and took these from her reverentially. She wore a misty-eyed expression, as if an old lover's photograph had slipped from the pages of a battered paperback.

'I bought those on holiday in Nice one summer. I'll keep them, I might wear those again. Ah, I have heard the mermaids singing, each to each, though they're not flannel, thank God, they're Pierre Cardin. Where on earth did you find that case? You've no reason to concern yourself with that,' she snapped, laying down the trousers, but Gwen, who considered her grandmother's presence to be sufficient permission, had already clicked open the thick brass buckle. The lid of the suitcase flopped back to reveal its torn and faded paisley-print lining, and six neat stacks of pressed and folded baby clothes.

'Granny!' Gwen breathed. 'Were those Dad's? Oh, *please* can I have them?'

'Absolutely not,' said Iris firmly, but was met by imploring looks from both girls, and a quavering lower lip from her granddaughter.

'No. Oh – *fine*. But I'd like to be clear that this does not constitute endorsement. Katy, I have not yet heard your opinion on the matter but I shall tell you for the record that I believe continuing with this pregnancy to be an act of self-sabotaging imbecility on my granddaughter's behalf, as she well knows. You may keep them if you insist. Lord knows what's in there. Your father's baby clothes, a baby blanket, and if I recall, an elaborately hideous collection of rather itchy cardigans knitted by Philip Alden's mother who had, as you will soon see, a great deal too much time on her hands.' She turned to go. 'I sincerely hope if they do anything they drive home a little reality. Those are clothes for a human, not a plaything. I am displeased.'

It was Katy who a moment later was wiping tears away and this decided Gwen's own course of emotional action, till then uncertain. She had many precious artefacts, but it had been so long since she'd unearthed anything new of her father's. A lump had risen in her own throat, but when she saw Katy crying she said firmly, 'Don't be silly.' Her father as an infant had not yet been her father; these were adorable but did not represent a person she could reasonably miss. She put her arm around her friend and realised, with a pounding heart, that it was possibly her first spontaneously maternal gesture.

Katy nodded and sniffed, wiping invisible mascara smears from beneath each eye with her ring fingers. 'I'm sorry. It's just, it's so nice. You might have pictures of your dad in some of these little outfits, and I just thought that when your baby comes you can take the same pictures, and – and that's really special. Oh, no, Gwen, please don't cry, I'm so sorry, please don't cry. They're beautiful. They're happy, as you said.'

They sat for a moment with their arms around one another. Gwen reached out reverentially to stroke a tiny playsuit in smocked white cotton, uneven mother-of-pearl buttons down its front. It was utterly unthinkable that a human was at that moment gestating within her, and would one day grow to fit these garments. Her throat constricted. She did not want to picture plump limbs within these tiny sleeves, nor the hot monkey cling of a tiny body. She wiped her nose inelegantly on her sleeve and said, 'I have to tell my mum, like, now – she'll be so shocked that there's stuff she hasn't seen, she's going to freak. And look at these, they're so gorgeous. I hope she's okay. She gets upset about my dad, you know. If she comes straight over when I text her and she's super sad do you mind hanging out with my granny just for a bit? Just for, like, ten minutes?'

Katy said that of course she wouldn't mind, Gwen's granny was fantastic, but that she would soon have to go in any case. Actually now, in fact. This had become urgently, pressingly true ever since Katy had seen those tiny, yellowing clothes, museum faded, inert, as lifeless as the man who'd once worn them. She was desperate to get on the Tube back to Totteridge where her own father, full-bellied and balding and a hale-and-hearty forty-five, would be there to give her a hug and to promise her, Scouts' honour, that he wouldn't die. Gwen's suitcase of Gothic, desiccating sleep suits, like the dead husks of abandoned snake skins, was intensely distressing.

'It's a sign,' Katy said firmly, retrieving her own sweater from beneath a pile of pillows. 'Even if your granny didn't want you to, your dad meant you to find them – he's looking over you and the baby.'

Gwen said, 'Mmm,' not very convincingly. She loathed such specific and improbable states as 'looking over', which evoked a nosy neighbour peering over a picket fence. She also disliked 'a sign', and particularly 'passed away', the latter because she felt it sounded somehow passive and a little foolish, as if her father had accidentally missed an exit on the motorway when, if anything, to die was to take the ultimate definitive action. And she did not like to have the pregnancy connected to her father. She had tried to tell herself he would be proud of her for choosing a hard, brave path but still, it seemed unlikely he'd go so far as to send gift baskets from on high. The only person who understood the delicate vocabulary of her bereavement was her mother. Gwen now needed urgently to speak to Julia. The girls parted, with equal relief. As soon as she could hear Katy downstairs taking polite leave of Iris, Gwen picked up her phone.

It rang and rang. Gwen hung up and immediately called back. Where was her mother? And why couldn't she sense, as of old, that she was needed? Gwen threw her phone onto the bed. The endless steady nausea was insupportable. Without Katy she no longer had the motivation to continue, and she felt hot, and teary, and possibly in need of a nap. She would take her treasures home, and she would wash them and iron them herself, and keep them in her room and she wouldn't allow her treacherous mother even to look at them. They were precious, and she could not let them frighten her with intimations of a flesh-and-blood reality to come. Julia did not deserve such relics. She was building a new life, and Gwen must do the same.

THIRTY-THREE

'This is no good, you know. By the time we reach the front it will have started,' Iris complained, shifting irritably from one foot to the other and peering around the group in front of them, searching for the source of the delay. She was with Philip at the O2 Centre cinema on the Finchley Road, waiting in line to buy their tickets for a documentary he was keen to see, about whales. 'Wales?' Iris had asked, puzzled, and Philip had clarified. On the assumption that an independently made wildlife documentary was unlikely to cause a box-office stampede they had not booked in advance, but when they arrived the queue snaked disconsolately around a Pac-Man configuration of security barriers. Iris glanced again at her watch.

'I don't think it matters a great deal if we miss five minutes. We know the gist.'

'You know the gist. Until five minutes ago I thought it was about scaling Snowdon.'

'If you prefer we could go downstairs to one of the places for some supper?'

Iris wrinkled her nose in distaste, as if he had suggested they forage for their dinner in the shopping-centre dustbins. 'Can't we go somewhere civilised every now and again? Coming to the pictures here is one thing but it's not exactly a culinary destination. In any case, I've utterly lost my appetite. This morning has quite literally sickened me. I feel ill.'

'Gwen seems —'

'Gwen is behaving like the stubborn infant that she is, and the most heartbreaking part is that she's so pleased with herself, and all the while she's careening towards a cliff. You should have seen her cooing over those baby clothes. She's overjoyed to be the centre of attention and what she doesn't realise is that she's simply ensuring in about seven months she will never be the centre of attention again. And that friend of hers is sweet enough but utterly air-headed and childish.'

'Well, they're children, so if they're a little childish you'll have to let them off.'

'I'd feel more comfortable if she had some contemporaries with a brain cell between them. Peer pressure ought to be what changes her mind. If she had some friends with a little ambition she would have made entirely different choices. If Julia had sent her to a decent school —'

'She's got a wonderful mother. And a kind stepfather. And us.'

'She'll need more than just us.'

They shuffled forward, the queue diminished by several faint-hearted patrons abandoning their positions, rather than any real progress at the tills. Iris tutted and moved her handbag from one shoulder to the other. 'Really, you would have thought the elderly ought not to have to stand around like this. That someone might let them— Oh, thank you so much. Yes, thank you. That's very kind. Come on –' she commanded, striding forward – 'thank you, yes. Thanks.

Now's the time to say if we're seeing this or not. Quick. Marine life, or we could give up and call it a night. Perhaps we should call it a night.'

'We're almost there.'

'I know, but I think I'm too depressed for fish. There are not one but *three* obstetric practitioners in Gwen's immediate family circle – I cannot understand how this was allowed to happen. How was it not put right, having happened? It's derangement. It's a tragedy. How am I expected to care about whales?' She had become grandly theatrical, which was a bad sign. But they had reached the front of the queue, and the moment had come to decide.

'I know. I do – we can give it a miss if you'd like.'

'I'm very tired,' said Iris, which was true, but an unchar-acteristic admission of fallibility. She stepped aside, back into the cheery mezzanine of the shopping centre. Philip followed her, apologising to a number of other patrons who had ceded their places to them.

They rode the escalators in silence. Then Iris said, hotly, as if he had contradicted her, 'It's a *travesty*. Gwen doesn't deserve— She's an innocent. She's an innocent and she has no idea, absolutely not the faintest idea, what's about to happen to her life. She thinks she'll have a dolly and all this gratifying attention she's commanded will go on and on, and instead her life is going to be torn limb from limb by ravening— I was going to offer anyway but if she nips it in the bud then I've told Julia I'll put her through art school. Tuition, accommodation, extra for blackmail, whatever it takes.' She stepped off at the bottom of the escalator and with an irritable gesture offered Philip a hand to disembark, which was accepted without comment. 'Are you walking or am I driving you?'

'You're driving me if you wouldn't mind. Of course it's a very generous idea, if they'd like it.'

'They're a bunch of ostriches, and I'm including the so-called adults in this situation. Mass inertia. Needless. *Needless.* And if she really goes through with this entirely dishonourable kamikaze manoeuvre I'm going to hire and subvention a nanny myself.' Iris began to hunt in her handbag for her car keys and Philip felt suddenly relieved to be going home. The whales could wait. He was weary, and Iris was in a dangerous temper.

'Do you remember that Italian au pair?' he asked, hoping to draw her back from the brink. It was sometimes possible to soften her, with care. 'May I hold your umbrella? You'll have a hand free. She was a nice girl. It was very helpful having someone.'

'Gioia. She was a bloody idiot,' said Iris shortly. She had located the keys and now set off at a clip into the dark car park. Philip strained to keep up, his knees singing in protest as he marched stiffly behind her, the umbrella angled forwards to shield Iris from the drizzle. A moment later she drew to an abrupt halt.

'Where is the bloody car?'

'Over there, I think. She was only homesick, wasn't she? Daniel liked her which was what mattered. She was good with him.'

'She left me high and dry, five minutes before I was due to join you in Paris for the weekend. Can you hold that thing a little higher, it's starting again. She was a selfish little girl. Ah, I see it there, thank goodness for the beeper thing. Giles had to bring Daniel out on his way to Bargemon.'

'Giles had to – what?' Philip slowed. He struggled to recall a summer, a weekend many years ago, a story from their canon of cherished stories. We were happy: here is Exhibit A. He lowered the umbrella, which was hurting his wrist. 'She brought him to us in Paris on her way to Naples. Gioia.'

'She was meant to, yes.'

'I don't understand.'

'Oh, darling, it just didn't line up.' Iris glanced at him, impatient or possibly wary. She seized the umbrella and held it rigidly upright in both hands. 'There was a coach that left from London and she was absolutely adamant about making her parents' wedding anniversary or some nonsense. It all ended on bad terms because she was a fool and I was cross and then I was absolutely in a fix. I couldn't leave the boy to travel by himself on the ferry.'

'Well, of course not but – I don't entirely understand. You left him with Giles, is that what you're saying? When you came to Paris?'

Iris had begun to walk again but Philip didn't move, and she was forced to turn around to address him. She had begun to look indignant. 'Yes, Philip, there's no need to sound so outraged, that's what I did. On balance it was expedient. You and I had had that awful row before you left and then you'd written a sweet letter about the two days you'd planned for us and I didn't think I ought to let you down. It's raining – can we talk about this in the car? Well, come and stand under this bloody umbrella then. Oh, *really*. Things were feeling a little unsteady. And it wasn't even a change of anyone's plans at all in the end, Giles just drove a slightly longer route to Bargemon, he was coming to France anyway. I couldn't exactly leave Daniel with the au pair when there was no au pair to leave him with. Look, I didn't want to cancel, and Giles offered to help me out of a fix and that was that. Why do you look so cross? He took his charge very seriously, I assure you – they had a wonderful time. Daniel told me all about it.'

Philip rubbed his eyes, slowly, and did not look up. 'You lied to me.'

Iris could think of no appropriate answer, for she and Giles had both lied to Philip a hundred times over the years, mostly about sex at parties or on assignments or for weekends in the Cotswolds, or late nights at work. She had always assumed Philip had taken for granted these many small deceptions. Calculating now, she realised that this revelation dated her affair with Giles long before it might otherwise have been suspected. Certainly years before the official record.

'You and Giles lied to me,' Philip repeated.

'It was only – this is madness, you and Giles were great friends later on. Please get under the thing.'

'You made my son lie to me.'

'Well, darling, there were other little white lies flying around in those days—' She halted, suddenly uncertain. This was dangerously close to heresy in the sealed, private world they'd spun; she was in high winds, and playing pre-cariously near to the cliff edge. The enchantment had kept them safe for almost five decades, a flexible, devoted love and companionship, enfolded in a cloak of tacit under-standing. She fell silent. The rules were the rules.

Philip said again, 'You made Daniel lie to me. He was a little boy. You put a lie between me and my son.'

'We had such a wonderful time that holiday, the three of us,' Iris said weakly. Philip's voice had broken as he spoke this last, awful and surely disproportionate accusation; she felt a tickle of panic that he had so misunderstood. 'He adored you, how can you think that anything could come between you—'

'Iris.' There was a pause as he removed his glasses, streaked and beaded with raindrops, flashing amber and saffron in the reflected light of slow-passing headlights.

'Better you had stayed with Giles,' he said quietly. 'Better some truth, finally, so there would be no, no *wound* between me and my son. Better anything than distance with my son, than a lie between us. He must have been so bewildered and you colluded with him, you and Giles, and made his father into a— I don't know, I don't know, I don't understand. And Daniel isn't here. He isn't here for me to tell him not to worry.' He took several steps backwards, unsteadily, away from her.

'We'll talk more in the car. Come on,' said Iris, turning decisively. 'Darling, this is madness, he was a child, he'd forgotten it by the time he'd had a crêpe and seen a little of Paris.' She felt perilously close to a full-blown row, something which had not happened, she now realised, since the day they'd finally signed their divorce papers. Or perhaps not since the day he had shouted at her for shouting at Julia for wearing black to Daniel's funeral. In any case, she couldn't stand to see him standing in this downpour, could not bear the way the rain had plastered his fine, white hair to his scalp, the way fat drops slipped down his cheeks like tears. Without glasses he looked vulnerable, and very old. How could Philip Alden be so old? He should not be out in this weather, at this time. She put her head down and strode the few remaining steps to draw him with her into the car. She turned on the engine, the heater, the heated seats. The first thing was to get him warm and dry, and then she could explain. But he had not followed her.

THIRTY-FOUR

It did not seem fair to involve James in her mother-in-law's unexpected packing but James presumed himself involved, and Julia was grateful. Whatever mattered to Julia was drawn without question into the inner circle of James's concern, a way of his she'd noticed and admired, early on. In any case, without his and Nathan's assistance the team would comprise only tiny, slender Julia herself; arthritic and unsteady Philip; and a queasy, ever more distractible Gwen, who at present did everything with irritating, self-satisfied lassitude. No doubt she would find several opportunities throughout the day to remind them that she couldn't lift heavy objects because she was pregnant, she couldn't join them for too many coffees or cups of tea because she was pregnant, she couldn't leave them a moment's peace to forget she was pregnant, because she was pregnant. For lightening the load and the atmosphere they needed James, even if no one else in the family would admit it.

The furniture would go with professional movers the following day, which was the formal date of sale, but there remained the *stuff*; velvet cushions the removal men were not permitted to touch; framed prints and pictures; three drawers of splitting Kodak photograph packets spilling muddled, slippery negatives; a great deal of musty, unused but beautifully pressed table linen; a white archive box of ancient telephones, from a black, mid-nineties cordless all the way back to an avocado Bakelite rotary, which enchanted Gwen. Supermarket bags of unidentifiable wires and chargers for items long discarded. Shadeless lamps in which expired bulbs wore a grey fuzz cap of static dust. A printer. A scanner. A cumbersome fax machine of sickly oat-coloured plastic with which Iris could not be enjoined to part, though it transpired that she only exchanged faxes with Philip, whom she also emailed, texted and instant-messaged. Box files containing hundreds of sallow, fading newspapers in which Iris had a byline. And books, and books, and books. Iris had supposedly been sorting and packing (certainly she had made frequent reference to her toils) and yet the house looked discouragingly unaltered. It had been the Alden family home in one configuration or another for decades. Julia had known of her mother-in-law's intentions for barely a fortnight, and this final exodus was supposed to be accomplished in a day.

'They'll do it all tomorrow if we add a few more hours to the booking,' Julia ventured, for the final time. She, James, Nathan and Gwen had arrived early as planned, armed with tape dispensers and scissors and marker pens, but she still nurtured the wild hope that Iris would permit the professional movers to do it all, and they could instead go to South End Green for eggs Benedict and cappuccinos. The man on the phone had quoted for the lot. They were thorough, he told her, she needn't lift a finger. His boys even packed the bog roll off the holder, don't you worry, love. Iris was having none of it. Boxes and bubble wrap had already been delivered.

'Darling, I won't have unknown gentlemen fishing around in my possessions,' trilled Gwen. Everyone laughed except James who would not, Julia knew, have dared even to smile at Iris's expense. Instead he rolled up his sleeves and began to construct the flat-packed cardboard boxes that were leaning in the hallway.

'Well, I won't,' Iris said, with an elegant and unapologetic shrug. She had dressed for the occasion in black slacks and a narrow-ribbed black cashmere sweater with a high turtleneck, unseen since the early years of their acquaintance. Unfamiliar enamelled bangles in cobalt and emerald clinked on her knobbed, narrow wrists – clearly this move had unearthed some long-lost, once-loved treasures. 'It would be ghastly to have them poking about. They'd manhandle everything and mix it all up and break things. I'd really much rather the family did it.' She kissed Julia, embraced Gwen and gave James a dry and unprecedented peck on the cheek. Julia felt briefly touched, until she remembered that Iris must also realise that James's presence was essential. 'Is Philip here yet?' she asked, prompted to remember the sweetest and most ludicrous manual labourer among them.

Iris kicked off neat, black rubber plimsolls and stalked back to the kitchen. Julia and Gwen followed her. 'Philip Alden's not here at present. Shall we start upstairs? Or here? Shall I make us some tea?'

Gwen sagged into a kitchen chair. 'It's *so* hot,' she said, which was true for no one except herself. 'I'm roasting.' She pulled her sweater over her head and fanned herself.

Julia averted her eyes in irritation. On the phone earlier Iris had made an unforgivable joke about giving Gwen the heaviest trunks to lift.

Iris nodded. 'Very well. Why don't you label boxes for us, that's a good, non-strenuous task. But you'll need to ask me as you go along, because the most important thing is to mark clearly the name of the room it's headed for, or it will all end up in the hallway there and be nightmarish. The rest of us can start in the bedroom. I've prepared piles. I'm rather pleased with my winnowing, there's a vast heap of *objets* to go to Norwood.'

'Shouldn't the writing be Philip's job? Maybe Gwen can fold things. He's been terribly elusive, by the way – is he all right? He's not answering my calls.'

'I'm sure he's right as rain. I didn't want to trouble him with all this – he's not coming. He can't lift anything anyway, he'd have been less than useless and got under our feet. And he hates me throwing anything away. We'd only have rowed.'

Julia started to say that she was sure Philip would nonetheless want to be included, but something in her mother-in-law's expression cautioned her, and she stopped.

'I don't see that it should take all that long if we're efficient. If you'll all come up with me perhaps someone could dismantle the computer, and then we'll start at the top.'

'I can do the computer, Granny.'

Gwen set off, and in the hall could be heard to inform Nathan that they were all to begin at the top of the house. Julia began to tidy the kitchen which was strewn on all surfaces with piles of bills and letters beneath yellow sticky notes. On the kitchen table was a stack of hardbacks in various conditions: *Lucky Jim*, *Women in Love*, *The Rainbow*, *Anna Karenina*, *Les Fleurs du Mal*. Julia ran her fingers over their spines.

'Giles's. They're all first or early editions. I thought I'd give them to Camilla.' Camilla was Giles's daughter, a journalist who lived in Brighton and kept urban chickens in an egg-shaped fibreglass hutch in her tiny back yard.

'That's thoughtful.'

'She's got most of his others – they ought all to be together. He left his collection here, mouldering in my office when he moved to France – oh, don't be so childish, when he *actually* moved to France. I kept saying he ought to take them – after all, why own them if you don't look at them? But he insisted I be custodian, and then he filled that house with cheap paperbacks instead. Typical Giles,' she finished fondly.

'Shall we post these or is she coming up soon?'

'Just pop them aside. I don't think we ought to trust them to Royal Mail, not that I wouldn't willingly see Lawrence dispatched into oblivion. We'll carry them loose.' These last were the ominous words Iris had spoken about a great many possessions. Julia imagined a column of hundreds of people moving like a line of toiling ants from Parliament Hill to the new flat, each ferrying one teaspoon, or a single mug.

'How much is actually packed?'

'Oh, there's barely anything left, I've worked and worked. Look, I'll show you.' Iris tripped lightly across the kitchen and flung open the pantry door to reveal a tower of neatly taped brown boxes. Julia felt a wave of relief.

'Shall I start taking these out? James found a parking space right outside. It might be good to get things out of the house.'

'That would be lovely, darling, and now I must go and supervise. God knows what the children are doing with my belongings. I'll send Thing to help you with your labours.' Iris then swept out, and Julia surveyed the contents of the pantry. 'P.A.'s Books' was scrawled across the top of one box. 'P.A.'s Clothes'. 'P.A.'s Med. textbks'. 'P.A.'s Tennis R. and Sportswr'. 'P.A.'s Papers'. And on the side of each the words, 'Second Bedroom'. 'Second Bedroom'. 'Second Bedroom'.

THIRTY-FIVE

A brief moment of respite. James at work, the delinquent, enervating, relentless children at school, and Julia alone in the house, alone with her own thoughts and alone, finally, with her piano. No students until four p.m. A few days ago James had come home with some Nigel Hess sheet music for her, a piece he adored, but she had not yet taken it from its bag. Of late, her free hours had been spent envisaging various calamitous paths Gwen's life might take as a teenage mother, and plotting every possible contingency. Now, turning the pages in silence, she felt her blood slow. Time contracted and folded in upon itself; in this stillness worry lifted, fractionally. This was the reason for James's gift – to coax her back to a pleasure she had been too guilty and frantic to permit herself. It would last, she knew, only as long as the concerto. But here on this bright, silent afternoon, here was meditation, and repair.

By the end of the year she would be a grandmother. A grandmother! Only in the last days had she forced herself to envisage it, as it felt right and necessary to confront what lay ahead. Gwen had made her decision and from now on, Julia resolved, would have no cause to doubt her support. She would bury her fear and her anxiety. She no longer discussed alternatives. She and James had made a conscious decision to alter their language, and to help one another to come to terms with what lay ahead. They would try not to call it 'a disaster', 'a nightmare', 'an accident' (at least not too often) but to say instead – a baby. For that was what the nightmare would become. Another person in their family by Christmas.

There had been years in which the longing for another child had consumed her. She had tormented Daniel with it until eventually he'd decreed that for their marriage they must draw a line, must formalise their contentment with their funny, mischievous little Gwen, and Julia had wept silently and had assented, continuing, in secret, to chart her ovulation, to take her temperature, to hope against hope. All that spilled and needless grief for an imagined, unknown soul, and all the while wasting precious, jewelled seconds with the real little girl around whom her whole world turned. Wailing for a paper cut on her fingertip while a fat, vermilion clot slid closer and closer to her heart.

And then James, and happiness, so many years later. Loneliness ended. She had surfaced from the submersion of parenthood, and filled her lungs. Who could bear to begin all that again? She had found passion and peace and a future with a man she loved, this time not for the children he would give her but deeply and purely for his own soul. James was all she wanted, and more than she'd ever dreamed.

She watched her own hands moving lightly on the keys. Green veins visible through fragile pale skin, a broken blood vessel between the third and forth knuckle of her right hand. Nails cut short for the piano. They would soon be the hands of a grandmother. The whole household would be beginning all over again, like it or not. James had swept into her life and made her feel young and hopeful, and in an instant Gwen had once again reminded her she was ancient. She turned the music back to the first page, and began to play.

The ringing of the phone came as an otherworldly intrusion, and she answered only to make it stop. There was a scrabbling sound and then Iris, panting and shrill. 'Julia! Thank God.'

Julia roused herself unwillingly from the treacle depths of the second movement – the pure, sweeping romance, its grand and unapologetic sentiment. When she raised the handset her own damp cheek surprised her; she had not known she had been crying.

'Are you all right?'

'No, I am absolutely not all right. I am the opposite of all right. I am absolutely – this is intolerable, and your concealment is unforgivable, after all our confidences—'

'Iris, hold on, what are you talking about?'

'He's seeing somebody!'

'What?'

'He's met someone. He's got a secret good-time girl, and I don't know who the hell you think you're protecting by playing ignorant but I know everything. I've just driven past him on Hampstead High Street having coffee with some ghastly, trashy, dumpy blonde and holding hands.'

It was as if she'd had a whisky and a Valium on a night flight, and was now being shaken urgently awake in order to pilot the plane. Julia blinked, and tried to focus. Her eyes moved forward through the music, still listening. She closed the pages and looked down.

'Was it Valentina? He's back at school, he shouldn't be anywhere near the High Street. Please don't tell me—'

'What? Who in God's name is Valentina? Why didn't you tell me?'

'Nathan's ex-girlfriend. Italian. Fake blonde. Bit trashy, as you say. But they can't have been holding hands, were they? Seriously?'

'Whose – what the hell are you talking about? Philip Alden's on the High Street with a woman. And don't tell me you don't know – I've no doubt you've all been cosy as ever whilst I've been sent to Coventry for something trivial from the Stone Age. Who is she?'

'Philip? I don't know anything, honestly, I've no idea – and we've not seen him at all, he's all but disappeared on me. He's in touch with Gwen, I know they email, that's it. The first time I'd seen him in ages was the other day and I suppose he was being a bit mysterious but I was so distracted and we only talked about Gwen . . . I did see someone dropping him off, but—'

'Blonde?' Iris demanded. 'Mop-like corkscrews of yellow sheep's wool? Outrageous, greasy dark roots? Fat? Clad in *jeans*?' This last spat like poison, as if jeans on such a person were tantamount to an SS uniform.

'I didn't see her legs, she was driving. But yes, curly blonde hair. I don't know who she is. I assumed she was a neighbour giving him a lift.'

'Well, they looked very neighbourly indeed just now. Very neighbourly. My God, the man's a quick worker. Although for all I know it's been *years*—'

'You sound upset. Come round, where are you?'

'I am not upset!' Iris roared. 'I am incredulous. I am at home – ha! How ludicrous. It's a travesty to use that word to describe this sterile, anonymous green-carpeted brassy waste-land of a building. I am in the spare room of my spare new abode. I'm in Room 101 of my sanitised, elevator-enhanced, elderly-friendly, Finchley-Road-accessible, joyless, white-walled, jumbo-sized coffin. I'm in a box, surrounded by boxes. I'm *filed*.'

'Come over, get a taxi. Come.'

'I'd like you to tell me why in God's name I am living in this purgatorial block if he doesn't need me to? Why, may I ask you, am I here? Why, if not to care for Philip Alden in his dotage, did I sell my beloved house with all its very *challenging stairs*?' Iris shrieked, with climactic hysteria. Julia struggled with this series of questions and the nested series of revelations embedded within them. Iris had only ever mentioned wanting financial freedom to enable Gwen's future; Julia had not understood that Philip's, too, had been planned for and secured, had possibly weighed more heavily on Iris's conscience even than her granddaughter's. Yet several things now made sense – the urgency with which she'd sold her house, though James and Julia had expressed every intention of taking care of Gwen and Nathan's needs themselves; the odd location of the new flat. Gwen's pregnancy seemed only the impetus for executing a plan long brewing. Had Iris actually expected him to move in with her again? Through the phone Julia could hear a musical scale of crashes, as if objects had fallen, or been hurled.

'Come over,' Julia said again, gently. 'I'll put the kettle on.'

'There's no need to speak to me like an invalid. And he stopped using his cards so I've not had the faintest idea where he's been or what he's been doing and until I clapped eyes on him just now I've been beside myself that he was starving in a gutter. He's not even been to Sainsbury's. It would have been considerate for someone to tell me that I no longer needed to expend endless time and energy worrying about him. Now I see I went above and beyond to even give it a second thought.'

'What cards?'

'Bank cards,' said Iris impatiently. 'I'd hardly take an interest in his library cards.'

'But how do you see his—'

'Well, we have a joint account, obviously,' and then before Julia had a chance to absorb this startling disclosure about a couple who had been separated since time immemorial, went on, 'and now there's all that money from the house just sitting in it that he hasn't touched while he makes some sort of *moral stand,* and he's probably still got his thermostat on *fifteen*, for God's sake, while he entertains his lady friend, and I live in an old people's home that he won't come to. It's quite hilarious.'

'But Iris, you don't really hate that flat, do you?'

'I do,' snapped Iris, tight and decisive. 'I hate it. I loathe and detest it and now it's where I live and that's the end of it. More fool me for feeling responsible for a doddering old imbecile feigning interest and dependence. Perhaps I shall move to France. Camilla never goes, she's always offering the house. I'm coming round. May I?'

Julia had never before known Iris ask permission for anything, and it moved her. 'Of course, come right now. I'm sure it's nothing. I'm sure he was just with a friend.'

THIRTY-SIX

Joan Perelman was a Scorpio, a part-time travel agent and full-time widow who lived, worked and bred miniature Schnauzers in a semi-detached pebble-dash in Stanmore, airy and spotless (despite the proliferating puppies), the mortgage of which she had recently and triumphantly finished paying off. She was sixty-six, had been only fifty when her Steve had died, and had been alone and lonely since then though she would never have admitted it, not even to the girls in her Thursday book club; perhaps not even to herself. Her two sons (journalist and doctor; Aquarius and Pisces), matching pair of fire-sign daughter-in-laws and five grandchildren all lived in Israel, and while she was glad they were settled, and happy for them that they were all together, it did make life in London very quiet.

She had been emailing Mr Philip Alden, MRCP, MD, FRCOS, FRCOG, intermittently for several months. He was supposed to be a speaker at an assembly for trainee holistic midwives in Paris organised by a British woman named Pamela Fuller who lived in Boston and who, though demanding, had given her a great deal of business over the years. Joan had made the travel arrangements for the last three of these retreats and so when Pamela had asked her to pin down an elusive participant, she'd hopped in the car armed with some encouraging soft-lit beauty shots of the Left Bank and a spa menu, as well as the material for the conference itself. She would coax him to commit, if Pamela so wished it.

It had been, as Joan had confided in her friend Cathy in the changing rooms after Hip Hop Hips, a whirlwind. Of course he was quite a bit older, but he had such a beautiful face, and clear, sad eyes that shone with humour and wisdom, and after setting her straight about the conference, which he had done almost immediately, he nonetheless offered her a coffee. This he made on the stove and then carried through on a precariously clattering tray. He had poured her coffee, offered her UHT milk, the sight of which had touched and saddened her, and had asked, with ever such a naughty twinkle in his eye, for her to tell him all about what he'd be missing. 'Tell me about the –' he'd reached for the top two brochures – 'tell me about the "bilingual past life regression refresher".' And so she had told him about having to find a simultaneous translator for the evening meditation masterclasses, and somehow she had then moved to other topics, and he had listened to her prattle about her son and his family visiting next week (staying with the *machatunim*, sadly, not with Joan) and her grandson's upcoming football party and the present she'd chosen (a kit to make a robot out of a drinks can; she didn't believe in video games though that was what he'd asked for), and Philip had asked all the right questions and said, how hard to have them all so far away. And then he'd told her about his son, Daniel, who'd died of cancer and she'd cried, and said sorry, it was awful of her to cry over a stranger's story but she'd just been so sad for him and here she was complaining that she had to fly to see her boys, sorry, sorry, and he'd said, solemnly and, as if he meant it – thank you. Then she had told him about Daisy who was due to whelp in less than a month, and he had taken such tender interest that Joan had relived the conversation over and over in the days that followed.

And it seemed that Philip had remembered too, for out of the blue he had phoned her weeks later, on a rainy evening in May, to ask about the dog. Moved to daring she'd asked, would he like to come for tea tomorrow to meet Daisy? And in case he'd got the wrong idea had added, stupidly, that she'd love to hear his medical opinion. He'd been reading up, he told her, when she was defrosting a spinach lasagne for supper and he was still, miraculously, in her kitchen. It would be an honour to be at the delivery. Since that day he had barely left her side. A week later Joan was due in Pinner for her grandson's eleventh birthday and it already seemed right, by then, that Philip should join her. He met the boys, he attended the birthday party, he helped with the assembly of the 7-Up can robot. It had been a short time, it was true, but they knew all they needed to know about one another. Unexpectedly, wonderfully, all-consumingly, it was love.

THIRTY-SEVEN

Gwen's exam weeks passed without incident which was in itself remarkable, under the circumstances. If pressed, she would reply that the day's module had gone 'okay', or 'fine', or in the case of an art history paper, 'all right, I think', and no more would be forthcoming. Each evening she sat down ravenous to supper, did an extremely brief spell of French vocabulary on the sofa and then retired to the bath where she would lie for an hour, occasionally memorising history dates but more often listening to a meditation track that she had recently downloaded from the Internet. Julia would walk past the bathroom and hear snatches of, 'allow your mind to empty like the waves receding', or more oddly, 'you can know anything you wish, if you simply wait in stillness for wisdom to enter'. Keeping up the Easter revision intensity for these final few days seemed a more sensible approach than waiting in stillness for wisdom to enter the cooling silted waters of a bathtub, but Julia recalled the tears and nightly hysteria of the GCSEs the year before and passed no comment. Gwen's morning sickness had been violent but unexpectedly brief and had now passed entirely, as had her fatigue. She no longer had any symptoms at all and, she would boast to anyone who'd listen, she felt entirely herself again and could forget about it for days at a time. Nonetheless she took herself to bed each night at nine p.m. 'to be responsible', and James and Julia had a series of improbably lovely evenings alone, curled together on the sofa, as it had never before been. And might never be again, Julia thought, with an ache in her throat. Gwen might be able to set aside her pregnancy while she finished off the year, but it could not be ignored much longer. She was ten weeks pregnant – in some ways very early; in others, late.

While Gwen apparently grew calmer, Nathan grew increasingly desperate. His own exams would not begin until the day hers ended and, for him, everything was still to play for. Oxford had asked for one A* and two As. He told Gwen that he did not have time to call her from school and she did not protest; she too was under pressure. Without the sound of her voice, it became surprisingly easy to pretend that nothing at home had changed. He was working every waking hour, and for efficiency's sake had increased these waking hours first to eighteen, then nineteen then, finally, to twenty a day. When his eyes closed over his books he drank coffee or took caffeine tablets, and then stayed longer at his desk to make effective use of the jittering insomnia. Charlie gave him eyedrops, and these helped with the burning and dryness. He would have all summer to recover.

There was nothing he had ever wanted as much as he wanted straight As, now. He would forgo all sleep, all pleasure, he would work until his hands seized and his brain bled. When term began it had been a relief to go back to the easy, studious camaraderie of his boarding house but it wouldn't have mattered. He could revise polynomials at the back of the 24 bus. He would have walked the streets reading about gene expression. He could have memorised the properties of transition metals at the foot of Eros at the heart of Piccadilly Circus while around him the pubs emptied, and the crowds flooded out of the theatres on the last Friday night before Christmas. He feared life closing down around him but he would fight his way free and Oxford would harbour him, offer safety, redemption. He was the embodiment of single-mindedness. He was indefatigable. He would succeed. He would fly.

THIRTY-EIGHT

Nathan's exams had finally begun that morning and since then James had carried his phone around the house, mooning and checking his watch and sighing with impatience like a lovestruck teenager. He was anxious to hear about this afternoon's mechanics. Physics had gone very well, he told her without looking up, frowning as he typed his reply; the question they'd expected about friction had come up and Nathan had aced it. It was his apparent confidence in the morning's module that had prompted this unwelcome discussion about next year. Julia continued to zest a lemon in silence, the sharp scent rising in her nostrils. She did not feel charmed, or generous, or celebratory, though she was in the midst of making a cake that she hoped would substitute for all those feelings. Gwen's own exams finished this afternoon.

They had made it through her AS fortnight with preternatural calm and harmony, but her daughter still had a year of school before she could be in Nathan's privileged position, considering universities, making plans, and what the hell did her future hold in any case, and how would she manage any of it if Nathan didn't stay in London? Julia would do whatever it took to prevent Gwen's own dreams from evaporating, but she did not intend to be left holding the baby while Nathan swanned off to Oxford, scot-free. It seemed obvious that he must live at home next year to help with his child, so obvious, in fact, that she had barely thought it needed discussion. He would still have the choice of many medical schools, several of which ranked among the best in the country.

The night before returning to Westminster, Nathan had announced over dinner with a faint but discernible touch of sorrow that he would no longer be applying to far-away Harvard, as if they would all be surprised and moved, and full of praise for a grand and unexpected sacrifice. Julia had only managed to say, 'I see,' and had asked to be handed the asparagus. Harvard? After Christmas her daughter would barely be able to go to the corner shops. For Julia and James too, the future to which they'd looked forward had become hazy with uncertainty – music festivals interrupted for feeds and tantrums; the new piano in a Lewes cottage vying for space with a shattered rainbow of plastic tat. Yet for Nathan Oxford remained the plan, and there had arisen this slim, prickling weal of irritation on the previously unspoiled surface of Julia and James's intimacy. They had approached it, circled and retreated without resolution. 'He might not get the grades,' James would offer, which really meant, *Peace, please, I love you, we've made it this far, we are united, please let's not fight*. And he might not get the grades, Julia knew, but the truth was that he almost certainly would. His teachers had long predicted straight A*s. And then what would happen? Whatever James might insist it was too far to commute.

He would have to turn it down. Julia found herself praying that he would miss his marks and so would not have to make a sacrifice for which he would almost certainly punish Gwen.

She considered Oxford. Its Brideshead splendour and indolence, the low click-thock of croquet mallet, the self-conscious delight of sub fusc and black tie and tail coats, emerald lawns and muddy riverbanks, of simply messing around in punts; of cobbled streets and echoing cloisters, wide-open quadrangles and covered markets, of squeaking bicycles, of dusty, leather-scented library corners where light streamed in through high windows onto the bowed and privileged heads below. Nathan would soon be handed the key on a velvet ribbon, and in the autumn would disappear into that enclosed and enchanted garden. And for Gwen, a life of schoolgirl motherhood. Oxford would never have been Gwen's world, she knew, but still, she had her own dreams. They'd walked around the animation department of the Leeds College of Art one half term and Julia had not been able to tear her gaze from Gwen's face. Her hungry eyes had taken in the banks of drafting tables, the modelling studio, the long rows of huge-screened iMacs. She'd turned to her mother with an expression of joyful disbelief and Julia had felt an unexpected pain at her daughter's impatience. *Don't grow up so fast*, she'd thought, *not yet*. Gwen had shown her round instinctively – here is where they do traditional frame-by-frame work; these puppets are for stop-frame animation; this must be the recording studio for voices; here's for 3-D, computer-generated work. Her little girl wanted to join this band of serious young people with their dyed hair, their septum piercings and eyebrow rings, their checked flannel shirts and army boots, their intense frowns over joystick and mouse and pencil and clay. And Julia had felt stricken, understanding for the first time that her daughter longed to leave her, and that it would happen soon, and Julia's world, without its centre, would quietly and catastrophically collapse. Gwen would take with her everything of meaning. It had been shortly after that visit to Leeds that she had agreed to a date with James.

No. There was no question that Nathan must live at home. He would have responsibilities, unimaginable though it was, and his second choice was not exactly a tragedy. Medicine at Imperial was not to be sneezed at. As Iris would say, you don't exactly sit shiva for medicine at Imperial. He didn't get to have the sex, the girlfriend, the intellect, the freedom and then, the crowning triumph, the Houdini act that spirited him away into a limestone paradise of books and beauty in that sweet city, with its gleaming infant-free spires. He couldn't have everything.

'I don't know what you want me to say.'

'I want you to talk to me. I want to understand why you're so against it. I want us to make plans —'

'But your plans involve your son sixty miles away from my daughter. And from *his* son or daughter, more to the point. For six years.'

'Oxford terms are only eight weeks long and he'll come back every weekend. Gwen's high-school terms will be way longer than that.'

'If we can get her back to school.'

'She has to, it shouldn't be a negotiation. And she'll have a huge amount of support during the week, she's never going to be alone. I've told you I'm going to be there for this baby. I'm going to do whatever I can to free them. No one's life should be derailed – you and I are here, and we can do it. And the other day Pamela was saying she could maybe also arrange to come over for two weeks of each term, if it helped—'

'What do you mean? *Our* life will be derailed! Our life is going to be totally derailed – I don't even recognise what's ahead of us . . . I'm almost fifty, James, it's too much to even think about starting all over again with an infant in the house. I don't know how it was for you and Pamela, maybe you had babies who slept through the night and never cried and sterilised their own bottles but I certainly didn't, I remember being so tired I felt jet-lagged, *all the time*, and I never imagined – of course we'll be there but you can't just decide you'll do it *for* him, and it's not as if we're talking about success or failure here, medical school is medical school and he should be grateful—' Julia halted quickly, though not before noticing that James had raised his eyebrows. She tried again. 'He should still be happy and excited about next year wherever he goes. I'm just saying, to get a medical degree from a great university is a triumph under any circumstances. He can go somewhere else, and most kids don't have that much choice even when they don't have a young baby. There's no reason to go so far away.' The idea of Pamela descending upon them was too alarming so this she ignored entirely.

'So far away? Julia, it's sixty-two miles, it's barely up the road.' James pointed behind him, towards the front door, towards Golders Green, towards junction eight of the M40, towards the rosy-gold horizon over which his golden son was to set sail. She knew what he valued – he had been to Harvard for both his degrees, and before Harvard Medical School, nauseating Pamela had read Natural Sciences at Christ's College, Cambridge. They were speaking more often these days and she could imagine their discussions – why ought their son to turn down a world-class institution when they could manage his temporary absence? Even for a good London college, it would be symbolic self-sacrifice. James could keep the baby cared for, the household mollified and managed, and would of course do it with better grace, better humour, and a great deal more competence than his teenage son. She understood it, in principle. It was atavistic. To launch your child into the world towards success and freedom, wasn't it this for which every parent strove, lifelong? If an impediment lay in Nathan's path James would raze it to the ground like a bulldozer, but in this case the impediment was her own child and she would not allow Gwen to be flattened for an indulged, over-privileged little so-and-so. She took a deep breath, and began her explanation again, from the beginning, and saw him grit his teeth with unaccustomed irritation. But then her phone rang and she sprang for it. It would be Gwen, reporting on the final exam. Those, at least, seemed to have gone without incident. James checked his own phone.

'Hi, my darling, how was it?'

'Mummy,' the voice on the other end was muffled and warped by digital interference. It sounded as if Gwen was underground, or perhaps underwater. 'Mummy, can you come?'

'I can't hear you very well, my darling, where are you? What happened? It's only one module, my love, I'm sure it will be okay.'

'I'm in the loos. Mummy, please come.' Julia heard a shuddering sob. 'I'm bleeding.'

THIRTY-NINE

When Nathan tiptoed in, Gwen was in her pyjamas on the sofa, her hair in two thick plaits, her knees drawn up, a hot-water bottle cradled in her arms. Behind her glasses her face was very white, her eyes fixed on the flickering television. She had the cuticle of her right thumb between her teeth, and did not appear to hear or sense him entering. The room was stuffy, the only light in the room the screen, and a reading lamp casting a yellow glow on the far wall.

Nathan hovered in the doorway, uncertain. He spoke her name softly, as though waking her from sleep, and she looked up and gave him a wan smile.

'You didn't have to come back.'

He sat down beside her, very gingerly. He did not know whether she was in pain, nor what to say if she was. What had been done to her, in the bright white sterility of the hospital? What had been taken?

'I mean, it's lovely that you did. But you've got two exams tomorrow.' Her voice was husky, as if her throat was very dry.

'You're more important,' he said fiercely. His father had said the same on the phone: exams tomorrow. But how could they possibly think he'd care about exams today? How could he stay in his boarding house tonight? His father's voice – filled with warmth and pity and a promise of his own reassuring solid presence, at that moment just out of reach, across London – had brought on such a violent lurch of homesickness that he could not have stayed in school another moment. As soon as he stepped out into Victoria Street, arm aloft, purposeful, he felt better. At first in the taxi he felt himself racing against the clock, in a panic to reach the heroine for the climactic scene in which he would be tested and would comfort her, and triumph. Nothing of these last, strange weeks had felt real – around him weird storms had raged, but when he kept his head down life remained unaltered, the threat too far ahead to fear, too abstract to comprehend. Now he felt electrified. Telling the driver 'as fast as you can' was manly and exhilarating. This was reality. But then the slow crawl of traffic, near-stasis in the red neon and clamour and spewing traffic of Edgware Road, and the film crew departed and left him alone, and he was no longer needed to perform. The adrenaline seeped away and left him shaking. No one was picking up the phone. He tried his mother, over and over, but it was mid-afternoon in Boston and she would be in clinic, inaccessible for hours. Then he had screwed shut his eyes and bitten the soft flesh between his thumb and index finger to try and punish himself into control; he had not been able to answer when the cab driver turned and asked him if he was all right. He did not understand the source of all this sorrow, only its magnitude, and that it had engulfed him.

He had expected hysteria at home, he realised; he had feared blood, or a confrontation of female biology. This muted calm was disconcerting, and made his role unclear.

She already had a hot-water bottle, and beside her on the coffee table lay a still life of sickroom requirements: a plate of biscuits, a cup of tea, a glass of water, a packet of chocolate buttons, a box of painkillers, a small packet of tissues, a weekly celebrity magazine. He had come home intending to nurse her, an evening of his own hard penance so he could go back to school having altered something. But her requirements had been met.

'Are you okay?' he asked foolishly. He leaned over to kiss her and she inclined her head towards him so he ended up catching her paternally on her hairline.

'I'm okay. Your dad got me an appointment with his friend tomorrow morning. Not that Claire person, someone else. It's nice of him – usually I'd have to wait longer. It'll be more comfortable after that, apparently.'

'Does it hurt?'

She shook her head. 'They said I could take paracetamol, but then when we got back your dad gave me – he said I didn't have to be hurting when he had something stronger that's okay to take. So he gave me something . . . American,' she finished. This speech had taken effort; she sank back onto the sofa, wearied by it.

'Lucky, Dad never gives me his good drugs. But I mean, *you're* okay. You're safe?'

'Yes. S'just one of those things. "Wasn't meant to be", or whatever.'

'But how can it just be—' His voice broke and now he took Gwen's white hand and raised it to his lips. He could not quite find her in the dark hollows of her eyes. It had begun to dawn on him what had not seemed real or possible before this loss – that he had almost had a child. A son, maybe. A moment later he found himself weeping. Gwen shifted to her knees and held his head tightly against her breast. 'How can it just be *gone*, just like that? That was our *baby*.'

'It's okay,' she whispered, 'everything's okay.' Her hand stroked his hair, but the more she soothed, the harder he wept. He did not want to stop. Nothing was okay. He had lost something in which he had never believed.

Upstairs, Gwen sank into bed. She had ordered Nathan back to school, back to his necessary responsibilities and the unaltered reality of exams. It had been a relief when his father drove him away and the house was silent again. When James returned she could vaguely hear his voice and her mother's mingled, soft and low in the kitchen, and for once she did not feel an angry impulse to eavesdrop, did not fear secrets or treachery. She knew they were speaking of her, and speaking tenderly. She did not deserve it.

Her mother had changed the sheets and refilled her hot-water bottle and this Gwen clutched to the dull ache in her abdomen – though in truth the pain was not bad, no worse than period cramps. After a moment James knocked and came in, with two tablets and a glass of water.

'In case you wanted something in the night. You could take one now and one after two a.m., if you wake.'

'Will it help me sleep?'

He nodded.

'It's not actually hurting that much. But can I take it anyway?'

'Just tonight, sure. One at a time, though. Gwen –' he paused in the doorway and ran a hand through his hair, gathering the front in his fist, a mannerism she recognised in Nathan – 'I'm so very sorry. I'm on call tonight but you know I won't leave this house unless I really have to. If you need anything in the night –'

'I know. Thanks.'

'Goodnight. Your mother will come in soon.'

'Wait!' She heard her own voice calling him back, and seconds later he returned and was at her bedside.

'Can I ask –' She had no vocabulary for her question but her hand was suddenly between James's, clasped tightly and shaken on each emphatic syllable.

'You did not make this happen, you hear me? *It is not possible.* It's not coffee or what you ate or what you didn't eat or a heavy box you lifted or anything within your control. This happens in one in five pregnancies, even at your age, and people don't talk about it and I have no idea why – it would spare a lot of women a lot of needless, toxic guilt. I would not bullshit you. I need you to hear me, okay?'

He would not look away, she knew, until she nodded.

The door closed, and she took a deep, unsteady breath. James had not understood. She had done this, not with her body but with her mind. She had wished away a baby. Overjoyed at the end of the fatigue and nausea, she hadn't known that for days she had been celebrating death within her. She had longed for liberation and in answer a violent, unexpected liberation had come.

Beneath her hot spread hands her abdomen was flat and unremarkable. In, out. She sank back into her pillow exhausted, washed into unconsciousness on a tide of Tramadol, and a rising steady surge of dark relief.

FORTY

Long ago on a different floor of that same hospital, Julia had cradled newborn Gwen and known her body's work: to shield this child from harm, lifelong. The cord between them was severed but her daughter pulsed in her veins and swelled her heart. Life, she promised her, would be a thing of beauty – no less was due to such unblemished perfection.

The arrogance! Vigilance could not keep her child beyond the reach of germs or falls or playground bullies, not from allergies nor fights with friends nor the teachers who found her unfocused or petulant, who couldn't see her unique brilliance and charm. Julia had failed so often, and then could only suffer for Gwen, suffer with Gwen, and try in the aftermath of each small calamity to make amends. And then Daniel had died and huge wet fawn eyes had looked up at Julia and pierced her, and she had read in their bewilderment, *How could you let this happen?*

Far taller than all her classmates, awkward and angular and exuding toxic sadness, for that first year Gwen had repelled the other girls. At the school gates they passed her by in flocks, tiny sparrows twittering, avoiding the unsettling spectacle of her bent, trudging form. In her hands an egg of Silly Putty constantly moulded and remoulded, on her back a grubby purple rucksack and in it the world's weight. She was not open or appealing but heavy-browed, frowning, angry, impossible to befriend. Julia picked her up each afternoon with a lead weight in her stomach. She couldn't make it better. Instead, she compensated.

Now such an adult misfortune, a complex, adult sorrow. It was obscene and unbearable to feel relief, seeing Gwen's face pale against the pale sheets, her daughter meek and bewildered, curled foetal beneath a winter duvet on long summer days. For her child's lost innocence, Julia wept. Such knowing, now, as no grown woman ought to know!

Within a week Gwen relinquished the daytime hours in bed, still rising very late but then managing to stay awake, clothed, communicative, till bedtime. She came to the supermarket with Julia, and to the post office. She waited in the car while Julia ran in to the dry cleaners. While Julia taught she lay on the sofa with magazines or her laptop or sat at the kitchen table, modelling a large, elaborate replica of the Hampstead Ladies' Bathing Pond. She clung close and Julia was grateful. So often in the last months she had been forced to stifle the instinct to reach out and draw her nearer; now Gwen sought the touch and care that Julia had so long craved. She had her only on loan, she knew, just until Nathan came home. But for the meanwhile it was a return to a rhythm as familiar as a heartbeat, mother and daughter together except when brief circumstance parted them and one waited patiently, and then a seamless return to one another. For the first week James stayed late at the hospital or did paperwork discreetly upstairs, and each evening Gwen worked on her models while Julia made dinner. At Gwen's suggestion they spring-cleaned. They sorted out Gwen's clothes. They cleared the drawers beneath her bed to make space for a proper archive of her models. They tidied the spice rack, the utensil drawer, the bookshelves of Julia's crowded little music room. They made easy order from small chaos. Her child had returned, prodigal, temporary, beloved, and Julia treasured each moment she was granted like a jewel.

For the Ponds, they packed as they always had. Towels, books, a pack of cards, warm clothes and a fleecy blanket for the moments just after an icy immersion. A picnic of peanut-butter sandwiches, carrot sticks, a bag of grapes, two red apples. The same lunch she and Gwen had favoured for this outing many summers ago. The weather had turned cloudy but this was England, and to wait for clear blue skies might be to wait for ever.

Safe from exhausting dissecting male eyes, the Ladies' Pond offers tranquil safety almost impossible to capture elsewhere. Gwen had brought an old black swimming costume from long-ago school lessons and in this she sat, comfortably cross-legged. Around them women relaxed. Stomach muscles released, shoulders hunched, flattering angles and postures abandoned. Freed. Gwen rolled onto her stomach on the towel and sprawled, face down, forehead resting on her rolled-up T-shirt. A brief flicker of sun lit the grass, was gone again, but hinted at return. Julia unpacked sandwiches, balled up foil, struggled briefly to unscrew Gwen's requested bottle of Coke.

Gwen said, mumbling into the earth, 'Can I ask you something?'

'Of course.'

Gwen raised herself to her elbows and began to pluck grass blades. 'So, Katy's the only person who knows . . . who knew I was pregnant, and Nathan's teachers know 'cause he was still at school and stuff and so James told them but no one else, and I've been thinking about what to do about my followers. Online, I mean. I always said it would be everything that happened in my life, not just the bits I wanted to show off, but it just feels a bit weird.'

Julia recoiled at the thought but said carefully, 'It seems a very exposing . . . What do you want to do?'

'I don't think I want to say anything. I mean, what would I do? Because I was planning this big reveal, you know, like with a little bump and an announcement in those old school wooden baby blocks, you know? Telling everyone that way about the baby. I just wanted to wait –' she gave a sideways glance towards her mother and then looked down again – 'just till you guys were a bit more used to it, and more . . . excited, and then tell everyone first on the blog, with this little stork and balloons and stuff.'

Julia's eyes filled. To think that Gwen had longed not only for acceptance, but enthusiasm. It would not have come, and then what? She wanted to reach out to stroke her daughter's cheek, her hair, but Gwen went on, 'But now it's like, I'd have to explain that I was pregnant and now I'm not pregnant at the same time and it just feels . . . I dunno. Wrong.'

'Some things are very painful to share, very private. And maybe it's too soon to even know how you feel yet.

It's okay to protect yourself and keep some things off the Internet. Then later you get to decide who you tell, if you want to, and who you don't.'

'You don't think it's dishonest not to put it up?'

'I don't,' said Julia firmly. 'I think it's brave.'

Gwen looked relieved. She rolled over and sat up, and reached for a sandwich. 'Okay. Then next I'm going to do the one of us here, because the Pond's going really well, I've almost finished it, and then the one after can be when Nathan finishes finally, and we can do something fun instead of me, like, dying on the sofa.' Here she rolled her eyes, and Julia had a glimpse of how it would be when Nathan returned – the miscarriage dismissed, cast off as embarrassing, or too much of a downer. 'I've been planning loads of amazing stuff. I'll meet him at Westminster so I could model that, but afterwards we're going to Covent Garden. D'you know you can check which street performers are going to be there? So I thought I'd plan out a few that would be amazing, and then there's this American sweet shop that Katy found so we'll go there as a surprise and buy stuff he likes from home, and then there's this bubble-tea place that's just opened, and then James is really into this barbecue idea which sounds cool if that's what Nathan wants. But basically, I'll organise the whole afternoon and then the best thing I'll model.' She peeled apart her remaining corner of sandwich and laid a carrot stick onto the slice with peanut butter on it, rolling this into a cigar. She frowned. 'It's been a bit weird that he's basically not been here for anything. We've talked on the phone but not really about what happened because he has people in his room a lot, and also he was studying and it seemed unfair to bring it up when he has to concentrate. But he keeps saying how he wished he could take care of me.' She bit the end off her rolled sandwich and said, her mouth full, 'I've been thinking, and I think we'll have a baby when I'm twenty-five. Or twenty-four.' Impossible not to see the flicker of challenge in her eyes. A test. Julia resolved not to fail.

'You'll see what feels right,' she said neutrally.

Gwen bit her lip. 'But it won't be this baby.'

'No, my darling.'

'It's like, another baby doesn't just make it okay about this baby, or make it like it never happened. You don't think –' She paused. 'You don't think James is just saying it to make me feel better, that there was nothing we could do? If there was something that was my fault I'd want to know.' They had covered this ground more than once before, and each time Gwen's guilt seemed fractionally eased.

'I don't. He's very straight. But if you wanted to talk to Claire again I'm sure she'd see you.'

'No, it's okay. It was a girl, I think. I'm so sure it was a girl. Do you believe mothers have instincts about these things?'

'I knew you were a girl.'

Gwen nodded, relieved to have her instincts affirmed, pleased, also, to have been recognised so early as herself. She wiped her hands on the grass and stood up inelegantly. She was going to swim, she announced, and it was clear from her tone that she wished to go alone. Julia took out a book, but did not open it. She watched Gwen climbing down into the slippery green of the pond, watched her daughter's long form move off through the murky water. A woman's body, now. A separate being, thinking her own closed, unguessable thoughts. She felt a sudden ache of longing for Gwen's own babyhood. It took so little to call it back, the private rapture of her new daughter's warm weight, slack and loose-jointed and slung, milk-drunk, across Julia's shoulder. Gwen in her arms had exuded an opiate. The tiny breaths against her neck, the sudden startles and then stillness and silence, the soft, urgent moans of baby dreams. Her finger gripped like a lifeline, unblinking grey eyes locked with her own in an exchange of silent promises. What would she give to start all over again, to be handed her infant daughter afresh, to file away each moment like a treasure, to do it right? She thought about the child her daughter had almost carried, and allowed the tears to come. She would listen harder. She would watch more closely. Next time she would be there to catch Gwen even before she slipped.

FORTY-ONE

On the morning of Nathan's final exam Gwen washed and straightened her hair. He had not been home for more than two weeks and the last time they had seen one another had been just after she'd returned from hospital when she had been curled on the sofa, barely responsive. She had been startled and touched by his devastation then, and it had shown her the right way to respond. Like a good army wife she had used her little strength to soothe him and patch him up and send him back into battle. When they'd spoken since, she'd done her best to sound cheerful, and to listen when he talked about school. It became easier and easier to sound okay, for she had begun to feel okay, but there was still a conversation missing; she had comforted him, but missed her own comforting. She wanted back the concern he'd shown that first night. She wanted praise for her bravery, and coddling for her trauma. And she wanted to remind him as much as possible of her old self. His last day at Westminster was a milestone; she had needed him, and now she could tell him so and they could be together. They could reassemble their bedroom (surely now the parents would allow it) and they would feel close again, and united. He would begin to fathom the leaden weight of all she felt, the dull guilt and the piercing flashes of disbelief. Nathan's love and admiration for her courage would lift the last sorrow from her shoulders like a cloak; he would be gallant, attentive, and she would shrug loose, would emerge poised and damaged, wiser and more beautiful, and walk free into the candlelight and music of the rest of her life. She could start to forget all she had learned about loneliness. In the darkness their fingertips would touch, and it would not be despair but safety, and connection.

In St James's Park the grass had just been cut, and the warm air was filled with drowsy summer. Passing crowds of tourists stayed dutifully on the paths, studying their maps and phones, invariably in search of either the Mall and onwards to Buckingham Palace, or Birdcage Walk and the Houses of Parliament. The Westminster boys lay on the freshly clipped lawns, blithe and privileged in charcoal suits and new freedom, playing a lazy, seated game of catch with a tight-crumpled ball of white paper that had once been an A-level exam sheet.

From his inside pocket Charlie drew a bottle of vodka and a packet of cigarettes while from the same hiding place in his own wrinkled jacket Nathan produced his hip flask. The sight of it made Gwen smile to herself.

A dark-haired boy loped over to join them and dropped his rucksack in the middle of the circle. This was Edmund, who sat next to Nathan in pure maths. Edmund had long ago dated Valentina briefly, which made him an object of interest. She studied his face for signs that he'd been branded in some manner by the Demon Barber.

'Champers?'

'Have you got? You star!'

'Gift from the olds. I've even got glasses.' Edmund unzipped his rucksack and began to flick plastic cups into their laps.

'Mixers?' asked Charlie.

'It's champagne, you muppet.'

'For the vodka.'

'Nope. Mixers are for pussies.'

'I'll go to the newsagent,' Gwen offered, seeing a way to participate whilst also getting away from his friends for a moment. She stood up, squinting in the sunshine. Her sunglasses were in her bag but she now worried they were babyish; when she bought them she'd thought the heart-shaped lenses quirky and original – here she felt uncertain.

'Top girl. Orange juice, cranberry juice, soda.'

Gwen looked at Nathan, waiting.

'What?'

'Wallet?'

'No cash? Here.' He handed her a twenty-pound note. 'Buy yourself something pretty.' His voice was hard and public, straining for cool and distance. He couldn't help it. Later he would coo and nuzzle her, overcompensating, anxious for reassurance that she would not hold him to the distance he himself had made.

The shops were further than she'd remembered. She decided to spend the rest of Nathan's money on catering, something that his friends would not have considered, and so bought cheese-and-onion crisps, Jaffa Cakes and three large bags of wine gums. The drinks were heavy, and the thin plastic bags were splitting by the time she was halfway back across the field. She managed to fit one bottle into her own bag, but the others had to be tucked awkwardly into the crook of each arm, and her return progress was cumbrous and slightly sweaty in the rising heat of the afternoon. Every few yards she had to stop and readjust her burdens.

There were ten or twelve teenagers cross-legged in a circle by the time she returned, mostly boys as well as two girls she didn't recognise, one of whom had her stockinged feet in, or near to, Charlie's crotch. The champagne and vodka bottles were empty, and a large Malibu was circulating.

'You can't mix Malibu and cranberry juice!' snorted Nathan, when he saw her. 'What were you thinking, woman?'

'It was vodka when I left.'

'Water into wine. Vodka into Malibu. Transubstantiation.' He widened his eyes. 'It's a miracle.'

'Transubstantiation's not water into wine, Fuller.' Beside him Edmund began to guffaw with tipsy laughter. 'Such a fucking Jew.'

Shocked, Gwen dropped the bottles rather heavily in the centre of the circle, but Nathan had only punched his friend rather lazily in the bicep and grinned. 'Well, what is it then? It'd be fucking impressive. Imagine turning Evian into Cab Sauv.'

'Communion wafer becomes the Body of Christ.' Edmund tossed his heavy hair from his eyes and tore into one of Gwen's bags of Kettle Chips, without acknowledgement. 'You take the host.' He laid a large crisp on his own extended tongue in illustration.

Nathan hooked his arm around Gwen's neck and pulled her closer, his exhalations loud and heavy against her ear. She was pleased by this display of possession and desire, and somewhat less pleased by the smell of his breath and slightly glazed look in his eyes. He had grown sloppy, and his laughter came in loud, forced shouts. The group was raucous with freedom but Nathan seemed further gone than the others, his head lolling, occasionally pulling her to him and plunging a rather clumsy tongue slightly too deep into her mouth.

The afternoon settled. The boys played a brief game of football but soon gave up in the heat, balled up their now obsolete school jackets and stretched back in the grass. Gwen lay down dutifully beside Nathan who rolled over and began to kiss her, messily and ostentatiously, until Charlie threw a wine gum at them and to Gwen's relief he stopped. She sat up again. By now she'd hoped to be alone with Nathan, perhaps somewhere in this park, walking, talking, holding hands, shaking their heads in awe at the extraordinary bond they now shared.

Today marked a momentous transition, and counting down towards it had steadied her in some of her darkest moments. She had pictured that first moment in which the huge oak doors creaked open. She'd imagined Nathan swinging her round with joy at his liberation, not only from school but from all the academic constraints that had hampered his ability to take care of her. Today, Nathan would assume the mantle of his responsibilities, solemn as a graduation gown. She would see him come back to her, and see her once again. It had already begun on the walk here when he had hung back from the others, had pulled her for a moment down a quiet stable mews, cobbled, blue-plaqued, and she had recognised in him the old fresh urgency, undiminished. Though she now found even the idea of sexual contact repellent, almost intolerable, her heart had leapt. Teenagers have always been forced to take these quiet public corners and make them private, temporarily, and here, with Nathan's heavy breath and roaming hands, was proof that they were once again normal teenagers. The daylight and his waiting friends ensured she was safe to sigh, and pull him tighter, and imitate his frustration. She found herself rising above the scene. She saw her red head bent close towards his dark one. They could have been parents, bound together inextricably and eternally. Can you believe it? Those two down there, kissing – for ever united. Look at them!

At half past four the group began to stir. There was a general agreement that they should go back to Yard and meet those who had been in afternoon exams and then move the celebrations to a pub behind Victoria Street, or perhaps to Marina's house in Vincent Square. Gwen tugged on Nathan's sleeve and whispered, 'Now we can go to Covent Garden.' It was already much later than she'd hoped. They would have to rush if they were to make it to the Taiwanese bubble-tea place, before heading home in time for James's barbecue.

'Come and meet Dom and the others from geography, *ma petite*.'

She shook her head. 'We're meant to do something just the two of us.'

'I tell you what.' Nathan stepped back unsteadily and slung an arm around Charlie's shoulders. 'This is what's going to happen. You go and do what you need to do in Covent Garden. She needs to go shopping,' he whispered confidentially to Charlie, 'and then you come back and meet us in the pub. We'll be in the pub, and you can come back and meet us.'

'Or at Marina's,' added one of the girls unexpectedly. She was a few feet away; though they had seemed busy gathering their belongings, collecting crisp packets, brushing grass from their clothing, everyone was in earshot.

Gwen shook her head again. 'I'm going.' Her voice came out louder than she'd intended. 'I'm not coming back again. I'm going home.'

'Okay, baby, have fun. I'll be home in . . . soon. I've just got very business – I've got very important business to attend to, which is the business of celebrating.'

She set off across the lawn and he loped a few steps to catch up with her.

'Are you pissed, baby?' he asked, in a different, private voice. She didn't care. Respect concealed from his friends had no value. Shouldn't he want to be alone with her?

'No,' she snapped, 'you're pissed.'

'Both can be true, in very different ways,' he said sorrowfully. 'The American way and the British. I prefer the English way, in this case. I'm pissed in the British sense – you're absolutely right and I highly, highly, highly, highly recommend it. Don't be pissed with me.'

'You said we'd talk after the exams. You said we'd hang out, and we'd talk about everything—'

'Fuck, seriously?' He bent down and began bundling his jacket into his school bag. 'Not *now*. I am not thinking about *that* today. It's literally the last thing I want to think about – I've just finished my exams. 'S'the end of my exams. 'S's my big day.'

'I spent the last day of my exams in hospital. And PS, it's all I think about. All the time. It's not like, a *choice,* I can't just decide, "Oh, I don't want to think about this today."'

'Well then, you should get over it,' he said shortly, standing up again.

She stared at him and he nodded vigorously, in agreement with himself.

'Seriously. Get over it! Come get drunk, come toast the end of my exams. You missed it for yourself because of the thing so come toast the end of your exams too! We should be celebrating the fact that you can drink, drinking's awesome. Not drinking is just . . . a waste. Come toast the fact that we had a fucking lucky escape, we got like a, a get-out-of-jail-free card, baby, we should be toasting. Cheers!' He raised an invisible glass to her, squinting slightly.

Perhaps he sensed that he had gone too far here as he then lurched forwards and tried to kiss her with sloppy tenderness, but Gwen jerked herself free and began to run across the lawn, lowering her head and succumbing, finally, to her sobs. When she reached the path she turned to see that Nathan had lit a cigarette, and with this dangling from his lower lip was bouncing a football from knee to knee with a maddening, surprising coordination. She did not wait, in case he didn't look up. *A lucky escape.* She hated him, and herself.

FORTY-TWO

Today Nathan would come back for the long summer holidays. It had been a blessed relief to be without him, but Gwen had been so excited earlier, racing up and down to model outfits, carefully painting too much garish colour on her pale face. For Gwen, and for James, Julia gathered her strength and went to welcome the children in the hallway when she heard the key.

It was Gwen alone, and she had been crying.

'Where've you been? What's wrong? What happened, Dolly?'

'Everything's fucking stupid!'

'What's stupid? Where's Nathan?'

'Who cares? I literally hate him. I hate my life. Stop asking me questions.'

Julia waited while Gwen kicked off her trainers on the doorstep, in the immediate path of anyone who might want to come in or out.

'You don't have to stand there looking at me like there's something wrong with me!' Even Gwen did not sound convinced by this complaint. She tried again. 'There's nothing wrong with me, *I'm fine*. Stop looking at me like I'm a fucking invalid!'

'Enough, now. I won't be spoken to like this. I don't know what's happened but you can't just come in here and instantly take it out on me. Where's Nathan? Why didn't he come home with you?'

'Nothing's happened,' Gwen whined, extending this last word over several seconds and pitches. She was now pulling her shoes back on.

'Where are you going?'

'It's literally none of your business! I'm going round the corner to make a phone call with some privacy, okay?'

After the front door slammed, Julia paused. Then she threw it open and called after her daughter.

'Wha-at?'

'Bring back some ice cream, Dolly, something nice that you really fancy.'

Gwen grunted non-committally, and then the gate swung shut behind her. Julia gave a small moan of anxiety. She should have spoken her conviction aloud in time to do something about it: it was a terrible idea for Nathan to come home for the summer.

In the kitchen, singing to Bon Jovi beneath a pair of Nathan's green, padded headphones, James had missed the shouting. Nathan had requested a barbecue for his first night of freedom, and James was making barbecue sauce. Saskia had just arrived from Boston and was sequestered upstairs with her friend Rowan, who was spending the night.

'Why didn't he come back with her?' he asked when Julia lifted an earphone to update him.

'I don't know. I think they've had an argument, she's in the most revolting mood. She'll be back any minute.'

'God save us. Where's that apricot jelly?'

'We can't still have that, it was from Christmas.'

'This'll blow your mind, I promise you. What did they fight about?'

Julia sank down into a chair. 'I have no idea but she seems really rattled, and now she's marched off again. I think she knows Saskia's here with Rowan and probably wanted to phone Katy and compose herself a bit. It might have been quite uncomfortable being around all Nathan's school friends, and I imagine she feels quite guilty and ambivalent about celebrating anything. She's so tired. And the last day of her exams – that was not a good day.'

James had found the remains of the apricot jam, as well as another unopened jar Julia didn't recognise that said 'FIGUE' in elaborate curlicues, and he was now dumping their contents into a stainless-steel bowl along with the entire squeezy bottle of ketchup. 'She's wiped out, she needs time. We'll just take it very easy for the summer,' he said, squirting, 'and make sure you guys get lots of time alone together. Mom-and-daughter time.'

Julia rose and put her arms around him, peering over his shoulder into the contents of his bowl. 'Thank you. That looks terrible,' she said, her chin moving against the solid curve of his bicep. He grinned. 'It's going to be awesome, just you wait. It's Nathan's all-time favourite. They've done it, you know. I'm so damn proud. They've been unbeliev-able little *mensches* for the last few weeks, both of them – it's a huge night tonight. We got these kids through . . . through a war zone. Think what they've been contending with, both of them. It's unimaginable. I really think she'll turn a corner now, you'll see. She's not had any space. Do you think I should make guacamole? The avocados are like bullets – I'd have to try and microwave them or something. Gwen likes hotdogs, right? I got ballpark hotdogs and relish. Next time we go to Boston I have to take you to a ballgame, you'll love it. Actually, you'll hate it but I'll love it. You'll love it when it's over, maybe.' He ducked to kiss her, behind her ear.

The day Nathan's exam timetable had been published James had swapped his clinic in order to be free to prepare this banquet. Along with the frankfurters, barbecued chicken and grilled peppers he had made some sort of Cuban-style sweetcorn with feta and mayonnaise, and had come back from Queen's Crescent with a watermelon the size of a small house pet. It felt far too soon to be celebrating anything but when consulted Gwen agreed it was still a good idea, and had even offered to bake Nathan an end-of-school cake – online she'd found a recipe for some elaborate confection that spilled out jelly beans. Gwen was surely the child more deserving of treats but Julia had been happy, at least, that she was once again planning creative activities. In any case, given Gwen's mood the cake now seemed rather unlikely. What little enthusiasm Julia had for the evening had evaporated. James had a great deal for which he ought to be grateful – his daughter was visiting from college, his son had finished senior school. She had a child enraged, beneath whose eyes bloomed mauve stains of exhaustion. It had only been, after all, a few weeks. Revelry was not her uppermost concern.

* * *

By nine p.m. Nathan still had not come home nor had he called, and Julia persuaded James to eat. Gwen had taken herself to bed, the first time that Julia had seen her be openly rude to Saskia who had tried and failed to convince her to have dinner with them. Gwen had responded with an unpleasant comment about James's cooking, had clattered around preparing herself Marmite toast, leaving butter, loaf, Marmite jar and a good many crumbs all over the counter, and had then clumped upstairs with her plate, looking thunderous.

'I'm going to sleep,' she told Julia, who had followed her upstairs, anxious. 'There's nothing to talk about – life is shit. I'm literally eating this toast and going to sleep in four seconds. See you tomorrow,' she relented, and allowed herself, stiffly, to be hugged. Julia held her daughter's bird-narrow frame for as long as she was permitted, and then returned to James and the girls. Her heart remained upstairs. The evening would be easier if Saskia had not brought home a stranger.

Rowan had arrived in a crisp white shirt with a sharply pointed collar, black tailored trousers that ended high above her ankles and were held up by black, snakeskin braces, and a pair of polished black brogues, very small. Her pallor was accentuated by comically oversized black-framed glasses, and pinned to one of the braces was an Art Deco crystal brooch, shaped like a Scottie dog. When they'd met at Christmas, Gwen had gazed down in open distrust at this severely attired pixie-person, and her scowl had hardened when Saskia said, 'Rowan's super creative – she makes loads of stuff, like you,' in a misguided attempt to find common ground. That had been her last visit. Julia hoped Gwen would sleep in, and that Rowan would leave early in the morning. Home should be a sanctuary, not Piccadilly Circus. Saskia's belongings were already strewn around her music room.

They ate on their knees in their square scrap of back garden. In his earlier enthusiasm James had grilled two packets of hot dogs and a cold stack of these, alongside a lukewarm mound of baked potatoes and a tray of now slightly wrinkling corn cobs, lay outside on a card table around his centrepiece, a heaped platter of barbecued chicken wings.

'At what point do we get worried about him?' James asked, though he had clearly begun to worry some time ago.

'I don't think he'll come back tonight, Dad.' Saskia frowned at her phone. She was sitting next to Rowan, cross-legged in the centre of a sunlounger, hunched over and typing furiously. 'I think he's pretty wasted.'

'What did he say? I'm glad he's communicating with someone, at least.'

'He's somewhere with Charlie. It's got a million spelling mistakes and then, "Tell Dad seed tortilla," and then a zillion emojis.'

'"Seed tortilla"?'

'"See you tomorrow", maybe.'

Rowan cocked her head, bird-like. 'God. I still think of your little brother as an actual child. It's insane to think of him old enough to drink, and now he's finished school! Super crazy.'

And he was nearly a father, thought Julia. *Super crazy.*

The girls both stood and announced that they were going out, and would come home quietly at an unspecified time. Neither offered to help clear away dinner. Julia regarded Saskia, who looked rather blowsy and dishevelled beside her sharp little friend. Her hair had grown too long, and though she had gained weight at college she had not bought clothes to accommodate it. Buttons strained. Julia dismissed the urge to tighten Saskia's bra straps, and to tie back her hair. Rowan, by contrast, had made an effort. She was severe-looking and not pretty, but had polished herself into a striking presence.

James pressed several ten-pound notes into Saskia's hand that were accepted without comment, and then the girls disappeared.

'What can I say? My people cater for emergencies.' James gave a resigned look at the groaning card table.

'I would have taken some of it to Philip tomorrow but I'm not sure he needs my deliveries any more. I must say, as bizarre as it all is, it is nice to think of him being taken care of. Strange. I never thought it would be Iris I'd have to worry about.'

'You don't have to worry about Iris, do you? She's been taking care of herself just fine since – what was his name?'

'Giles.'

'Right. Since Giles moved to France.' James gave her a cheeky grin, proud to have absorbed this family vernacular, and Julia shrugged off the ungenerous part of her that considered his use of it unseemly.

'She hasn't really been *alone* alone, she's had Philip on the other end of the phone. And text. And email. And fax machine. Even when Giles was in the picture they were always in touch.'

'Well, she couldn't expect him to be at her beck and call for ever if they weren't in a relationship any longer. What was he getting out of it?' James asked reasonably, and Julia fell silent, considering. Iris and Philip had seemed immovable as a mountain range and yet, unexpectedly, Philip had moved. What had seemed hewn from granite had shivered to pieces like glass.

'I was thinking, I probably should have figured he'd want to spend tonight with his friends. Your old dad's barbecued wings aren't the most rock-and-roll way to mark your high-school graduation. If that damn kid is not coming back I'm opening another beer. Would you like one?'

Julia shook her head. Her plate had been sitting on her knee and she moved it to the grass. James went inside, returning with his beer and a roll of cling film, and began to wrap up the chicken. 'I should have figured. I mean, when you think of the last few weeks – the kid needs a break.'

'Gwen needs a break.'

An edge in her voice made James stop. 'Of course she does. There's no competition. We're never going to play that game, baby – let's not start. There's only one team here.' He dragged his chair over and sat and faced her, looking serious. 'It's been awful and they both need a break. Thankfully it's not Gwen's style to go out drinking like a frat boy, and my son – every now and again he gets the urge to behave like the dumb teenage boy that he is.'

'But she has been longing for time alone with him. You've seen, she's been so generous with him, she's made a monumental effort not to disturb him while he was working. Now he's free he should have understood that. She's been counting the days. It's not just party time now that exams are over, these aren't normal circumstances.' Unable to stop herself she added, 'He has responsibilities.'

James stood up again. For a moment she thought he looked pained, but then he picked up a wrapped dish in each hand and headed back into the kitchen. 'They're not normal circumstances. You're right, and it's my fault – I should have drawn his attention to it.'

'It's not your fault in any way.'

'Come on.'

'Come on what?'

'Come on, let's not fight the kids' fights.'

She fell silent. He was right, of course, but Gwen's destructive temper was contagious, and Julia felt an urge to keep pushing. Instead she took his beer from the table and blew a low note across the mouth of the bottle, like a ship's horn. 'Okay,' she said after a moment, decisive. 'I'm sorry. I've caught Gwen's mood. Give me the frankfurters. Will you bring the ketchup back out?'

FORTY-THREE

'We need this,' James announced the next morning, battling a holdall into the boot of the car.

Nathan mumbled something and James came round to the back window.

'What?'

'I said, *like a hole in the head.*'

'That hole in your head is called a hangover, my boy. I offered intravenous fluids, you said no, my next best offer is a walk on the beach. You can get two hours' quality sleep in the car. Righty-ho then,' he added, in an execrable British accent. Nathan closed his eyes.

A day in Sussex seemed an ambitious plan, but James was insistent. It was the weekend, Saskia was with them, the weather was beautiful, and now was the time to begin a slow piecing back together. He was taking them all to Camber Sands. 'This family needs airing,' he'd told Julia early that morning, and with that, at least, she was inclined to agree. But she was fairly sure that Gwen and Nathan had not yet spoken to one another, and Gwen's reproachful glances over breakfast had been painful to witness. A London day trip might have been more sensible.

From the passenger seat, Julia turned to smile encouragingly at the children but received no response. Nathan and

Gwen, sullen and uncooperative, were looking anywhere but at one another. Saskia shifted and laid her head on Gwen's shoulder.

'Sleepy,' she mumbled. 'Ro and I sat up talking for ages when we came home.' She leaned across Gwen to address her brother. 'What time was it you got in?'

'Dunno. Three, maybe?'

'Right, but then he made us sit up with him and make him scrambled eggs and listen to his drunken rambling. You were going on and on about the Egg McMuffin being your personal madeleine.'

Sandwiched in the middle Gwen scowled, and then leaned forward between the seats and turned up the volume of the radio. Finally James climbed into the driver's seat, and announced that they were ready.

For the first hour they drove in silence. The road glinted in the sunshine and Nathan grudgingly yielded his sunglasses to his father so he could see to drive, and then threw his head back and covered his eyes in the crook of his arm. Saskia hummed intermittently to the radio, and Julia watched her own daughter's face in the rear view mirror and worried, and worried. She should have told James to take his own kids to the beach, and she and Gwen should have spent the day alone. This was too much for her, with Nathan in a temper and vacant, saccharine Saskia whom they had not seen for months and who had once again become a semi-stranger.

At Maidstone James swung the car into a service station. 'McDonald's. Sas gave me the idea, I absolutely insist. Your challenge, should you choose to accept it, is to compile the most unhealthy combination of items you can think of.

Someone get me the fish thing with fries, nuggets and a chocolate milkshake.' He turned and winked at Nathan. 'Next best thing to intravenous fluids.' Julia wondered why he seemed to find his son's excessive drinking to be amusing rather than reprehensible. Nathan slipped wordlessly from the car.

But McDonald's turned out to be an excellent idea. Back on the road with steaming paper bags, the children revived. Gwen spoke, voluntarily, to say that her cheeseburger was 'the best'. Nathan, finishing his second Big Mac, observed that fat and salt combined had magical restorative properties, and began to call out musical suggestions to his father. Saskia dipped a chicken nugget in Gwen's ketchup and nudged her gently with an elbow.

After a while Gwen said, 'I so should have got a milkshake,' and Julia was surprised to see Nathan take his from between his knees and offer it to her. James, who had been lifting his own from the cup holder to hand over his shoulder, glanced briefly at Julia and smiled, and Julia gave a tiny shrug and sipped her black coffee in silence. They drove on through Kent and south, to East Sussex.

They were not the only people drawn to the water. The queue for the car park stretched back more than a mile and so Julia, keen to preserve the fragile good tempers, did not object when James said they should go ahead. They took what they could carry and began to make their way along the road towards the shore, Gwen and Nathan lagging behind. Julia found herself walking with Saskia. She did not have the energy for someone else's daughter. She had been dreading Saskia's arrival in the house – another personality, more needs, emotional, practical, dietary. Last night, seeing

Saskia and Rowan together she had been riven with envy at their carelessness, their intimacy. Lucky, light-hearted, untraumatised. Katy had been to visit only once, carrying a small white orchid in Marks & Spencer cellophane and looking utterly petrified. Gwen did not seem to answer her phone any more, except to Nathan.

Julia's mind was upon the reconciliation taking place behind them; it took effort to turn her attention to the girl and think of a conversation she might begin. She settled on their location, the weather, the white-streaked purple bells of sea bindweed flourishing along the path. All this, so close to London, they should remember it year-round and come more often – and all the while thinking, *Has that little shit apologised? Has he let her speak? Will he give her a chance to tell him everything she suffered, and what it means to her?* As they mounted the dunes she paused for a moment, craning backwards, and spotted Gwen's red hair, still a way off in the distance.

Saskia began to screw her toe into the fine sand. 'It's been weird to be so far away with all this stuff happening to my family. I've been worried about my brother and Gwen and everyone and, I dunno, it's just easier to be here. Now I know that, like, even though this super-sad thing happened it's all going to be okay.'

Julia was startled; a moment ago they had been discussing the dune grass, and whether or not the beach would have a changing room. She and Saskia had never before had a conversation with any content.

'Is that your sense now? It's going to be okay?'

Saskia nodded. 'Definitely. I just can't even imagine what she went through, you know? And on top of everything there must have been this guilt that she'd let you guys down by getting pregnant in the first place, and she was agonising and agonising and then out of nowhere comes this massive stark reminder that we don't actually get to decide a lot of the time. Like, we're not in control at all. You don't think of someone having a miscarriage at sixteen. My mom says it's actually no less common then than any other time, and it's just one of those things. But that doesn't make it any easier when it's actually happening to *you* and not to all those other people. I just feel better being here with you guys so I can see them. And yeah, so I think they'll be okay. A sad thing happened that was no one's fault, and they love each other. And that's it.'

This was the longest speech Julia had ever heard Saskia make and she was struck by the girl's compassion. Now, something eased within her, remembering she liked James's daughter. Saskia would be kind to Gwen.

'They love each other,' Saskia said again, watching Gwen and Nathan approach across the car park. She spoke with admiration. Their arms were around one another and Nathan had taken Gwen's bag so she had nothing to carry. They were talking intently, not smiling, but not arguing. Gwen's palm was pressed to Nathan's chest. Julia turned away. Teenage relationships were always roller coasters, but how had the whole family ended up trapped with them on the ride?

The beach was crowded, utterly unlike her last visit when she and James had come alone and walked for miles along wide empty stretches of blond sand, met only by the odd dog walker and a few determined enthusiasts flying kites in the stiff winter wind. Today the heat had drawn hundreds of families, gathered in untidy sprawls behind candy-striped windbreaks, and in sinking plastic chairs. There were not enough umbrellas – tender English flesh was laid out everywhere like the aftermath of a massacre, gently roasting in the unaccustomed heat. Julia and Saskia unrolled towels, and Julia had read a chapter of her novel by the time Gwen and Nathan approached, fingers interlaced. Intermittently, Julia's eye was drawn to the baby at the centre of a large family group nearby. Naked but for a watermelon-pink sunhat, she was banging a tube of sunscreen onto the towel beneath her, pausing only when her mother spooned mashed banana into her mouth. Watching recalled to Julia the passionate, consuming Stockholm syndrome; the beautiful tyranny of early motherhood. She wondered how Gwen felt to see the slideshow exhibition of new parenthood enacted beside them throughout the afternoon – the endless soothing, changing, feeding – but Gwen showed no signs of having noticed.

FORTY-FOUR

'It's just so nice to meet you.' Joan's loose nest of blonde curls bounced as she nodded. Over the crook of her arm was a pink paper bag, from which white creamy shredded paper overflowed. In her other hand was a bunch of tall sunflowers, which she pressed shyly into Julia's hands.

'Thank you so much, they're beautiful. Come in,' said Julia, brightly and irrelevantly, since they were already in. For Philip she had resolved to make this new woman feel welcome, but could not shake the fear that she had entered accidentally into an illicit affair. 'If she tells you to call her Granny,' Iris had told Gwen, 'I'm calling the lawyers.' Iris had visited only that morning and her presence still hung in the air, like woodsmoke. Julia wondered if Philip could smell Chanel No. 5, and lingering, imperious disdain. But Philip, holding a coat and a small, mint-green ostrich leather handbag with a long gold chain, had barely taken his eyes from Joan. His hair had been swept up and forwards, in a rather stylish cut. He was, Julia realised, startled, wearing jeans.

Footsteps thundered above them and Nathan appeared, striding into the hall with a hand already extended to shake Philip's, as if about to welcome him into a glass-walled corner office for an interview. Gwen padded down after him, drawing with her a scent of nail polish and acetone. The fingernails of one hand were painted green, with white polka dots, Nathan too, Julia noticed, had a single green thumbnail. Julia made introductions, and they moved to the kitchen where James was brewing a pot of tea and unwrapping a banana bread from the market. He wiped his hands and came forward to greet them.

'How is it to be free, at long last?' Philip asked Nathan. He was still holding Joan's light mackintosh which he smoothed every now and again, a patient, attentive valet. Julia took it from him and hung it over a chair, along with the handbag. Joan fussed and protested and said she mustn't worry, but then began to move kitchen chairs around so that Philip might have one with arms.

'Supercalifragilisticexpialidocious,' Nathan told him. Gwen came to sit beside him and from the pocket of his jeans he produced her bottles of nail polish, one green, one white, and set them before her. 'Delivered. You remain unsmudged. I never intend to do any exams again. I'm not going to medical school, I've told my father already. I'm going to become a crab fisherman in Thailand.'

'When my boys were doing A levels it was a nightmare,' said Joan, accepting the mug of tea that James handed her before sliding it immediately towards Philip. 'But then it's all over before it's begun, and suddenly that's it, before you know it. And all these doctors in the family, you'll sail through.' She looked from James to Philip, and back to Nathan. 'Isn't it a funny thing, all these obstetricians in the family? Both your parents and Phil.'

Iris would die, thought Julia, turning away to hide her smile. She would spontaneously combust. Philip Alden. Phil.

'On a good day obs and gynae is the best job in the world,' James told her. 'On a bad day I wish I was a plumber.'

'Will you deliver babies, like your parents?'

'No,' said Nathan, rather too firmly. 'I'm going to do oncology.'

'Oh, isn't that wonderful, we need young men like you.' Joan pressed a hand to her heart. 'My Steve had lung. And your Daniel had liver, Phil said.' She turned to Julia who nodded, though her eyes flew to Gwen, who did not take kindly to discussions of her father's cancer, certainly not to such abbreviated, familiar references to it. But Gwen was at the sink rinsing a punnet of strawberries and either hadn't heard, or hadn't minded.

'What a *mensch*.' Joan looked around for affirmation and found it in Gwen who was looking at Nathan with an irritating pride. Nathan himself looked down modestly at his hands. He rubbed a finger over his green-painted thumbnail and it smeared. Gwen giggled and dispatched him upstairs for polish remover and cotton wool.

'Where will he study next year?' Joan took Philip's hand across the table, and squeezed it. 'Josh, that's my eldest, was at Guy's and St Thomas's and he made some lovely friends, though they did work him very hard. I must say, I know it's not what matters but it's nice for the parents that all the medicine's best in London, isn't it. He did six months of cleft palates in Guatemala, but mostly he was just down in Lambeth and even that feels far away when it's your eldest and you're used to having them upstairs. Aaron went to Birmingham. Has he decided?'

'He's got a place at Oxford,' James told her, while at the same time Gwen said, 'He might stay in London.'

'My goodness, isn't that something?' Joan blinked and nodded several times and looked rather uncertainly from Gwen to James.

James said nothing but stood and moved to the head of the table where he began to slice the banana cake rather formally, as if carving a side of roast beef. Gwen ran her finger round and round the edge of her empty plate. There was no longer any reason for Nathan to stay in London; Gwen's convenient misfortune had liberated him. He would go to New College, Oxford, and Gwen, with one more year of school ahead, would pine.

James distributed slices of cake and then left for the hospital, apologising to Joan, who apologised in return for having taken him away from his patients for even this long. After he'd gone Joan gave Philip a small querying glance, received a nod and then turned to Gwen. She was still holding a paper bag on her lap and this she handed over, hurriedly.

'I hope it's all right, but this is just a very little something. I had a pattern and I just thought, something cosy. Good for snuggling on the sofa.'

The gift turned out to be a white knitted blanket with a perfect rainbow cabled into its centre. 'It's gorgeous,' Gwen breathed. 'This is amazing, I can't believe you can do this! Thank you *so much*.' She hugged Joan, who flushed, looking pleased.

'Oh, it's only practice it needs. I can teach you if you'd like, you'd pick up cable in no time. Phil told me that you liked rainbows, so.'

'I do, and I love knitting, I just haven't had that much practice. I do mostly polymer clay, and a tiny bit of oils. But knitting's cool 'cause you can do it while you do other stuff, like watching TV or whatever. I've been sitting at home a lot for the last few weeks – I could have knitted myself, like, a whole house.'

Joan's expression softened. 'You know, when I first married I had baby fever, and I thought it would be easy peasy. I got pregnant straight away and at eight weeks I had a mis.' Julia froze, horrified. Gwen was looking down at the folded blanket on the table, unmoving, and it was impossible to see her face. 'The hardest time of my life, till then. And back then no one talked about it, we were just meant to get on with it, pull your socks up, try for another, make it right that way. I don't know why anyone thinks that's the answer – it isn't. Or isn't for everyone. I didn't want to try again so we didn't, not for two more years. I was scared that maybe my body couldn't do it and it would all happen the same way. And I was very sad for a time. So sad. But then I started to get better and then all those years later when I lost my Steve all I could think was, "We had those precious years together first, just the two of us, just to be married." And I've got my boys, and that time we had, back then I wouldn't have chosen it for all the world I was so desperate to have a family, but they were beautiful years. We got to know each other. We grew up. I can't wish it differently.' She ran her fingers idly over each coloured arc of the rainbow in turn. 'I like rainbows too, you know. They're hopeful. My first Schnauzer dam was called Rainbow because she had these lovely stripy markings, not really what you'd want in a pure Schnauzer, very odd, that's why I got her in the end, the breeder said no one would take a funny-looking scrap like that so she was left on the shelf, but in the poodle crosses it just came out beautifully. And what a temperament. Twelve, she lived to. She was my precious girl, she saved me, after Steve. She saved me.'

Julia was cringing, waiting for some unforgivable rudeness, and felt a rush of anger when Gwen raised her head and she saw a tear slip down her face. But Gwen was looking at Joan intently. She said, 'We had Mole, and he saved me, too.'

'They just know, don't they, dogs,' Joan agreed, and she and Gwen smiled at one another.

FORTY-FIVE

A, A, A, B, C. Oxford would not take him. Imperial would not take him. It was King's College London, another world-class institution, and it was unimaginable, and it was the end of the world. Controlled while on the line to Nathan's housemaster, James had put the phone down, paused, and then slammed his palm into the door frame leaving a fine spiderweb of cracks beneath the heel of his hand. The next minutes were a blur, from which Julia could only recall the gist of her own soothing, reasonable words – she had talked about perspective, about difficult circumstances, about a sense of achievement, personal fulfilment and who you actually were as a human being mattering more than historic names – but only moments later found herself screaming that he should think himself bloody lucky his child was being educated at all when her own child's life had come close to ruin; somehow James was roaring that she wanted Nathan to fail just because Gwen made destructive choices; her outraged denial of this indefensible accusation had been loud, but had not been convincing to either of them.

She hadn't wanted Nathan to fail. But Gwen had suffered, and Nathan's impermeable cheer, his impending success, the new stage he was impatient to begin had all filled her with envy. He seemed shatterproof, and she could not quite let go of its unfairness. It was Gwen's strength and affliction to feel to the quick even a glancing blow, while Nathan had been so effectively in denial about its existence that the loss of his child made no lasting impression. And now to grieve for something so petty – how could James truly think a university so important? It was ludicrous. What message did James's own disappointment convey to his child about what mattered in life? She would have liked a little less emphasis placed on the boy's curriculum vitae, a little more placed on his character. No. Julia could not pity Nathan. Nor could she like him, even in these last weeks when his devotion to Gwen had apparently returned and redoubled.

James and Julia went to bed in a frosty silence, unaccustomed and distressing to both of them. They had never before raised their voices in anger and it was only now, after the smashing of that precious, celebrated myth (*We are a couple who always speak with gentleness; we are a couple who sleep each night face to face; we are a couple unlike other couples*) that each had realised the wonder of it. After all, they had weathered more treacherous storms. As parents they made very different choices, true, but James had proven himself wise and generous to his marrow, a better man even than she'd known. And Julia's gratitude, above all else, had never left her. She had expected to live the rest of her life without love and had found James, and had never before lost sight of that revelation. But tonight she had abandoned her gratitude when James had seemed to forget his own. He made it clear he blamed Gwen. An act of sabotage. Had he really said that? Not quite, but almost.

In the middle of the night, she woke to find that they had moved together in sleep and were entwined, arms and legs wrapped tightly around one another, the sheets kicked off and entangled at their feet. James was sleepily kissing her face, her eyelids, her mouth, and she had begun to cry and to whisper frantic words of love and of apology before it began to dawn that what had roused them both was furious shouting, somewhere in the house. They froze, pressed tightly chest to chest, breath held as if sharing a narrow hiding place. Against her cheek Julia felt James furrow his brow as he listened. He dropped his forehead against her collarbone, and rolled over with an exhausted groan. Julia fumbled on the floor for her dressing gown and followed James downstairs. As she passed her practice room the door opened and Saskia emerged, sleep-tousled and squinting, mumbling something indistinct.

'It's fine, go back to sleep,' Julia whispered, and Saskia nodded wordlessly and closed her eyes and the door again.

It was three o'clock in the morning and on the ground floor of the house both of their children were screaming, voluble and operatic. Over James's shoulder Julia looked down and saw Gwen at the foot of the stairs, dressed in tartan brushed cotton pyjama shorts and a faded Rainbow Brite T-shirt. She had worn this at seven or eight years old and called it back into service as an ironic retro item, though it seemed to Julia that she had been seven or eight only yesterday and there was nothing ironic about a child in child's clothing, however much midriff it now exposed. Gwen's hair was electric, huge and wild around her pale face, and she was pacing back and forth in the narrow hall as if barring the front door, a scrawny and gesticulating Cerberus.

'You can't! You can't say that, you can't, you can't just rewrite everything!' Gwen's thick glasses slipped to the end of her nose on a slick of tears and sweat, and she was forced to pause and push them back up with her forefinger. 'It's not fair!'

'Hey. Keep your voices down. What's wrong with you? Where've you been, Nathan? I've been calling you. Come here – I've been worried. We needed to talk today.'

Neither teenager gave any indication that they could hear James speaking. Nathan lurched into view from the kitchen and began to repeat that Gwen was insane, out of her mind, impossible to reason with. His voice was loud, slurred with alcohol and outrage, and he had the hood of his sweatshirt tightened low over his brow so that his face was in shadow and he looked as if he were about to commit a mugging, or an act of light vandalism. Gwen, who had begun to hyperventilate, was gulping back strangled hiccups of rage between each choked word of accusation.

James rushed to pull his son into a tight bear hug as Julia went to embrace her daughter. Gwen did not succumb easily, her long limbs stiff and flailing, her narrow shoulders heaving with jagged, desperate breaths.

'Shh. Breathe, Dolly. What is going on?' Julia pushed back the few damp curls that had stuck to Gwen's sweating brow just as James, in less compassionate tones, turned and demanded, 'What the hell is going on down here? Why are you shouting at him?' He had one arm thrown over Nathan's shoulder, his hand upon his son's chest, upon his notionally broken heart. Nathan's eyes were pink-rimmed and bloodshot. Crying? Drugs, maybe? Julia did not feel particularly sympathetic to either cause. She glared at James.

'Ask her,' Nathan said bitterly, pointing. 'She's having a psychotic break. She's actually psychotic. I haven't done anything wrong. My life is officially over now, thank you, thank you very much. You can't actually keep me chained in this house any more, I'm not a hostage, I'm allowed time off for good fucking behaviour. And I'm allowed to say that the reason my life is over is—'

'Your life is not over, you got amazing grades—'

'Oh, yeah, they're really amazing. They're amazing for a retard. Amazing for a school like yours where everyone does Goat Milking and General Studies and fucking *Art*, amazing for you with your accidental, "Oh, I only care about rainbows and glitter and oops! I get As." '

'Art is just as important as what you do!'

Nathan turned unsteadily on his heel and set off towards the front door and Gwen shrieked with incoherent rage, shaking Julia off and chasing him. 'Stop walking away from me! Come back! COME BACK!'

'Enough,' hissed James, springing forwards to bar Nathan's exit. Gwen and Nathan paused and looked at him. 'Nathan, I want to talk to you, properly. But this is not the way, and you are not walking out of this house again tonight, do you understand? You both sort your asses out like civilised adults.'

Nathan, who had been looking slightly queasy and fleetingly contrite, now raised his face in a sneer. 'Oh, because we never heard you and Mom yelling, never. It was nothing but raindrops on roses and whiskers on kittens in our house growing up. One endless picnic. Like the fucking Waltons.'

James now looked thunderous. 'Stop. Cursing. Both of you. You will behave like human beings in this house, and like the adults you claim to be. I don't care if you are seventeen or seventy, this is unacceptable. We need to sit down and talk, I promise you, we just need to—'

'What are you even talking about? Nothing's going to be okay, and by the way, you can't promise me shit because my life is over already, because she has chopped my balls off. Literally one by one, my balls have been chopped off – she's torn them off with her teeth like a Rottweiler. "It is all rather unexpected and disappointing, Fuller,"' he quoted, shaking his head sorrowfully and stroking the air beneath his chin as if pulling on a beard, '"so unexpected and disappointing but *under the circumstances . . .*" I knew it was a mistake that you told Markham, now he's all like, "Under the circumstances it's lucky you're not in a ditch." "Under the circumstances it's lucky you're not a crack addict eating from the trash under Waterloo Bridge." "Under the circumstances we'd have been happy if you'd dropped out of school and got a job licking the toilets clean at McDonald's, we'd have been jolly proud of you *under the circumstances*".'

Gwen gave a gasp, outrage mingled with disbelief. 'You're such a snob! And there aren't any circumstances! Your circumstances are literally exactly how they were before – it's made no difference whatsoever, your life never changed even one per cent. We've all been walking on eggshells for you pretending that any of this actually matters, like your *school exams* were the most important thing in the world. Do you even know how stupid that is? Do you know anything about the real world at all? Newsflash – no one cares at all about your A levels, literally no one. And you never let me talk about the fact that we lost our baby, you don't care, you've just had everyone pretend that the whole thing never even happened, like *our baby* never even happened. It's the stupidest thing I've ever heard, it's the most selfish – and now you're blaming me and – and you're the most immature, disgusting—' She broke off, weeping extravagantly. Julia tried to put an arm around her again, to guide her back upstairs, and was once more abruptly pushed off.

Nathan spread his hands and gestured around, gathering looks of sympathy from an imagined crowd of supporters, though only Gwen and Julia were facing in his direction, neither inclined to solicitude. Julia now stepped forwards. 'Go to bed,' she ordered, attempting the same commanding air that James had achieved moments earlier. 'Enough. We will talk as a family in the morning. I'm sorry you feel you've had a hard day, Nathan. I know you don't want to hear it right now but I think in time you'll come to be very proud of yourself. You've had a shock, but now it's three o'clock in the morning. Go to bed. Now, please.'

'I was under the impression this was a free country.' Nathan was not looking at her but instead continued his slurred address to the invisible audience, now in the galleries. 'I was under the impression people could air their dirty laundry in the privacy of their own homes. This is my home, isn't it? I was under the impression it was good to talk about our feelings. To *express*.'

'Yeah, Julia,' said Gwen, which startled Julia and came as an unexpectedly painful betrayal, 'it's actually none of your business. It's not like I tried to get involved when you guys were screaming at each other earlier.'

'We weren't screaming,' Julia protested, as Nathan began a rather hollow, mirthless laugh. 'Pots and kettles all over the place. 'S'like living in a kitchen cupboard. We're all mad here,' he added, smiling in a way that suggested that the spectators in the dress circle had appreciated this reference. 'I'm mad, you're mad. They're Hare and Hatter, baby. Visit either you like, they're both mad.'

'They were screaming,' Gwen told him. 'They were, while you were out. When they couldn't get hold of you and they were worrying and then they phoned the school, they were screaming their heads off at each other for ages.'

'Love's young dream. The lesson in all of this, baby, is that there's no such thing as perfect anything, it's all just PR bullshit, 's'what I've been saying to you all along if you recall, and you didn't want to hear it. I get called cynical so often that people forget to call me right, which I also am, but cynical's just sensible. There, that's my bumper-sticker contribution. Cynical's sensible, and it's all sunshine and roses until you start fighting and then the next stage is, "*It's not you – it's us. Mommy and Daddy still love you both very much.*" 'S'amazing how everyone reverts to cliché. Here's a cliché – life's a bitch. Life's a bitch, and then you die. Everyone knows I'm right, we're all dancing on the *Titanic* and no one will admit the Emperor's got his cock out. Now please come here.' Nathan opened his arms and Julia was astonished to see Gwen move into them, grateful and without hesitation. She had hunched over automatically, so that he might put his arms over her shoulders. Moments ago Gwen had been almost unhinged with righteous fury; now she had buried her face against his neck and was stroking his hair and murmuring inaudibly. Julia thought she caught the words 'going to be . . .' and 'I hate . . .' but could not hear and so did not know what Gwen hated. Julia, with sharp clarity, hated Nathan. Still too inebriated to modulate his voice, Nathan began to whisper loudly and ardently into the fox-red cloud of Gwen's hair that he loved her, that he was sorry about the baby, their poor baby, that he hadn't meant it, that he had never been so unhappy. 'I don't understand,' he kept saying, 'I don't understand.' Julia watched his hands roaming up and down her daughter's narrow, bent back, the sharp shoulder blades, the knobbed spine visible beneath faded cotton, his gestures both of reassurance and perhaps preliminary sexual advance. Julia looked away in disgust. She heard footsteps and saw James heading upstairs. He gave a grim little smile and gestured to Julia to give up, to join him and together they retired to their bedroom, feeling fragile and somehow brutalised. In the living room, Gwen and Nathan were still crying and kissing, kissing and crying, cupping each other's faces in desperation, drawing one another in as if they were reuniting or perhaps parting before an uncertain future on the chill, grey platform of a wartime train station.

FORTY-SIX

'Not good,' said Julia, in response to her mother-in-law's enquiry. An exhalation could be heard through the phone. Without warning Iris had taken herself to France; her displeasure came through with a Gallic hinted shrug, and the imagined aroma of lavender, and pastis. Julia stepped out of the lift from the underground car park and battled to release the chain of a tethered supermarket trolley, one-handed. 'You can't even begin to imagine how horrible it was yesterday. It was as if everyone finally lost their minds, once and for all. I said such awful things and James looked so hurt and I still couldn't stop myself. The only thing I'm longing to say and can't is that I hate his son, and I want him out of my house. And Gwen's absolutely insistent that everything will be fine once Nathan gets over yesterday and it won't be, I saw his face. He'll never forgive her – not for Oxford, not for getting pregnant. And not for her results. Which, by the way, I am bloody proud of.' Julia bit her lip and stared glassily into her empty trolley. 'Though not as proud as I am of how courageous she's been recently. Unlike James, I have not brought up my daughter to believe that grades reflect the value of a person.'

She had come to lean on James so completely that thinking of it gave her vertigo, yet now it was James's son about whom she needed counsel and, almost without realising, she had begun to withdraw from the safety of their private, holy confessional. Now she took her fears to Iris, leaving with James the banalities, the palliatives, the careful and protective white lies so essential to a new family. We are all fine. It's fine. Your son is a fine, upstanding citizen, I'm so fond of him. Of course he needs to blow off steam. A small, unnerving gulf had opened, a crack in the earth between them two inches wide, a mile deep. She had come to the supermarket for fruit and eggs, and tuna steaks for this evening's dinner, and to rant in guaranteed, luxurious privacy. She did not care about fruit or eggs or tuna. Now she was wandering up and down the aisles of Waitrose looking blankly at product after product, and offloading her anxiety onto Iris. Iris, whom she longed to visit in Parliament Hill, whose face she longed to see. Iris, who no longer lived in Parliament Hill, who made fresh starts with such dignity, who had taken the sorrow she refused to acknowledge to the far side of the Channel.

It had been many years since Julia had been to Giles's house in Bargemon. Gwen had been eight, engrossed by her crochet kit, utterly uninterested in Giles's attempts to teach her tennis or Julia's to take her down to the ponds to visit the squat fat interesting toads. Gwen had sat cross-legged by the swimming pool making pink and purple coasters shaped like four-petalled flowers, her tongue clamped between her teeth with stern concentration. She would do nothing else. It had been uncomfortably like having their own little sweat shop, Daniel had observed, staffed with one extremely diligent child labourer. When she'd run out of fuchsia they'd expected the coaster craze to fizzle but instead she had begged and pleaded, hopping from foot to foot, and Julia had driven her the hour and a half back into Nice to find a haberdashery.

The house, Iris had assured her, had barely changed since that summer. It was rather quiet, perhaps, but several people in the village remembered her. Julia pictured her mother-in-law outside on the highest of the terraces, sitting at a terracotta-tiled table beneath the thick-leafed shade of an ancient fig tree. Iris herself was a blank in this image. It was high summer, and possibly 40 degrees, but surely she wasn't in anything as undignified as a bathing suit? Loose white linen, possibly, and a broad straw hat. Would she always be chic, even in complete, unbroken solitude? Then Iris brought her back into the fluorescent chill of Waitrose by saying, 'Well, you do have rather different child-rearing approaches, put it that way. It's tricky to bring two sets of values together so late in the day, but I must say I don't think Thing has it entirely wrong—'

'And that's fine, but what about bringing up children to be kind, or to be thoughtful, or to take responsibility for their actions, or to trust their own intuition? I don't understand – he puts such value on generosity in his own behaviour and with his kids he has this blind spot – the most important thing above everything is pedalling away on this hamster wheel. He can't think that's what matters most in life, and yet he does. It's just so, so *narrow*. A degree doesn't make you happy.'

'Hamsters don't pedal. I agree that one can be equally miserable with an Oxford degree as without, but you do see why he's disappointed when it was such a close thing.

And I do think the ex-wife has some fairly substantial expectations for the boy, too.'

Julia was glaring into a chiller cabinet at an array of Cheddars and Wensleydales and Red Leicesters. Did they need cheese? She couldn't remember. She threw several blocks into the trolley, then replaced one. When she reached the end of the aisle she hesitated and returned for it, dragging her trolley backwards. 'I couldn't care less what loony Pamela thinks. I can't see how the pregnant women of Boston have coped today when she's spent every waking hour phoning either Nathan or James. Or me, to ask for Nathan or James. And meanwhile James is finally having to confront the reality that Nathan – shock horror – isn't necessarily a genius. What's to say he would have got anything different anyway? Maybe he didn't mess up and these are the marks he deserves. Till yesterday James was genuinely resolute that the last months wouldn't have to cost Nathan anything, as long as we all worked hard enough, as if we could manage it away so beautifully that no one would even have to break their stride, but now he needs to give his son a kick up the backside and get him to stop behaving like such a bloody child, and to come home, stop drinking, get a bit of perspective. None of this will matter remotely in the long run – Oxford, not-Oxford, who cares? He's in a ludicrously privileged position. And he can't just leave Gwen in this awful limbo that she won't even admit she's in – he has to tell her if it's over. Enough's enough. I'd like to see them all prioritise some *values*, not just marks.'

'Have you and Thing talked this morning?'

'About what? What is there to say? I feel as if we're speaking different languages. But I do know his son can't behave like this and live under my roof.'

'It isn't just your roof.'

'Exactly,' said Julia, ignoring what she suspected had been Iris's point. 'It's Gwen's childhood home. She has a right to feel safe, and looked after, and secure. If they break up—'

'Listen, darling.' Ice clinked in a glass and Julia felt a stab of envy, picturing pale Provençal sunshine, chilled rosé under a sheen of condensation, *bleu de Bresse* weeping on a board of olive wood, *magret de canard*, the air heavy with ripe figs and citronella smoke, a hot and honeyed escape from muddy reality. Iris had been made unhappy by a change of circumstances and had thrown back her shoulders, and booked a ticket to France. She would give no straight or definitive answer about her return. She had wanted to sell her house, so she'd sold her house. She had wanted to go to France, and a few weeks later had taken up residence in Bargemon. She made apparently effortless fresh starts. Julia flung several cartons of fat-free yoghurt into her trolley with unnecessary force. 'I'm so glad you phoned me,' Iris went on. 'You need to get this off your chest, and I must say it's rather a relief not to hear you Pollyanna-ing around the place but now you're going to hear me say the opposite of what I usually tell you. It's all very well to be expressive and let things out in a relationship and everything else, but this time you simply can't do it. You must call me or at a push Philip Alden, if he can find the time between picking up Viagra prescriptions and manicuring poodles to answer the telephone, but for God's sake don't say any of this at home. He'll never forgive you. You feel aggrieved by his child and he feels aggrieved by yours, so please stop talking about them. I agree that you are very different sorts of parents but the beauty of your position is that you don't have to bother finding common ground because you don't have to parent together, so none of it matters in the slightest. Just leave one another to get on with it. Your efforts now need to be directed back towards your own business.'

Julia wheeled slowly through the biscuit aisle, then reversed again to snatch a treacherous roll of Marie biscuits. Philip was bringing Joan for tea. 'We're supposed to be going out for dinner tomorrow night. James insisted.'

'Don't you go out for dinner all the time?'

'I can't even think . . . we've not been out the two of us since before everything happened. Months ago. We're actually meant to be going to Milan for the weekend in a few weeks – James has those Rossini tickets – but I can't even think about that just yet.'

'Listen to yourself. Anyone would think you had survived a nuclear holocaust. *Everything happened*, as you so coyly put it, and was horrid, but we need a firm return to real life now, please. I'm desperately relieved to hear you're getting a weekend away soon. Listen to me. Put on something attractive, get your hair done, go out tomorrow, for the love of God. All this micromanaging of the almost-adult is unhealthy for absolutely everyone. Why don't you book a hotel for the night?'

'We *can't*.'

'I don't see why not, but then what do I know. Listen, enjoy tomorrow evening. I must go, I've decided to lunch every day in the square, I can't lurk in this house just because – I can't just *sit here*. Come and visit.'

She was gone, and Julia too was alone again, wheeling her trolley towards the tills and unpacking onto the conveyer belt her various acquisitions, having forgotten almost everything for which she'd come.

FORTY-SEVEN

Gwen slept intermittently all afternoon, stirring only briefly when her mother came in from shopping and sat beside her silently for a time, stroking her hair. When she next woke she was alone and it was cooler, the sky through the window a bank of dense bruise-dark cloud. There were voices downstairs and she knew without hesitation that Nathan was in the house.

The ground had shifted. When they had eventually gone to bed last night he'd seemed full of a determined, unfocused, angry passion, had pulled her to him urgently but it had been without affection or even much aware-ness of her. Afterwards he had turned his back to her in brooding silence, and later must have crept out while she lay sleeping for she'd woken alone, and a new, sick sense of foreboding had kept her cocooned beneath the muf-fling safety of the covers. His absence filled the room that morning. It squatted lead-heavy on her chest, and she had the sudden understanding that they could have weathered his physical removal to Oxford, and that if he had won the place she'd so feared she would have cost him nothing, and might still have been his girlfriend. Now he was going nowhere, but in his bitter disappointment he was moving beyond her reach.

She had planned to change. She had wanted to brush her hair. She had wanted to paint her nails, and find her push-up bra, and paint black kohl over the red rims of her bloodshot eyes. Instead, unaltered, she padded downstairs where she knew he'd be.

Gwen entered the living room to find Saskia's friend Rowan sitting neatly on top of Saskia's closed suitcase, cross-legged like a pixie. She wore a white vest and black denim dungarees, small, very round mirrored sunglasses, and burgundy lipstick on a very white face.

'It's a travesty,' Rowan was saying. 'Hi, Gwen, cute bracelet. I'm going to climb into this suitcase and come with you. I'm going to slip into your pocket.'

'Come with me!' Saskia said, and Rowan sprang to her feet so the two could embrace, rocking from side to side in one another's arms savouring their maudlin, pantomime sadness. Nathan was lounging in an armchair and as Gwen entered he did not look up, but instead smiled towards his sister with her friend, indulgent, paternal. Behind her James came in with the car keys.

'I'm so sorry, guys, but I have to take Miss Saskia. The time has come.'

Rowan stuck out her lower lip in protest. 'Boo,' she said, 'boo, boo. Let her stay! We say let her stay for ever.'

'Believe me, if I could I would. Take it up with the college – they claim they need her back.'

'Transfer to Magdalen,' Rowan said, finally removing the mirrored sunglasses and letting them fall. They were, Gwen now saw, on a long chain of black-and-gold links that hung around her neck. 'Come back with me, you know it's the only sensible thing to do.'

'Magdalen? Only losers go to Oxford – all the cool kids are going to King's.' Nathan swept back his hair. To hear him, Gwen thought, you would never know that he had cried for most of last night.

'I'm taking this suitcase and we're going in five minutes. Four minutes. Who's coming with me?'

Nathan raised his hand. 'I'm coming. Rowan? You in?'

'I hadn't really thought about it. I'd love to but I don't have a means of getting home again.'

'I can be your means,' said James, pausing to set down the suitcase he held. 'I'll drop you home. But if you're coming we're all leaving now, now. Gwen?' he asked, squeezing her shoulder. Gwen shook her head. The presence of the others dropped a cloak of public silence and propriety over her; Nathan's inaccessibility beyond it was insupportable. He still had not looked at her. When they were next alone, he would say things she did not want to hear.

Outside, James began to hoot the car horn and Nathan jogged out after the others. After a moment Saskia returned. Gwen swallowed, thickly. Saskia's loss severed yet another fine wire of connection with Nathan and left her perilous.

Saskia took Gwen's face between her hands, squeezing her cheeks, shaking Gwen gently from side to side. 'Please don't let my brother be a dick.'

'I don't know how I can stop him.' A tear slipped down each cheek.

'Oh no, don't be sad, I'm sorry. You're still my sister, please don't cry. You are, I mean it, that's the amazing thing. You'll always be my sister whatever happens. Always.'

Gwen nodded tightly. It was not true, of course. Saskia was Nathan's sister. Gwen had nobody.

'I thought I'd be able to talk to him on the way home this evening but then Rowan came to Heathrow with us, so I had to drop her back. I had to listen to him pretend to be fine instead.'

'Well, where is he now?' asked Pamela. She sounded faintly accusing, as though James might have mislaid their son like a dry-cleaning ticket, or a bunch of keys.

'Asleep, it's two a.m.'

'Are you at work? Why are you awake?'

'Yes,' James lied, closing the kitchen door behind him and lowering his voice. 'On call, my house officer rang. Shoulder dystocia and postpartum haemorrhage and – I can't talk about it twice,' said James, who had not, in fact, even talked about it once, and was a poor liar. He was not on call, and the prolonged dystocia had been first thing this morning, an unpleasant enough birth that he felt guilty using it now as an excuse. The mother had been morbidly obese and suffering gestational diabetes and he ought to have insisted on a section, but she had cried and pleaded and James, overtired after yesterday's emotional scenes, had not had the energy to resist her. She had tried to push, and the newborn had suffered brachial plexus damage. James did not, now, feel good about this decision.

The truth was that he couldn't sleep, had longed for someone to talk to, and had no wish to wake Julia as he did not trust himself to remain civil. She had accused him of having no sense of perspective, of snobbery, of inhabiting an elite and rarefied plane while discarding 'what really matters'. Hadn't she heard anything he'd confided about his background? About his own childhood? Did she really think that names and labels were what mattered to him? To accuse him of snobbery was risible – and the hypocrisy had taken his breath away. All he had ever taught his son was the value of hard work, of discipline, of aspiration. It was far more indulgent to raise a child to think that academic education was an irrelevance as long as their self-esteem was thriving, or whatever the hell it was she believed. What really matters? What horseshit. Meanwhile, along the way, Julia had lobbed a series of adjectives at his son for which, twenty-four hours later, he was still struggling to forgive her. Selfish. Immature. Self-absorbed. Inconsiderate. All these on a day when Nathan had needed not condemnation but comfort, a day when the memory of Gwen's monumental selfishness was heightened, its consequences livid and raw. Julia accused Nathan of disrespect, of behaving badly towards Gwen. Well, Nathan had his whole life ahead and it was understandable if he did not want to remain in a joyless and precociously serious mini-marriage with an infantile, spoiled little girl who whined with hectoring and imperious neediness. James found himself grieving the Oxford loss afresh. As well as everything else it would have granted Nathan total liberty from Gwen.

He'd walked away expecting any minute that Julia would calm down, follow him upstairs and apologise, and when she hadn't he had grown angrier, and more resentful. Pamela, who loved Nathan as he did, would understand.

'Was the baby okay?'

'What baby?'

'Shoulder dystocia? Never mind, never mind. Nathan sounds terrible. Should I come, do you think?'

'No,' said James reflexively, but then thought for a moment. 'Maybe, actually. I think we should sit down with him. I still can't believe it. Mr Markham is shocked, we've talked twice today. When did you speak to Nathan?'

'Darling, I've spoken to him twenty-five times today, it's precisely why I'm worried. He barely called all summer and now it's like the Batphone. I popped to one of Beth's deliveries this morning and when I switched my phone on I had eleven missed calls. I think I should come. It's only three weeks till the Paris conference in any case – I could come and just stay through. Are you okay? You sound very cross.'

'You make it sound as if I haven't been taking care of him.'

'Jamesy, I don't know what's afoot with you, but I said absolutely no such thing. I said the boy phones his mother.'

'Julia called him vindictive for blaming Gwen. I don't see who else we should blame.'

'Julia's delusional,' said Pamela shortly.

'We had a crazy fight yesterday,' James admitted.

'I'm amazed you have the energy to fight with everything else going on. You know, I feel I ought to do something nice for Gwen. She's one of the most spoiled little girls I've ever met and I am absolutely consumed with loathing. For my own sanity I need karmic balance. I should give her a gift.'

James, long familiar with Pamela's complex and contradictory theology of giving, said nothing. He had many times been on the receiving end of these presents of karmic redress, and they were usually tied in a stinging ribbon of acid.

'Listen, for God's sake, if you really think it's over between them don't let him have break-up sex with her – she'll get pregnant again, I promise you. Don't laugh, I'm absolutely serious, she will. She's a conniving little so-and-so who will have to readjust to the idea that she's not the centre of the universe,' Pamela concluded, apparently abandoning all thoughts of good karma. 'Enough flinging herself around like Ophelia and then pulling that bloody exam rabbit out of the hat. *Her* life's on track. She made her bed.'

'Yes. But look what it cost Nathan to lie in it. What I don't understand,' James went on, feeling a guilty rush of disloyalty and relief, 'is how it can be possible to put such a premium on children's happiness and self-fulfilment or whatever, with no understanding that encouraging academic success teaches precisely the delayed gratification that is essential to later happiness in the real, adult world. Happiness isn't having your needs met instantly, like an infant. Fulfilment in later life is effort rewarded. In work, in relationships, in marriages . . .' Here he trailed off, thinking it unwise to pursue a discussion of marital fulfilment with his ex-wife.

'You can't eat happiness,' said Pamela shortly. Her pragmatism had always been robust, if incongruous. 'A joyous adolescence playing with Play-Doh won't pay the gas bills later on. And more to the point, someone somewhere will say no to the girl, and then what will happen? She'll fall apart.'

'Julia thinks I'm pushy. She called me a snob.'

'Take it as a compliment. Has Nathan said anything to you about America?'

James opened the fridge and stared blankly into its depths. 'He's missed the applications, no? I thought we'd agreed not.'

'That was mid-debacle, if you recall, when the shackles of imminent teenage parenthood awaited him in London. He could start spring semester, it wouldn't take much, quick SATs, personal statement. Wentworth will write him a reference, and with that he'd be a shoo-in everywhere. What are you chewing? It's loud. Even Harvard's still not out of the question with good enough referees.'

'Chicken from yesterday, I'm starving. My God, that would be incredible. It would have blown my mother's mind, two grandkids at college. A son and a grandson at Harvard! That's what she busted her ass for, to get me out of Dorchester, to teach me—'

'Take a little credit, you got yourself out. You won the scholarships. And,' she conceded, seizing an opportunity to criticise Julia obliquely, 'your mother taught you the value of hard work. We can sort it out, you know, there are enough Ivy League schools. I'll come to London, and we'll powwow.'

Someone else was awake in the house. James heard footsteps, and the floorboards above his head creaked as one of the children padded across the landing to the bathroom.

'I'd better go.'

'Good luck. I'm really not sure I'd eat yesterday's chicken at the Free, you know,' said Pamela, confusing James until he remembered he'd said he was at work. 'It's bad enough on day one. Consider a few days a week of veganism. Or even just Meatless Mondays. You'll feel better, I promise. I'll email when I've booked flights. Kiss, kiss. Ciao, ciao.'

FORTY-EIGHT

Julia and James had come to an uneasy truce. Resenting, fearing, longing for the extra hour away from Gwen, Julia thought they should save time and drive, but on James's insistence they had instead walked in late-summer dusk across the bottom of the Heath, keeping pace in a silence that might have been lingering animosity, or new shyness. They went to the Bull and Last for smoked salmon and warm soda bread and sharp, strong gin and tonics; for space, for fresh air, and above all else for respite from the house, which hummed with steady and claustrophobic tension. Julia had steeled herself for protest, and had been unprepared for Gwen simply saying, 'Okay, Mummy,' in a small, dull voice, and then subsiding back onto the sofa with a look of such blank and eloquent wretchedness that Julia had immediately opened her mouth to say that she wouldn't go. The next moment she'd caught sight of James's grave, tired face and had bitten her tongue.

'I know, I know, we need to talk about the children,' she'd said earlier, when he told her he'd made a reservation, and he'd looked hurt and said softly, 'We need to *not* talk about the children.' He was right, but knowing it hadn't eased her conscience as the front door closed behind them.

How good it would be to walk away. What a relief, not to see that flushed and tear-greased pleading resentful face. What soothing music the silence would be, free from Gwen's voice, petulant, disconsolate; what restorative paradise away from all the weeping. To be alone with James. Julia ached to stay, and longed to flee.

She must not forget that Gwen had chosen this relationship with Nathan. Yet who would choose this? A hurt and angry little girl couldn't know what she had fought for, and those who understood should have tried harder to stop her. *It's my fault*, but then again, *Gwen stamped her feet and demanded adulthood*. And on and on, tramping the same tight and tedious circuit over old, worn ground, the same regrets unending, unresolved.

Julia refused a starter and then, barely settled at the table, they almost rowed. James said irritably that they might as well get a takeaway and a taxi home if she had only allowed twenty minutes for the meal; they'd better start back now, in fact, it had been a wonderful evening and, after all, they'd exceeded their yearly allowance of fun. He looked cross and flushed, and he was in the right once again. She noticed that he had shaved, and put on a favoured, dry-clean-only white shirt. He had come home that afternoon with a bunch of creamy white and violet-streaked lisianthus, now in a vase on the piano. She said, quickly, it had only been that she wasn't that hungry but of course there was no rush – she'd have a green salad to be companionable if he was getting two courses – and she watched him decide to believe her, electing to avoid the fight. 'And maybe some olives first?' she added as the waitress moved to leave them, returning her small notepad to the pocket of her apron.

When their drinks came Julia raised her glass and said, 'To us,' and saw relief in James's face. Across the table his after-shave reached her, lime and faint, spiced woodsmoke. She began to feel lighter, threw her shoulders back, pushed the candle aside and reached for his hands.

'In this family we are the original couple,' James told her, clinking his highball glass against hers again. Beneath the table his knees closed around her own and squeezed gently. 'We need to remember how we all got here. It's us. Everything else can be figured out.'

'The original couple? You mean, like in the garden?'

'Right. You'd better Adam and Eve it.'

'I don't know this is Paradise, at the moment.' She intended to say this playfully but it had sounded bitter and she arrested her own train of thought before she could pursue the analogy any further. She did not want either of them hunting for serpents. 'London's rubbing off on you, very impressive,' she added quickly, changing the subject, and James rattled through his brief cockney lexicon – apples and pears; Sherbet Dab; septic tank (this one, meaning an American, was new to her) – concluding with a demand for another butchers at the drinks menu. Another pitfall dodged, and she relaxed again. Their food came. Julia found that she was ravenous, and taking pleasure in a meal for the first time in months.

She had no conversation, could think of nothing except to express over and over her disloyal relief and gratitude that they were not at home. Whenever she attempted to speak it was this that rose to her lips: *Thank God we're away.* But each felt the other's child had done their damage and so had fallen naturally onto the enemy team. James was her best friend, yet could no longer receive such confidences. How she longed for the release: *I can't bear it any longer; Gwen's passive misery is suffocating me; I've worried myself sick about her, lifelong; I am tired.*

For a while they ate in silence, until James clattered down his knife and fork, dropped his head back and said, addressing the ceiling, 'God, it's good to get away with you, I'm sick of those fucking children. We need to do this more often, seriously. For God's sake let's go to Milan for longer, let's make it a week. I need you. I miss you. I know they've needed us but it's relentless and never-ending – they're like, they're like *vampires*.'

Julia's eyes filled. 'I miss you too. I can't bear this. I know, you're right, I feel bled dry.' That was the way back – not my child to blame, not your child. A safe, bland plural. *The children.* She risked a question, though she feared the answer. 'Do you ever feel like we're being punished for being people? Instead of parents? I kept telling myself it was for Gwen too, that it would be good for her to have a man in the house, have a father figure and a family and – but it was because I wanted it so much. I wanted you so much. You came along and changed everything and I was just drunk on it. I was thinking like a person, instead of like a parent. I let myself want.'

'You should want,' he said fiercely. 'Christ, Julia, you *are* a person.'

'We could have waited – maybe this was all because we rushed them. We could have moved in together once they'd all left home and it was just us – why didn't we wait?'

James had been shaking his head, disagreeing before she'd even finished. 'Life is so damn short. I didn't want to *date* you, I wanted to make a life with you. This life, the life we have. Every day I didn't wake up next to you was wasted.' He seized her hand. 'With you I'm who I'm meant to be – you teach me how to be. Your honesty, your gentleness, your generosity – I've never known anyone who loves like you do, you give with your whole self. It's humbling, and you do it so quietly, and utterly without guile. You know, when I first met Philip, before he even told me you taught piano or suggested I take lessons, he had already told me a story about you. He said that you'd been dropping by with meals for more than ten years and not once had you ever said you'd cooked for him, always that you'd made too much by accident and he was doing you a favour. "She's terrible at judging quantities, my daughter-in-law," that's what he said, and he said it with such love and I remember thinking, now there's a woman with *grace*. And I was right. And I found you and in every way you're more beautiful than I ever could have imagined and somehow, impossibly, it turns out that in a few years I'll be sixty when I'm sure last week I was twenty-two, and I'm not waiting around . . . and yes, I could have moved out when we found out about the kids – we could have said okay, we tried, we'll go back to our apartment and I'll come for dinner every Tuesday and Friday or what-ever and keep the kids apart that way and when they leave home I'll move back in, but we made a commitment to be a family. And don't forget we said that was an important lesson for them, too, you don't just quit when things get hard. We live together now, we work through our shit as a family. If we'd waited we would still be waiting.' For a moment James closed his eyes. 'You know what, I actually can't pursue it. We did the right thing for us, and in any case what's done is done. I'm sorry, baby, can we just not? I cannot think about them any longer, not for one damn second. Can we just get this –' he glanced down at the dessert menu – 'can we just get this Ferrero Rocher ice cream, and focus on that instead? I'm having a Sauternes.'

In the early days, Julia remembered, they had planned for family harmony and anticipated it with patient conviction – the initial disruption, and eventually a grudging, more settled, united normality. Love invites magical thinking. *But how did we believe such a fairy tale? We had no alternative better than wild, empty hope as we careened towards a cliff edge. Yet – I wanted. I want.*

She kissed his rough knuckles, where they still held her own hand. It pleased him when she showed her commitment to this evening, and so she asked for a rhubarb crumble that she did not want and saw his brow clear, as she'd known, or hoped, it would. She then excused herself. In the bathroom she checked her messages, where a text from Gwen said with unsophisticated yet devastating efficacy, I HOPE YOU'RE HAVING FUN. I LOVE YOU, MUMMY. Unwilling to be manipulated and manipulated nonetheless, Julia buried her phone back in her bag, and returned stiffly to James. When he asked whether she wanted to see what was on at the Everyman Cinema she shook her head and said she was sorry but she was really a little tired. It had been a very long week. 'It's been wonderful,' she told him, stroking his clean-shaven cheek. 'Really.' She pretended not to see the look of disappointment on his face, and when he asked for the bill she did not protest.

* * *

It had not been their most successful dinner but it had not ended in a row, and at present that was the best for which either of them could hope. James and Julia walked home hand in hand, in an easier silence.

As they passed Parliament Fields the floodlights were on, and what appeared to be a women's athletic club had colonised the grassy slope and field. Four runners in striped club Lycra crouched in the starting blocks while the rest zipped themselves in and out of tracksuits, tightened fluorescent shoelaces, touched toes, stretched impressive, geometric calf muscles. The gun fired, and James and Julia paused, leaning on the railings to watch as young legs pounded the baked rust of the track, young arms pumped with savage determination. A hush had fallen among the spectators.

Nearest to them sat a dark-browed girl with tight black curls, waiting alone, knees pulled up beneath her chin, skinny arms wrapped around them, her face tense with concentration as she watched her teammates, or rivals, hurdling below. She reached up to retie her pony-tail and something in the gesture was so familiar, the stern contracted eyebrows, the spread-palmed, businesslike gathering in of unruly corkscrews, that Julia caught her breath. James made to move, but Julia put out a hand to stop him. She wanted to see *this* girl run.

Between races there were long breaks; the coaches began an intense discussion by the far bend, heads together over a clipboard; no one moved to right the hurdles that had fallen. After a while James pushed himself back from the railings and said, 'I don't know how long middle-aged men are meant to watch teenage girls doing calisthenics in tiny shorts, you know, if they're not actually racing. I'm starting to feel a little creepy,' and Julia dragged herself away. As they left, the black-haired girl remained apart from the others, bending to stretch the backs of her legs, pulling her nose towards her own shins with fierce, quick little bounces. As they reached the footbridge, they heard the starting gun.

The shops of Queen's Crescent stay open late, offering a charade of purpose to the gangs of teenagers who patrol it. The chicken shop serves chips and battered saveloys till the small hours; the halal butchers do intermittent business until midnight, radio tuned to the muezzin, two brothers beneath the buzzing fluorescent light strips behind a display of lamb shoulders and blood-dark livers glossy as polished glass. Next door the greengrocers play the cricket coverage with equal reverence, their narrow doorway flanked by plywood steps heaped with taro, okra, yams, jackfruit, as well as plastic buckets filled with less exotic fare – red peppers, Granny Smiths, pale tomatoes – on sale, along with booze and fags, straight through till morning. To this strip of scrappy, eclectic commercial enterprise come local kids to meet and mate, retiring to its darker side streets for interludes of tender privacy.

When they turned off the Malden Road, James halted. He took Julia's elbow, slowing her, turning her, pulling her back towards him. 'There's no rush,' he murmured into her hair. 'Home's not going anywhere.'

She leaned into him. They stood unmoving and she felt his warmth against her; her own blood heat, her own breath slow, and deepen. This, after all, was what mattered. Tonight had all been for this fleeting, vital union, the current of energy restored between them; the body reminded. He and she.

Over her shoulder, James caught a movement in the shadows on the other side of Malden Road. On the far corner of Queen's Crescent two teenagers embraced; a boy in a hooded sweatshirt, his hands lost beneath the denim jacket of the slight, black-haired girl he was kissing. The boy's hands locked beneath the girl's backside; he lifted her up, mouths still pressed together, and with her neat legs wrapped around his hips he backed up several steps against the wall, almost disappearing into the darkness. Small white hands roamed up and down his bent shoulders, coming to rest on either side of his face. James caught a glimpse of the boy's sweatshirt and jerked his head to the left, almost pushing Julia over. He reached out instantly for her hand.

'Come,' he said urgently, 'let's go home.' He began to stride on but his eyes had clouded, and as Julia followed she turned to where his gaze had been a moment before. She saw what he had wanted to conceal – Nathan, grinding in a horrible, porn-inspired hip rotation against an equally feverish little Rowan. Before James could stop her Julia stepped forward instinctively, into the road. A car swerved to avoid her with an angry flashing of headlights and a fist held to the horn.

Nathan glanced up, and the colour drained from his face. He whispered something to Rowan who buried her face in his neck, shaking her head with what might have been laughter. Julia stumbled back onto the pavement and began to walk, and then run, towards the house. At their gate James caught up with her and reached for her arm. She shook him off violently and did not turn, but once she reached their front door she hesitated and then stepped back. For a moment she stood with hands on hips, trying to recover her breath.

'Julia.'

She looked past him, vaguely, down the street. 'I can't go in. I have no idea what to say to her.' Her voice was flat, expressionless. 'You will have to talk to – your son. Obviously he has to move out. Obviously he has to go.'

FORTY-NINE

Her little girl was curled into a comma, her thumb slack in her mouth, index finger resting lightly on the bridge of her nose. In sleep she frowned, brows drawn low together, the other fist clenched on the pillow beside her. The room was hot and stuffy, the windows closed against the cool, clear summer night. Gwen had kicked off the covers and her long, pale, freckled legs were pulled up to her chest, defensive. So much passionate feeling, even in unconsciousness. Her fierce red hair loose, spread behind her huge and untamed, like Boudicca, Julia thought, stroking back the bright curls that had fallen over Gwen's hot forehead. A young warrior, tensed for battle as she dreamed. In sleep, she drew Julia backwards in time. Even as a new mother Julia had ached with longing for the infant that still lay in her arms, living over and over in her mind's eye the moment Gwen would crawl, then walk, then release her hand on the first day of nursery and one day pack a bag and shatter her heart. She had held six-week-old Gwen to her chest and lowered her head and sobbed and when Daniel had tried to help, to take the baby from her, she had clutched Gwen jealously to her and could only cry, *'She's so perfect,'* meaning, *Please God let this last.* This time too would pass in a heartbeat, and tomorrow or the next day her daughter would be eighteen, or twenty, or twenty-five, no longer in need. No longer hers.

On the bedside table Gwen had laid out a scene, lit up now by a silver wash of moonlight. She had used the inside of a shoebox as well as its top; the scene spilled out on two levels. On top of the box everyone had gathered. It was a party, or a parade, and behind them a cardboard backdrop of balloons and glitter and fireworks. Iris, in sunglasses, wielded a huge, outsized croissant. Philip and Joan were arm in arm, four black-and-white woolly dogs frolicking ahead of them on pink cotton leads. Saskia had a string bag filled with tiny books over one shoulder and a ring-bound notebook in her hands, and danced to the unheard music that filled her ears through miniature headphones. Nathan, ahead of her, wore a white coat and a broad grin and had a stethoscope plugged into his ears, its head held against the obscenely inflated chest of a blonde in a bikini – unlike the family she was cardboard, and in only two dimensions. And furthest away, in the far corner James and Julia embraced, their gazes locked.

Below, inside the shoebox itself was white, and at first glance looked empty. Julia bent to look. Gwen had made a new version of herself for this scene, a tenth of the size of everyone else, the little body only roughly hewn in modelling clay. Her face was hidden in her hands. In that huge blank space she looked desolate. By her feet a tiny scrap of paper, a tiny pencilled 'I'm sorry' scrawled, doll-size, and above her the parade continued, unaware. Julia touched the minute sculpture and found the clay still soft. Within her something broke, barely perceptible, a snap like a dry twig underfoot.

Gwen had cast a pillow to the floor and Julia sat down and pulled this into her lap, holding it to her chest beneath crossed arms. She leaned back against the side of the bed.

When she opened her eyes it had begun to grow light outside, first oyster grey, then faded tulip pink. Pale London sunshine, chill and morning-damp. The birds began, first the low fluting call of a wood pigeon, and then the twittering gossip of brown sparrows assembled outside in the cherry tree. She heard the diesel rumbling of the 24 bus on the Malden Road; outside, the creak and crash of a nearby front gate. Across London Philip would already have risen, moving softly so as not to wake Joan, creeping downstairs to retrieve the newspaper and to prepare the precarious cup of tea it brought him happiness to take to her each morning. An hour ahead on her pine-green French hillside, Iris would be waking to another day of thick golden sunshine and empty silence broken only by the frogs and crickets, and the chug and hiss of sprinklers beneath her window. She would make coffee on the stove, heating milk, laying a cup and saucer on a tray, a teaspoon, a small warmed jug. Later she would sit in the village square beneath the plane trees and study a production she would see when she returned to London. Erect and dignified in her white linen and her loneliness.

And downstairs, James. Julia could hear him moving around the kitchen, though it was barely dawn. She wondered if he had slept. He had come in as angry as she had been – she'd seen his face and barely recognised it. Angry with Nathan, angrier with Gwen, raging with Julia for having witnessed his son behaving with such callous immaturity. She had caught him out being imperfect, and knew from experience that for each to bear witness to the foolishness of the other's child became quickly unforgivable.

But hours had passed and James would already be calm. He would have poured himself a glass of wine and talked himself round. Julia had all but banned his son from the house; to carry on James would decide to forget she had spoken that banishment. His door must always be open to his boy – no other way for him was possible.

Their love had seemed enduring and immutable, huge and sturdy as an ancient redwood, and was in the end, she saw, so easily felled. No matter how broad the trunk, each light fall of the axe deepens the wound and now, though it still appeared to stand, its roots were severed. Just a single stroke and the whole vast tree would crack and topple. She would not bear its slow precarious decay. For in the half-shadows of Queen's Crescent she had seen James's expression and had understood, as she had never before allowed herself to believe, that he hated Gwen. She realised with a sharp contraction of pain that he hated Gwen as she herself hated Nathan, for he had nurtured such wild, unrealistic hopes for his son, only to see them dashed to pieces against the solid enduring bulk of Gwen's foolishness. James hated her daughter. The thought fell into her consciousness with the steady clarity of a stone dropped in still water and settled there, black and solid. She had seen his hostility, and could not unsee it. By now he would have hidden it, packed it tidily away again beneath the right words and an appearance of limitless tender understanding. But she would raise her daughter only with love, and for that, she now understood, she must raise her daughter alone.

She would not be needed long. Three years, maybe four, while Gwen made her painful, inelegant transition into womanhood and strode, or tiptoed, or limped out into the world. Gwen would leave and Julia would be – where? But she could not think of it. That sorrow was inevitable and didn't, couldn't, alter her course now. Julia took a breath and stood. Then she went downstairs to break her own heart. Wasn't this, after all, a mother's love? And if she could not know it yet, one day Gwen would learn.

PART FOUR

FIFTY

'I just wanted to say enjoy, darling.'

It was Iris. In the foyer of the Everyman, Julia wedged the phone between ear and shoulder and continued to hunt for her ticket in the recesses of her battered bag. As usual her mother-in-law had caught her at a moment of minor panic; Julia stepped aside to allow other, more organised cinema-goers ahead of her. Out came pens, dry-cleaning tickets, loose Polo mints, car keys, and then a block of fresh fudge wrapped in striped grease-paper, a miniature pot of clotted cream and another of strawberry jam. There, beneath this odd collection, was the ticket. Julia had come from an early supper at a nearby gastropub with the new Dr and Mrs Alden, who had just returned from a week-end in Cornwall. It was in Joan's nature to package up and distribute to loved ones what she herself had barely had time to enjoy or even experience – in another bag Julia also carried a pair of luminous green and sapphire sea-glass coasters, a tea towel printed with a recipe for cheese-and-onion pasties, and a white cardboard box tied with pink curling ribbon, containing scones. 'They've gone hard since this morning,' Joan had fussed, dithering while she presented them, as if she might decide at the last minute to take the unsatisfactory treats back again. 'You must promise you'll do them in the oven a little.' Over fish and chips ('so we can pretend we're still at the seaside') Joan recounted their adventures in Tintagel where the purchase of these souvenirs, as well as innumerable others for her sons, daughters-in-law and assorted grandchildren, seemed happily to have occupied the visit. She and Philip were full of praise for the weather and the coast, and Joan was only sorry they'd had to leave the dogs, who would have loved the beach. By way of atonement Daisy had joined them for dinner, gently head-butting Philip's shins in gratitude for each scrap he delivered, tenderly, beneath the table. He had caught a little sun, Julia had noticed.

'Thank you. I'm late already – I don't know how I always do this.' Julia switched her mobile from beneath her left ear to her right and offered her ticket to the usher.

'Go, go,' Iris commanded. 'I'm envious. I must say I'm rather theatre-starved out here. A feistier Desdemona than Verdi's, no? There was meant to be a wonderful revival in Milan last summer, but of course the Met's the Met. These live link-up things are so clever, though I do wish people didn't feel they had to munch their way through it like ruminants – it's still opera even at the cinema. Oh, and listen, if you speak to Gwendolen tell her that Katy left some sort of fuchsia straw fedora number in their room. I only spotted it when I got back from dropping them at the train.'

'I'll text her. I've been instructed not to ring.'

'Quite right. And it's not important, no doubt she can pick up something equally hideous in Italy. It feels like it's made of polythene, or polyester or polystyrene – I don't know, something flammable. They're absolutely fine, by the way, though Gwendolen's done something ghastly with her hair, did you know?'

'She sent me a picture last week. I wasn't sure if it was that bad in real life.'

'Worse. Sort of carroty-blonde, and patchy. Never mind, it will perhaps fend off the Italians. Enjoy, darling. All those tenors. How bad can it be?'

Julia switched off her phone and went in. She was directed to a wide leather armchair in the back row and she set down her glass of wine to curl into the cushions, pulling her knees up beneath her. She had Pinot Noir and Rossini. What more could she want? Some company, perhaps. The seat beside hers was empty. But Anne had cancelled at the last moment and Gwen could never be dragged to opera even had she been in London. In any case it was time, Julia had long known, to get used to doing things on her own.

She spotted him just before the house lights fell. At the front, sharing a burgundy velvet sofa and a small bowl of popcorn with Claire, his former registrar. Claire's cropped hair had grown long and heavy down her back, and she was laughing as she reached forward into the bowl. Her other hand wasn't visible, but might have been on James's knee.

It had been a year. It was, Julia told herself, only to be expected. Yet still she found she was fumbling on the floor for her blazer and her gifts from Joan, hearing loose change and unknown possessions spill from her handbag as she leaned forwards. Claire was young and wore leather trousers, and had been unquestioningly attentive and compassionate and efficient when they had needed her on a very dark morning in spring, last year. Julia would go home. She would not listen to the Rossini, which she now realised would have been a mistake. Under cover of darkness she left, knocking her wine over into her vacated seat and whispering a hurried apology to the usher without pausing to explain. She would not sit alone, watching them from the shadows.

James caught her wrist in the lobby.

'Julia.'

'Hello.'

'You're leaving.' This sounded like an accusation, and she flushed.

'I didn't think you'd seen me.'

'I hadn't. Claire did.'

'How is Claire?'

'What? Oh, good, she's good, she's moved to the Homerton. How are you?'

Julia assured him she was fine, without elaborating. She did not say, *I have plans to become someone else.* After months of prevarication she had made an appointment at the salon for the following morning – she intended to shear her hair off, blunt and neat and high above her shoulders, and to colour it the true blonde for which Iris and her hairdresser had always lobbied. It was happening tomorrow. Tomorrow she would become her new self: sharper, better defined, more definitive. Today, by accident, she still resembled the person she had always been. But she had no way to explain any of this and instead said, 'Anne was meant to be – she had to work, in the end. How are you? How is Nathan?'

'He's good. Great. Loving it. Rowing, the whole deal. I'll see him next week, I'm stopping on my way to California.'

He seemed to hesitate and then rushed on, 'I've been offered a job at UCSF, I'm going to talk to some people, check out some apartments, get a feel . . . It's a research post again. Better weather. Much better Chinese food, you know, which is definitely something to consider.' He had been speaking very quickly but now seemed to catch himself, and slowed. His hair on one side stood on end where he'd held it briefly in his fist. He added softly, 'Time for a change, maybe.'

Julia pulled her jacket tighter. From the auditorium came the sounds of the orchestra tuning, loud and discordant, a sweltering afternoon in Lincoln Center beamed live into this mild north London summer evening. Any minute the overture would begin, and she would no longer be able to ensure her composure.

'Do send my best to Claire and – and, I'm happy for you both.'

He frowned. 'Thanks.'

She began to walk away, but after only a few steps he called after her, 'I'm – we're just friends, really.'

She turned back to see his face change almost instantly, from embarrassment to hesitation, or perhaps it was a trace of defiance. 'I've been lonely.'

She said again, more softly, 'I'm happy for you.'

'Stop saying that,' he said irritably. He was wearing a pair of dark trousers she recognised, and a shirt that she did not. Behind him a woman's laughing face was magnified, chiselled by falling photographic sunlight and shadows on a huge framed playbill; a documentary he and she had seen together here, last year, in a former lifetime. The espresso machine behind the counter buzzed and thrummed. Julia began to search for her keys and James stepped forward, as if to bar her way. 'Where are you going now?'

'Home.'

'How's Gwen?'

'Shouldn't you get back in?'

He waved this suggestion away, dismissing it. 'Where's she going in September?'

'Leeds, in the end. She's Interrailing with Katy at the moment. Last heard of somewhere between Bargemon and Dubrovnik.'

'Quiet without them, no?'

'Yes. And less laundry.'

'And less laundry,' he agreed, holding her gaze. It was Julia, after a heartbeat, who looked away. In the mirrored wall beside them the lobby extended, doubled, and she became aware of their reflections: a slight, pale woman, face upturned; a tall man with new threads of silver in his fair hair, thumbs hooked into his pockets, his shoulders raised in a tense shrug. She shifted slightly to avoid the sight of these two awkward strangers.

James said nothing further and yet made no move to return to the darkened cinema, from which were now clearly audible the galloping opening bars of the overture, eliding almost immediately into the plangent lovesick strains of hope and longing that would follow. Soon the foreshadowing of bloodshed, between bars of pomp and flourish. True love vanquished. Foolish, needless death. James glanced back towards the closed doors of the auditorium and Julia dared to look at him, studying his profile for signs of – what? He had not changed. Here was the face for which she searched in every crowd, scanning; hoping. All her life she would know its contours as her own. She had no right to wish him anything but happiness.

She said, 'I can hear Iago, I think.'

'So what? You already made me miss the whole thing once in Milan.' And then seeing she looked stricken he sobered. 'That wasn't funny, I'm sorry. I'm nervous.'

'Nothing makes you nervous.'

'That's not true. Unlicensed fireworks make me nervous. Pigeons. You.'

It was her turn now to smile. In the cinema behind them Otello was disembarking, welcomed by the grateful Doge as a son of Venice. Love, hoped Otello, would crown all his achievements in battle. His audience in Belsize Park knew better.

'It sounds so optimistic. Rossini has a way of making impending heartbreak sound so cheerful. Poor Otello.'

'Poor Desdemona,' James countered.

'Victims of their own flawed characters.'

'You think? Or of circumstance.'

'One leads to the other.'

'I think,' James said softly, 'that you're being very hard on them.'

Without warning the couple in the mirror moved towards one another; she closed her eyes to feel his arms enfold her, one hand warm at the nape of her neck, his forehead resting lightly, for a moment, against her own. Her lungs filled with the scent of him; spice and citrus and skin. Against her cheek she felt his fist close, momentarily, in the falling mass of her hair. Then he released her, and was gone. For as long as she could, she held her breath. She remained until the doors of the cinema closed behind him.

On Haverstock Hill she waited for the lights to change. Dusk was falling, London muted and softened by the thickening darkness. She would go home. Back to prim tidiness and silence, to objects untouched since she alone had touched them. Back to still, close air. But tonight, before the words she now knew that she would write to him, she could hope. That their two fragile human hearts continued to beat each hour she knew to be a miracle. A car slowed to let her cross and she nodded her thanks and found, when she reached the far side, that she was smiling. She had seen him. He might still love her; either way she would love him all her life. She felt her chest expand and fill. Tonight, she would open the French windows. She would sit in the garden. She would listen, after all, to the Rossini.